INTRODUCTORY
CIRCUIT THEORY

INTRODUCTORY CIRCUIT THEORY

Ernst A. Guillemin

PROFESSOR OF ELECTRICAL COMMUNICATION
DEPARTMENT OF ELECTRICAL ENGINEERING
MASSACHUSETTS INSTITUTE OF TECHNOLOGY

NEW YORK · JOHN WILEY & SONS, INC.
LONDON

Library of Congress Catalog Card Number: 53–11754

Printed in the United States of America

To my sophomores, whose enthusiastic
cooperation has been the inspiration
for this work

P R E F A C E

For the orientation of the reader of this volume, it should be pointed out that this is the first of a contemplated sequence. The second volume will begin with a study of the approximation properties and uses of Fourier series in connection with circuit problems, and will lead logically into a discussion of Fourier and Laplace transform theory, its correlation with the classical differential equation viewpoint, and its application to analysis and synthesis procedures. The remainder of this volume will deal with an introduction to synthesis on a survey level, including some conventional filter theory and the closely related topic of transmission lines. The advanced aspects of (linear, passive, bilateral) network analysis and synthesis will be the subject of one or two final volumes. Work on the second volume has been interrupted in favor of proceeding immediately with the advanced part which is more urgently needed.

The present volume, as its title states, is intended to be an introductory treatment of electric circuit theory—the text for a first course in circuits for undergraduate students majoring in electrical engineering or for physics students who need a good orientational background in the subject. It is the result of my past five years' experience in getting our E.E. sophomores headed in the right direction and our physics sophomores provided with a broad orientation in circuit principles and a flexible attitude toward their use. I feel that circuit theory (that is, *linear, passive, lumped, finite, bilateral* circuit theory—hereafter called just plain circuit theory) is the electrical engineer's bread and butter, so to speak. He needs to know this subject well before he can tackle any of the other subjects in his curriculum; and it is of the utmost importance that his first course shall provide him with a set of basic concepts and ways of thinking that will not become obsolete throughout the rest of his undergraduate and graduate years. He should be started off with the same basic concepts and processes of analysis that he will be using in his doctorate research or in his professional work four or five years later. He will not understand them so well or be able to use them with the same facility as a sophomore, but he should never have to unlearn or discard any of his earlier concepts later on. His thoughts as a sophomore should sprout from the same roots that will feed and sustain his creative thinking throughout his professional life. In other words, his first course should not be a "terminal" first course but the beginning of a career.

I have always held that, where the teaching of basic concepts and procedures are concerned, no distinction should be made between the so-called "elementary" and the "advanced" methods. We refer to things as being "advanced" only so long as we understand them insufficiently well ourselves to be able to make them clear in simple terms. Once we understand a subject fully and clearly, it is no longer difficult to make it understandable to the beginner. And, if we do not warn the beginner beforehand, he will not be able to distinguish when we are teaching him the "elementary" methods and when the "advanced." Such a distinction will reside only in the teacher's mind; to the student both will be equally novel and equally clear.

I am pointing out these things because some teachers, upon perusing the pages of this book, may consider some of the topics dealt with (as well as the general level of the work) to be somewhat more advanced than is ordinarily considered appropriate for sophomore or junior students. It is important to remember in this regard that a concept is not necessarily more difficult for the student because it happens to be unfamiliar to the teacher. Conceptually none of the material in this book is any more difficult than that involved in the differential or integral calculus which we consider quite appropriate for the sophomore level. Compared with the old-fashioned brand of circuits course, the work is more challenging, to be sure, but it is also far more interesting. To my students, who are my most ardent and reliable critics, there is nothing drab about this subject any longer. Their enthusiasm and morale are high, and the future looks bright and exciting to them. This is how things should be.

Let me be a little more specific about the ways in which the introductory treatment in this book differs from most. Primarily it hits harder at the things that are more fundamental, and attempts in every way possible to present basic ideas and principles so as to promote flexible thinking in terms of them and facile use of them in their application to a wide variety of simple practical problems.

We teachers talk much about fundamentals, but sometimes we don't get very close to them. Take the matter of setting up equilibrium equations for an electric circuit. The very first step is to decide upon a suitable set of variables. They must be independent, and must be adequate to define the state of the network at any moment. The usual approach to the selection of variables is to choose a set of mesh currents or loop currents. But do we stop to consider how we can be sure that these will be independent and adequate, or whether they are reversibly, uniquely, and unambiguously related to the branch currents? No. We take all this for granted, and we also take for granted that the student will straighten this "obviously simple" matter out for himself. He doesn't realize it at the time, but right here he stores up a lot of trouble for himself that does not show until much later in his career when he meets a slightly unorthodox situation and suddenly discovers that he can't even get started on it.

A similar and even more confusing situation exists when we attempt to choose a set of voltages as variables as in node analysis. This topic, even the instructor admits, never gets across. Needless to say, I don't think we are being very fundamental about these things. Of course, our usual defense is to say that this is not a very important aspect of circuit theory anyway; it's one of these advanced topics too highbrow for sophomores; and, besides, no practical engineer ever uses it anyway. This last remark is really one for the book. Of course he doesn't use it. How can he, when he doesn't understand what it's all about and never had it explained to him or was shown its possibilities? As for the topic being too highbrow for sophomores, this is plain nonsense (to which my sophomores will most vehemently attest).

So far as the practical potential of this item is concerned, let me mention just one of a number of pertinent incidents that occurred recently. A group of engineers concerned with the Bonneville power development in the Pacific Northwest were having a conference here, and one of them described a new approach to the analysis problem which is particularly effective for such power-distribution networks and leads to a systematized computational procedure that beats using the old network analyzer all hollow. This "new" approach consists in picking an appropriate tree and identifying the link currents with loop currents, the tree in this instance being the distribution system and the links being the branches formed by the sources and loads. It seems that power engineers also can benefit by a more fundamental approach to circuit theory!

Another topic that is essential in getting closer and giving more emphasis to fundamentals is the use of scale factors and the process of normalization. We tell the student at the outset that we are going to restrict our discussion to *linear* circuits, but do we clearly impress upon him the significance of this property or how we can capitalize on it? Many of my graduate students, as well as many engineers in industry, are not aware of the implications of this property and of its usefulness if suitably exploited. In fact, the conventional procedure in teaching circuit theory deliberately obscures this important aspect of the subject through overemphasizing what is mistakenly regarded as a "practical" attitude. I can well remember, in my own circuits course that I attended as a sophomore, that the excitation in the numerical problems was invariably 110 volts or 220 volts or some other value in current practice. It was believed by the teacher (and still is by some today) that we must make the student aware of such practical values of voltage; that it is an important collateral function of an introductory circuits course to enlighten our young men about the magnitudes of significant quantities in current practical use.

To begin with, our students of today are not so stupid as all that. They already know that common "house current" is supplied at 110 and 220 volts, and they even know that the frequency is 60 cycles per second (except in some parts of Canada), and a host of other practical data too numerous to mention. Furthermore, these factual data about practical values should be and are far more appropriately presented in a correlated laboratory subject. It is much more important to emphasize that the assumption of 1 volt or 1 ampere as an excitation value is entirely sufficient to take care of any eventuality regarding source intensity. Moreover, if we do this, we achieve a certain simplification of the numerical work, in that we have one less factor to carry through the pertinent multiplications and divisions, and we become ever so much more clearly aware of the implication of the linear property of networks and of the distinctions to be made between power calculations and voltage or current calculations, because the necessary factors by which the solution must afterward be multiplied are different.

A similar argument may be advanced concerning the specification of frequency. Unless there seems to be an urgent need to do otherwise, it is far more instructive to assume 1 radian per second as the frequency of an a-c source. Through learning how he can subsequently adapt the response thus found to any other value of excitation frequency, the student acquires a far better appreciation of the fundamental way in which circuit behavior depends upon frequency as a parameter; and again a very material advantage is gained with regard to the numerical computations. This latter item alone is more important as a practical matter than many readers might suppose. I had occasion recently to set up an analysis procedure on a research project in an industrial laboratory and neglected to suggest frequency scaling. The ensuing calculations fairly bristled with fantastic powers of 2π and 10, causing all sorts of silly errors and absurd results. A program of frequency scaling that brought all the relevant parameter values (critical frequencies and such) into the range 1–10 straightened things out in a hurry. (The men in this research group, incidentally, were trained as physicists; so the lack of our teaching procedures to provide a sufficiently clear understanding of fundamentals is apparently not restricted to engineering courses.)

The matter of element values lies within the framework of these same discussions because of its intimate relation to frequency and amplitude scaling. Most of the problems in this book involve element values (henrys, farads, ohms) in the range 1–10. Here, again, critics will argue that these values are unrealistic and may give our students mistaken ideas concerning usual practical values. To this challenge I reply: (a) Our students are not that dumb. (b) They have lived and will live in the world of reality where they have ample opportunity to find out what "really goes." (c) They are concurrently taking a coordinated laboratory subject where they cannot help but become aware of the fact that 1 farad is a rather large capacitance. (d) It is much more important for them to learn how, for purposes of calculation, we can so normalize our problem as to bring the element values into a range where powers of 10 are absent or at least reduced to a minimum. In fact, it is this normalized problem that yields what are sometimes called "universal curves" representing the pertinent circuit response under a wide variety of conditions.

There are other important consequences of linearity that cannot be overstressed such as the additive property (superposability of solutions) and the fact that excitation and response functions as a pair may be differentiated or integrated any finite number of times without their appropriateness one to the other being destroyed. But of utmost and supreme importance is the proper discussion of and approach to the impedance concept. In this connection we cannot regard transient analysis as an advanced topic to be dealt with later on. Transient analysis *must* precede the discussion of a-c steady-state response in order that the true character of the impedance function may be recognized. Unless this phase of an introduction to circuit theory is properly accomplished, the student will be left with a false notion about the impedance concept that he will have to unlearn later on before he can acquire a mentally clear picture of what an impedance really is and of the omnipotent role it plays in circuit behavior. To teach the impedance concept initially in its conventional restricted form regarding a-c steady-state response materially impedes a later understanding of its true nature and causes a waste of student time and effort that we cannot afford today. In this regard I have frequently observed that many of my graduate students have greater difficulty mastering the impedance concept than some of my better sophomores whose mental attitude is not preconditioned by some limited viewpoint.

Besides, the time has passed when we could regard the discussion of transient response of circuits as a luxury item in our E.E. curriculum. The widespread use of electronic-control devices and the increased importance of communication links in our fast-moving modern world have made that attitude as obsolete as the rotary converter. A discussion of the transient behavior of circuits is a *must* in our present physics as well as in our E.E. curricula at least. And it is wrong to think that it logically belongs in a later discussion following the introductory subject. Without an appreciation of the natural behavior of at least some simple circuits it is not possible to present the impedance concept because the natural frequencies are the quantities by which the impedance is determined, apart from an unimportant constant multiplier. The impedance is thus more intimately related to the transient behavior than to the so-called steady-state response, although it characterizes both. This intimate relation between the transient and steady-state behavior of circuits is extremely important as a fundamental principle, and we cannot claim to be hitting at fundamentals unless this item is dealt with properly.

In close relationship with this interpretation of the impedance function is the concept of complex frequency and its graphical representation in the complex frequency plane. Through this means, the evaluation of an impedance for a given applied frequency is reduced to a geometrical problem that in many practical cases can be solved by inspection, especially where reasonable approximations are allowable. Further exploitation of these same ideas leads us, in a logical manner, to interpret similarly the evaluation of the constants determining the transient response, and ultimately to all of the practically useful results ordinarily regarded as being obtainable only through use of Laplace transform methods. Such a wealth of knowledge about circuits lies within this conceptual framework that, without question, it may be regarded as the foundation of circuit theory; yet the conventional "first course" in circuits as it is now presented (with few exceptions) makes no mention of these things.

Finally the principle of duality may be mentioned as an important fundamental concept that should be prominent throughout the discussions comprising an introductory treatment of circuit theory. Here the term "throughout" is used literally, since the principle of duality is not a topic that can effectively be disposed of by a concentrated discussion injected at some seemingly appropriate point, but instead is best dealt with by touching upon it again and again, bringing out each time some additional important aspect or application of this useful concept.

Considering the general structure of this book, it is significant to point out that the first three chapters may be regarded as a separate unit which could be used as the text for a rather solid subject in d-c circuits or resistance circuits if this seemed appropriate. Similarly, the succeeding Chapters 4 through 8 form a closely knit unit that can be used separately. In fact this portion of the book was written in such a way that it could be used independently as the text for a one-semester subject, provided the students had previously been exposed to Kirchhoff's laws and simple resistance circuits in their physics course. If only one semester can be devoted to circuits (as with our physics students), then this material offers a reasonable compromise, while the availability of the discussions in the first three chapters as collateral reading material (to be consulted either concurrently or at any later time) serves as a stopgap in lieu of being able to provide a really adequate foundation at this point in the curriculum. If two semesters can be devoted to the introductory circuits subject, then Chapters 1 through 9 form an appropriate text, and Chapter 10, which rounds off and generalizes some of the previous discussions, remains as a collateral reading assignment or as a reminder that the study of circuit theory really has no ending. In any event, the student who later goes on with advanced work in network analysis and synthesis will need the material of Chapter 10 as a necessary background. Thus the book may serve a dual purpose, as indeed it has served during the period of its development, the one-semester version being appropriate for our physics students and the two-semester one for the E.E.'s.

It is only fair to warn the potential reader that this book will prove only moderately satisfactory as a reference work. Thus the discussion relevant to any significant item like Thévenin's theorem, duality, the reciprocity theorem, source transformations, etc., will not be found nicely packaged within certain pages. Discussion of such items as well as that pertinent to various fundamental principles are scattered throughout the book—a first presentation here, a little more there, and still more later on. The reason for this kind of piecemeal presentation is that the book is intended to be used as a text, and the learning process is a piecemeal procedure. We like at any stage to have some repetition of what we already know, presented with the addition of a few new ideas, followed by some illustrations, and then by further additions, etc. Another reason for this type of presentation is the dual purpose the book is meant to serve. Any repetitiousness resulting from these objectives I hope the reader will find pleasing rather than otherwise.

At this point I would like to make some specific comments on the material in the various chapters and the reasons for its particular mode of presentation. The first two chapters are the result of years of practice and much troubled thinking about how best to present the subject of establishing equilibrium equations for a network, and why, in spite of all my efforts, there always remained so much confusion and so little confidence in the student's mind about this topic. At long last I think I have found the answer to this perplexing question, and Chapters 1 and 2 embody that answer. Thus the conventional approach (and I am as guilty as anyone of having followed it) attempts to present too much at once and achieves only confusion. The various methods using tensor or matrix algebra suffer from the same defect. Moreover, they fail to discuss adequately the most important issue of network geometry, and in other respects are not suitable for an introductory presentation.

The process of establishing equilibrium equations involves actually four topics which individually require careful thought and concentration for clear understanding. When these are superimposed to form one conglomerate mass, it is little wonder that nothing but misunderstanding and muddled thinking results.

The first topic is that of selecting an appropriate set of variables and establishing the relations between these and the branch variables. It is concerned only with the network geometry (no mention need nor should be made at this point of Kirchhoff's laws, or the volt-ampere relations for the elements, or the sources). The topic involves a number of subtleties, and its understanding requires a reasonably good appreciation of the principle of duality, but these matters can be clarified easily if we exclude at this time everything else except the purely geometrical properties, as is done in Chapter 1.

Having selected variables, we are in a position to write equilibrium equations, and so the discussion of the Kirchhoff laws and how to apply them is the next logical topic. The third topic concerns the volt-ampere relations for the branches; and now we can combine topics 1, 2, 3 to form the equilibrium equations in terms of the chosen variables. Finally comes the discussion of sources, and our problem of establishing equilibrium relations is done.

Compare this with the usual procedure of writing Kirchhoff law equations immediately in terms of loop currents. Here the four steps outlined above are all tossed into the pot at once and stirred together. The result is a violent case of indigestion, unless we so restrict and simplify the network structure as to render the end result trivial.

I might mention, incidentally, that the discussions in Chapter 1 are rather complete, perhaps more so than might be regarded appropriate or necessary in an introductory course. In answer to such comment I can only say that, when I wrote the chapter, I could see no point in deliberately stopping before I had finished what I had to say and what I consider to be a minimum of necessary material to form a good background on which to build later. To postpone the discussion of some of this material seemed unwise, since a subsequent continuation (perhaps in another volume) would have to repeat parts of the earlier arguments in order to achieve coherence in the presentation as a whole. I don't think that the availability of more information than one cares to assimilate at the moment should pose any serious problem. Chapter 1 may profitably be read and reread several times by the student at various stages in his educational program.

With regard to the geometrical aspects of duality, which play an important part in the topic of Chapter 1, I found it convenient to invent names for two things that to my knowledge at least had not previously been named. Thus the dual of a cut set I have named a "tie set," and the dual of a tree a "maze." These names seemed most appropriate to me, and I hope the reader will find them appropriate also.

Chapter 3 is a collection of topics, all of which are directly or indirectly concerned with expediting the process of obtaining solutions. Systematic elimination procedures, solution by determinants, special artifices applicable where various types of symmetry prevail, short methods usable with ladder structures, wye-delta transformations, source transformations (which are what Thévenin's and Norton's theorems amount to), the reciprocity theorem (frequently an effective aid in obtaining a desired result), a knowledge of how power calculations must be made (the fact that these effects when caused by separate sources are *not* additive in contrast to currents and voltages which are), the transformations that leave power relations invariant, the equivalence relations pertinent to the tee, pi, bridged-tee and lattice structures—all these things are useful when we are dealing with the business of constructing solutions. I feel that they belong together and that it is useful to make a first presentation of them while discussing the restricted case of resistance networks where there are no other complications to interfere with their assimilation. Although here, as in Chapter 1, the treatment may seem to be somewhat more inclusive than is essential at an introductory level, no serious difficulty need thereby be created, since the relative emphasis given to various topics can always be appropriately adjusted.

In this chapter an attempt is made to have the various topics introduce themselves logically rather than be forced upon the reader's attention in a haphazard fashion. Thus, having discussed network geometry, and having shown how a numerical set of equations may be solved by systematically eliminating variables, what is more logical than for the reader to become curious about the geometrical implications of this elimination process? The elimination of a node potential should correspond geometrically to the elimination of a node, and the elimination of a mesh current to the elimination of the pertinent mesh. Such a correlation, which is indeed possible, not only leads logically to a presentation of wye-delta or delta-wye transformations and their generalizations, but does so with a minimum of disagreeable algebra, as contrasted with other presentations of this item, particularly in the general star-mesh case. A particularly simple proof of the reciprocity theorem which likewise fits in with the pattern set by the systematic elimination procedure is achieved through showing that the symmetry of the parameter matrix characterizing the equilibrium equations is unchanged by a typical step in this procedure.

Chapter 4, which introduces the volt-ampere relations for the inductance and capacitance elements and shows that inductance networks and capacitance networks are dealt with by means of the same methods applicable to resistance networks, is primarily concerned with a discussion of the unit step and impulse functions, in terms of which various more arbitrary source functions and switching operations may conveniently be described. In connection with the impulse function, it has been stated that the subtleties involved in its interpretation are too difficult for a class at the sophomore level and that the concept is too abstract and unreal. Neither criticism is consistent with our prevailing attitude. The limit process involved in the definition of the impulse is precisely of the same nature as that pertinent to the formation of a derivative or of an integral. If the comprehension of this sort of limit process is too much for a sophomore, then we shall also have to give up trying to teach him the differential calculus.

As for the impulse being unreal, nothing could be further from the truth. In our daily life we frequently see things bumping into other things. Take a bat hitting a baseball for instance. The ball changes its velocity from minus to plus in a wink—and that's short enough (compared with the time of flight of the ball) to be negligible. For all practical purposes the ball acquires its kinetic energy of flight in no time. If we want to be fussy about this situation and say that the nonzero time of impact must be considered and so we really are not dealing with an impulse in its true sense, then to be consistent we should be equally fussy about the step function, because a change in value (of a force for instance) cannot occur instantly either; yet we no longer object to step functions in our engineering analysis, because we have lived with this concept longer and are used to it. Our mathematical methods of analysis always represent an idealization of the true state of affairs, and the impulse function involves nothing different in this respect from all the other mathematical concepts that we are accustomed to use.

Engineering analysis involving singularity functions of all orders is becoming so common today that we can no longer neglect making our students familiar with them at an early stage. My chief reason for introducing the impulse as well as the step when I first wrote this text material was the desire to use Thévenin's and Norton's theorems with capacitance and inductance elements in the transient state. Since these elements involve differentiation and integration, it was clear that a step function might have to be differentiated in the course of solving a problem by these means. To deprive the student of this flexible way of dealing with transient problems, I felt, was not in keeping with my basic objectives, and so I moved the presentation of singularity functions from the graduate curriculm into the sophomore year.

It might also be pointed out that the early introduction of these concepts into the study of circuit theory develops a more open-minded attitude on the part of the student toward characteristic behavior patterns. In my student days, for example, we were told that the current in an inductance just had to be continuous. Though this is true in most practical situations, it is much better not to make such sweeping assertions. It is far more instructive to show the student that a discontinuous current can be produced in an inductance only through the application of a voltage impulse but that physical conditions may sometimes approximate this kind of excitation function.

Chapter 5 deals with the transient response of simple circuits, making use of all the artifices mentioned above. The primary objective is to give the student a physical understanding of transient response in first- and second-order cases, together with a facile way of dealing with the pertinent mathematical relationships, so that he will develop an easy and circumspect approach to problems of this sort, rather than always use the same mathematically ponderous and slowly moving machinery of the "general case." In this respect I have seen some awful crimes committed, particularly by students who have learned the Laplace transform method. They are determined to Laplace-transform everything that comes their way, and they get so they can't solve the simplest problem without this machinery. They can't write down the discharge of a capacitor through a resistance without Laplace-transforming the poor thing to death. I don't want any of my students to get into a fix like that. I want them to know their simple transients as well as they know their own names, and Chapter 5 aims to give them the kind of workout that can accomplish this end.

In Chapter 6 we come to *la pièce de résistance* as the French would say. Here we introduce the sinusoid, the notion about complex frequency, the impedance concept, its interpretation in terms of the natural frequencies of the circuit, graphical portrayal of the pole-zero pattern in the s-plane, evaluation of impedances through geometrical visualization of their frequency factors, interpretation of resonance as a near coincidence between applied and natural frequencies, reciprocal and complementary impedances, magnitude and frequency scaling, vector diagrams, and other related aspects pertinent to this general theme. Transients and steady states are stirred together into a pretty intimate mixture, with the impedance function keeping order and clarifying all of the pertinent interrelationships. The circuits dealt with are for the most part still the simple ones touched upon in Chapter 5 so that the student will have no difficulty following the mathematical steps while getting used to the many new concepts and methods of interpretation presented here. A few more elaborate element combinations, such as the constant-resistance networks and double-tuned circuits, are discussed toward the end of this chapter in order to show the student how simple a matter it is to deal with such situations in terms of the rather powerful tools which the earlier discussions have placed at his command.

Chapter 7 introduces a formal discussion of energy and power relations. Instead of the conventional restriction in the derivation of pertinent quantities to in-phase and out-of-phase components of current and voltage, an attempt is made to develop a more physical appreciation of these phenomena through specific attention to the stored energy functions and their significance in the sinusoidal steady state, along with the role played by the dissipation function. Thus the definition of reactive power as the product of the voltage and the quadrature component of current leaves the student with no physical picture of what this quantity is or why it exists and needs to be considered. When it is seen to be proportional to the difference between the average values of the stored energies, its significance begins to be appreciated in physical terms. Through expressing impedances in terms of energy functions, through their determination by these means, and through the ability thus to perceive from a single-frequency computation the whole course of their behavior in a given vicinity (for instance, the determination of the impedance behavior in a resonance vicinity and computation of the factor Q), the student is given a glimpse of how energy and power considerations may be useful in a much broader sense than merely for the computation of energy consumption.

The object of Chapter 8 is to provide the means for dealing with more extensive and more random circuits in the sinusoidal steady state than the simple ones so far considered. Most important in this regard is the consideration of mutual inductive coupling. The traditional stumbling block involved in the treatment of random situations, namely, the determination of algebraic signs, is overcome by a systematic approach which is straightforward in its use for the computation of pertinent parameter matrices on both the loop and node bases.

In Chapter 9 the subject of transient response is generalized, first, through consideration of the so-called a-c transients and, second, through development of the complete solution for any finite lumped network, leading to a result that is identical in form with, but much more simply derived than, that alternately obtainable through Laplace transform methods supplemented by complex integration. It is in these discussions that the concept of complex frequency is fully developed and illustrated by a consideration of the exact coincidence between excitation and natural frequencies (perfect resonance). It is shown how all the many useful theorems ordinarily derived only by Fourier and Laplace transform methods are easily and rigorously established by inspection of the form of the solution for the general case, and these theorems (or *properties* as I prefer to call them) are discussed and illustrated by means of numerous examples.

These examples were constructed by starting from assumed pole-zero configurations for the desired transfer functions and synthesizing the pertinent networks. Thus, for the first time in the history of textbooks on transient analysis, the reader is presented with illustrative examples involving higher than second-order systems. He will find a multiple-order pole problem other than the hackneyed RLC circuit for the critically damped case; and he will find examples that are representative of useful response characteristics, as well as illustrative of the theoretical analysis that precedes them.

Before the advent of synthesis it was not possible to construct really interesting illustrative examples. If a circuit with more than two or three meshes was assumed, the solution of a characteristic equation of high degree was immediately involved, and the resulting random character of the response obtained after much disagreeable work was hardly representative of anything interesting. Being able to start from a pole-zero pattern and work in both directions (to a network on the one hand, and to its transient response on the other) opens up a host of possibilities that were not available to the textbook writer of the past. Within a limited space, I have made the most of this situation in working out a set of illustrative examples for Chapter 9.

Chapter 10, as mentioned previously, supplies a certain generality and completeness to the derivation of equilibrium equations and energy relations that have been discussed already but have not been established in this way. Thus, when the reader reaches this chapter, he will be familiar with all the topics it contains except the mathematical methods needed to state them in perfectly general and yet compact and concise form. The final item is a critical discussion of the principle of duality and of the results derivable from it in the light of the broader viewpoint just presented. The story of network theory is, of course, nowhere nearly completed at this point, but, since one volume cannot contain all of it, this seems to be a reasonable point at which to stop.

I should probably say something about historical notes (who did what, when, and why) and references to source material and all that, because with few exceptions I haven't done any of this sort of thing. As a matter of fact, if one takes the works of Kirchhoff, Helmholtz, Cauchy, Lord Rayleigh, and maybe a few others of similar standing and vintage, there isn't much else that is needed to establish the background for network theory. If a student has the inclination to "do some digging" (most of them prefer not to) to ferret out historical facts, he will have no difficulty finding the bibliographical help and the encouragement from his instructor that he needs. I do not mean to belittle the importance of having some historical background on the evolution of science and mathematics (and network theory), but the wherewithal to go into this aspect of things is already available. I would rather confine my limited energies (and heaven knows they are limited!) to making available the things that are not now available.

One final point. In the teaching of this subject I regard it as important to remind the student frequently that network theory has a dual character (no connection with the principle of duality); it is a Dr. Jekyll–Mr. Hyde sort of thing; it is two-faced, if you please. There are two aspects to this subject: the physical and the theoretical. The physical aspects are represented by Mr. Hyde—a smooth character who isn't what he seems to be and can't be trusted. The mathematical aspects are represented by Dr. Jekyll—a dependable, extremely precise individual who always responds according to established custom. Dr. Jekyll is the network theory that we work with on paper, involving only pure elements and only the ones specifically included. Mr. Hyde is the network theory we meet in the laboratory or in the field. He is always hiding parasitic elements under his jacket and pulling them out to spoil our fun at the wrong time. We can learn all about Dr. Jekyll's orderly habits in a reasonable period, but Mr. Hyde will continue to fool and confound us until the end of time. In order to be able to tackle him at all, we must first become well acquainted with Dr. Jekyll and his orderly ways. This book is almost wholly concerned with the latter. I am content to leave Mr. Hyde to the boys in the laboratory.

And, speaking of the "boys in the laboratory," that is to say, the able and cooperative staff who assist in administering this material to our undergraduate students, I wish here to thank them one and all for their many helpful suggestions and their enthusiastic cooperation throughout the period of this "five-year plan." I cannot name one without naming them all, and I cannot name them all because I can't be sure that I won't miss one or two. So they'll all have to remain nameless; however, for the time being only. It won't be long before each one makes a name for himself as some have already.

And that is all, except to wish you all a pleasant voyage—through the pages of this book and wherever you may be going.

E. A. GUILLEMIN

Wellesley Hills
November 1953

C O N T E N T S

CONTENTS

Introduction

Although the discussions in this book, and those in the ones to follow it, are restricted to the simplest class of electrical networks, the reader should not expect that he will find them to be either simple or restricted as to scope and practical importance. Regarding their importance, it may be pointed out that an understanding of the theory of this simplest class of networks is an indispensable prerequisite to the study of all others; and as to scope it is significant to observe that because of their simplicity one is able to develop the theory of this class of networks to a remarkable degree of completeness. As a result, this theory plays a dominant role in the study and development of almost all electrical devices and systems, and is therefore as fundamental to the intellectual equipment of the electrical engineer as is a knowledge of mathematics to the physicist.

With these remarks the primary mission of this introduction is accomplished. The following paragraphs are intended to provide the uninitiated reader with a bit of an idea as to what an electrical network is, and to define the simple class of networks mentioned above. Actually it is illusory to suppose that the reader who is totally unacquainted with this subject will derive much benefit from an exposure to such a definition of terms, since he will understand them clearly only after he has gained a considerable background in network theory. On the other hand, such remarks may provide the reader with a sufficient initial orientation to enable him to gain a proper perspective as he progresses with the studies that lie ahead.

The relevant operating characteristics of a large proportion of all electrical devices are adequately described through a knowledge of currents and voltages as time functions at appropriately selected points or point pairs. The significant behavior of an electronic amplifier, for example, is characterized in terms of its volt-ampere relations at specified input and output terminal pairs; the performance characteristics of a transmission line for the distribution of electric energy or for the conveyance of electric signals representing coded information are expressible in terms of relative voltage and current values at appropriate points along the line; the behavior of a motor-generator set is conveniently studied in terms of the voltage and current input to the motor relative to the voltage and current output from the generator; the electrical characteristics of an ordinary light bulb are adequately described in terms of the voltage-current relations at its terminals.

In some of these devices, other features besides the electrical ones are usually of interest also, as are, for example, the mechanical phenomena involved in the operation of the motor-generator set, or the light spectrum emitted from the light bulb referred to above. A separation of the nonelectrical from the purely electrical studies in such cases is, however, usually desirable, and can always be accomplished under an appropriately chosen set of environmental conditions. It may additionally be necessary to make simplifying approximations and idealizations in order to render the electrical features of the problem manageable in reasonable terms, but, when this is done, the resulting representation of the original device is commonly described by the term "electric circuit" or "network."

While the electric circuit may thus be an idealized or skeletonized representation of the electrically relevant features of some physical unit in which these circuit characteristics are only incidental or at most partially influential in controlling its structure and behavior, there are important instances where the circuit is the whole device and its function is that of a controlling unit in a larger system. The electric "wave filters" and "corrective networks" essential to long-distance telephone communication circuits, or the "control networks" in servo mechanisms are examples of this sort. Here the electric circuit no longer plays an incidental role but takes its place along with other important electro-mechanical or electronic devices as a highly significant unit or building block essential to the successful operation of modern power, communication, or control systems.

Dominant in their effect upon the volt-ampere behavior of an electric circuit are its energy-storage and energy-dissipation properties. Energy storage takes place in the electric and magnetic fields associated with the network, while energy dissipation is practically ever-present because of resistance offered to the flow of electric charge through conductors. Three things, therefore, dominate in molding the electrical behavior of a network: namely, the two associated fields and the dissipative character of its various conducting paths. Although their effects are physically superimposed throughout any actual device, the idealization referred to above frequently permits one to assign them to separate portions of the physical system and to regard these portions as having negligible dimensions. Thus one speaks of certain "lumped" parts as having resistive characteristics alone, others as having influence only upon the associated magnetic fields, and a third group related solely to the pertinent electric fields.

These parts are spoken of as the *lumped parameters or elements* of a circuit. They are of three kinds: the resistance parameter or dissipative element, the inductance parameter which is related to the associated magnetic fields, and the capacitance parameter appropriate to the pertinent electric fields. Physical embodiments of these network parameters or elements (appearing wherever their occurrence is deliberate rather than incidental) are familiar to the reader as resistors (usually made of metallic wire having poor conductivity), inductors such as wire coils, and capacitors (frequently in the form of metallic sheets or plates separated by a thin film of insulating material). It is important to observe that these physical embodiments are not exact representations for the separate circuit elements which, by definition, are "pure" in the sense that each one contains none of the other two. In any physical resistor, for example, some inductive and capacitive effects are unavoidable, as are resistive and capacitive effects in a physical inductor, etc. These frequently unwanted effects present in physical resistors, inductors, and capacitors are commonly referred to as "parasitics." Since any physical device with its known parasitic elements can always be represented to a sufficient degree of approximation in terms of theoretically pure elements, a method of circuit analysis based upon pure elements alone is both adequate and useful.

The relationship of voltage across an element to the current through it, which is commonly referred to as its pertinent *volt-ampere relationship*, is in most cases a linear one (throughout reasonable operating ranges), and the appropriate constant of proportionality is designated as the "value" of that element.

There are devices in which the values of network elements are functions of the voltage across them or of the current carried by them. For example, an iron-cored coil represents an inductance element whose value is dependent upon the coil current; an electron tube represents a resistance which varies with the applied voltage. Such elements are said to be *nonlinear* because the voltage is not linearly proportional to the associated current (or to the current derivative or integral, whichever is pertinent). It is important to distinguish networks that contain such elements from those that do not, and to recognize significant differences in their response characteristics, for these differences form the basis upon which the selection of specific types of elements is made in the practical use of circuits.

There are some devices, linear as well as nonlinear, whose voltage or current transmission properties depend upon their orientation with respect to the points of excitation and observation. These are spoken of as being *unilateral* devices or elements; and wherever the usual ones need to be distinguished from these, they are referred to as *bilateral* elements.

Another important distinction having a bearing upon network behavior is made according to whether the network does or does not contain energy sources or constraints other than those explicitly given by the associated excitation. If it does, then one may expect at times to get more power out than one puts into the network, or to obtain a continued response even in the absence of a power input. When a network contains such implicit energy sources and/or constraints, it is called *active;* otherwise it is referred to as being *passive.*

The finite, lumped, linear, passive bilateral network is the simplest regarding methods of analysis needed in a study of its behavior under various operating conditions. To an introductory understanding of the physical and mathematical aspects of this type of network, the discussions of the present volume are directed.

Network Geometry
and
Network Variables

1 The Classification of Networks

Linear passive networks are distinguished from one another according to the kinds of elements that are involved, and in the manner of their interconnection. Thus a given network consisting of resistance elements alone is referred to as a *resistance network;* and *inductance* or *capacitance networks* are similarly defined as such in which only inductances or capacitances are involved. Next in order of complexity are the so-called *two-element* types, more precisely the *LC* networks (those containing inductance and capacitance elements but, by assumption, no resistances), the *RC* networks in which inductive effects are absent, and *RL* networks in which capacitive effects are absent. The *RLC* network then represents the general case in the category of linear passive networks.

2 The Graph of a Network

Quite apart from the kinds of elements involved in a given network is the all-important question of *network geometry* that concerns itself solely with the manner in which the various elements are grouped and interconnected at their terminals. In order to enhance this aspect of a network's physical makeup, one frequently draws a schematic representation of it in which no distinction is as yet made between kinds of elements. Thus each element is represented merely by a line with small circles at the ends denoting terminals. Such a graphical portrayal showing the geometrical interconnection of elements only, is called a *graph* of the given network. Figure 1 shows an example of a network as it is usually drawn so as to distinguish the various kinds of elements [part (a)] and how this same network appears when only its geometrical aspects are retained [the graph of part (b)]. The numbers associated with the various branches are added for their identification only. The terminals of the branches (which are common to two or more branches where these are confluent) are referred to as *nodes*.

5

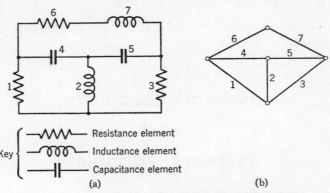

Key: —⌇WⱲ⌇— Resistance element
      —⌁₀₀₀⌁— Inductance element
      —‖— Capacitance element

(a)   (b)

FIG. 1.   A network schematic and its graph.

There are situations in which various parts of a network are only inductively connected as in part (a) of Fig. 2 where two pairs of mutually coupled inductances are involved.   Here the corresponding graph (shown in part (b) of Fig. 2) consists of three separate parts; and it is seen also

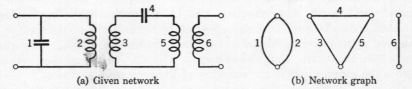

(a) Given network   (b) Network graph

FIG. 2.   The schematic and graph of a network consisting of several separate parts.

that a node may be simply the terminus of a single branch as well as the point of confluence of several branches.

With the graph of a network there are thus associated three things or concepts: namely, *branches, nodes, and separate parts.*   The graph is the skeleton of a network; it retains only its geometrical features.   It is useful when discussing how one should best go about characterizing the network behavior in terms of voltages and currents and in deciding whether a selected set of these variables are not only independent but also adequate for the unique characterization of the state of a network at any moment.

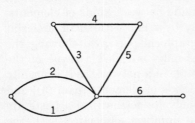

FIG. 3.   The graph of Fig. 2 coalesced into one part.

In this regard it is apparent that an economy can be effected in situations like the one in Fig. 2 through permitting one node in each of the separate parts to become coincident, thus uniting these parts, as is shown in the graph of Fig. 3.

Except for the fact that the superimposed nodes are constrained to have the same electric potential, no restrictions are imposed upon any of the branch voltages or currents through this modification which reduces the total number of nodes and the number of separate parts by equal integer values. In subsequent discussions it is thus possible without loss in generality to consider only graphs having one separate part.

3 The Concept of a "Tree"

The graph of a network places in evidence a number of closed paths upon which currents can circulate. This property of a graph (that it contain closed paths) is obviously necessary to the existence of currents

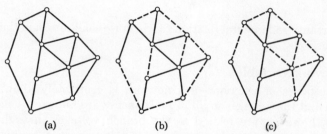

(a)   (b)   (c)

Fig. 4. A graph and two possible trees (solid lines).

in the associated network. It is a property that can be destroyed through the removal of judiciously chosen branches.

In Fig. 4 the graph of a given network is shown in part (a), and again in parts (b) and (c) with some of the branches represented by dotted lines. If the dotted branches were removed, there would remain in each of the cases shown in (b) and in (c) a graph having all of the nodes of the original graph (a) but no closed paths. This remnant of the original graph is called a "tree" for the reason that its structure (like that of any tree) possesses the significant property of having no closed paths.

More specifically, a tree is defined as any set of branches in the original graph that is just sufficient in number to connect all of the nodes. It is not difficult to see that this number is always $n_t - 1$ where n_t denotes the total number of nodes. For, if we start with only the nodes drawn and no branches, it is clear that the first added branch connects two nodes, but thereafter one additional branch is needed for each node contacted. If no more than the minimum number of $n_t - 1$ branches are used to connect all of the nodes, then it is likewise clear that the resulting structure contains no closed paths, for the creation of a closed path involves the linking of two nodes that are already contacted, and hence involves the use of more branches than are actually needed merely to connect all of the nodes.

For a given network graph it is possible to draw numerous trees, since the process just described is not a unique one. Each tree, however, connects all of the n_t nodes, and consists of

$$n = n_t - 1 \qquad\qquad (1)$$

branches, which are referred to, in any given choice, as the *tree branches*. The remaining branches, like the ones shown dotted in parts (b) and (c) of Fig. 4, are called *links*. If there are l of these, and if the total number of branches in the network graph is denoted by b, then evidently

$$b = l + n \qquad\qquad (2)$$

an important fundamental relation to which we shall return in the following discussions.

4   Network Variables

The response or behavior of a network is completely known if the currents and the voltages in all of its branches are known. The branch currents, however, are related to the branch voltages through fundamental equations that characterize the volt-ampere behavior of the separate elements. For instance, in a resistance branch the voltage drop (by Ohm's law) equals the current in that branch times the pertinent branch resistance; in a capacitance branch the voltage equals the reciprocal capacitance value times the time integral of the branch current; and in an inductance branch the voltage is given by the time derivative of the current with the inductance as a proportionality factor. Although the last-mentioned relations become somewhat more elaborate when several inductances in the network are mutually coupled (as will later be discussed in detail), their determination in no way involves the geometrical interconnection of the elements. One can always, in a straightforward manner, relate the branch voltages directly and reversibly to the branch currents.

We may, therefore, regard either the branch currents alone or the branch voltages alone as adequately characterizing the network behavior. If the total number of branches is denoted by b, then from either point of view we have b quantities that play the role of unknowns or variables in the problem of finding the network response. We shall now show that either set of b quantities is not an independent one, but that fewer variables suffice to characterize the network equilibrium, whether on a current or on a voltage basis.

If in a given network a tree is selected, then the totality of b branches is separated into two groups: the tree branches and the links. Correspondingly, the branch currents are separated into tree-branch currents and link currents. Since a removal or opening of the links destroys *all* closed paths and hence by force renders all branch currents zero, it becomes clear that the act of setting only the link currents equal to zero forces all currents in the network to be zero.* The link currents alone hold the power of life and death, so to speak, over the entire network. Their values fix all the current values; that is, it must be possible to express all of the tree-branch currents uniquely in terms of the link currents.

The inference to be drawn from this argument is that, of the b branch currents in a network, only l are independent; l is the smallest number of currents in terms of which all others can be expressed uniquely. This situation may be seen to follow from the fact that all currents become zero when the link currents are zero. Thus it is clear that the number of independent currents is surely not larger than l, for, if one of the tree-branch currents were claimed also to be independent, then its value would have to remain nonzero when all the link currents are set equal to zero, and this condition is manifestly impossible physically. It is equally clear on the other hand that the number of independent currents is surely not less than l, for then it would have to be possible to render all currents in the network zero with one or more links still in place, and this result is not possible because closed paths exist so long as some of the links remain.

Thus, in terms of currents, it must be possible to express uniquely the state of a network in terms of l variables alone. As will be shown later, these variables may be any appropriate set of link currents (according to the specific choice made for a tree), but more generally they may be chosen in a large variety of ways so that numerous specific requirements can be accommodated.

Analogously one may regard the branch voltages as separated into two groups: the tree-branch voltages, and the link voltages. Since the tree branches connect all of the nodes, it is clear that, if the tree-branch volt-

---

* In these considerations it is not necessary that we concern ourselves with the manner in which the network is energized although some sort of excitation is implied since all currents and voltages would otherwise be zero, regardless of whether the links are removed or not. If the reader insists upon being specific about the nature of the excitation, he may picture in his mind a small boy tossing coulombs into the capacitances at random intervals.

ages are forced to be zero (through short-circuiting the tree branches, for example), then all the node potentials become coincident, and hence *all* branch voltages are forced to be zero. Thus, the act of setting only the tree-branch voltages equal to zero forces all voltages in the network to be zero. The tree-branch voltages alone hold the power of life and death, so to speak, over the entire network. It must be possible, therefore, to express all of the link voltages uniquely in terms of the tree-branch voltages.

Exactly n of the branch voltages in a network are independent, namely, those pertaining to the branches of a selected tree. Surely no larger number than this can be independent because one or more of the link voltages would then have to be independent, and this assumption is contradicted by the fact that all voltages become zero through short-circuiting the tree branches alone. On the other hand, no smaller number than n voltages can form the controlling set, for it is physically not possible to force all of the node potentials to coincide so long as some tree-branch voltages remain nonzero.

Thus one recognizes that the state of a network can uniquely be characterized either by means of $l = b - n_t + 1$ currents or by $n = n_t - 1$ $= b - l$ voltages. The currents may, for example, be any set of link currents, and the voltages may be any set of tree-branch voltages. Since, in general, $n \neq l$, the characterization of a network in terms of current variables involves a different number of unknowns than does its characterization in terms of voltage variables. There is nothing inconsistent about this conclusion since we are at present considering the question of independence among voltages or currents from a geometrical point of view only. Dynamically, the number of independent variables associated with a given physical system determines uniquely its so-called degrees of freedom; their number depends neither upon any algebraic method of derivation nor upon the manner in which the variables are defined. It is, however, not appropriate to raise these questions at this time, since we are at the moment considering only those features of our problem that are controlled by the geometrical aspects of the given network.

5   The Concept of Loop Currents; Tie Sets and Tie-Set Schedules

It is possible to give to the link currents an interesting geometrical interpretation that is useful when these are selected as a set of variables. This interpretation is best presented in terms of a specific example. In Fig. 5(a) is shown a simple network graph and in parts (b), (c), and (d) of the same figure are several possible choices for a tree. For the tree of part (b), the branches numbered 1, 2, 3, 4 are the links. If one of these is inserted into the tree, the resulting structure has just one closed path or loop, which is different for each link. Thus, for this choice of tree, a distinct set of closed paths is associated with the respective links. In Fig. 6(a) these are indicated by loop arrows, numbered to correspond to the similarly numbered links with which they are associated and

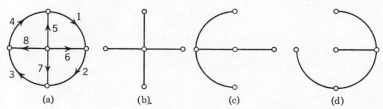

FIG. 5.   A graph and three possible trees.

directed (as indicated by these loop arrows) so as to be confluent with the respective link currents. Thus loop 1 is formed by placing link 1 alone into the tree of Fig. 5(b); loop 2 is formed by placing link 2 alone into this tree; etc.

This procedure suggests that we may give to the link currents a new interpretation, namely, that of being *circulatory* currents or loop currents.

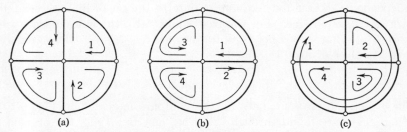

FIG. 6.   Closed paths or loops corresponding, respectively, to the three trees shown in Fig. 5.

Each link current is thus identified with a loop current; the remaining tree-branch currents are clearly expressible as appropriate superpositions of these loop currents, and hence are uniquely determined by the link currents, as predicted earlier.

If the branch currents in the network graph of Fig. 5(a) are denoted by $j_1, j_2, \cdots, j_8$, numbered to correspond to the branch numbering, and if the loop currents of the graph of Fig. 6(a) are denoted by i_1, i_2, i_3, i_4, then we can make the identifications

$$j_1 = i_1, \qquad j_2 = i_2, \qquad j_3 = i_3, \qquad j_4 = i_4 \qquad (3)$$

Through comparison of Figs. 5(a) and 6(a) one can then readily express the remaining tree-branch currents as appropriate superpositions of the loop currents, thus,

$$j_5 = i_1 - i_4$$

$$j_6 = i_2 - i_1$$

$$j_7 = i_3 - i_2 \tag{4}$$

$$j_8 = i_4 - i_3$$

or, being mindful of the relations 3, have

$$j_5 = j_1 - j_4$$

$$j_6 = j_2 - j_1$$

$$j_7 = j_3 - j_2 \tag{5}$$

$$j_8 = j_4 - j_3$$

These last four equations express the tree-branch currents, uniquely and unambiguously, in terms of the link currents. Thus, of the eight branch currents in the graph of Fig. 5(a), only four are geometrically independent. These four are appropriate to the set of links associated with any selected tree. For the tree of Fig. 5(b), the link currents are j_1, j_2, j_3, j_4. For the tree of Fig. 5(c) they are j_1, j_2, j_5, j_7. Here we may write, in place of Eqs. 3,

$$j_1 = i_1, \qquad j_2 = i_2, \qquad j_5 = i_3, \qquad j_7 = i_4 \tag{6}$$

These loop currents circulate on the contours indicated in Fig. 6(b), which again are found through inserting, one at a time, the branches 1, 2, 5, 7 into the tree of Fig. 5(c). The tree-branch currents in this case are expressed in terms of the loop currents by the relations

$$j_3 = i_2 + i_4$$

$$j_4 = i_1 - i_3$$

$$j_6 = i_2 - i_1 \tag{7}$$

$$j_8 = i_1 - i_2 - i_3 - i_4$$

which are found by inspection of Figs. 5(a) and 6(b) through noting that the currents in the tree branches result from the superposition of pertinent loop currents.

Through substitution of Eqs. 6 into 7, one again obtains the tree-branch currents expressed in terms of the link currents

$$j_3 = j_7 + j_2$$
$$j_4 = j_1 - j_5$$
$$j_6 = j_2 - j_1 \tag{8}$$
$$j_8 = j_1 - j_2 - j_5 - j_7$$

thus making evident once more the fact that only four of the eight branch currents are geometrically independent.

The reader is cautioned against concluding that *any* four of the eight branch currents may be regarded as an independent set. The branches pertaining to a set of independent currents must be the links associated with a tree, for it is this circumstance that assures the independence of the currents. Thus the branch currents j_5, j_6, j_7, j_8, for example, could not be a set of independent currents because the remaining branches 1, 2, 3, 4 do not form a tree. The concept of a tree is recognized as useful because it yields a simple and unambiguous method of deciding whether any selected set of branch currents is an independent one. Or one can say that the tree concept provides a straightforward method of determining a possible set of independent current variables for any given network geometry.

Part (d) of Fig. 5 shows still another possible choice for a tree appropriate to the graph of part (a), and in Fig. 6(c) is shown the corresponding set of loops. In this case one has

$$j_4 = i_1, \qquad j_5 = i_2, \qquad j_7 = i_3, \qquad j_8 = i_4 \tag{9}$$

and through superposition there follows that

$$j_1 = i_1 + i_2 = j_4 + j_5$$
$$j_2 = i_1 - i_3 - i_4 = j_4 - j_7 - j_8$$
$$j_3 = i_1 - i_4 = j_4 - j_8 \tag{10}$$
$$j_6 = -i_2 - i_3 - i_4 = -j_5 - j_7 - j_8$$

When dealing with networks having large numbers of branches and correspondingly elaborate geometries, one must have a less cumbersome and more systematic procedure for obtaining the algebraic relationships between the branch currents and the loop-current variables. Thus it is readily appreciated that the process of drawing and numbering the reference arrows for the loops, and subsequently obtaining by inspection the appropriate expressions for the branch currents as algebraic sums of pertinent loop currents, can become both tedious and confusing in situations involving complex geometries.

A systematic way of indicating the loops associated with the selection of a particular tree is had through use of a schedule such as 11, which

Loop No.	Branch No.							
	1	2	3	4	5	6	7	8
1	1	0	0	1	0	−1	0	1
2	0	1	1	0	0	1	0	−1
3	0	0	0	−1	1	0	0	−1
4	0	0	1	0	0	0	1	−1

(11)

pertains to the graph of Fig. 5(a) with the tree of part (c) and hence for the loops shown in Fig. 6(b). To interpret this schedule we note that the first row, pertaining to loop 1, indicates that a circuit around this loop is equivalent to traversing in the positive reference direction, branches 1, 4, and 8, and, in the negative reference direction, branch 6. None of the remaining branches participate in forming the contour of loop 1, and so their corresponding spaces in the first row of the schedule are filled in with zeros. The second row is similarly constructed, noting that the pertinent loop contour is formed through traversing branches 2, 3, and 6 positively, and branch 8 negatively. Thus the successive rows in this schedule indicate the confluent sets of branches that participate in forming the various correspondingly numbered loops, due attention being given (and indicated through appropriate algebraic signs) to the confluence or counterfluence of respective branch and loop reference arrows.

A most interesting and useful property of this schedule is now revealed through attention to its columns, for we note that their elements are the coefficients in an orderly written set of equations expressing the branch currents in terms of the loop currents. Interpretation of the columns of schedule 11 in this way yields the equations

$$j_1 = i_1 \qquad\qquad j_5 = i_3$$
$$j_2 = i_2 \qquad\qquad j_6 = -i_1 + i_2$$
$$j_3 = i_2 + i_4 \qquad\qquad j_7 = i_4 \qquad\qquad (12)$$
$$j_4 = i_1 - i_3 \qquad\qquad j_8 = i_1 - i_2 - i_3 - i_4$$

which are seen to agree with Eqs. 6 and 7.

The reason why this schedule has the property just mentioned may best be seen through supposing that it is originally constructed, by columns, according to the relationships expressed in Eqs. 12. One subsequently can appreciate why the resulting rows of the schedule indicate the pertinent closed paths, through noting that the nonzero elements of a row are associated with branches traversed by the same loop current, and these collectively must form the closed path in question.

The actual construction of the schedule may thus be done in either of two ways, viz.: by rows, according to a set of independent closed paths (for example, those associated with a selected tree), or by columns, according to a set of equations expressing branch currents in terms of loop currents. If constructed by columns, the rows of the schedule automatically indicate the closed paths upon which the associated loop currents circulate; and, if constructed by rows from a given set of closed paths, the columns of the resulting schedule automatically yield the pertinent relations for the branch currents in terms of the loop currents. This type of schedule (which for reasons given later is called a *tie-set schedule*) is thus revealed to be a compact and effective means for indicating both the geometrical structure of the closed paths and the resulting algebraic relations between branch currents and loop currents.

Regarding this relationship, one may initially be concerned about its uniqueness, since there are fewer loop currents than branch currents. Thus, if asked to solve Eqs. 12 for the loop currents in terms of branch currents, one might be puzzled by the fact that there are more equations than unknowns. However, the number of independent equations among this set just equals the number of unknown loop currents (for reasons given in the preceding discussion), and the equations collectively form a consistent set. Therefore the desired solution is effected through separating from Eqs. 12 an independent subset and solving these. Knowing that the equations were originally obtained through choice of the tree of Fig. 5(c), thus designating branch currents j_1, j_2, j_5, j_7 as a possible independent set, indicates that the corresponding equations among those given by 12 may be regarded as an independent subset. These yield the identifications $i_1 = j_1$, $i_2 = j_2$, $i_3 = j_5$, $i_4 = j_7$ as indicated in Eqs. 6 for this choice of tree.

It is, however, not essential that the independent subset chosen from Eqs. 12 be this particular one. Thus, if we consider the tree of Fig. 5(d) as a possible choice, it becomes clear that branch currents j_4, j_5, j_7, j_8 are an independent set. The corresponding equations separated from 12, namely,

$$j_4 = i_1 - i_3$$
$$j_5 = i_3$$
$$j_7 = i_4$$
$$j_8 = i_1 - i_2 - i_3 - i_4$$
(13)

may alternatively be regarded as an appropriate independent subset. Their solution reads

$$i_1 = j_4 + j_5$$
$$i_2 = j_4 - j_7 - j_8$$
$$i_3 = j_5$$
$$i_4 = j_7$$
(14)

Noting from Eqs. 8 that $j_4 + j_5 = j_1$, and that $j_4 - j_7 - j_8 = j_2$, it is clear that 14 agrees with the former result.

Four of the eight Eqs. 12 are independent. A simple rule for picking four independent ones is to choose those corresponding to the link currents associated with a possible tree. Any four independent ones may be solved for the four loop currents. Substitution of these solutions into the remaining equations then yields the previously discussed relations between tree-branch currents and link currents.

There should be no difficulty in understanding this situation since the previous discussion has made it amply clear that the link currents or loop currents are an independent set and all other branch currents are uniquely related to these. Equations 12 are consistent with this viewpoint and contain all of the implicit and explicit relations pertinent thereto. Hence their solution cannot fail to be unique, no matter what specific approach one may take to gain this end.

Although a schedule like 11 may be constructed either by columns or by rows, the usual viewpoint will be that it is constructed by rows from an observation of those sets of confluent branches forming the pertinent closed paths. The latter are placed in evidence, one by one, through imagining that all the links are opened except one, thus forcing all but one of the link or loop currents to be zero. The existence of a single loop current energizes a set of branches forming the closed path on which this loop current circulates. This set of branches, called a *tie set*, is indicated by the elements in the pertinent row of the tie-set schedule.

If the geometry of the network graph permits its mappability upon a plane or spherical surface without crossed branches, then we may regard any tie set as forming a boundary that divides the total network into two portions.* Hence, if the branches in such a set are imagined to shrink longitudinally until they reduce to a single point, the network becomes "tied off" so to speak (as a fish net would by means of a draw string), and the two portions bounded by the tie set become effectively separated except for a common node. It is this interpretation of the tie set that suggests its name.

Although there are several important variations in this procedure for establishing an appropriate set of current variables, we shall leave these for subsequent discussion and turn our attention now to the alternate procedure (dual to the one just described) of formulating a set of network variables on a voltage basis.

6 The Concept of Node-Pair Voltages; Cut Sets and Cut-Set Schedules

On the voltage side of the network picture, an entirely analogous situation prevails. Here we begin by regarding the tree-branch voltages as a possible set of independent variables in terms of which the state of a network may uniquely be expressed. Since the tree branches connect all of the nodes, it is possible to trace a path from any node to any other node in the network by traversing tree branches alone; and therefore it is possible to express the difference in potential between any pair of nodes in terms of the tree-branch voltages alone. Moreover, the path connecting any two nodes via tree branches is unique since the tree has no closed loops and hence offers no alternate paths between node pairs. Therefore, the potential difference between any two nodes, referred to as the pertinent *node-pair voltage*, is uniquely expressible in terms of the tree-branch voltages. The link voltages, which are a particular set of node-pair voltages, are thus recognized to be uniquely expressible in terms of the tree-branch voltages.

Let us illustrate these principles with the network graph of Fig. 5(a), and choose initially the tree given in part (b) of this same figure. If the branch voltages are denoted by v_1, v_2, $\cdots$, v_8, numbered to correspond to the given branch numbering, then the quantities v_5, v_6, v_7, v_8 are the

---

* For a graph not mappable on a sphere (for example one that requires a doughnut-shaped surface), some but not all tie sets have this property. This point is discussed further in Art. 9.

tree-branch voltages and hence may be regarded as an independent set. They may simultaneously be regarded as node-pair voltages, and, since they are to serve as the chosen set of variables, we distinguish them through an appropriate notation and write

$$e_1 = v_5, \qquad e_2 = v_6, \qquad e_3 = v_7, \qquad e_4 = v_8 \qquad (15)$$

This part of the procedure parallels the use of a separate notation for the loop currents i_1, i_2, $\cdots$ when choosing variables on a current basis. There the link currents are identified with loop currents; in Eqs. 15 the tree-branch voltages are identified with node-pair voltages.

The remaining branch voltages, namely the link voltages, are now readily expressible in terms of the four tree-branch or node-pair voltages 15. Thus, by inspection of Fig. 5(a) we have

$$v_1 = -v_5 + v_6 = -e_1 + e_2$$
$$v_2 = -v_6 + v_7 = -e_2 + e_3$$
$$v_3 = -v_7 + v_8 = -e_3 + e_4 \qquad (16)$$
$$v_4 = -v_8 + v_5 = -e_4 + e_1$$

The procedure in writing these equations is to regard each link voltage as a potential difference between the nodes terminating the pertinent link, and to pass from one of these nodes to the other via tree branches only, adding algebraically the several tree-branch voltages encountered.

If the tree of Fig. 5(c) is chosen, the branch voltages v_3, v_4, v_6, v_8 become the appropriate independent set, and we make the identifications

$$e_1 = v_3, \qquad e_2 = v_4, \qquad e_3 = v_6, \qquad e_4 = v_8 \qquad (17)$$

The expressions for the link voltages in terms of these read

$$v_1 = -v_4 + v_6 - v_8 = -e_2 + e_3 - e_4$$
$$v_2 = -v_3 - v_6 + v_8 = -e_1 - e_3 + e_4$$
$$v_5 = v_4 + v_8 = e_2 + e_4 \qquad (18)$$
$$v_7 = -v_3 + v_8 = -e_1 + e_4$$

The results expressed in Eqs. 16 and 18 bear out the truth of a statement made in Art. 4 to the effect that any set of tree-branch voltages may be regarded as an independent group of variables in terms of which the remaining branch voltages (link voltages) are uniquely expressible. In the network graph of Fig. 5, any tree has four branches. Hence, of the eight branch voltages, only four are geometrically independent.

These may be the ones pertinent to any selected tree; and the rest are readily expressed in terms of them.

In dealing with more complex network geometries it becomes useful to establish a systematic procedure for the selection of node-pair voltage variables and for the unique expression of the branch voltages in terms of them. The accomplishment of this end follows a pattern that is entirely analogous (yet dual) to that described in the previous article for the current basis. That is to say, we seek to construct a schedule appropriate to the voltage basis in the same way that the tie-set schedule is pertinent to the current basis. To this end we must first establish the geometrical interpretation for a set of branches which, for the voltage basis, plays a role analogous to that defined for the current basis by a tie set (or confluent set of branches forming a closed loop). The latter is placed in evidence through opening all of the links but one, so that all loop currents are zero except one. The analogous procedure on a voltage basis is to force all but one of the node-pair (i.e., tree-branch) voltages to be zero, which is accomplished through short-circuiting all but one of the tree branches. This act will in general simultaneously short-circuit some of the links, but there will in any nontrivial case be left some links in addition to the one nonshort-circuited tree branch that are likewise not short-circuited and will appear to form connecting links between the pair of nodes terminating the pertinent tree branch. This set of branches, which is called a *cut set*, is the desired analogue of a tie set, as the following detailed elaboration will clarify.

Consider again the network of Fig. 5(a) and the tree of part (b) of this figure, together with the pertinent stipulation of node-pair voltages as expressed by Eqs. 15. The cut-set schedule appropriate to this situation reads as given in 19.

Node Pair No.	Branch No.							
	1	2	3	4	5	6	7	8
1	-1	0	0	1	1	0	0	0
2	1	-1	0	0	0	1	0	0
3	0	1	-1	0	0	0	1	0
4	0	0	1	-1	0	0	0	1

$$(19)$$

It is customary to regard the node-pair voltages e_1, e_2, e_3, e_4 as rises, while the branch voltages are drops. For this reason the reference arrow for an e is opposite to that for the v that it is numerically equal to. With this fact in mind let us consider in detail the construction of schedule 19 by its rows, referring for this purpose to Fig. 5. Since by Eqs. 15, $e_1 = v_5$, we observe that the terminals of branch 5 constitute node pair 1, and the tip end of the reference arrow for e_1 is at the tail end of the reference arrow for branch 5. Analogous remarks apply to the other three node pairs which are the terminals of branches 6, 7, and 8.

To determine the cut set associated with node pair 1, we regard e_1 as the only nonzero node-pair voltage; that is, branches 6, 7, and 8 are short-circuited. Under these conditions it should be clear that links 2 and 3 are likewise short-circuited, but that links 1 and 4 together with tree branch 5 remain nonshort-circuited. These three branches, therefore, constitute the cut set pertinent to node pair 1, and the corresponding elements in the first row of schedule 19 thus are the only non-zero ones.

Now, as to the algebraic signs of these nonzero elements, we note that a positive e_1 would cause currents that are confluent with the reference arrows in branches 4 and 5, and counterfluent with the reference arrow in branch 1. The sign given to the nonzero element is chosen positive for confluence and negative for counterfluence.

Similarly, node pair 2 is identified with the terminals of branch 6. To place in evidence the associated cut set, we imagine the other tree branches to be short-circuited, whence the nonshort-circuited branches are 1, 2, and 6. The sign convention just described yields plus signs for branches 1 and 6, and a minus sign for branch 2. Construction of the remaining rows in this cut-set schedule follows the same pattern.

If we now regard the columns in this schedule as containing the coefficients in an orderly written system of equations expressing the branch voltages in terms of the node-pair voltages, we have

$$
\begin{aligned}
v_1 &= -e_1 + e_2 & v_5 &= e_1 \\
v_2 &= -e_2 + e_3 & v_6 &= e_2 \\
v_3 &= -e_3 + e_4 & v_7 &= e_3 \\
v_4 &= e_1 - e_4 & v_8 &= e_4
\end{aligned}
\tag{20}
$$

These agree with the results expressed by Eqs. 15 and 16. Hence we see that the cut-set schedule 19 could alternatively have been constructed by columns according to Eqs. 15 and 16, or the equivalent Eqs. 20.

The cut set is that group of branches that becomes energized when its pertinent node-pair voltage is the only nonzero one among all of the node-pair voltages, just as the tie set is that group of branches that becomes energized when its pertinent loop current is the only nonzero one among all of the loop currents. It is clear, therefore, that the cut sets may alternatively be found from Eqs. 20 through picking out the branches corresponding to those nonzero v's that result from considering the e's to be nonzero one at a time; and it is thus appreciated that the construction of a cut-set schedule may be done either by rows according to the method first described or by columns according to a set of equations like those given by 20. If constructed by rows, through picking out the cut sets, the columns of the schedule automatically yield the associated relations for the branch-voltage drops in terms of the node-pair voltages; and, if constructed by columns, the rows of the schedule automatically yield the associated cut sets.

An important geometrical characteristic of a cut set is recognized from the following consideration. If all but one of the branches in a tree become short circuits, then only the two nodes at the ends of the nonshort-circuited branch survive. Or we may say that the totality of nodes in the network separate into two groups; all the nodes of one group become superimposed at one end of the nonshort-circuited branch, and all the nodes of the second group coincide at the other end of this branch. If we think of grasping these two groups of nodes separately, one in each hand, and regard the branches as though they were elastic bands, then the cut set in question is that set of branches that is stretched as we pull our hands apart. If we were to cut these stretched branches, the original network graph would be cut into two subgraphs, one of which we would be holding in each hand. It is this interpretation that suggests the name "cut set."

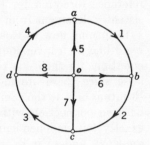

A cut set quite generally is thus seen to be any group comprising a minimum of branches so selected that the act of cutting them separates the network into two parts. We can visualize the selection of a cut set as being done by picking up in one hand some of the nodes in the network and pulling these away from the rest (which may be thought of as fastened somehow to the plane of the paper); the stretched branches form a cut set.

Fig. 7. Designation of the nodes in the graph of Fig. 5 by letters o, a, b, c, d.

With this interpretation in mind let us again consider the formation of the cut-set schedule 19 based upon the graph of Fig. 5(a) with the tree of part (b) of that figure and hence for the node-pair voltages defined by Eqs. 15. In Fig. 7 this graph is redrawn with the nodes lettered so we can refer to them specifically.   Branches 5, 6, 7, 8 constitute the tree.   Node-pair voltage e_1 equals v_5, and the tip of its reference arrow is at node o. To find the cut set corresponding to this node-pair voltage, the remaining tree branches are regarded as short circuits, whence the nodes b, c, d are seen to coincide with the node o.   In our right hand we, therefore, imagine picking up nodes o, b, c, d, and with our left hand holding node a. The tip end of the reference arrow for e_1 is in our right hand; hence the positive reference direction for branches in the associated cut set is from our right hand to our left hand.   The stretched branches clearly are those numbered 1, 4, 5.   The reference arrows on 4 and 5 are confluent with the positive reference direction for this node pair while that on branch 1 is counterfluent.   Construction of the first row of schedule 19 is thus clear.

To construct the second row we observe that $e_2 = v_6$, and so the tip end of e_2 is again at node o.   This time branches 5, 7, 8 are regarded as short circuits; so the nodes picked up in our right hand become o, a, c, d, and the positive reference direction for the cut-set branches is again divergent from our right hand.   The cut set consists of branches 1, 2, 6, with 1 and 6 positive and 2 negative.

For e_3 the picked-up nodes are o, a, b, d, and for e_4 they are o, a, b, c. It is useful always to consider picking up that group of nodes that coincides at the tip end of the pertinent node-pair voltage; then the positive reference direction for the branches in the associated cut set is consistently divergent from the picked-up nodes.

Returning now to Eqs. 20, a few additional remarks may be in order regarding their inversion.   That is to say, if we were asked to solve these equations for the e's in terms of the v's, the question of uniqueness may arise since there are more equations than unknowns.   However, the situation here is the same as has already been discussed for the current basis in connection with Eqs. 12.   Namely, among Eqs. 20 there are exactly four independent ones (as many as there are independent unknowns), and so it is merely a matter of separating four independent equations from the given group and solving these.   The last four are obviously independent and yield the definitions chosen for the e's in the first place.   However, we can alternatively choose say the first three and the fifth.   Their solution yields

$$e_1 = v_5$$
$$e_2 = v_1 + v_5$$
$$e_3 = v_1 + v_2 + v_5 \tag{21}$$
$$e_4 = v_1 + v_2 + v_3 + v_5$$

but Eqs. 16 show that

$$v_1 + v_5 = v_6$$

$$v_1 + v_2 + v_5 = v_7 \tag{22}$$

$$v_1 + v_2 + v_3 + v_5 = v_8$$

Hence the solutions 21 again agree with the definitions 15.

Of Eqs. 20, four are independent. Not *any* four are independent, but there are no more than four independent ones in this group, and there are several different sets of four independent ones that can be found among them. A simple rule for picking four independent ones is to choose those corresponding to the branch voltages of a possible tree. The solution to these yields the expressions for the e's in terms of the v's; and substitution of these solutions for the e's into the remaining equations yields the previously discussed relations between link voltages and tree-branch voltages. The cut-set schedule which contains the information regarding the geometrical character of the cut sets, as well as the algebraic relationships between the implied node-pair voltages and the branch voltages, is thus seen to be a compact and effective mode of expressing these things. It does for the formulation of variables on the voltage basis what the tie-set schedule does for the establishment of a system of variables on the current basis. Continued use will be made of both types of schedules in the following discussions.

7 Alternative Methods of Choosing Current Variables

The procedure for selecting an appropriate set of independent current variables in a given network problem can be approached in a different manner which may sometimes be preferred. Thus, the method given in Art. 5, which identifies the link currents with a set of loop-current

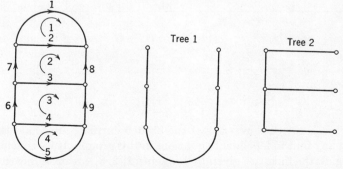

Fig. 8.   A graph with meshes chosen as loops, and two possible trees.

variables, leaves the tie sets or closed paths upon which these currents circulate to be determined from the choice of a tree, whereas one may prefer to specify a set of closed paths for the loop currents at the outset.

Consider in this connection the graph of Fig. 8. In addition to providing the branches with numbers and reference arrows, a set of loops have also been chosen and designated with the circulatory arrows numbered 1, 2, 3, 4. These loops, incidentally, are referred to as *meshes* because they have the appearance of the meshes in a fish net. It is a common practice in network analysis to choose, as a set of current variables, the currents that are assumed to circulate on the contours of these meshes. Having made such a choice, we must know how to relate in an unambiguous and reversible manner, the branch currents to the chosen mesh currents.

This end is accomplished through setting down the tie-set schedule corresponding to the choice made for the closed paths defining the tie sets. With reference to the graph of Fig. 8 one has, by inspection, schedule 23 and the columns yield

Mesh No.	Branch No.								
	1	2	3	4	5	6	7	8	9
1	1	−1	0	0	0	0	0	0	0
2	0	1	−1	0	0	0	1	−1	0
3	0	0	1	−1	0	1	0	0	−1
4	0	0	0	1	−1	0	0	0	0

(23)

$$j_1 = i_1 \qquad j_4 = -i_3 + i_4 \qquad j_7 = i_2$$

$$j_2 = -i_1 + i_2 \qquad j_5 = -i_4 \qquad j_8 = -i_2 \qquad (24)$$

$$j_3 = -i_2 + i_3 \qquad j_6 = i_3 \qquad j_9 = -i_3$$

The mesh currents in terms of the branch currents are found through solving any four independent equations in this group. If we consider tree 1 in Fig. 8, the links are given by branches 1, 2, 3, 4, thus indicating that the first four of Eqs. 24 are independent. These yield

$$i_1 = j_1$$
$$i_2 = j_1 + j_2$$
$$i_3 = j_1 + j_2 + j_3 \tag{25}$$
$$i_4 = j_1 + j_2 + j_3 + j_4$$

Substitution into the remaining Eqs. 24, gives

$$j_5 = -j_1 - j_2 - j_3 - j_4$$
$$j_6 = j_1 + j_2 + j_3$$
$$j_7 = j_1 + j_2 \tag{26}$$
$$j_8 = -j_1 - j_2$$
$$j_9 = -j_1 - j_2 - j_3$$

These express the tree-branch currents in terms of the link currents.

If instead, we choose tree 2 in Fig. 8, the branches 1, 5, 8, 9 become links. The corresponding equations in group 24, namely,

$$i_1 = j_1$$
$$i_4 = -j_5$$
$$i_2 = -j_8 \tag{27}$$
$$i_3 = -j_9$$

are independent and give the expressions for the mesh currents in terms of the link currents. With these, the remaining Eqs. 24 yield again the tree-branch currents in terms of the link currents, thus:

$$j_2 = -j_1 - j_8$$
$$j_3 = j_8 - j_9$$
$$j_4 = -j_5 + j_9 \tag{28}$$
$$j_6 = -j_9$$
$$j_7 = -j_8$$

It is readily seen that the results expressed by Eqs. 25 and 26 are consistent with those given by Eqs. 27 and 28. That is to say, the choice of a tree has nothing to do with the algebraic relations between the loop currents and the branch currents; it merely serves as a convenient way of establishing an independent subset among Eqs. 24. In the present very simple example, one can just as easily pick an independent subset without the aid of the tree concept; however, in more complex problems the latter can prove very useful.

In approaching the establishment of a set of current variables through making at the outset a choice of closed paths, a difficulty arises in that the *independence* of these paths is in general not assured. A necessary (though not sufficient) condition is that *all* branches must participate in forming these paths, for, if one or more of the branches were not traversed by loop currents, then the currents in these branches in addition to the loop currents would appear to be independent. Actually, the loop currents chosen in this manner could not be independent since altogether there can be only l independent currents.

A sufficient (though not necessary) procedure to insure the independence of the closed paths (tie sets) is to select them successively in such a way that each additional path involves at least one branch that is not part of any of the previously selected paths. This statement follows from the fact that the paths or tie sets form an independent set if the l rows in the associated tie-set schedule are independent: that is, if it is not possible to express any row in this schedule as a linear combination of the other rows. If, as we write down the successive rows in this schedule, each new row involves a branch that has not appeared in any of the previous rows, that row can surely not be formed from a linear combination of those already chosen, and hence must be independent of them.

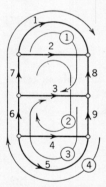

A glance at schedule 23 shows that this principle is met. Thus, construction of the first row involves only branches 1 and 2. The second row introduces the additional branches 3, 7, 8; the third row adds branches 4, 6, and 9, and the last row involves the previously unused branch 5. It is not difficult to convince oneself that, if one designates only *meshes* as closed paths (which is, of course, possible only in a graph that is mappable on a plane or sphere), then the rows in the associated tie-set schedule can always be written in such a sequence that the principle just described will be met. This simple choice in a plane mappable graph, therefore, always assures the independence of the closed paths and hence does the same for the implied mesh-current variables.

FIG. 9. A modified choice of loops for the graph of Fig. 8 that turns out not to form an independent set.

However, it is quite possible for the l rows in a tie-set schedule to be independent while not fulfilling the property just pointed out. Thus, as already stated above, this property of the rows is a sufficient though not necessary condition to insure their independence. When closed paths are chosen in a more general manner, as they sometimes may be, it is not always evident at the outset whether the choice made is acceptable. To illustrate this point, let us reconsider the network graph of Fig. 8 with the choice of closed paths shown in Fig. 9. The tie-set schedule reads as in 29, and hence the expressions for the branch currents in terms

Loop No.	Branch No.								
	1	2	3	4	5	6	7	8	9
1	1	0	−1	0	0	0	1	−1	0
2	0	1	0	−1	0	1	1	−1	−1
3	0	0	1	0	−1	1	0	0	−1
4	1	0	0	0	−1	1	1	−1	−1

(29)

of the loop currents are

$$j_1 = i_1 + i_4 \qquad j_4 = -i_2 \qquad j_7 = i_1 + i_2 + i_4$$

$$j_2 = i_2 \qquad j_5 = -i_3 - i_4 \qquad j_8 = -i_1 - i_2 - i_4 \qquad (30)$$

$$j_3 = -i_1 + i_3 \qquad j_6 = i_2 + i_3 + i_4 \qquad j_9 = -i_2 - i_3 - i_4$$

as may also be verified by inspection of Fig. 9.

To investigate the independence of the chosen loops, we observe that the choice of tree 1 in Fig. 8 indicates that the branch currents j_1, j_2, j_3, j_4 form an independent set. Hence the first four of Eqs. 30 should be independent. They obviously are not, since the right-hand members of the second and fourth equations are identical except for a change in algebraic sign. Hence the loops indicated in Fig. 9 are not an independent set, notwithstanding the fact that they are l in number and collectively traverse all of the branches.

If we modify the choice of loops in Fig. 9 merely by shifting the part of loop 4 that traverses branch 1 onto branch 2, the resultant set is found to be an independent one.* It should thus be clear that the choice of an

* It might be noted, incidentally, that the rows of the correspondingly modified schedule 29 do not fulfill the property that each successive one involves at least one new branch. Nevertheless these rows are independent.

independent set of loops (or tie sets) is in general not a matter that is evident by inspection, although one has a straightforward procedure for checking a given selection. Namely, the chosen set of loops are independent if the l rows of the associated tie-set schedule are independent; and they are, if it is possible to find in this schedule a subset of l independent columns (i.e., l independent equations among a set like 30). The simplest procedure for making this check among the columns is to pick those columns corresponding to the links of *any* chosen tree. These must be independent if the l rows of the schedule are to be independent. They are if the pertinent equations (like the first four of 30 in the test discussed in the previous paragraph) have unique solutions. Usually one can readily see by inspection whether or not such solutions exist. An elegant algebraic method is to see if the determinant of these equations is nonzero. Thus the nonvanishing of the determinant formed from the subset of columns corresponding to the links of a chosen tree suffices to prove the independence of an arbitrarily selected set of closed paths.

In the case of graphs having many branches this method may prove tedious, and so it is useful to be aware of alternative procedures for arriving at more general current-variable definitions, should this be desirable. Thus one may make use of the fact that the most general tie-set schedule is obtainable through successive elementary transformations of the rows of any given one, and that such transformations leave the independence of the rows invariant. We may, for example, start with a schedule like 23 that is based upon a choice of meshes so that its rows are surely independent. Suppose we construct a new first row through adding to the elements of the present one the respective elements of the second row. The new schedule is then as shown in 31.

Loop No.	Branch No.									
	1	2	3	4	5	6	7	8	9	
1	1	0	−1	0	0	0	1	−1	0	(31)
2	0	1	−1	0	0	0	1	−1	0	
3	0	0	1	−1	0	1	0	0	−1	
4	0	0	0	1	−1	0	0	0	0	

Loops 2, 3, 4 are still the meshes 2, 3, 4 of Fig. 8. However, loop 1 is now the combined contour of meshes 1 and 2, as a comparison of the first row of the new schedule with the graph of Fig. 8 reveals. If we modify this new schedule further by constructing a new second row with elements equal to the sum of the respective ones of the present rows 2, 3, and 4, there results another schedule that implies a loop 2 with the combined contours of meshes 2, 3, and 4. It should thus be clear that more general loops or tie sets are readily formed through combining linearly a set of existing simple ones. So long as only one new row is constructed from the combination of rows in a given schedule, and if the pertinent old row is a constituent part of this combination, the procedure cannot destroy the independence of a given set of rows.

Each new schedule has the property that its columns correctly yield the expressions for the branch currents in terms of the implied new loop currents. That is to say, since transformation of the schedule through making linear row combinations implies a revision in the choice of loops, it likewise implies a revision in the algebraic definitions of the loop currents. Nevertheless the relations expressing the branch currents in terms of these new loop currents is still given by the coefficients in the columns of the schedule. For example, we would get for schedule 31 the relations

$$j_1 = i'_1 \qquad\qquad j_4 = -i'_3 + i'_4 \qquad j_7 = i'_1 + i'_2$$

$$j_2 = i'_2 \qquad\qquad j_5 = -i'_4 \qquad\qquad j_8 = -i'_1 - i'_2 \quad (32)$$

$$j_3 = -i'_1 - i'_2 + i'_3 \qquad j_6 = i'_3 \qquad\qquad j_9 = -i'_3$$

where primes are used on the i's to distinguish them from those in Eqs. 24 which are pertinent to schedule 23.

Comparison of Eqs. 24 and 32 reveals the transformation in the loop currents implied by the transformation of schedule 23 to the form 31, namely:

$$i_1 = i'_1$$

$$i_2 = i'_1 + i'_2$$

$$i_3 = i'_3 \qquad\qquad\qquad (33)$$

$$i_4 = i'_4$$

This result is at first sight somewhat unexpected. Thus the transformation from schedule 23 to schedule 31 implies leaving the contours for the loop currents i_2, i_3, i_4 the same as in the graph of Fig. 8, but changes the contour for loop current i_1. Offhand we would expect the algebraic definition for i_1 to change and those for i_2, i_3, and i_4 to remain the same. Instead we see from Eqs. 33 that i_1, i_3, and i_4 are unchanged while i_2 changes.   Nevertheless Eqs. 32 are correct, as we can readily verify through sketching in Fig. 8 the altered contour for loop 1 and expressing the branch currents as linear superpositions of the loop currents, noting this altered path for i_1.   The results expressed by Eqs. 33, therefore, are surely correct also.

The mental confusion temporarily created by this result disappears if we concentrate our attention upon schedule 23 and Eqs. 24 and ask ourselves: What change in relations 24 will bring about the addition of row 2 to row 1 in schedule 23 and leave rows 2, 3, and 4 unchanged? The answer is that we must replace the symbol i_2 by $i_1 + i_2$, for then every element in row 2 will also appear in row 1, in addition to the elements that are already in row 1, and nothing else will change.   The lesson to be learned from this example is that we should not expect a simple and obvious connection between the contours chosen for loop currents and the algebraic definitions for these currents, nor should we expect to be able to correlate by inspection changes in the chosen contours (tie sets) and corresponding transformations in the loop currents until experience with these matters has given us an adequate insight into the rather subtle relationships implied by such transformations.

The reason for our being misled in the first place is that we are too prone to regard the choice of contours for loop currents as *equivalent* to their definition in terms of the branch currents, whereas in reality the fixing of these contours merely *implies* the algebraic relationships between the loop currents and branch currents (through fixing the tie-set schedule); it does *not* place them in evidence.

The most general form a linear transformation of the tie-set schedule may take is indicated through writing in place of 33

$$i_1 = \alpha_{11}i'_1 + \alpha_{12}i'_2 + \cdots + \alpha_{1l}i'_l$$

$$i_2 = \alpha_{21}i'_1 + \alpha_{22}i'_2 + \cdots + \alpha_{2l}i'_l$$

$$\tag{34}$$

$$\cdot \quad \cdot \quad \cdot \quad \cdot \quad \cdot \quad \cdot \quad \cdot \quad \cdot \quad \cdot \quad \cdot \quad \cdot \quad \cdot$$

$$i_l = \alpha_{l1}i'_1 + \alpha_{l2}i'_2 + \cdots + \alpha_{ll}i'_l$$

in which the α's are any real numbers. If $i_1 \cdots i_l$ are an independent set of current variables, then $i'_1 \cdots i'_l$ will be independent if Eqs. 34 are independent; that is, if they possess unique solutions (which they will if their determinant is nonzero). In general the currents $i'_1 \cdots i'_l$ will no longer have the significance of circulatory currents or loop currents, although for convenience they may still be referred to by that name. They will turn out to be some linear combinations of the branch currents.

If such a very general set of definitions for the loop currents is desired, one can approach the construction of an appropriate tie-set schedule directly from this point of view, which we will illustrate for the network graph of Fig. 8. Thus let us suppose that one wishes to introduce current variables which are the following linear combinations of the branch currents:

$$i_1 = -j_1 + j_2 - j_3 + j_4 - 3j_9$$

$$i_2 = j_2 + 2j_3 + j_6 - j_8$$

$$i_3 = j_1 + j_3 + j_5 + j_7 + j_9$$

$$i_4 = j_2 + 2j_4 + j_6 + j_8$$

(35)

The first step is to rewrite these expressions in terms of l (in this case four) branch currents. To do this we may follow the usual scheme of picking a tree and finding the relations for the tree-branch currents in terms of the link currents. For tree 1 of Fig. 8, these are given by Eqs. 26. Their use transforms Eqs. 35 into

$$i_1 = 2j_1 + 4j_2 + 2j_3 + 1j_4$$

$$i_2 = 2j_1 + 3j_2 + 3j_3 + 0j_4$$

$$i_3 = 0j_1 - 1j_2 - 1j_3 - 1j_4$$

$$i_4 = 0j_1 + 1j_2 + 1j_3 + 2j_4$$

(36)

having the solutions

$$j_1 = 0i_1 + \tfrac{1}{2}i_2 + 3i_3 + \tfrac{3}{2}i_4$$

$$j_2 = \tfrac{1}{2}i_1 - \tfrac{1}{2}i_2 - \tfrac{3}{2}i_3 - 1i_4$$

$$j_3 = -\tfrac{1}{2}i_1 + \tfrac{1}{2}i_2 - \tfrac{1}{2}i_3 + 0i_4$$

$$j_4 = 0i_1 + 0i_2 + 1i_3 + 1i_4$$

(37)

Using Eqs. 26 again we have the additional relations

$$j_5 = 0i_1 - \tfrac{1}{2}i_2 - 2i_3 - \tfrac{3}{2}i_4$$
$$j_6 = 0i_1 + \tfrac{1}{2}i_2 + 1i_3 + \tfrac{1}{2}i_4$$
$$j_7 = \tfrac{1}{2}i_1 + 0i_2 + \tfrac{3}{2}i_3 + \tfrac{1}{2}i_4 \tag{38}$$
$$j_8 = -\tfrac{1}{2}i_1 + 0i_2 - \tfrac{3}{2}i_3 - \tfrac{1}{2}i_4$$
$$j_9 = 0i_1 - \tfrac{1}{2}i_2 - 1i_3 - \tfrac{1}{2}i_4$$

The results in Eqs. 37 and 38 yield tie-set schedule 39, which more

Loop No.	Branch No.								
	1	2	3	4	5	6	7	8	9
1	0	$\tfrac{1}{2}$	$-\tfrac{1}{2}$	0	0	0	$\tfrac{1}{2}$	$-\tfrac{1}{2}$	0
2	$\tfrac{1}{2}$	$-\tfrac{1}{2}$	$\tfrac{1}{2}$	0	$-\tfrac{1}{2}$	$\tfrac{1}{2}$	0	0	$-\tfrac{1}{2}$
3	3	$-\tfrac{3}{2}$	$-\tfrac{1}{2}$	1	-2	1	$\tfrac{3}{2}$	$-\tfrac{3}{2}$	-1
4	$\tfrac{3}{2}$	-1	0	1	$-\tfrac{3}{2}$	$\tfrac{1}{2}$	$\tfrac{1}{2}$	$-\tfrac{1}{2}$	$-\tfrac{1}{2}$

$$(39)$$

compactly contains this same information. This is the schedule that is implied by definitions 35 for the loop-current variables, which no longer possess the geometrical interpretation of being circulatory currents.

As we shall see in the following chapter, the tie-set schedule plays an important role in the formulation of the equilibrium equations appropriate to the chosen definitions for the current variables. The present discussions, therefore, provide the basis for accommodating such a choice, regardless of its generality or mode of inception. Thus we have shown that the process of selecting an appropriate set of current variables can take one of essentially three different forms:

1. The approach through choice of a tree and identification of the link currents with loop currents. In this process the algebraic definitions for the loop-current variables are as simple as they can be, but one exercises no direct control over the nature of the closed paths or loops.

2. The approach through a forthright choice of loops or tie sets. Here the procedure exercises direct control over the paths upon which the current variables are assumed to circulate (a simple choice being

the meshes of a mappable network), but no facile control is had regarding the associated algebraic definitions of the loop currents.

3. The approach through making an initial and arbitrarily general choice for the algebraic definitions of the current variables (like those given by Eqs. 35). In this case the variables no longer possess the simple geometrical significance of circulatory currents. This approach will probably seldom be used, and is given largely for the sake of its theoretical interest.

8   Alternative Methods of Choosing Voltage Variables

When voltages are chosen as variables, we similarly have three possible variations which the form of the approach may take. The first, which is discussed in Art. 6, proceeds through choice of a tree and the identification of tree-branch voltages with node-pair voltage variables. In this process (like procedure 1 mentioned above for the choice of current variables), the algebraic definitions for the node-pair voltages are as simple as they can be, but little or no direct control can be exercised over the geometrical distribution of node pairs. A second form of procedure, which permits a forthright choice of node pairs at the outset, and a third, in which the process is initiated through an arbitrarily general choice for the algebraic definitions of the voltage variables, are now presented in detail.

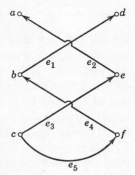

FIG. 10. A possible choice of node-pair voltages for the graph of Fig. 8.

To illustrate how a designation of node-pair voltage variables may be approached through the initial selection of an appropriate set of node pairs, let us consider the network of Fig. 8. In Fig. 10 are indicated the nodes of this network, lettered a, b, $\cdots$, f for ease of reference, and a system of lines with arrowheads intended to indicate a choice of node pairs and reference directions for the voltage variables e_1, e_2, $\cdots$, e_5. These arrows are not to be confused with branches of the network; yet, if we momentarily think of them as such, we notice that the structure in Fig. 10 has the characteristics of a tree, for it connects all of the nodes, and involves the smallest number of branches needed to accomplish this end. Hence this choice for the variables $e_1 \cdots e_5$ is an appropriate one since the variables surely form an independent set, and their number equals the number of branches in any tree associated with a network having these nodes. In making a forthright choice of node pairs it is sufficient to see to it that the system of reference arrows accompanying this choice (whether actually drawn or merely implied) forms a structure that has a tree-like character.

Using the principles set forth in Art. 6, one can construct cut-set schedule 40 appropriate to the choice of node pairs indicated in Fig. 10

Node Pair No.	Branch No.									Picked-Up Nodes
	1	2	3	4	5	6	7	8	9	
1	-1	-1	0	0	0	0	0	-1	0	d
2	1	1	0	0	0	0	-1	0	0	a
3	1	1	-1	0	0	0	-1	1	-1	a, e
4	-1	-1	1	0	0	-1	1	-1	0	b, d
5	-1	-1	1	-1	-1	-1	1	-1	1	b, d, f

(40)

for the network graph of Fig. 8. In this schedule we have included a last column indicating the nodes picked up in the formation of the respective cut sets. Thus, with reference to Fig. 10, if e_1 is regarded as the only nonzero node-pair voltage, nodes a, b, c, e, f coincide at the tail end of e_1 while node d alone occupies the tip end. Hence cut set 1 is found through picking up node d alone and (all other nodes remaining fixed) noting the set of branches in the network of Fig. 8 that are stretched by this procedure. The associated signs are positive or negative according to whether the respective branch reference arrow is divergent from or convergent upon the picked-up node or nodes.

The cut set pertinent to e_2 is found through regarding all other node-pair voltages as being zero so that nodes b, c, d, e, f coincide at the tail end of e_2 while node a marks the tip end. Picking up this node stretches the branches 1, 2, and 7 in the graph of Fig. 8, and the reference arrows on branches 1 and 2 are divergent while that on branch 7 is convergent. Similarly, with e_3 alone nonzero, nodes a, e coincide at the tip end of e_3 while nodes b, c, d, f coincide at the tail end. The picked-up nodes are a and e, and the corresponding cut set is then seen by inspection of Fig. 8. The reader can thus readily check the remaining rows in cut-set schedule 40.

According to the columns of this schedule we can now immediately write

$$v_1 = -e_1 + e_2 + e_3 - e_4 - e_5 \qquad v_6 = -e_4 - e_5$$

$$v_2 = -e_1 + e_2 + e_3 - e_4 - e_5 \qquad v_7 = -e_2 - e_3 + e_4 + e_5$$

$$v_3 = -e_3 + e_4 + e_5 \qquad v_8 = -e_1 + e_3 - e_4 - e_5 \quad (41)$$

$$v_4 = -e_5 \qquad v_9 = -e_3 + e_5$$

$$v_5 = -e_5$$

The correctness of these may readily be checked with reference to Figs. 8 and 10, remembering again that the v's are drops and the e's are rises. For example, v_1 is the voltage drop from node a to node d. If we pass from a to d via the system of node-pair voltage arrows in Fig. 10, we observe that we first traverse the arrows for e_2 and e_3 counterfluently, and then the arrows for e_5, e_4, and e_1 confluently. Since confluence indicates a rise in voltage, the terms for e_1, e_4, and e_5 are negative. There should be no difficulty in thus verifying the remaining equations in set 41.

One could have written Eqs. 41 from inspection of Figs. 8 and 10 to start with and thus constructed schedule 40 by columns, whence the rows would automatically yield the cut sets. This part of the procedure is thus seen to be the same as with the alternate approach given in Art. 6. So is the matter regarding the solution of Eqs. 41 for the node-pair voltages in terms of the branch voltages. One selects any five independent equations from this group and solves them. Again the selection of a tree in the associated network graph (such as tree 1 or 2 in Fig. 8) is a quick and sure way to spot an independent subset among Eqs. 41, and the remaining ones will then yield the appropriate expressions for the link voltages in terms of tree-branch voltages, as discussed previously.

In this method of approach to the problem of defining an appropriate set of independent voltage variables, a rather common procedure is to choose the potential of one arbitrarily selected node as a reference and designate as variables the potentials $e_1 \cdots e_n$ of the remaining nodes with respect to this reference. Thus, one node serves as a datum or reference, and the node pairs defining the variables $e_1 \cdots e_n$ all have this datum node in common. The quantities $e_1 \cdots e_n$ in this arrangement are spoken of as *node potentials* and are referred to as a "node-to-datum" set of voltage variables.

The rather simplified choice of node pairs implied in this specialized procedure is in a sense the parallel of choosing meshes for loops in the specification of current variables. This theme is elaborated upon in Art. 9 where the dual character of the loop and node procedures is stressed and the implications of this duality are partially evaluated.

The equivalent of Fig. 10 for a choice of node-pair voltages of this sort is shown in Fig. 11, pertinent to the network graph of Fig. 8. Again, for the moment regarding the arrows in this diagram as branches, we see that it has tree-like character and hence that such a node-to-datum set of voltages is always an independent one.

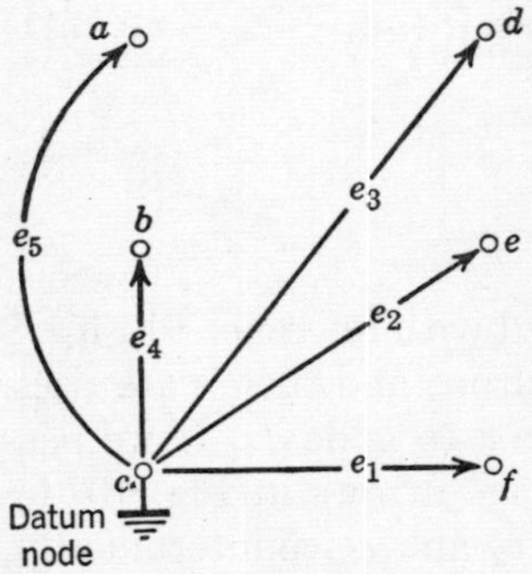

FIG. 11. A node-to-datum choice of node-pair voltages for the graph of Fig. 8.

The cut sets appropriate to this group of node-pair voltages are particularly easy to find since we observe that setting all but one of the node-pair voltages equal to zero causes all of the nodes to coincide at the datum except the one at the tip end of the nonzero voltage. Hence the branches divergent from this single node form the pertinent cut set. With reference to Fig. 8, cut-set schedule 42 is thus readily obtained.

Since the node-pair voltages are the potentials of the separate nodes with respect to a common datum, each branch voltage drop is given by the difference of two node potentials, namely those associated with the nodes terminating the pertinent branch. If the latter touches the datum node, then its voltage drop is given by a single node potential

Node No.	Branch No.									Picked-Up Nodes
	1	2	3	4	5	6	7	8	9	
1	0	0	0	-1	-1	0	0	0	1	f
2	0	0	-1	0	0	0	0	1	-1	e
3	-1	-1	0	0	0	0	0	-1	0	d
4	0	0	1	0	0	-1	1	0	0	b
5	1	1	0	0	0	0	-1	0	0	a

(42)

(with proper algebraic sign). These observations are borne out by the fact that all of the columns in schedule 42 have either two or one nonzero elements; those with a single nonzero element pertain to branches touching the datum node. The branch voltages in terms of the node potentials are thus formed either by inspection of Figs. 8 and 11 or from the columns of schedule 42 to be

$$v_1 = -e_3 + e_5 \qquad v_4 = -e_1 \qquad v_7 = e_4 - e_5$$

$$v_2 = -e_3 + e_5 \qquad v_5 = -e_1 \qquad v_8 = e_2 - e_3 \qquad (43)$$

$$v_3 = -e_2 + e_4 \qquad v_6 = -e_4 \qquad v_9 = e_1 - e_2$$

The node potentials in terms of the branch voltages are found from these by the usual process of selecting from these equations a subset of five independent ones. According to tree 1 of Fig. 8, the last five are such a subset. Their solution yields

$$e_1 = -v_5$$

$$e_2 = -v_5 - v_9$$

$$e_3 = -v_5 - v_8 - v_9 \qquad (44)$$

$$e_4 = -v_6$$

$$e_5 = -v_6 - v_7$$

and the remaining equations in set 43 then give the following expressions for the link voltages in terms of the tree-branch voltages

$$v_1 = v_5 - v_6 - v_7 + v_8 + v_9$$

$$v_2 = v_5 - v_6 - v_7 + v_8 + v_9$$

$$v_3 = v_5 - v_6 + v_9 \qquad (45)$$

$$v_4 = v_5$$

It is interesting to observe how more general node-pair voltage definitions are derivable from the simple node-to-datum set through carrying out linear transformations on the rows of cut-set schedule 42. Thus, suppose we form from this one a new schedule through adding the elements of the second row of 42 to the respective ones of the first row,

Node Pair No.	Branch No.									Picked-Up Nodes
	1	2	3	4	5	6	7	8	9	
1	0	0	-1	-1	-1	0	0	1	0	e, f
2	0	0	-1	0	0	0	0	1	-1	e
3	-1	-1	0	0	0	0	0	-1	0	d
4	0	0	1	0	0	-1	1	0	0	b
5	1	1	0	0	0	0	-1	0	0	a

$$(46)$$

giving schedule 46. The columns yield

$$v_1 = -e'_3 + e'_5 \qquad v_4 = -e'_1 \qquad v_7 = e'_4 - e'_5$$
$$v_2 = -e'_3 + e'_5 \qquad v_5 = -e'_1 \qquad v_8 = e'_1 + e'_2 - e'_3 \quad (47)$$
$$v_3 = -e'_1 - e'_2 + e'_4 \qquad v_6 = -e'_4 \qquad v_9 = -e'_2$$

Solution of the last five now reads

$$e'_1 = -v_5$$
$$e'_2 = -v_9$$
$$e'_3 = -v_5 - v_8 - v_9 \qquad\qquad (48)$$
$$e'_4 = -v_6$$
$$e'_5 = -v_6 - v_7$$

and comparison with Eqs. 44 reveals that

$$e_1 = e'_1$$
$$e_2 = e'_1 + e'_2$$
$$e_3 = e'_3 \qquad\qquad (49)$$
$$e_4 = e'_4$$
$$e_5 = e'_5$$

This result suggests that the node-pair voltage diagram has changed from the form shown in Fig. 11 to that shown in Fig. 12, since the potential of node e with respect to the datum (which in Fig. 11 is e_2) now is equal to the sum of e'_1 and e'_2. We note further that, when e'_1 is the only nonzero voltage, nodes e and f coincide at the tip end of e'_1; so the associated cut set is found through picking up these two nodes, as is also indicated in schedule 46. The picked-up nodes corresponding to the remaining node-pair voltages evidently remain the same as before, and hence the rest of the cut sets are unchanged.

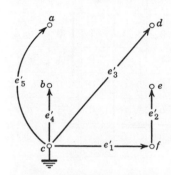

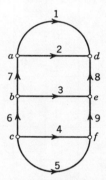

FIG. 12. Revision in the node-pair voltage definitions of Fig. 11 corresponding to a transformation of cut-set schedule 42 to form 46.

FIG. 13. The graph of Fig. 8 with node designations as given in Figs. 10, 11, and 12.

Other simple transformations in schedule 46 may similarly be interpreted. For example, if row 3 is added to row 4, the picked-up nodes for cut set 4 become d and b, which in Fig. 12 implies that the tail end of e'_3 shifts from the datum to node b, and we will find that now $e_3 = e''_3 + e''_4$ where the double prime refers to the latest revision of the set of node-pair voltages (the rest of the e's remain as in Eqs. 49 with double primes on the right-hand quantities).

One soon discovers upon carrying out additional row combinations in schedules 42 or 46 that it is by no means always possible to associate a node-pair voltage diagram like the ones in Figs. 10, 11, or 12 with the resulting node-pair voltages, for the reason that some of these are likely no longer to be simply potential differences between node pairs but instead are more general linear combinations of the branch voltages.

The same is true if one constructs a cut-set schedule (as is also a possible procedure) by making arbitrary choices for the picked-up nodes. To illustrate such a method we may consider again the graph of Fig. 8 which is redrawn in Fig. 13 with the nodes lettered as in Figs. 10, 11, and 12. Cut-set schedule 50 is constructed by simply making an arbitrary choice for the picked-up nodes relating to the pertinent cut sets.

The term "node pair" here retains only a nominal significance since we are not at all assured that the implied voltage variables are potential

Node Pair No.	Branch No.									Picked-Up Nodes
	1	2	3	4	5	6	7	8	9	
1	0	0	0	0	0	0	−1	−1	0	a, d
2	0	0	0	0	0	1	0	0	1	c, f
3	1	1	1	1	1	0	0	0	0	a, b, c
4	−1	−1	−1	0	0	0	0	0	−1	d, e
5	0	0	−1	−1	−1	0	0	1	0	e, f

$$(50)$$

differences between node pairs. We are at this stage in the procedure not even assured that the implied voltage variables form an independent set. What we have done is to choose cut sets in an altogether random manner, which is analogous to choosing closed loops in a random manner when approaching the problem on a current basis. We can readily check whether the implied voltage variables are an independent set and find out what they are by writing down the relations specified by the columns of schedule 50, thus:

$$v_1 = e_3 - e_4 \qquad v_4 = e_3 - e_5 \qquad v_7 = -e_1$$

$$v_2 = e_3 - e_4 \qquad v_5 = e_3 - e_5 \qquad v_8 = -e_1 + e_5 \qquad (51)$$

$$v_3 = e_3 - e_4 - e_5 \qquad v_6 = e_2 \qquad v_9 = e_2 - e_4$$

That such a set of equations exists is manifest since schedule 50 is obtainable through a linear transformation of the rows in schedule 42, and the property of the columns to yield the branch voltages in terms of the implied node-pair voltages is not lost through such a transformation. Hence, if Eqs. 51 possess unique solutions for the voltage variables $e_1 \cdots e_5$, these exist, and cut-set schedule 50 is appropriate to them. Equations 51 do possess unique solutions if there exists among them an independent subset of five equations appropriate to any tree of the graph of Fig. 13 or 8. Picking tree 1 in Fig. 8 designates v_5, v_6, v_7, v_8, v_9 as independent tree-branch voltages and hence stipulates that the last five equations in set 51 should be independent. It is readily seen that they are, for they yield the solutions

$$e_1 = -v_7$$

$$e_2 = v_6$$

$$e_3 = v_5 - v_7 + v_8 \tag{52}$$

$$e_4 = v_6 - v_9$$

$$e_5 = -v_7 + v_8$$

We may conclude that the cut sets in schedule 50 are independent, and Eqs. 52 tell us what the implied voltage variables are in terms of the branch voltages. The first two are simple potential differences between nodes, but the remaining three are not. There is no reason why the selected voltage variables have to be potential differences between nodes. So long as they form an independent set, and we know the algebraic relations between them and the branch voltages, they are appropriate.

Lastly let us consider for the same network of Fig. 8 the following set of independent linear combinations of the branch voltages as a starting point:

$$e_1 = -v_1 + v_3 + v_4 + 2v_6 + 2v_7 + 5v_8 + 5v_9$$

$$e_2 = -v_2 + v_3 + v_4 - v_5 + v_6 + v_7 + 4v_8 + 4v_9$$

$$e_3 = -v_2 + 2v_3 - v_5 + v_6 + 3v_8 + 2v_9 \tag{53}$$

$$e_4 = -v_1 + 2v_3 - v_5 + v_6 - v_7 + 2v_8 + v_9$$

$$e_5 = v_3 - v_5 + v_6$$

Through use of Eqs. 45 one can eliminate all but five of the branch voltages and get definitions 53 into the form

$$e_1 = v_5 + 2v_6 + 3v_7 + 4v_8 + 5v_9$$

$$e_2 = v_6 + 2v_7 + 3v_8 + 4v_9$$

$$e_3 = v_7 + 2v_8 + 3v_9 \tag{54}$$

$$e_4 = v_8 + 2v_9$$

$$e_5 = v_9$$

The solutions to these equations together with Eqs. 45 yield the complete set of relations for the branch voltages in terms of $e_1 \cdots e_5$, thus

$$v_1 = e_1 - 3e_2 + 2e_3 - e_5$$

$$v_2 = e_1 - 3e_2 + 2e_3 - e_5$$

$$v_3 = e_1 - 3e_2 + 3e_3 - e_4 + e_5$$

$$v_4 = e_1 - 2e_2 + e_3$$

$$v_5 = e_1 - 2e_2 + e_3 \qquad\qquad (55)$$

$$v_6 = e_2 - 2e_3 + e_4$$

$$v_7 = e_3 - 2e_4 + e_5$$

$$v_8 = e_4 - 2e_5$$

$$v_9 = e_5$$

These results may be summarized in cut-set schedule 56. Thus we see

Node Pair No.	Branch No.								
	1	2	3	4	5	6	7	8	9
1	1	1	1	1	1	0	0	0	0
2	−3	−3	−3	−2	−2	1	0	0	0
3	2	2	3	1	1	−2	1	0	0
4	0	0	−1	0	0	1	−2	1	0
5	−1	−1	1	0	0	0	1	−2	1

(56)

that any stated algebraic definitions for the voltage variables can be accommodated, although their usual simple geometrical interpretation is no longer applicable. The independence of definitions 53, incidentally, is verified through noting that Eqs. 54 possess solutions.

9 Duality

In the foregoing discussions regarding the appropriate selection of current or voltage variables, the reader will undoubtedly have noticed a number of similarities and analogies between the procedures pertinent to these two methods of approach. We wish now to call specific attention to this aspect of our problem so that we may gain the circumspection that later will enable us to make effective use of its implications. In a word, this usefulness stems from the fact that two situations which, on a current and voltage basis respectively, are entirely analogous, have identical behavior patterns except for an interchange of the roles played by voltage and current, while physically and geometrically they are distinctly different. Not only can one recognize an obvious economy in computational effort resulting from this fact since the analysis of only one of two networks so related yields the behavior of both, but one can sense as well that an understanding of these ideas may lead to other important and practically useful applications, as indeed the later discussions of our subject substantiate.

A careful review of the previous articles in this chapter shows that essentially the same sequence of ideas and procedures characterizes both the loop and the node methods, but with an interchange in pairs of the principal quantities and concepts involved. Since the latter are thus revealed to play a dual role, they are referred to as dual quantities and concepts. First among such dual quantities are current and voltage; and first among the dual concepts involved are meshes and nodes or loops and node pairs. Since a zero current implies an open circuit and a zero voltage a short circuit, these two physical constraints are seen to be duals. The identification of loop currents with link currents and of node-pair voltages with tree-branch voltages shows that the links and the tree branches likewise are dual quantities. The accompanying table gives a more complete list of such pairs.

Dual Quantities or Concepts

Current	Voltage
Branch current	Branch voltage
Mesh or loop	Node or node pair
Number of loops (l)	Number of node pairs (n)
Loop current	Node-pair voltage
Mesh current	Node potential
Link	Tree branch
Link current	Tree-branch voltage
Tree-branch current	Link voltage
Tie set	Cut set
Short circuit	Open circuit
Parallel paths	Series paths

It should be emphasized that duality is strictly a *mutual* relationship. There is no reason why any pair of quantities in the table cannot be interchanged, although each column as written associates those quantities and concepts that are pertinent to one of the two procedures commonly referred to as the loop and node methods of analysis.

Two network graphs are said to be duals if the characterization of one on the loop basis leads to results identical in form with those obtained for the characterization of the other on the node basis. Both graphs will have the same number of branches, but the number of tree branches in one equals the number of links in the other; or the number of independent node pairs in one equals the number of independent loops in the other. More specifically, the equations relating the branch currents

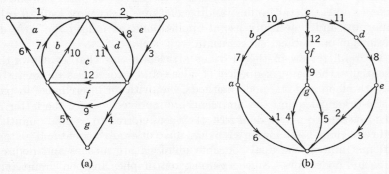

Fig. 14.   A given graph and its dual.

and loop currents for one network are identical in form to the equations relating the branch voltages and the node-pair voltages for the other, so that these sets of equations become interchanged if the letters i and j are replaced, respectively, by e and v, and vice versa. For appropriately chosen elements in the branches of the associated dual networks, the electrical behavior of one of these is obtained from that of the other simply through an interchange in the identities of voltage and current.

Apart from the usefulness that will be had from later applications of these ideas, a detailed consideration of the underlying principles is advantageous at this time because of their correlative value with respect to the foregoing discussions of this chapter.

Geometrically, two graphs are dual if the relationship between branches and node pairs in one is identical with the relationship between branches and loops in the other. The detailed aspects involved in such a mutual relationship are best seen from actual examples. To this end, consider the pair of graphs in Fig. 14. Suppose the one in part (a) is given, and we are to construct its dual as shown in part (b). At the outset we observe that the graph of part (a) has seven meshes and five independent node pairs (a total of six nodes). Hence the dual graph must have seven independent node pairs (a total of eight nodes) and five meshes. The total number of branches must be the same in both graphs.

In proceeding with the construction of the dual of (a), one may begin by setting down eight small circles as nodes—one for each mesh in the graph of part (a), and an extra one that can play the part of a datum node if we wish to regard it as such, although any or none of the eight nodes needs to be considered in this light. We next assign each of these seven nodes to one of the seven meshes in the given graph, as is indicated in Fig. 14 through the letters a, b, $\cdots$, g. The procedure so far implies that we are considering as tie sets those confluent branches in graph (a) that form the contours of meshes and as cut sets those branches in the dual graph that are stretched in the process of picking up single nodes. At least, this implication is true of the nodes a, $\cdots$, g that are assigned to specific meshes; the cut set pertaining to the remaining unassigned node will correspond to a tie set in graph (a) that will reveal itself as we now proceed to carry out the process of making all tie sets in the given graph identical to all the cut sets in its dual.

Initially let us disregard reference arrows entirely; these will be added as a final step. To begin with mesh a, we observe that it specifies a tie set consisting of branches 1, 6, 7; therefore the cut set formed through picking up node a in the dual graph must involve branches 1, 6, 7, and so these are the branches confluent in node a. Similarly the branches 7, 10 form the tie set for mesh b, and therefore these branches are confluent in node b of the dual graph; and so forth. The actual process of drawing the dual graph is best begun by inserting only those branches that are common to any two tie sets and hence must be common to the respective cut sets. That is to say, we note that any branches that are common to two meshes in the given graph must be common to the two corresponding nodes in the dual graph and hence are branches that form direct connecting links between such node pairs. For example, branch 7 is common to meshes a and b, and hence branch 7 in the dual graph connects nodes a and b; similarly branch 10 links nodes b and c; branch 11 links nodes c and d; and so forth.

In this way we readily insert branches 7, 10, 11, 8, 12, 9, and then note that the remaining branches 1, 2, 3, 4, 5, 6 in the original graph form a tie set that must be identical with the cut set of the dual graph that is associated with the remaining unassigned node. Hence these branches, which have one terminus in an assigned node, are the ones that must be confluent in the remaining node. The latter is thus seen to be assignable to the loop formed by the periphery of the given graph. In a sense we may regard this periphery as a "reference loop" corresponding to the originally unassigned node playing the role of a "reference node," although the following discussion will show that this view is a rather specialized one and need not be considered unless it seems desirable to do so.

Now, as to reference arrows on the branches of the dual graph we note, for example, that the traversal of mesh a in a clockwise direction is confluent with the reference arrow of branches 1 and 6, and counterfluent with the reference arrow of branch 7. Hence on the dual graph we attach reference arrows to branches 1 and 6 that are divergent from node a, and provide branch 7 with an arrow that is convergent upon this node.

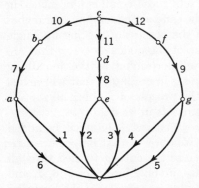

FIG. 15. A graph topologically equivalent to that in Fig. 14b.

That is to say, we correlate clockwise traversal of the meshes with divergence from the respective nodes, and then assign branch arrows in the dual graph that agree or disagree with this direction, according to whether the corresponding branch arrows in the given graph agree or disagree with the clockwise direction for each corresponding mesh. We could, of course, choose a consistent counterclockwise traversal of the meshes, or in the dual graph choose convergence as a corresponding direction. Such a switch will merely reverse *all* reference arrows in the dual graph (which we can do anyway), but we must in any case be consistent and stick to the same chosen convention throughout the process of assigning branch reference arrows. This is done in the construction of the graph of Fig. 14(b), as the reader may readily verify by inspection.

Being mindful of the fact that duality is in all respects a mutual relationship, we now expect to find that the graph (a) of Fig. 14 is related to the graph (b) in the same detailed manner that (b), through the process of construction just described, is related to (a). Thus we expect the meshes of (b) to correspond to nodes in (a) as do the meshes of (a) to the nodes in (b). However, we find upon inspection that such is not consistently the case. For example, the mesh in graph (b) having its contour formed by the consecutively traversed branches 1, 7, 10, 12, 9, 4 corresponds in graph (a) not to a single node, but instead is seen to be the dual of the group of three nodes situated at the vertexes of the triangle formed by the branches 2, 3, 11, since the act of simultaneously picking up these nodes reveals the same group of branches 1, 7, 10, 12, 9, 4 in graph (a) to be a cut set.

This apparent inconsistency is easily resolved through consideration of a slight variation in the construction of the dual of graph (a) as shown in Fig. 15. Here all meshes correspond to the nodes of graph (a) in Fig. 14 in the same way that the meshes of graph (a) correspond to nodes in the graph of Fig. 15, as the reader should carefully verify. The additional·principle observed in the construction of the graph of Fig. 15 is that the sequence of branches about any node is chosen to be identical with that of the similarly numbered branches around the respective mesh, assuming a consistent clockwise (or counterclockwise) direction of circuitation around meshes and around nodes. For example, the branches taken in clockwise order around mesh a of the graph of Fig. 14(a) are numbers 1, 7, 6; around node a in the graph of Fig. 15 this sequence of branches corresponds to counterclockwise rotation. Correspondingly, the clockwise sequence of branches around mesh c in Fig. 14(a) is 10, 11, 12, and this is the counterclockwise sequence of the corresponding branches around node c in Fig. 15. This correspondence in the sequence of branches is seen to hold for all meshes and their corresponding nodes not only between meshes in Fig. 14(a) and nodes in Fig. 15 but also between the meshes in Fig. 15 and their corresponding nodes in Fig. 14(a). The duality between these two graphs is indeed complete in every respect.*

So far as the relationships between branch currents and loop currents or between branch voltages and node-pair voltages are concerned, however, these must be the same for the graph of Fig. 14(b) as they are for the graph of Fig. 15, since both involve fundamentally the same geometrical relationship between nodes and branches, as a comparison readily reveals. For this reason it is not essential in the construction of a dual graph to preserve branch-number sequences around meshes and nodes as just described unless one wishes for some other reason to make meshes in the dual graph again correspond to single nodes in the original graph. From the standpoint of their electrical behavior, the networks whose graphs are given by Figs. 14(b) and 15 are entirely identical. These graphs are, therefore, referred to as being *topologically* † *equivalent*, and either one may be regarded as the dual of Fig. 14(a), or the latter as the dual of either of the networks of Figs. 14(b) and 15.

An additional interesting example of dual graphs is shown in Fig. 16. The meshes $a, b, c, \cdots$ in the graph of part (a) correspond to similarly

---

* The correlation of clockwise rotation in one graph with counterclockwise rotation in its dual is an arbitrary choice. One can as well choose clockwise rotation in both, the significant point being that a consistent pattern is adhered to.

† The mathematical subject dealing with the properties of linear graphs is known as *topology*.

lettered nodes in the graph of part (b); and, conversely, the meshes in graph (b) correspond to nodes in part (a). It will also be observed that the sequences of branches around meshes and around corresponding nodes agree; and it is interesting to note in this special case that, although both graphs have the form of a wheel, the spokes in one are the rim seg-

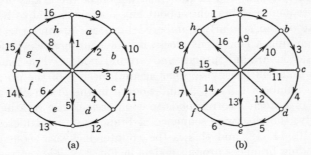

(a)   (b)

Fig. 16.   A pair of dual graphs.

ments of the other. It is further useful to recognize that these graphs may be redrawn as shown in Fig. 17, where they take the form of so-called *ladder* configurations with "feedback" between their input and output ends. Removing link 16 in the graph of Fig. 16(a) corresponds to short-circuiting link 16 in the dual graph of part (b), since open- and

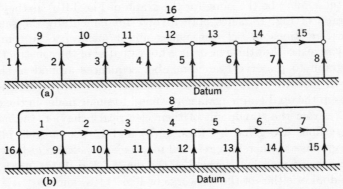

Fig. 17.   The dual graphs of Fig. 16 redrawn in the form of unbalanced ladder networks.

short-circuit constraints are dual concepts (as previously mentioned). In graph 17(b) this alteration identifies the first node on the left with the datum, thus in effect paralleling branches 1 and 9 at the left and branches 8 and 15 on the right. Such ladder configurations are much used in practice, and it is therefore well to know that the dual of a ladder is again a ladder with the essential difference that its series branches correspond to shunt branches in the given ladder, and vice versa.

It is helpful, in the process of constructing a dual graph, to visualize the given one as mapped upon the surface of a sphere instead of on a plane. If this is done, then the periphery appears as an ordinary mesh when viewed from the opposite side of the sphere. For example, if the graph of Fig. 16(a) is imagined to consist of an elastic net and is stretched over the surface of a sphere until the periphery contracts upon the opposite hemisphere, and if one now views the sphere from the opposite side so as to look directly at this hemisphere, then the periphery no longer appears to be fundamentally different in character from an ordinary mesh, for it now appears as a simple opening in the net, like all the other meshes. Thus the branches 9, 10, 11, 12, 13, 14, 15, 16 forming the contour of this mesh appear more logically to correspond to the similarly numbered group of branches in the dual graph 16(b) emanating from the central node which, like all the other nodes, now corresponds to a simple mesh in the given graph.

When, in the choice of network variables, one identifies loop currents with link currents and node-pair voltages with tree-branch voltages, it will be recalled that each tie set consists of one link and a number of tree branches, while each cut set consists of one tree branch and a number of links. Since the tie sets of a given graph correspond to cut sets in the dual graph, one recognizes that the tree branches in one of these graphs are links in the other. That is to say, corresponding trees in dual graphs involve complementary sets of branches. In Fig. 16, for example, if one chooses the branches 1, 2, 3, 4, 5, 6, 7, 8 in graph (a) as forming a tree, then the corresponding tree in graph (b) is formed by the branches 9, 10, 11, 12, 13, 14, 15, 16. Or, if in graph (a) we choose branches 1, 2, 3, 4, 12, 13, 14, 15 as forming a tree, then in graph (b) the corresponding tree is formed by branches 5, 6, 7, 8, 9, 10, 11, 16.

It should now be clear, according to the discussion in the preceding articles, that, if in a given graph we pick a tree and choose the complementary set of branches as forming a tree in the dual graph, then the resulting equations between branch currents and loop currents in one of these graphs becomes identical (except for a replacement of the letters j and i, respectively, by v and e) with those relating branch voltages and node-pair voltages in the dual graph. In the graphs of Fig. 16, for example, we may choose branches 1 to 8 inclusive as the tree of graph (a) and branches 9 to 16 inclusive as the tree of graph (b). Then in graph (a), the branch currents $j_9, j_{10}, \cdots, j_{16}$ are respectively identified with loop currents $i_1, i_2, \cdots, i_8$, while in graph (b) the branch voltages v_9,

v_{10}, $\cdots$, v_{16} are respectively identified with node-pair voltages e_1, e_2, $\cdots$, e_8. For the tree-branch currents in graph (a) we then have, for example, $j_2 = -i_1 + i_2 = -j_9 + j_{10}$; $j_3 = -i_2 + i_3 = -j_{10} + j_{11}$, etc.; while for the link voltages in graph (b) we have correspondingly $v_2 = -v_9 + v_{10} = -e_1 + e_2$; $v_3 = -v_{10} + v_{11} = -e_2 + e_3$, etc. The reader may complete these equations as an exercise, and repeat the process for several other trees as well as for the graphs of Fig. 14.

It should likewise be clear that similar results for a pair of dual graphs and their current and voltage variables are obtained if for one graph one chooses meshes as loops and in the other the corresponding nodes as a node-to-datum set of node pairs. In this case it may be desirable to regard the unassigned node as a datum and the corresponding peripheral mesh as playing the role of a datum mesh. Since more general choices of loops or of node pairs may be expressed as linear combinations of these simple ones, it is seen that the parallelism between the current and voltage relations of dual networks holds in all cases, regardless of the approach taken in formulating defining relations for network variables.

It is important, however, to note a restriction with regard to the existence of a dual graph. This restriction may most easily be understood through recognizing that all possible choices of tie sets in a given network must correspond to cut sets in its dual, and vice versa. In this connection, visualize the given graph as some net covering the surface of a sphere, and a tie set as any confluent group of branches forming a closed path. As mentioned at the close of Art. 5, let us think of inserting a draw string along this path and then tying off, as we might if the sphere were an inflated balloon. We would thus virtually create two balloons, fastened one to the other only at a single point where the contracted tie set has become a common node for the two subgraphs formed by the nets covering these balloons. Whether we thus regard the tie set as contracted or left in its original form upon the sphere, its primary characteristic so far as the present argument is concerned lies in the fact that it forms a boundary along which the given network is divided into two parts, and correspondingly the totality of meshes is divided into two groups.

In the dual graph these correspond to two groups of nodes. If we think of grasping one of these node groups in each of our two hands and pulling them apart, the stretched branches place in evidence the cut set corresponding to the tie set of the original graph. The act of cutting this set of branches is dual to the tying-off process described above, since by this means the dual graph is separated into two parts which are, respectively, dual to the two subgraphs created by contracting the tie set.

Duality between the original graph and its dual demands that to every creatable cut set in one of these there must correspond in the other a tie set with the property just described. It should be clear that this requirement cannot be met if either network is not mappable upon a sphere but requires the surface of some multiply connected space like that occupied by a doughnut or a pretzel. For example, if the mapping of a graph requires the surface of a doughnut, then it is clear that a closed path passing through the hole is not a tie set because the doughnut is not separated into two parts through the contraction of this path. The surface of a simply connected region like that of a sphere is the only surface on which *all* closed paths are tie sets. There is obviously no corresponding restriction on the existence of cut sets, since we can visualize grasping complementary groups of nodes in our two hands and, through cutting the stretched branches, separating the graph into two parts regardless of whether the geometry permits its being mapped upon a sphere or not.

Thus, mappability upon a sphere is revealed as a necessary condition that a tie set in the original graph shall correspond to *every possible* cut set in its dual, and hence the latter is constructible only if the graph of the given network is so mappable.*

10 Concluding Remarks

As expressed in the opening paragraphs of the previous article, the object in discussing the subject of duality is twofold. First, duality is a means of recognizing the analytical equivalence of pairs of physically dissimilar networks; so far as mappable networks are concerned, it essentially reduces by a factor of two the totality of distinct network configurations that can occur. Second, and no less useful, is the result that the principle of duality gives us two geometrically different ways of interpreting a given situation; if one of these proves difficult to comprehend, the other frequently turns out to be far simpler. This characteristic of the two geometrical interpretations of dual situations to reinforce the mental process of comprehending the significance of either one we wish now to present through a few typical examples.

Suppose, for a given mappable graph, we consider a node-to-datum set of voltage variables. That is to say, we pick a datum node, and choose as variables the potentials of the remaining nodes with respect to this datum. If we now wish to obtain algebraic expressions for these node voltages in terms of a like number of independent branch voltages, the simplest procedure is to select a tree and recognize that each node potential is then uniquely given by an algebraic sum of tree-branch

---

* Further detailed discussion of these as well as all foregoing principles presented in this chapter are given throughout the succeeding chapters dealing with their application. A general method for the construction of dual networks and the evaluation of their properties is given in the last article of Ch. 10.

voltages, since the path from any node to the datum via tree branches is a unique one. The geometrical picture involved and the pertinent algebraic procedure are simple and easily comprehensible.

Contrast with this the completely dual situation. For a given mappable graph, we consider the mesh currents as a set of appropriate variables, and ask for the algebraic expressions for these in terms of a like number of independent branch currents. Since the latter may be regarded as the currents in a set of links associated with a chosen tree, the initial step in the procedure is clearly the same as in the previous situation. At this point, however, the lucidity of the picture is suddenly lacking, for we do not appear to have a procedure for expressing each mesh current as an algebraic sum of link currents that has a geometric clarity and straightforwardness comparable to the process of expressing node potentials in terms of tree-branch voltages, and yet we feel certain that there must exist a picture of equivalent clarity since to every mappable situation there exists a dual which possesses all of the same features and with the same degree of lucidity. Our failure to find the mesh situation as lucid as the one involving node potentials must be due to our inability to construct in our minds the completely dual geometry. Once we achieve the latter, our initial objective will easily be gained, and our understanding of network geometry will correspondingly be enhanced.

It turns out that our failure to recognize the dual geometry stems from an initial misconception of what is meant by a *mesh*. Since we use the term *mesh* to connote a particular kind of *loop*, namely the simplest closed path that one can trace, we establish in our minds the view that the term mesh refers to the contour (the associated tie set) instead of the thing that it should refer to, namely the *space* surrounded by that contour! A mesh is an opening—not the boundary of that opening. This opening is the dual of a node—the point of confluence of branches.

A tree consists of nodes connected by tree branches. The dual of a tree branch is a link. Therefore the dual of a tree should be something that consists of spaces (meshes) connected by links. If we add to the mental picture created by these thoughts the fact that traversing a branch longitudinally and crossing it at right angles are geometrically dual operations (since a branch voltage is found through a longitudinal summation process while a branch current is given by a summation over the cross section), we arrive without further difficulty at the geometrical entity that must be recognized as the dual of a tree. *It is the space surrounding the tree.*

This space is subdivided into sections by the links. Each of these sections is a mesh; and one passes from mesh to mesh by crossing the links, just as in the tree one passes from node to node by following along the tree branches. Figure 18 shows in part (a) a graph in the form of a rectangular grid and in part (b) a possible tree with the links included as dotted lines. The space surrounding the tree, and dual to it, is best described by the word *maze* as used to denote a familiar kind of picture puzzle where one is asked to trace a continuous path from one point in this space to another without crossing any of the barriers formed by the tree-like structure.

Such a path connecting meshes m and n is shown dotted in part (b) of the figure. It is clear that the path leading from one mesh to any other is unique, just as is the path from one node to another along the tree

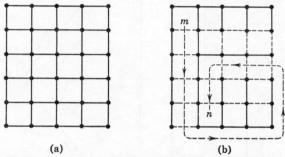

(a)   (b)

Fig. 18.   A graph; a possible tree and its dual which is interpreted as a maze.

branches. In passing along a path such as the one leading from mesh m to mesh n, one crosses a particular set of links. These links characterize this path just as a set of confluent tree branches characterize the path from one node to another in a given tree.

Having recognized these dual processes, we now realize that we have not been entirely accurate in the foregoing discussions where we refer to a loop current as being dual to a node-pair voltage. The latter is the difference between two node potentials, and its dual is, therefore, the difference between two mesh currents, like the currents in meshes m and n in Fig. 18(b). The difference $(i_m - i_n)$ is algebraically given by the summation of those link currents (with due attention to sign) characterizing the path from m to n, just as a node-pair voltage (potential difference between two nodes) equals the algebraic sum of tree-branch voltages along the path connecting this node pair. The difference $(i_m - i_n)$, which might be called a *mesh-pair current*, is the real dual of a node-pair voltage. With the addition of the maze concept to our interpretation of network geometry, we have acquired a geometrical picture for the clarification of the algebraic connection between mesh-current differences and link currents that is as lucid as the familiar one used to connect node-potential differences with tree-branch voltages.

These matters are further clarified through more specific examples. In Fig. 19 is shown a simple network graph [part (a)], its dual [part (b)], and a schematic indicating a choice of node-to-datum voltages characterizing the dual graph [part (c)]. In the graph of part (a) the tree branches are the solid lines, and the links (branches 1, 2, 4, 5, 6) are shown dotted. In the dual graph of part (b), these same branches (1, 2, 4, 5, 6) form the tree, and the rest are links. The datum node surrounds the whole dual

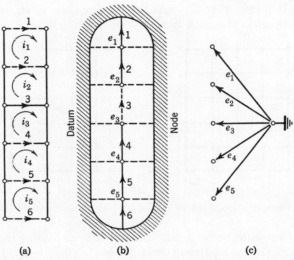

(a)　　　　　　　(b)　　　　　　　(c)

Fɪɢ. 19. A network graph (a), its dual (b), and a node-to-datum choice of node-pair voltages (c) corresponding to the mesh currents in (a). The tree branches (solid) in (a) become links (dotted) in (b) and vice versa.

graph. Mesh currents $i_1, i_2, \cdots, i_5$ are chosen to characterize the graph (a), while correspondingly the node potentials $e_1, e_2, \cdots, e_5$ characterize the dual graph (b).

Starting with the dual graph, it is evident that the expressions for the e's in terms of the tree-branch voltages read

$$e_1 = v_1$$

$$e_2 = v_2 + v_1$$

$$e_3 = -v_4 - v_5 - v_6 \qquad (57)$$

$$e_4 = -v_5 - v_6$$

$$e_5 = -v_6$$

Analogously, the mesh currents in terms of the link currents in graph (a) must be given by

$$i_1 = j_1$$

$$i_2 = j_2 + j_1$$

$$i_3 = -j_4 - j_5 - j_6 \qquad (58)$$

$$i_4 = -j_5 - j_6$$

$$i_5 = -j_6$$

One can verify these last results either by expressing the link currents as superpositions of the loop currents in the following manner,

$$j_1 = i_1$$

$$j_2 = i_2 - i_1$$

$$j_4 = i_4 - i_3 \qquad (59)$$

$$j_5 = i_5 - i_4$$

$$j_6 = -i_5$$

and solving for the i's, or by noting that each mesh current (like a node potential) is the difference between the current circulating on the contour of that mesh and the datum mesh current, which is visualized as circulating on the periphery of the entire graph. In this sense the datum mesh is the entire space outside the graph, just as the datum node in the dual graph surrounds it. Following the pattern set in Fig. 18(b) for expressing mesh-current differences in terms of link currents, one readily establishes Eqs. 58 as representing the situation depicted in graph (a) of Fig. 19, and simultaneously recognizes how the algebraic signs in these equations are related to the reference arrows involved.

Consider now the same networks, but with an altered choice for the voltage and current variables. In Fig. 20(a) are shown the paths for the new loop currents. The dual graph is not repeated in this figure, but part (b) shows the diagram for the choice of node-pair voltages in the dual graph that correspond to the new loop currents in graph (a). All variables corresponding to this revised choice are distinguished by primes. So far as the voltage picture is concerned, one has little difficulty in recognizing that one now has

$$e'_1 = e_2 - e_1 = v_2$$

$$e'_2 = e_1 = v_1$$

$$e'_3 = e_5 = -v_6 \tag{60}$$

$$e'_4 = e_4 - e_5 = -v_5$$

$$e'_5 = e_3 - e_4 = -v_4$$

and so, by analogy, the corresponding relations for the loop currents in terms of the link currents of the graph in part (a) of Fig. 20 must be

$$i'_1 = i_2 - i_1 = j_2$$

$$i'_2 = i_1 = j_1$$

$$i'_3 = i_5 = -j_6 \tag{61}$$

$$i'_4 = i_4 - i_5 = -j_5$$

$$i'_5 = i_3 - i_4 = -j_4$$

These can readily be verified through the usual procedure of writing expressions for the link currents in terms of the loop currents and solving. It is more interesting, however, to establish them entirely by analogy to the dual voltage situation, for we learn in this way more about the manner in which the loop currents are related to the link currents. Thus a loop current like i'_3, for example, surrounds three meshes, and correspondingly the node-pair voltage e'_3 contributes to the potentials of the three nodes o, p, q [Fig. 20(b)]. In forming the cut set associated with e'_3 we would pick up nodes o, p, q, whereas in forming the tie set associated with i'_3 we may say that we "pick up" the meshes whose combined contour places that tie set in evidence.

Having established the fact that picking up meshes is dual to picking up nodes, and recognizing that loop currents, as contrasted to mesh currents, circulate on the resulting contours of groups of meshes, we are in a position to sketch the node-pair voltage diagram [like part (b) of Fig. 20] corresponding to a chosen loop-current diagram [like part (a) of Fig. 20], provided one exists, and, by analogy to the dual voltage equations, obtain directly the pertinent relations for the loop currents.

Since for cut sets picked at random there does not necessarily correspond a set of "node-pair voltages" that are simple potential differences between pairs of nodes, it is analogously true that for loops (i.e. tie sets) picked at random there does not necessarily correspond a set of "mesh-pair currents" that are simple differences between currents in pairs of meshes. In the example of Fig. 20, pertinent to Eqs. 60 and 61, the conditions are chosen so that one does obtain e's that are potential

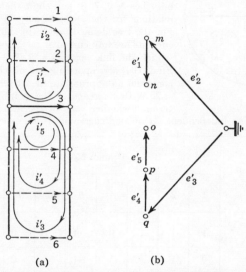

(a)   (b)

FIG. 20. A revised choice of loop currents in the graph of Fig. 19(a) and the corresponding revision in the node-pair voltage definitions for the dual graph.

differences between nodes and i's that are mesh-current differences, but, when loops are picked at random, it is in general no longer possible to give any simple geometrical interpretation to the implied current relationships, just as on the voltage side of the picture a straightforward interpretation fails when cut sets are chosen at random.

Wherever simple relationships do exist, the principle of duality is distinctly helpful in clarifying them. For example, in comparing parts (a) of Figs. 19 and 20, one might be tempted to conclude offhand that $i'_1 = i_2$, or $i'_5 = i_3$ because the contours on which these pairs of currents circulate are the same. As pointed out in Art. 7, it is fallacious to imply that there is any direct relation between the contours chosen for loop currents and their algebraic expressions in terms of link currents. Equations 61 show that the above offhand conclusions are false. Use of the duality principle, as in the preceding discussion, shows why they are false.

PROBLEMS

1. For the graph shown, pick the indicated meshes as loops and write a corresponding tie-set schedule. Select an independent set of columns as those pertinent to the links of a chosen tree, and from the corresponding equations find expressions for the mesh currents i_1, i_2, i_3, i_4 in terms of branch currents. Do this specifically for (a) the tree composed of branches 1, 2, 3, 6; (b) the tree composed of branches 5, 6, 7, 8; and show that the two sets of relations for the i's in terms of j's are equivalent. For the tree defined under (b) show that the mesh currents are link currents.

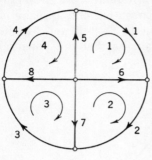

PROB. 1.

Pick the link currents 4, 5, 7, 8 as loop currents. Find the corresponding set of closed paths, and construct an appropriate tie-set schedule.

2. With reference to the graph of Prob. 1, determine whether each of the accompanying tie-set schedules defines an independent set of loop currents. If so, express the loop cur-

Loop No.	Branch No.							
	1	2	3	4	5	6	7	8
1	1	1	1	0	1	0	0	−1
2	0	1	1	1	−1	1	0	0
3	1	0	1	1	0	−1	1	0
4	1	1	0	1	0	0	−1	1

Loop No.	Branch No.							
	1	2	3	4	5	6	7	8
1	1	1	0	0	1	0	−1	0
2	0	1	1	0	0	1	0	−1
3	0	0	1	1	−1	0	1	0
4	1	0	0	1	0	−1	0	1

rents in terms of the currents in links 1, 2, 3, 4. In each case, trace the closed paths traversed by the loop currents.

Express the currents in branches 5, 6, 7, 8 in terms of the link currents 1, 2, 3, 4.

3. Given the accompanying tie-set schedule and its associated graph, trace the

Loop No.	Branch No.											
	1	2	3	4	5	6	7	8	9	10	11	12
1	−1	−1	0	0	1	1	0	0	0	−1	0	1
2	0	0	1	1	0	0	−1	−1	0	−1	0	1
3	1	0	0	1	0	1	1	0	1	0	−1	0
4	0	−1	−1	0	−1	0	0	−1	1	0	−1	0
5	1	1	1	1	0	0	0	0	0	0	0	0

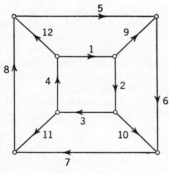

PROB. 3.

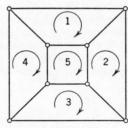

PROB. 4.

closed paths traversed by the implied loop currents and tell whether they form an independent set.

4. Designating meshes for the graph of the preceding problem as indicated in the accompanying sketch, write down a corresponding tie-set schedule, and express the rows in the schedule of Prob. 3 as linear combinations of the rows in this new one. Now determine the answer to Prob. 3 by noting whether it is possible to construct these row combinations through *successive* simple combinations of rows, starting with the schedule on the mesh basis. (At each stage in this process of successive modifications, any row may be replaced by a combination of that row and others in the *same* schedule only.)

5. For the graph of Prob. 3 write down a cut-set schedule corresponding to (a) a tree composed of branches 1, 3, 4, 9, 10, 11, 12; (b) a tree composed of branches 6,

7, 8, 9, 10, 11, 12; identifying, in each case, the node-pair voltages with the tree-branch voltages. For each choice of tree, express the link voltages in terms of the tree-branch or node-pair voltages.

6. For the graph of Prob. 3 and the designation of nodes shown in the accompanying sketch, choose 0 as the datum node, and write a cut-set schedule for the node-to-datum voltages, $e_1, \cdots, e_7$. Express these in terms of each of the two sets of tree-branch voltages specified in Prob. 5.

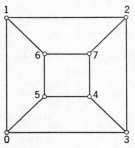

PROB. 6.

7. With reference to the graph of Prob. 3 and the node designation given in Prob. 6, determine which of the following sets of node pairs are independent, and for each of the latter construct a pertinent cut-set schedule, and express the node-pair voltages in terms of the branch voltages of tree (a) in Prob. 5: (a) 02, 04, 13, 17, 26, 35, 57; (b) 02, 06, 13, 15, 24, 46, 57; (c) 02, 06, 13, 15, 24, 36, 37.

8. Construct the dual of the graph in Prob. 3, giving the appropriate numbering and reference arrows for all branches. On this dual graph indicate a set of mesh currents dual to the node-to-datum voltages of Prob. 6, and show that the cut-set schedule written there is now the appropriate tie-set schedule. Show further that the relations for the mesh currents in terms of link currents are identical in form with the expressions for the node potentials in terms of tree-branch voltages found in Prob. 6.

9. For the dual graph of Prob. 8 define loop-current variables (mesh-pair currents) that are dual to each of the independent sets of node-pair voltages specified in Prob. 7. Show in each case that the appropriate tie-set schedule is identical with the pertinent cut-set schedule of Prob. 7, and thus find the relations between the loop currents and the link currents dual to the branch voltages in tree (a) of Prob. 5. For each set of independent loop currents (making use of the appropriate tie-set schedule) find the associated set of closed paths and trace these in the dual graph.

10. Through making appropriate linear combinations, show that any set of linearly independent rows is reducible to the particular set shown here, in which ele-

$$
\begin{array}{cccccc}
1 & x & x & x & x & \cdots \\
0 & 1 & x & x & x & \cdots \\
0 & 0 & 1 & x & x & \cdots \\
0 & 0 & 0 & 1 & x & \cdots \\
& \cdot & \cdot & \cdot & \cdot & \cdot \quad \cdot \quad \cdot
\end{array}
$$

ments marked x may have any finite values (including zero). If necessary, some column interchanges (corresponding to changes in branch numbering) are, of course, permitted at any stage in the transformations. Thus show that, if the l rows of a tie-set schedule are independent, it must always be possible to find at least one set of l independent columns.

11. If the links corresponding to the chosen tree of any given graph are numbered 1, 2, $\cdots$, l, and loop currents are defined as $i_1 = j_1$, $i_2 = j_2$, $\cdots$, $i_l = j_l$, show that the first l columns of the tie-set schedule represent a matrix having 1's on its prin-

cipal diagonal (upper left to lower right) and all other elements zero (called a *unit* matrix). Compare this situation with that in the previous problem.

12. Draw a regular pentagon with branches numbered 1 to 5 and additional branches 6 to 10 so that each vertex (node) is connected with every other one. For any appropriate cut-set schedule prove that any four of the columns 1 to 5 or 6 to 10 are independent.

13. With reference to the graph of the preceding problem, consider any appropriate tie-set schedule, and prove that any six of its columns including either 1 to 5 or 6 to 10 are independent.

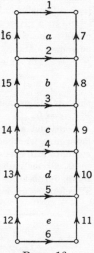

PROB. 16.

14. Consider a graph in which a branch connects every node with every other node. Determine the number n of independent node pairs and the number l of independent loops in terms of the number of total nodes n_t. Compute the number of equilibrium equations needed for this graph on the loop and node bases for the cases $n_t = 2, 3, 4, 5, 10, 50, 100$, and tabulate the results.

15. Consider a three-dimensional graph in the form of a uniform cubical grid with n_s nodes on a side and n_s^3 total nodes. Show that the number of independent loops is $l = 2(n_s^3 - 1) - 3(n_s^2 - 1)$. Make a table showing the numbers n and l for $n_s = 2, 3, 4, 5, 10, 100$.

16. Consider the graph shown here, and choose a tree consisting of the branches 6 to 16 inclusive. Let the loop currents be the link currents $i_k = j_k$ for $k = 1 \cdots 5$, and construct the pertinent tie-set schedule. Define a second set of loop currents as those circulating in the clockwise direction around the boundaries of the meshes a, b, c, d, e, and construct a second tie-set schedule appropriate to this choice of current variables.

Referring to the respective rows of the first schedule by the numerals $1 \cdots 5$ and to those of the second by the letters $a \cdots e$, express the rows (tie sets) of each schedule as the appropriate linear combinations of rows in the other schedule. For example:

$$a = 1 - 2; \quad b = 2 - 3; \quad \text{etc.} \quad \text{and} \quad 5 = e; \quad 4 = d + e; \quad \text{etc.}$$

These are the *topological* relationships between the two sets of closed paths involved in the definition of loop currents. Now find the *algebraic* relationships between the set of loop currents $i_1 \cdots i_5$ and the set $i_a \cdots i_e$; that is to say, express the $i_1 \cdots i_5$ in terms of $i_a \cdots i_e$, and vice versa. Compare the topological and the algebraic relationships thus found, and note carefully the distinction that must be made between them.

17. With reference to the situation in Prob. 16, suppose we introduce some new loop currents as the mesh-current differences given by the algebraic relationships

$$i_A = i_b - i_a; \quad i_B = i_c - i_a; \quad i_C = i_d - i_b; \quad i_D = i_e - i_c; \quad i_E = i_e$$

Determine the tie-set schedule appropriate to these new loop currents, and thus find the set of closed contours on which they circulate (that is to say, find the topological transformation that accompanies the above algebraic transformation).

On the other hand, construct from the second schedule in Prob. 16 a new one whose rows are the combinations: $b-a, c-a, d-b, e-c, e$ (paralleling the above algebraic transformations), and sketch in the graph of Prob. 16 the set of closed paths appropriate to this new schedule. Denoting the loop currents circulating upon these contours by i_I, i_{II}, i_{III}, i_{IV}, i_V, use the new schedule to determine their values in terms of the branch currents, and thus get the expressions for $i_I \cdots i_V$ in terms of $i_a \cdots i_e$ (that is to say, find the algebraic transformation that accompanies the above topological transformation).

18. In a given network having the graph of Prob. 16, the branches 1, 2, $\cdots$, 6 contain the windings of a set of relays whose desired operation depends upon the currents in these branches being equal in pairs thus: $j_1 = j_2$, $j_2 = j_3$, $j_3 = j_4$, $j_4 = j_5$, $j_5 = j_6$. Through introducing as current variables the differences

$$i_1 = j_1 - j_2, \quad i_2 = j_2 - j_3, \quad i_3 = j_3 - j_4, \quad i_4 = j_4 - j_5, \quad i_5 = j_5 - j_6$$

these relations could be expressed as a set of simpler null conditions $i_1 = 0$, $i_2 = 0$, $\cdots$, $i_5 = 0$.

Construct a tie-set schedule appropriate to this choice of current variables, and determine whether or not it is an independent set. If so, express all of the branch currents in terms of these current variables.

19. Given that the tie-set schedule shown was obtained from a set of mesh currents, reconstruct the geometrical network, numbering all branches and including all reference arrows.

Loop No.	Branch No.								
	1	2	3	4	5	6	7	8	9
1	1	1	0	0	0	0	1	-1	0
2	0	0	1	1	0	0	0	1	-1
3	0	0	0	0	1	1	-1	0	1

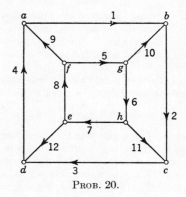

PROB. 20.

20. With reference to the graph shown in the adjacent sketch it is proposed to define a set of node-pair voltages as

$$e_1 = e_b - e_a \qquad e_5 = e_f - e_e$$

$$e_2 = e_c - e_b \qquad e_6 = e_g - e_f$$

$$e_3 = e_d - e_c \qquad e_7 = e_h - e_g$$

$$e_4 = e_e - e_d$$

in which e_a, e_b, $\cdots$ are the potentials of the separate nodes with respect to some common datum. (a) Construct the pertinent cut-set schedule. (b) Draw the tree corresponding to this cut-set schedule. (c) Are the rows of this schedule independent? Give your reasoning. (d) Indicate seven independent columns.

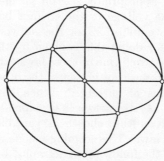

PROB. 21.

21. A graph is formed by the lines of intersection of the three mutually orthogonal coordinate planes with each other and with the surface of a concentric sphere, as indicated in the sketch. How many independent variables are involved: (a) on a current basis, (b) on a voltage basis? Is it possible to choose the currents in the quadrant arcs as forming an independent set? Show your reasoning.

CHAPTER TWO

The Equilibrium Equations

1 Kirchhoff's Laws

Having chosen an appropriate set of geometrically independent variables, on either the voltage or the current basis, one is interested next in expressing the equilibrium of the network in terms of these. The means available for doing this is given by the so-called Kirchhoff laws, of which there are two. One of these laws expresses a fundamental equilibrium condition in terms of voltages; the other expresses an analogous condition in terms of currents. When currents are chosen as variables, equilibrium of the network is expressed by means of the voltage law; when voltages are chosen as variables, equilibrium is expressed by the current law. This seeming inconsistency will adequately be elaborated upon in the following paragraphs, but first let us become acquainted with the Kirchhoff laws themselves.

We shall begin with a discussion of the voltage law, and in preparation for this discussion let us recall what is meant by voltage. "Voltage" is a shorter way of saying "electric potential difference." Electric potential is work or energy; that is to say, it is a scalar quantity like temperature, or quantity of water, or altitude above sea level. The fact that it is at any moment a scalar function of *position only* (i.e., a *single-valued* scalar) is the important thing so far as Kirchhoff's voltage law is concerned. Thus we can speak of the electric potential of any point in a network with respect to the potential of some arbitrary point chosen as reference, just as we can speak of the altitude of any point in a mountainous terrain with respect to sea level chosen as an arbitrary reference. By the single-valued character of either of these functions we imply that the value found for the function at some point relative to that at another is independent of the route chosen in traversing from one of these points to the other in the course of actually carrying through a measurement or computation.

Suppose, for example, that we are to measure the altitude of the tip of Mt. Washington in New Hampshire with respect to some bench mark at its base by the customary methods used in surveying. We do this through successively measuring the differences in altitude between appropriately chosen intermediate points extending over some circuitous route having its ends respectively at the bench mark and at the mountain top. Assuming errors in measurement to be negligible, the net difference in altitude is expected to be independent of the route chosen. A similar conclusion applies in the case of any other single-valued scalar function, and the electric potential is such a one.

Now suppose we were to go on a surveying trip, start from some arbitrary bench mark, traverse all over the mountainous terrain, and finally return to the same bench mark. In this case we would expect to find a *zero* net difference in altitude, as is manifestly clear from the fact that the end points of our circuit are identical. Formal expression of this obvious fact in the analogous electrical case is the essence of Kirchhoff's *voltage law.* Let us elaborate slightly.

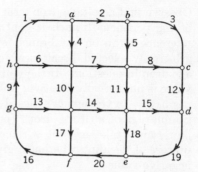

FIG. 1. Network graph relative to the discussion of Kirchhoff's laws.

Refer to the network geometry shown in Fig. 1, and suppose we proceed around the periphery, touching in succession upon nodes a, b, c, d, e, f, g, h, and returning to node a.

The potential of node a minus the potential of node b is the "drop" in potential from a to b, or the *voltage drop* v_2 in branch 2. Similarly v_3 is the voltage drop in branch 3 and equals the potential of node b minus that of node c. Proceeding in this way around the periphery, we see that the following equation is true

$$v_2 + v_3 + v_{12} + v_{19} + v_{20} + v_{16} + v_9 + v_1 = 0 \qquad (1)$$

This is Kirchhoff's voltage law expressed for the closed loop formed by the periphery. Numerically the values of some of these voltage drops must, of course, be negative; otherwise the sum of all of them could not be zero. We speak of Eq. 1 as representing an *algebraic* sum. If some voltage drop like v_2 is numerically negative, then evidently the potential of node a is less than that of node b (both referred to the same reference, of course).

Interpretation of the physical meaning of Eq. 1 is aided by use of the altitude analogue; that is, by regarding the nodes in the graph of Fig. 1 as bench marks in a mountainous terrain, and the voltage drops like v_2, v_3 as drops in altitude between the pertinent bench marks in the reference-arrow directions. Thus a rise in altitude in a given direction between two bench marks can alternately be regarded as a numerically negative drop.

One can trace through many additional closed paths in the network graph of Fig. 1. For example, starting again at node a and proceeding in succession to nodes b, c, d, e, and f, one may return to node a via the confluent set of branches 17, 10, and 4. In this case the voltage-law equation reads

$$v_2 + v_3 + v_{12} + v_{19} + v_{20} - v_{17} - v_{10} - v_4 = 0 \qquad (2)$$

Observe that a voltage-drop term is algebraically negative when traversal of the pertinent branch is contrary to its reference arrow. Thus the reference arrow on any branch is just what its name implies, namely an arbitrarily selected direction which we agree to call positive for the voltage drop in question. If the voltage drop actually has this direction, its value is numerically positive; if it has the opposite direction, its value is negative. In traversing a closed circuit within the terrain, the algebraic summation of altitude drops (potential drops between pertinent node pairs) must take account of reference-arrow directions, as must also the process of deciding whether a given drop has a numerically positive or negative value.

Thus, if bench mark e, for example, is higher than bench mark d, then v_{19} is numerically negative; and, since its algebraic sign in Eq. 2 is plus, we see that this term involves an arithmetic subtraction. In branch 10, on the other hand, the actual drop in altitude may be contrary to the arrow direction so that v_{10} has a negative value. The corresponding term in Eq. 2 becomes numerically positive, as is appropriate since we actually experience a drop in altitude when we encounter branch 10 in traversing the circuit to which Eq. 2 applies.

The Kirchhoff voltage law thus expresses the simply understandable fact that the algebraic sum of voltage drops in any confluent set of branches forming a closed circuit or loop must equal zero. Symbolically this fact may be expressed by writing

$$\Sigma \pm v = 0 \qquad (3)$$

where the Greek capital sigma is interpreted as a summation sign and the quantities $\pm v$ which are summed are voltage drops, with due regard to the possible agreement or disagreement of their pertinent reference arrows with the (arbitrary) direction of traversal around the loop, thus indicating the choice of the plus or minus sign respectively.

It is interesting to observe an important property of equations of this type with reference to a given network geometry such as that shown in

Fig. 1. Suppose we write voltage-law equations for the upper left-hand corner mesh and its right-hand neighbor, thus:

$$v_1 + v_4 - v_6 = 0$$
$$v_2 + v_5 - v_7 - v_4 = 0 \tag{4}$$

Addition of these two equations gives

$$v_1 + v_2 + v_5 - v_7 - v_6 = 0 \tag{5}$$

which we recognize as an equation pertinent to the closed loop which is the periphery of the two meshes combined. The reason for this result is that branch 4, which is common to both meshes, injects the terms $+v_4$ and $-v_4$ respectively into the two Eqs. 4, and hence cancels out in their addition.

It is immediately clear that such cancelation of voltage terms will take place in the summation of any group of equations relating to meshes for which these terms correspond to branches common to the group of meshes. Suppose we write separate equations for the meshes immediately below those to which Eqs. 4 refer, thus:

$$v_6 + v_{10} - v_{13} + v_9 = 0$$
$$v_7 + v_{11} - v_{14} - v_{10} = 0 \tag{6}$$

Adding Eqs. 4 and 6, we have

$$v_1 + v_2 + v_5 + v_{11} - v_{14} - v_{13} + v_9 = 0 \tag{7}$$

This equation is pertinent to the periphery of the block of four upper left-hand meshes in the graph of Fig. 1. If all the equations for the separate meshes in this graph are added, one obtains Eq. 1 relating to the periphery of the whole graph. The student should try this as an exercise.

We now turn our attention to an analogous law in terms of branch currents: the so-called Kirchhoff *current law*. The electric current in a branch is the time rate at which charge flows through that branch. Unless the algebraic sum of currents for a group of branches confluent in the same node is zero, electric charge will be either created or destroyed at that node. Kirchhoff's current law, which in essence expresses the principle of the conservation of charge, states therefore that an algebraic summation of branch currents confluent in the same node must equal zero. Symbolically this fact is expressed by writing (as in Eq. 3):

$$\Sigma \pm j = 0 \tag{8}$$

As illustrations of this law suppose we write equations of this sort for nodes a and h and the one immediately to the right of h in Fig. 1.

These read

$$-j_1 + j_2 + j_4 = 0$$

$$j_1 + j_6 - j_9 = 0 \qquad (9)$$

$$-j_4 + j_7 + j_{10} - j_6 = 0$$

Each equation states that the net current diverging from a pertinent node equals zero.

Now suppose we add the three Eqs. 9. This gives

$$j_2 + j_7 + j_{10} - j_9 = 0 \qquad (10)$$

Branch currents j_1, j_4, and j_6 cancel out in the process of addition. Reference to the graph of Fig. 1 reveals that these branches are *common* to the group of three nodes in question, while the branches to which the remaining currents in Eq. 10 refer terminate only in one of these nodes.

An interesting interpretation may be given the resulting Eq. 10. If we regard the portion of the graph of Fig. 1 formed by branches 1, 4, and 6 alone (referred to as a *subgraph* of the entire network) as enclosed in a box, then Eq. 10 expresses the fact that the algebraic sum of currents divergent from this box equals zero. In other words, the current law applies to the box containing a subgraph the same as it does to a single node. That is to say, it is not possible for electric charge to pile up or diminish within a box containing a lumped network any more than it is possible for charge to pile up or diminish at a single node. This fact follows directly from the current law applied to a group of nodes, as shown above, and yet students usually have difficulty recognizing the truth of this result. They somehow feel that in a box there is more room for charge to pile up, and so it may perhaps do this, whereas at a single node it is clear that the charge would have to jump off into space if more entered than left the node in any time interval. The above analysis shows, however, that what holds for a simple node must hold also for a box full of network.

2   Independence among the Kirchhoff Law Equations

Equilibrium equations are a set of relations that uniquely determine the state of a network at any moment. They may be written in terms of any appropriately chosen variables; the uniqueness requirement demands, however, that the number of independent equations shall equal the number of independent variables involved. We have seen earlier that the state of a network is expressible either in terms of $l = b - n_t + 1$

independent currents (for example, the loop currents) or in terms of $n = n_t - 1 = b - l$ independent voltages (for example the node-pair voltages). On a current basis we shall, therefore, require exactly l independent equations; and on a voltage basis exactly n independent equations will be needed.

For these equations we turn our attention to the Kirchhoff laws. It is essential to determine how many independent equations of each type (the voltage-law and the current-law types) may be written for any given network geometry. Consider first the voltage-law equations, and assume that these have been written for all of the nine meshes of the network graph in Fig. 1. Incidentally, this graph has 20 branches and a total of 12 nodes ($b = 20$, $n_t = 12$). Hence $l = 20 - 12 + 1 = 9$, which just equals the number of meshes. Any tree in this network involves $n = 11$ branches. There are 9 links, and hence there are 9 geometrically independent loop currents.

From what has been pointed out in the previous article, it is clear that a voltage-law equation written for any other loop enclosing a group of meshes in Fig. 1 may be formed by adding together the separate equations for the pertinent meshes. Such additional voltage-law equations clearly are not independent. The inference is that one can always write exactly l independent equations of the voltage-law type.

This conclusion is supported by the following reasoning. Suppose, for any network geometry, a tree is chosen, and the link currents are identified with loop currents. For the correspondingly determined loops a set of voltage-law equations are written. These equations are surely independent, for the link voltages appear separately, one in each equation, so that it certainly is not possible to express any equation as a linear combination of the others. Each of these equations could be used to express one link voltage in terms of tree-branch voltages. This fact incidentally substantiates what was said earlier with regard to the tree-branch voltages being an independent set and the link voltages being expressible uniquely in terms of them (see Art. 6, Ch. 1).

Now any other closed loop for which a voltage-law equation could be written must traverse one or more links since the tree branches alone can form no closed paths. If in this equation the previous expressions for the pertinent link voltages are substituted, the resultant equation must reduce to the trivial identity $0 \equiv 0$, since no nontrivial relation can exist among tree-branch voltages alone (the tree-branch voltages are independent and hence are not expressible in terms of each other). It follows, therefore, that the voltage-law equation written for the additional closed loop expresses no independent result. There are indeed exactly l independent voltage-law equations.

Let us turn our attention now to the Kirchhoff current-law equations and see how many of these may be independent. Referring again to the graph of Fig. 1, suppose we begin writing equations for several nodes adjacent to each other. If we examine these equations carefully, we observe that each contains at least one term that does not appear in the others. For example, if we consider the equations written for nodes a and h, it is clear that the terms involving j_2 and j_4 do not appear in the equation for node h, and that the j_6 and j_9 terms in the equation for node h do not appear in the one for node a. If we also write an equation for the node immediately to the right of h, this one contains terms with j_7 and j_{10} which are not contained in either of the equations for nodes a or h. Such sets of equations are surely independent, for it is manifestly not possible to express any one as a linear combination of the others so long as each has terms that the others do not contain.

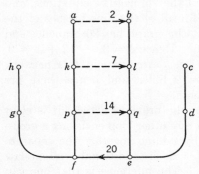

Fig. 2. A tree for the graph of Fig. 1. The cut-set pertinent to node pair f–e consists of tree branch 20 and the links shown dotted.

As we proceed to write current-law equations for additional nodes in the graph of Fig. 1, the state of affairs just described continues to hold true until equations have been written for *all but one* of the nodes. The inference is that exactly $n = n_t - 1$ independent equations of the current-law type can always be written. This conclusion is supported by the following reasoning.

Suppose, for any network geometry, a tree is chosen, and the tree-branch voltages are identified with node-pair voltages. For the correspondingly determined node pairs, a set of Kirchhoff current-law equations are written. The set of branches taking part in the equation for any node pair is the pertinent cut set, just as the group of branches involved in the voltage-law equation for any loop is the tie set for that loop. The cut set pertinent to the node pair defined by any tree branch evidently involves that tree branch in addition to those links having one of their ends terminating upon the picked-up nodes (see Art. 8, Ch. 1).

Figure 2 illustrates the choice of a tree for the network graph of Fig. 1, and, with respect to the node pair f, e joined by branch 20, indicates by dotted lines the links that take part in the pertinent cut set. Since the tree-branch voltage v_{20} is identified with the respective node-pair voltage, the latter has its reference arrow pointing from f to e. That is to say, the picked-up nodes are e, q, l, b, c, d. Hence the pertinent current-law equation reads

$$j_{20} - j_{14} - j_7 - j_2 = 0 \tag{11}$$

Schedules like 40, 42, 46 in Art. 8 of Ch. 1 are helpful in writing the current-law equations for a chosen set of node pairs, for the elements in the rows of such a schedule are the coefficients appropriate to these equations.

Suppose that current-law equations like 11 are written for all of the node pairs corresponding to the n tree branches. These equations are surely independent, for the tree-branch currents appear separately, one in each equation, so that it certainly is not possible to express any equation as a linear combination of the others. Each of these equations could be used to express one tree-branch current in terms of the link currents. This fact incidentally substantiates what was said earlier with regard to the link currents being an independent set and the tree-branch currents being expressible uniquely in terms of them (see Art. 5, Ch. 1).

Now any other cut set pertinent to a node pair for which a current-law equation could be written would have to involve one or more tree branches, since the tree connects all of the nodes, and therefore no node exists that has not at least one tree branch touching it. If in such an additional current-law equation one substitutes the expressions already obtained for the pertinent tree-branch currents, the resultant equation must reduce to the trivial identity $0 \equiv 0$, since no nontrivial relation can exist among link currents alone (the link currents are independent and hence are not expressible in terms of each other). It follows, therefore, that the current-law equation written for any additional node pair expresses no independent result. There are indeed exactly n independent current-law equations.

3   The Equilibrium Equations on the Loop and Node Bases

Having established the fact that the state of a network can be characterized uniquely either in terms of a set of l loop currents or in terms of a set of n node-pair voltages, and having recognized that the numbers of independent Kirchhoff voltage-law and current-law equations are l and n respectively, the conclusion is imminent that the equilibrium condition for a network can be expressed in either of two ways: (a) through a set of l voltage-law equations in which the loop currents are the variables, or (b) through a set of n current-law equations in which the node-pair voltages are the variables. These procedures, which are referred to respectively as the *loop* and *node methods* of expressing network equilibrium, are now discussed in further detail.

Consider first the *loop method*. The voltage-law equations, like Eq. 1, p. 65, involve the branch-voltage drops. If these equations are to be written with the loop currents as variables, we must find some way of expressing the branch voltages in terms of the loop currents. These expressions are obtained in two successive steps.

The branch voltages are related to the branch currents by the volt-ampere equations pertaining to the kinds of elements (inductance, resistance, or capacitance) that the branches represent; and the branch currents in turn are related to the loop currents in the manner shown in Ch. 1. Detailed consideration of the relations between branch currents and branch voltages is restricted at present to networks involving resistances only. Appropriate extensions to include the consideration of inductance and capacitance elements will follow in the later chapters.

Let the resistances of branches 1, 2, 3, $\cdots$ be denoted by r_1, r_2, r_3, etc. Then the relations between all the branch voltages and all the branch currents are expressed by

$$v_k = r_k j_k \quad \text{for} \quad k = 1, 2, \cdots, b \tag{12}$$

The complete procedure for setting up the equilibrium equations on the loop basis will be illustrated for the network graph shown in Fig. 3. Part (a) is the complete graph, and part (b) is a chosen tree. Branches

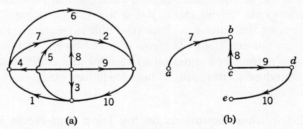

FIG. 3. A nonmappable graph (a), and a possible tree (b).

1, 2, $\cdots$, 6 are links, and the link currents $j_1, j_2, \cdots, j_6$ are identified respectively with the loop currents $i_1, i_2, \cdots, i_6$.

The following tie-set schedule is readily constructed from an inspection of the resulting closed paths pertinent to these six loop currents [as the reader should check through placing the links 1, 2, $\cdots$, 6, one at a time, into the tree of Fig. 3(b)]. The Kirchhoff voltage-law equations written for these same loops are immediately obtained through use of the coef-

Loop No.	Branch No.									
	1	2	3	4	5	6	7	8	9	10
1	1	0	0	0	0	0	1	−1	1	1
2	0	1	0	0	0	0	0	1	−1	0
3	0	0	1	0	0	0	0	0	−1	−1
4	0	0	0	1	0	0	1	−1	0	0
5	0	0	0	0	1	0	0	−1	1	1
6	0	0	0	0	0	1	−1	1	−1	0

(13)

ficients in the rows of this schedule, thus:

$$
\begin{aligned}
v_1 + v_7 - v_8 + v_9 + v_{10} &= 0 \\
v_2 + v_8 - v_9 &= 0 \\
v_3 - v_9 - v_{10} &= 0 \\
v_4 + v_7 - v_8 &= 0 \\
v_5 - v_8 + v_9 + v_{10} &= 0 \\
v_6 - v_7 + v_8 - v_9 &= 0
\end{aligned}
$$

(14)

while the columns of the same schedule furnish the coefficients in the following equations for the branch currents in terms of the loop currents:

$$
\begin{aligned}
j_1 &= i_1 & j_6 &= i_6 \\
j_2 &= i_2 & j_7 &= i_1 + i_4 - i_6 \\
j_3 &= i_3 & j_8 &= -i_1 + i_2 - i_4 - i_5 + i_6 \\
j_4 &= i_4 & j_9 &= i_1 - i_2 - i_3 + i_5 - i_6 \\
j_5 &= i_5 & j_{10} &= i_1 - i_3 + i_5
\end{aligned}
$$

(15)

If we assume for the branch resistances the values

$$
\begin{aligned}
r_1 = 2, \quad r_2 = 1, \quad r_3 = 5, \quad r_4 = 3, \quad r_5 = 4 \\
r_6 = 7, \quad r_7 = 6, \quad r_8 = 10, \quad r_9 = 8, \quad r_{10} = 9 \text{ ohms}
\end{aligned}
$$

(16)

then $v_1 = 2j_1$, $v_2 = j_2$, $v_3 = 5j_5$, $v_4 = 3j_4$ volts, and so forth. Use of Eqs. 15 then gives

$$
\begin{aligned}
v_1 &= 2i_1 & v_6 &= 7i_6 \\
v_2 &= i_2 & v_7 &= 6(i_1 + i_4 - i_6) \\
v_3 &= 5i_3 & v_8 &= 10(-i_1 + i_2 - i_4 - i_5 + i_6) \qquad (17) \\
v_4 &= 3i_4 & v_9 &= 8(i_1 - i_2 - i_3 + i_5 - i_6) \\
v_5 &= 4i_5 & v_{10} &= 9(i_1 - i_3 + i_5)
\end{aligned}
$$

The desired loop equilibrium equations are obtained through substituting these values for the v's into Eqs. 14. After proper arrangement of the results, one finds

$$
\begin{aligned}
35i_1 - 18i_2 - 17i_3 + 16i_4 + 27i_5 - 24i_6 &= 0 \\
-18i_1 + 19i_2 + 8i_3 - 10i_4 - 18i_5 + 18i_6 &= 0 \\
-17i_1 + 8i_2 + 22i_3 + 0i_4 - 17i_5 + 8i_6 &= 0 \\
16i_1 - 10i_2 + 0i_3 + 19i_4 + 10i_5 - 16i_6 &= 0 \\
27i_1 - 18i_2 - 17i_3 + 10i_4 + 31i_5 - 18i_6 &= 0 \\
-24i_1 + 18i_2 + 8i_3 - 16i_4 - 18i_5 + 24i_6 &= 0
\end{aligned}
$$

$$(18)$$

Considering next the *node method* of writing equilibrium equations we observe first that the current-law equations, like Eq. 11 above, involve the branch currents. If these equations are to be written with the node-pair voltages as variables, we must express the branch currents in terms of the node-pair voltages. To do this, we note that the branch currents are related to the branch voltages through Eqs. 12, and the branch voltages in turn are related to the node-pair voltages in the manner shown in Ch. 1. Equations 12 are now more appropriately written in the form

$$
j_k = g_k v_k \quad \text{for} \quad k = 1, 2, \cdots, b \tag{19}
$$

in which g_1, g_2, g_3, $\cdots$ are respectively the reciprocals of r_1, r_2, r_3, $\cdots$ and are referred to as the branch conductances (expressed in mhos).

With reference to the network graph of Fig. 3 and the tree shown in part (b) of that figure, let the tree-branch voltages v_7, v_8, v_9, v_{10} be identified respectively with the node-pair voltages e_1, e_2, e_3, e_4. The following cut-set schedule is then readily constructed from an inspection of Fig. 3, noting the picked-up nodes pertinent to these four node pairs.

Node Pair No.	Branch No.										Picked-Up Nodes
	1	2	3	4	5	6	7	8	9	10	
1	-1	0	0	-1	0	1	1	0	0	0	a
2	1	-1	0	1	1	-1	0	1	0	0	c, d, e
3	-1	1	1	0	-1	1	0	0	1	0	a, b, c
4	-1	0	1	0	-1	0	0	0	0	1	a, b, c, d

(20)

The Kirchhoff current-law equations corresponding to this choice of node pairs are immediately obtained through use of the coefficients in the rows of this schedule (the algebraic sum of currents in the branches of any cut set must equal zero), thus:

$$-j_1 - j_4 + j_6 + j_7 \qquad\qquad = 0$$
$$j_1 - j_2 + j_4 + j_5 - j_6 + j_8 = 0$$
$$-j_1 + j_2 + j_3 - j_5 + j_6 + j_9 = 0$$
$$-j_1 + j_3 - j_5 + j_{10} \qquad\qquad = 0$$

(21)

while the columns of the same schedule furnish the coefficients in the following equations for the branch voltages in terms of the node-pair voltages

$$v_1 = -e_1 + e_2 - e_3 - e_4 \qquad v_6 = e_1 - e_2 + e_3$$
$$v_2 = -e_2 + e_3 \qquad\qquad v_7 = e_1$$
$$v_3 = e_3 + e_4 \qquad\qquad v_8 = e_2$$
$$v_4 = -e_1 + e_2 \qquad\qquad v_9 = e_3$$
$$v_5 = e_2 - e_3 - e_4 \qquad\qquad v_{10} = e_4$$

(22)

For branch conductances corresponding to the resistance values 16, one has $j_1 = 0.5v_1$, $j_2 = v_2$, $j_3 = 0.2v_3$, $j_4 = 0.333v_4$, and so forth.

Use of Eqs. 22 then gives

$$j_1 = 0.5(-e_1 + e_2 - e_3 - e_4) \qquad j_6 = 0.143(e_1 - e_2 + e_3)$$

$$j_2 = -e_2 + e_3 \qquad\qquad\qquad j_7 = 0.167e_1$$

$$j_3 = 0.2(e_3 + e_4) \qquad\qquad\quad j_8 = 0.1e_2 \qquad\qquad (23)$$

$$j_4 = 0.333(-e_1 + e_2) \qquad\qquad j_9 = 0.125e_3$$

$$j_5 = 0.25(e_2 - e_3 - e_4) \qquad\quad j_{10} = 0.111e_4$$

The desired node equilibrium equations are obtained through substituting these values for the j's into Eqs. 21. After proper arrangement, the results read

$$1.142e_1 - 0.976e_2 + 0.643e_3 + 0.500e_4 = 0$$

$$-0.976e_1 + 2.326e_2 - 1.893e_3 - 0.750e_4 = 0$$

$$0.643e_1 - 1.893e_2 + 2.218e_3 + 0.950e_4 = 0 \qquad (24)$$

$$0.500e_1 - 0.750e_2 + 0.950e_3 + 1.061e_4 = 0$$

In summary it is well to observe that the procedure for setting up equilibrium equations involves, for either the loop or node method, essentially three sets of relations:

(a) The Kirchhoff equations in terms of pertinent branch quantities.
(b) The relations between branch voltages and branch currents.
(c) The branch quantities in terms of the desired variables.

The coefficients in the rows and in the columns of the appropriate tie-set or cut-set schedule supply the means for writing the relations (a) and (c) respectively. The relations (b), in the form of either Eqs. 12 or Eqs. 19, are straightforward in any case.

The desired equilibrium equations are obtained through substituting relations (c) into (b), and the resulting ones into (a). In the loop method, the branch quantities in the voltage-law equations (a) are voltages while the branch quantities in (c) are currents. In the node method, the branch quantities in the current-law equations (a) are currents while the branch quantities in (c) are voltages. The relations (b) are needed in either case to facilitate the substitution of (c) into (a); that is to say, this substitution requires first a conversion from branch currents to branch voltages or vice versa. It is this conversion that is supplied by the relations (b) which depend upon the circuit elements (resistances or conductances in the above example).

The tie-set or cut-set schedule is thus seen to play a dominant role in either method since it summarizes in compact and readily usable form all pertinent relations except those determined by the element values.

The rows of a tie-set schedule define an independent set of closed paths, and hence provide a convenient means for obtaining an independent set of Kirchhoff voltage-law equations. Any row of a cut-set schedule, on the other hand, represents all of the branches terminating in the subgraph associated with one or more nodes. Since the algebraic sum of currents in such a set of branches must equal zero, the rows of a cut-set schedule are seen to provide a convenient means for obtaining an independent set of Kirchhoff current-law equations.

The columns of these same schedules provide the pertinent relations through which the desired variables are introduced. They are useful not only in the process of obtaining the appropriate equilibrium equations, but also in subsequently enabling one to compute any of the branch quantities from known values of the variables.

In situations where the geometry is particularly simple, and where correspondingly straightforward definitions for the variables are appropriate, one may, after acquiring some experience, employ a more direct procedure for obtaining equilibrium equations (as given in Art. 6) which dispenses with the use of schedules.

4 Parameter Matrices on the Loop and Node Bases

It should be observed that the final equilibrium Eqs. 18 and 24 are written in an orderly form in that the variable i_1 (resp. e_1) appears in the first column, the variable i_2 (resp. e_2) in the second column, and so forth. Taking this arrangement for granted, it becomes evident that the essential information conveyed by Eqs. 18, for example, is contained with equal definiteness but with increased compactness in the array of coefficients

$$[R] = \begin{bmatrix} 35 & -18 & -17 & 16 & 27 & -24 \\ -18 & 19 & 8 & -10 & -18 & 18 \\ -17 & 8 & 22 & 0 & -17 & 8 \\ 16 & -10 & 0 & 19 & 10 & -16 \\ 27 & -18 & -17 & 10 & 31 & -18 \\ -24 & 18 & 8 & -16 & -18 & 24 \end{bmatrix} \tag{25}$$

known as the *loop-resistance parameter matrix*. Equilibrium Eqs. 24 are similarly characterized by the following *node-conductance parameter matrix*.

$$[G] = \begin{bmatrix} 1.142 & -0.976 & 0.643 & 0.500 \\ -0.976 & 2.326 & -1.893 & -0.750 \\ 0.643 & -1.893 & 2.218 & 0.950 \\ 0.500 & -0.750 & 0.950 & 1.061 \end{bmatrix} \tag{26}$$

The term *matrix* is a name given to a rectangular array of coefficients as exemplified by forms 25 and 26. As will be discussed in later chapters, one can manipulate sets of simultaneous algebraic equations like those given by 18 and 24 in a facile manner through use of a set of symbolic operations known as the rules of matrix algebra. These matters need not concern us at the moment, however, since the matrix concept is at present introduced only to achieve two objectives that can be grasped without any knowledge of matrix algebra whatever, namely: (a) to recognize that all of the essential information given by the sets of Eqs. 18 and 24 is more compactly and hence more effectively placed in evidence through the rectangular arrays 25 and 26; (b) to make available a greatly abbreviated method of designating loop- or node-parameter values in numerical examples.

The second of these objectives may better be understood through calling attention first to a common symbolic form in which equations like 18 are written, namely thus:

$$r_{11}i_1 + r_{12}i_2 + \cdots + r_{1l}i_l = 0$$
$$r_{21}i_1 + r_{22}i_2 + \cdots + r_{2l}i_l = 0$$
$$\cdot \quad \cdot \quad \cdot \quad \cdot \quad \cdot \quad \cdot \quad \cdot \quad \cdot \quad \cdot \quad \cdot \quad \cdot \quad \cdot \quad \cdot \quad \cdot$$
$$r_{l1}i_1 + r_{l2}i_2 + \cdots + r_{ll}i_l = 0$$

$$(27)$$

Here each coefficient is denoted by a symbol like r_{11}, r_{12}, and so forth. The corresponding matrix reads

$$[R] = \begin{bmatrix} r_{11} & r_{12} & \cdots & r_{1l} \\ r_{21} & r_{22} & \cdots & r_{2l} \\ \cdot & \cdot & \cdot & \cdot \\ r_{l1} & r_{l2} & \cdots & r_{ll} \end{bmatrix} \qquad (28)$$

The general coefficient in this matrix is denoted by r_{sk} in which the indexes s and k can independently assume any integer values from 1 to l. Observe that the first index denotes the *row position*, and the second one denotes the *column position* of the coefficient with respect to array 28.

Analogously, a set of node equations like 24 would symbolically be written

$$g_{11}e_1 + g_{12}e_2 + \cdots + g_{1n}e_n = 0$$
$$g_{21}e_1 + g_{22}e_2 + \cdots + g_{2n}e_n = 0$$
$$\cdot \quad \cdot \quad \cdot \quad \cdot \quad \cdot \quad \cdot \quad \cdot \quad \cdot \quad \cdot \quad \cdot \quad \cdot \quad \cdot \quad \cdot \quad \cdot$$
$$g_{n1}e_1 + g_{n2}e_2 + \cdots + g_{nn}e_n = 0$$

$$(29)$$

with the matrix

$$[G] = \begin{bmatrix} g_{11} & g_{12} & \cdots & g_{1n} \\ g_{21} & g_{22} & \cdots & g_{2n} \\ \cdot & \cdot & \cdot \cdot \cdot & \cdot \\ g_{n1} & g_{n2} & \cdots & g_{nn} \end{bmatrix} \tag{30}$$

Identification of loop Eqs. 27 in analytic form, with the specific numerical Eqs. 18 would necessitate (without use of the parameter-matrix concept) writing

$$r_{11} = 35, \quad r_{12} = -18, \quad r_{13} = -17, \quad \cdots \tag{31}$$

which is clearly an arduous and space-consuming task compared with writing down the numerical matrix 25. Use of the matrix concept takes advantage of the fact that the row and column *position* of a number identifies it as a specific r_{sk} value; it is no longer necessary to write identifying equations like those given by 31. Similar remarks apply to the numerical identification of parameters on the node basis and the usefulness of the corresponding parameter-matrix notation.

5   Regarding the Symmetry of Parameter Matrices

The parameter matrices 25 and 26 given above have an important and interesting property in common which is described as their *symmetry*. For example, in matrix 25 we note that $r_{12} = r_{21} = -18$, $r_{13} = r_{31} = -17$, $r_{14} = r_{41} = 16$, and so forth. More specifically, matrix 25 is said to possess symmetry *about its principal diagonal*, the latter being represented by the elements $r_{11} = 35$, $r_{22} = 19$, $r_{33} = 22$, etc. on the diagonal extending from the upper left- to the lower right-hand corner of the array. Elements symmetrically located above and below this diagonal are equal. Symbolically this symmetrical property is expressed by the equation

$$r_{sk} = r_{ks} \tag{32}$$

Similar remarks apply to the node-conductance matrix 26.

This symmetry of the parameter matrix is neither accidental nor inherent in the physical property of linear networks. It is the result of having followed a deliberate procedure in the derivation of equilibrium equations that need by no means always be adhered to.

In order to understand the nature of this procedure, let us recall first that the process of deriving equilibrium equations involves predominantly the two sets of relations designated in the summary in Art. 3 as (a) the Kirchhoff-law equations and (c) the defining equations for the chosen variables. [The circuit element relations (b) are needed in carrying out the substitution of (c) into (a) but are not pertinent to the present argument.] On the loop basis the variables are loop currents, and the Kirchhoff equations are of the voltage-law type; on the node basis the variables are node-pair voltages, and the Kirchhoff equations are of the current-law type.

The choice of a set of loop-current variables involves the fixing of a set of loops or closed paths (tie sets), either through the choice of a tree and the identification of link currents with loop currents or through the forthright selection of a set of geometrically independent loops. The writing of Kirchhoff voltage-law equations also necessitates the selection of a set of geometrically independent loops, *but this set need not be the same as that pertaining to the definition of the chosen loop currents.* If the same loops *are* used in the definition of loop currents and in the writing of the voltage-law equations, then the resulting parameter matrices become symmetrical, but if separate choices are made for the closed paths defining loop currents and those for which the voltage-law equations are written, then the parameter matrices will not become symmetrical.

Thus a more general procedure for obtaining the loop equilibrium equations involves the use of two tie-set schedules. One of these pertains to the definition of a set of loop-current variables (as discussed in Art. 5, Ch. 1); the tie sets in the other one serve merely as a basis for writing the voltage-law equations. Instead of using the rows and columns of the same schedule for obtaining relations (a) and (c) respectively in the summary referred to above, one uses the rows of one schedule and the columns of another. The reader should illustrate these matters for himself by carrying through this revised procedure for the numerical example given above and noting the detailed changes that occur.

Analogously, on the node basis, one must choose a set of geometrically independent node pairs and their associated cut sets for the definition of node-pair voltage variables, and again for the writing of the Kirchhoff current-law equations. The second selection of node pairs and associated cut sets need not be the same as the first, but, if they are (as in the numerical example leading to Eqs. 24), then the resulting parameter matrix becomes symmetrical.

Thus a more general procedure for obtaining the node equilibrium equations involves the use of two cut-set schedules. One of these pertains to the definition of a set of node-pair voltage variables (as discussed in Art. 6, Ch. 1); the cut sets in the other one are utilized in writing current-law equations. Instead of using the rows and columns of the same schedule, one uses the rows of one schedule and the columns of another.

The significant point in these thoughts is that the choice of variables, whether current or voltage, need have no relation to the process of writing Kirchhoff-law equations. It is merely necessary that the latter be an independent set; the variables in terms of which they are ultimately expressed, may be chosen with complete freedom.

When the same tie sets are used for voltage-law equations and loop-current definitions, or the same cut sets are used for current-law equations and node-pair voltage definitions, then we say that the choice of variables is *consistent* with the Kirchhoff-law equations. It is this consistency that leads to symmetrical parameter matrices.*

The question of symmetry in the parameter matrices is important primarily in that one should recognize the deliberateness in the achievement of this result and not (as is quite common) become confused into thinking that it is an inherent property of linear passive bilateral networks to be characterized by symmetrical parameter matrices. We shall, to be sure, follow the usual procedure that leads to symmetry, not only because it obviates two choices being made for a set of loops or node pairs, but also because symmetrical equations are easier to solve, and because a number of interesting network properties are more readily demonstrated. So in the end we follow the customary procedure, but with an added sense of perspective that comes from a deeper understanding of the principles involved.

6 Simplified Procedures That Are Adequate in Many Practical Cases

We have given the preceding very general approach to the matter of forming the equilibrium equations of networks because, through it as a background, we are now in a position to understand far more adequately and with greater mental satisfaction the following rather restricted but practically very useful procedures applicable to many geometrical network configurations dealt with in practice. Thus, in many situations

---

* These matters were first pointed out by the author at an informal round-table conference on network analysis and synthesis sponsored by the AIEE at its midwinter convention in 1938. The discussions (supplemented by a distribution of pertinent mimeographed notes) included derivation of the general loop and node equilibrium equations for bilateral networks in symmetrical or dissymmetrical form and the consequent possibility of obtaining symmetrical matrices for networks containing unilateral elements through an appropriate definition of variables. During the past 15 years the presentation of this material was continually simplified through classroom use.

encountered in engineering work, the network geometry is such that the graph may be drawn on a plane surface without having any branches cross each other. As mentioned in Art. 9, Ch. 1 such a network is spoken of as being "mappable on a plane," or more briefly as a mappable network. The network whose graph is shown in Fig. 3 is not of the mappable variety, but the one given by the graph in Fig. 1 is.

When the equilibrium equations for a mappable network (such as that shown in Fig. 1) are to be written on the loop basis, it is possible to choose as a geometrically independent set of closed loops the meshes of this network graph (as pointed out in Art. 7 of Ch. 1). A simple example of this sort is shown in Fig. 4 in which the meshes are indicated by circulatory arrows. The corresponding voltage-law equations are

$$v_1 - v_4 = 0$$
$$v_2 - v_5 = 0$$
$$v_3 - v_6 = 0 \tag{33}$$
$$v_4 + v_5 + v_6 = 0$$

The branch currents in terms of the loop currents are seen to be given by

$$j_1 = i_1 \qquad j_4 = i_4 - i_1$$
$$j_2 = i_2 \qquad j_5 = i_4 - i_2 \tag{34}$$
$$j_3 = i_3 \qquad j_6 = i_4 - i_3$$

Suppose the branch resistance values are

$$r_1 = 5, \quad r_2 = 10, \quad r_3 = 4, \quad r_4 = 2, \quad r_5 = 10, \quad r_6 = 5 \tag{35}$$

Equations 34 multiplied respectively by these values yield the corresponding v's by means of which Eqs. 33 become expressed in terms of the loop currents. After proper arrangement this substitution yields

$$7i_1 + 0i_2 + 0i_3 - 2i_4 = 0$$
$$0i_1 + 20i_2 + 0i_3 - 10i_4 = 0$$
$$0i_1 + 0i_2 + 9i_3 - 5i_4 = 0 \tag{36}$$
$$-2i_1 - 10i_2 - 5i_3 + 17i_4 = 0$$

with the symmetrical matrix

$$[R] = \begin{bmatrix} 7 & 0 & 0 & -2 \\ 0 & 20 & 0 & -10 \\ 0 & 0 & 9 & -5 \\ -2 & -10 & -5 & 17 \end{bmatrix} \tag{37}$$

A simple physical interpretation may be given to these equations by reference to Fig. 5 in which the same network as in Fig. 4 is redrawn with the branch numbering and reference arrows left off but with the branch resistances and their values indicated. The term $7i_1$ in the first of Eqs. 36 may be interpreted as the voltage drop caused in mesh 1 by loop current i_1 since the total resistance on the contour of this mesh is 7 ohms; the rest of the terms in this equation represent additional voltage drops caused in mesh 1 by the loop currents i_2, i_3, i_4, respectively. Since no part of the contour of mesh 1 is traversed by the currents i_2 and i_3, these

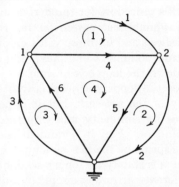

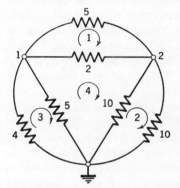

FIG. 4. A mappable network graph in which the meshes are chosen as loops.

FIG. 5. The resistance network whose graph is shown in Fig. 4. Element values are in ohms.

can cause no voltage drop in mesh 1; hence the coefficients of their terms in the first of Eqs. 36 are zero. The term $-2i_4$ takes account of the fact that loop current i_4, in traversing the 2-ohm resistance, contributes to the voltage drop in mesh 1 and that this contribution is negative with respect to the loop reference arrow in mesh 1.

The second of Eqs. 36 similarly expresses the fact that the algebraic sum of voltage drops caused in mesh 2 by the various loop currents equals zero. Only those terms have nonzero coefficients whose associated loop currents traverse at least part of the contour of mesh 2. The value of any nonzero coefficient equals the ohmic value of the total or partial mesh 2 resistance traversed by the pertinent loop current, and its algebraic sign is plus or minus, according to whether the reference direction for this loop current agrees or disagrees, respectively, with the reference arrow for mesh 2. Analogous remarks apply to the rest of Eqs. 36.

With this interpretation in mind, one can write the loop-resistance matrix 37 directly. Thus the coefficients on the principal diagonal are, respectively, the total resistance values on the contours of meshes 1, 2,

3, $\cdots$. The remaining coefficients are resistances of branches common to a pair of meshes, with their algebraic signs plus or minus according to the confluence or counterfluence of the respective mesh arrows in the pertinent common branch. Specifically, a term r_{sk} in value equals the resistance of the branch common to meshes s and k; its algebraic sign is plus if the mesh arrows have the same direction in this common branch; it is minus if they have opposite directions.

In a mappable network, with the meshes chosen as loops and the loop reference arrows consistently clockwise (or consistently counterclockwise), the algebraic signs of *all* nondiagonal terms in the loop-resistance matrix are *negative*. It is obvious that this procedure for the derivation of loop equilibrium equations yields a symmetrical parameter matrix ($r_{sk} = r_{ks}$) since a branch common to meshes s and k, whose value determines the coefficient r_{sk}, is at the same time common to meshes k and s.

This simplified procedure for writing down the loop equilibrium equations directly (having made a choice for the loops and loop currents) does not, of course, require mappability of the network, but it is not difficult to appreciate that it soon loses its simplicity and directness when the network geometry becomes random. For, in a random case it may become difficult to continue to speak of meshes as simplified versions of loops; moreover, their choice is certainly no longer straightforward nor is the designation of loop reference arrows as simple to indicate. Any given branch may be common to more than two meshes; the pertinent loop reference arrows may traverse such a branch in random directions, so that the nondiagonal coefficients in the parameter matrix will no longer be consistently negative. Although the simplified procedure may still be usable in some moderately complex nonmappable cases, one will find the more general procedure described earlier preferable when arbitrary network geometries are encountered.

An analogous simplified procedure appropriate to relatively simple geometries may be found for the determination of node equilibrium equations. In this simplified procedure the node-pair voltage variables are chosen as a node-to-datum set, as described in Art. 8 of Ch. 1. That is, they are defined as the potentials of the various single nodes with respect to a common (arbitrarily selected) datum node, as illustrated in Ch. 1 by Fig. 11 for the network graph of Fig. 8. The cut sets (which determine the Kirchhoff current-law equations) are then all given by the groups of branches divergent from the single nodes for which the pertinent node potentials are defined.

With regard to the network of Fig. 4 one may choose the bottom node as the datum or reference and define the potentials of nodes 1 and 2 respectively as the voltage variables e_1 and e_2. Noting that the pertinent cut sets are the branches divergent from these nodes, the current-law equations consistent with this selection of node-pair voltages are seen to read

$$j_1 + j_4 - j_6 - j_3 = 0$$
$$-j_1 - j_4 + j_2 + j_5 = 0$$

(38)

The branch voltages in terms of the node potentials are, by inspection of Fig. 4,

$$v_1 = e_1 - e_2 \qquad v_4 = e_1 - e_2$$
$$v_2 = e_2 \qquad v_5 = e_2$$
$$v_3 = -e_1 \qquad v_6 = -e_1$$

(39)

The branch conductances corresponding to the resistance values 35 are

$$g_1 = 0.2, \quad g_2 = 0.1, \quad g_3 = 0.25, \quad g_4 = 0.5, \quad g_5 = 0.1, \quad g_6 = 0.2$$

(40)

Equations 39 multiplied respectively by these values yield the corresponding j's in terms of the node potentials. Their substitution into Eqs. 38 results in the desired equilibrium equations, which read

$$1.15e_1 - 0.70e_2 = 0$$
$$-0.70e_1 + 0.90e_2 = 0$$

(41)

with the symmetrical node-conductance matrix

$$[G] = \begin{bmatrix} 1.15 & -0.70 \\ -0.70 & 0.90 \end{bmatrix}$$

(42)

A simple physical interpretation may be given to the node equilibrium Eqs. 41 that parallels the interpretation given above for the loop equations. Thus the first term in the first of Eqs. 41 represents the current that is caused to diverge from node 1 by the potential e_1 acting alone (that is, while $e_2 = 0$); the second term in this equation represents the current that is caused to diverge from node 1 by the potential e_2 acting alone (that is, while $e_1 = 0$). Since a positive e_2 acting alone causes current to converge upon node 1 (instead of causing a divergence of current), the term with e_2 is numerically negative. The amount of current that e_1 alone causes to diverge from node 1 evidently equals the value of e_1 times the total conductance between node 1 and datum when $e_2 = 0$ (that is, when node 2 coincides with the datum). This total conductance clearly is the sum of the conductances of the various branches divergent from node 1; with reference to Fig. 5 (in which the given parameter values are resistances) this total conductance is $1/5 + 1/2 + 1/5 + 1/4 = 1.15$, thus accounting for the coefficient of the term with e_1 in the first of Eqs. 41.

The current that e_2 alone causes to diverge from node 1 can traverse only the branches connecting node 1 directly with node 2 (these are the 2-ohm and 5-ohm branches in Fig. 5), and the value of this current is evidently given in magnitude by the product of e_2 and the net conductance of these combined branches. In the present example the pertinent conductance is $1/2 + 1/5 = 0.70$ mho, thus accounting for the value of the coefficient in the second term of the first of Eqs. 41 (the reason for its negative sign has already been explained). A similar interpretation is readily given to the second of Eqs. 41.

Thus these equations or their conductance matrix 42 could be written down directly by inspection of Fig. 5, especially if the branch-resistance values are alternately given as branch-conductance values expressed in mhos. The elements on the principal diagonal of $[G]$ are, respectively, the total conductance values (sums of branch conductances) divergent from nodes 1, 2, $\cdots$ (in a more general case there will be more than two nodes). The nondiagonal elements of $[G]$ *all* have negative algebraic signs, for the argument given above in the detailed explanation of Eqs. 41 clearly applies unaltered to all cases in which the node-pair voltage variables are chosen as a node-to-datum set. In magnitude, the nondiagonal elements in $[G]$ equal the net conductance values (sums of branch conductances), for those branches directly connecting the pertinent node pairs. More specifically, the element g_{sk} in $[G]$ equals the negative sum of the conductances of the various branches directly connecting nodes s and k. If these nodes are not directly connected by any branches, then the pertinent g_{sk} value is zero. Note that the consistent negativeness of the nondiagonal terms follows directly from the tacit assumption that any node potential is regarded as positive when it is *higher* than that of the datum node. This situation parallels the consistent negativeness of the nondiagonal terms in the $[R]$ matrix obtained on the loop basis for a mappable network in which all the mesh reference arrows are chosen consistently clockwise (or consistently counterclockwise), whence in any common branch they are counterfluent.

7 Sources

When currents and their accompanying voltage drops exist in a resistive network, energy is being dissipated. Since at every instant the rate of energy supply must equal its rate of dissipation, there can be no voltages or currents in a purely resistive or in any "lossy" network unless there are present one or more sources of energy.

Until now the role played by sources has not been introduced into the network picture and indeed their presence has nothing whatever to do with the topics discussed so far. Sources were purposely left out of consideration for this reason, since their inclusion would merely have detracted from the effectiveness of the discussion. Now, however, it is time to recognize the significance of sources, their characteristics, and how we are to determine their effect upon the equilibrium equations.

Their most important effect, as already stated, is that without them there would be no response. This fact may clearly be seen, for example, from the loop equilibrium Eqs. 36 for the network of Fig. 5. Since these four equations involving the four unknowns i_1, i_2, i_3, i_4 are independent, and all of the right-hand members are zero, we know according to the rules of algebra that none but the trivial solution $i_1 = i_2 = i_3 = i_4 = 0$ exists. That is to say, in the absence of excitation (which, as we shall see, causes the right-hand members of the equations to be nonzero) the network remains "dead as a doornail."

It was pointed out in the introduction that an electrical network as we think of it in connection with our present discussions is almost always an artificial representation of some physical system in terms of idealized quantities which we call the circuit elements or parameters (the resistance, inductance, and capacitance elements). We justify such an artificial representation through noting (a) that it can be so chosen as to simulate functionally (and to any desired degree of accuracy) the actual system at any selected points of interest, and (b) that such an idealization is essential in reducing the analysis procedure to a relatively simple and easily understandable form.

Regarding the sources through which the network becomes energized or through which the physical system derives its motive power, a consistent degree of idealization is necessary. That is to say, the sources, like the circuit elements, are represented in an idealized fashion. We shall see that actual energy sources may thus be simulated through such idealized sources in combination with idealized circuit elements. For the moment we focus our attention upon the idealized sources themselves.

Although the physical function of a source is to supply energy to the system, we shall for the time being find it more expedient to characterize a source as an element capable of providing a fixed amount of voltage or a fixed amount of current at a certain point. Actually it provides both voltage and current, and hence an amount of power equal to their product, but it is analytically essential and practically more realistic to suppose that either the voltage or the current of the source is known or fixed. We could, of course, postulate a source for which both the voltage and the current are fixed, but such sources would not prove useful in the simulation of physical systems, and we must at all times be mindful of the utility of our methods of analysis.

When we say that the voltage or the current of a source is fixed, we do not necessarily mean that it is a constant, but rather that its value or sequence of values as a continuous function of the time are independent of all other voltages and currents in the entire network. Most important in this connection is the nondependence upon the source's own voltage, if it is a current, or upon its own current if it is a voltage. Thus a so-called idealized voltage source provides at a given terminal pair a voltage function that is independent of the current at that terminal pair; and an idealized current source provides a current function that is independent of the voltage at the pertinent terminal pair.

By way of contrast, it is useful to compare the idealized source as just defined with an ordinary passive resistance or other circuit element. In the latter, the voltage and current at the terminals are related in a definite way which we call the "volt-ampere relationship" for that element. For example, in a resistance the voltage is proportional to the current, the constant of proportionality being what we call the value of the element in ohms. At the terminals of an ideal voltage source, on the other hand, the voltage is whatever we assume it to be, and it cannot depart one jot from this specification, regardless of the current it is called upon to deliver on account of the conditions imposed by its environment. An extreme situation arises if the environment is a short circuit, for then the source is called upon to deliver an infinite current; yet it does so unflinchingly and without its terminal voltage departing in the slightest from its assigned value. It is, of course, not sensible to place an ideal voltage source in such a situation, for it then is called upon to furnish infinite power. The ideal voltage source is idle when its environment is an open circuit, for then the associated current becomes zero.

Similarly, at the terminals of an ideal current source the current is whatever we assume it to be, and it cannot depart from this specification, regardless of the voltage it is called upon to produce on account of the conditions imposed by its environment. An extreme situation arises in this case if the environment turns out to be an open circuit, for then the source must produce an infinite voltage at its terminals since the terminal current, by definition, cannot depart from its specified value. Like the short-circuited voltage source, it is called upon to deliver infinite power, and hence it is not realistic to place an ideal current source in an open-circuit environment. This type of source is idle when short-circuited, since the associated voltage is then zero.

In the discussion of Kirchhoff's voltage law we found it useful to think of voltage as analogous to altitude in a mountainous terrain. The potentials of various points in the network with respect to a common reference or datum are thought of as being analogous to the altitudes of various points in a mountainous terrain with respect to sea level as a common reference. Instead of an actual mountainous terrain, suppose we visualize a miniature replica constructed by hanging up a large rubber sheet and suspending from it various weights attached at random places. Since altitude is the analogue of voltage, the problem of finding the altitude of various locations on the sheet (above, say, the floor as a common reference) is analogous to determining the potentials of various nodes in an electrical network with reference to a datum node.

Suppose first that we consider the electrical network to have no sources of excitation; all node potentials are zero. The analogous situation involving the rubber sheet would be to have it lying flat on the floor. To apply a voltage excitation to the network may be regarded as causing certain of its node potentials to be given fixed values. Analogously, certain points in the rubber sheet are raised above the floor to fixed positions and clamped there. As a result, the various nodes in the electrical network whose potentials are not arbitrarily fixed, assume potentials that are consistent with the applied excitation and the characteristics of the network. Analogously, the freely movable portions of the rubber sheet assume positions above the floor level that are consistent with the way in which the sheet is supported at the points where it is clamped (analogous to excitation of the electrical network) and the structural characteristics of the sheet with its system of attached weights.

It is interesting to note from the description of these two analogous situations that electrical excitation by means of voltage sources may be thought of as arbitrarily fixing or clamping the voltage at a certain point or points. A voltage source is thus regarded as an applied *constraint*, like nailing the rubber sheet to the wall at some point.

Ideal current sources when used to excite an electric network may likewise be regarded as applied constraints. In any passive network the currents and voltages in its various parts are in general free to assume an array of values subject only to certain interrelationships dictated by the structure of that network, but, without any excitation, all voltages and currents remain zero. If we now give to some of these voltages and currents arbitrary nonzero values, we take away their freedom, for they can no longer assume any values except the specified ones, but the remaining voltages and currents, whose values are not pegged, now move into positions that are compatible with the network characteristics interrelating all voltages and currents, and with the fixed values of those chosen to play the role of excitation quantities. As more of the voltages and currents are clamped or fixed through the application of sources, fewer remain free to adjust themselves to compatible values. Finally, if all voltages and currents were constrained by applied sources, there would be no network problem left, for everything would be known beforehand. In the commonest situation, only a single voltage or current variable is constrained through an applied source; determination of the compatible values of all the others constitutes the network problem.

Various ways in which sources are schematically represented in circuit diagrams are shown in Fig. 6. Parts (a), (b), and (c) are representations of voltage sources, whereas part (d) shows the representation for a current source. Specifically (a) and (b) are common ways of indicating

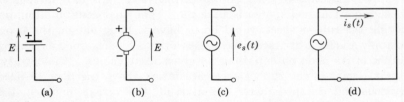

Fig. 6. Schematic representations for sources. (a) A constant voltage (battery), (b) a constant voltage (d-c generator), (c) arbitrary voltage function, (d) arbitrary current function.

constant-voltage sources, also called "direct current" or "d-c" voltage sources. The schematic (a) simulates a battery, for example, a dry cell in which the zinc electrode (thin line) is negative and the carbon electrode (thick line) is the positive terminal. The d-c source shown in (b) is drawn to resemble the commutator and brushes of a generator. The symbolic representation in (c) is intended to be more general in that the wavy line inside the circle indicates that $e_s(t)$ may be any function of time (not necessarily a sinusoid, although there is an established practice in using this symbol as the representation for a sinusoidal generator). It should be particularly noted that $e_s(t)$ in the symbolic representation of part (c) may be *any* time function and, in particular, may also be used to denote a constant-voltage source (d-c source).

Part (d) of Fig. 6 shows the schematic representation for a current source in which $i_s(t)$ is any time function and hence may be used to denote a constant or d-c source as well as any other.

In all of these source representations it will be noted that a reference arrow is included. This arrow does *not* imply that the source voltage or current is assumed to act in the indicated direction but only that, if it should at any moment have this direction, it will at that moment be regarded as a positive quantity. The reference arrow establishes a means for telling when the quantity $e_s(t)$ or $i_s(t)$ is positive and when it is negative. A source voltage is said to "act in the direction of the reference arrow" when it is a voltage rise in this direction. The $+$ and $-$ signs of parts (a) and (b) of Fig. 6 further clarify this statement. In most of the following work the representations shown in parts (c) and (d) will be used.

It should not be overlooked that the representations in Fig. 6 are for *ideal* sources. Thus the voltage between the terminals in the sketch of part (c) is always $e_s(t)$ no matter what is placed across them. Likewise the current issuing from the terminals in the sketch of part (d) is always $i_s(t)$ no matter what the external circuit may be. An actual physical voltage source may, to a first approximation, be represented by placing a resistance in series with the ideal one so that the terminal voltage decreases as the source current increases. A physical current source may similarly be represented to a first approximation through the ideal one of part (d) with a resistance in parallel with the terminals, thus taking account of the fact that the net current issuing from the terminals of the combination depends upon the terminal voltage, and decreases as this voltage increases. These matters will further be elaborated upon in the applications to come later on.

It is common among students that they have more difficulty visualizing or grasping the significance of current sources than they do in the understanding of voltage sources. A contributing reason for this difficulty is that voltage sources are more commonly experienced. Thus our power systems that supply electricity to our homes and factories are essentially voltage sources in that they have the property of being idle when open-circuited. Sources that are basically of the current variety are far less common. One such source is the photoelectric cell which emits charge proportional to the intensity of the impinging light and hence is definitely a current source; it clearly is idle when short-circuited because it then delivers no energy. Another device that is commonly regarded as a current source is the pentode vacuum tube. Its plate current is very nearly proportional to its grid excitation under normal operating conditions, and hence, for purposes of circuit analysis, it is appropriate to consider it as being essentially a current source. In any case it can with very good accuracy be regarded as an ideal current source in parallel with a resistance.

Whether actual sources are more correctly to be regarded as voltage sources or as current sources is, however, a rather pointless argument since we shall soon see that *either* representation (in combination with an appropriate arrangement of passive circuit elements) is always possible no matter what the actual source really is. Again we must be reminded that circuit theory makes no claim to be dealing with actual things. In fact it very definitely deals only with fictitious things, but in such a way that actual things can thereby be represented. Like all other methods of analysis, circuit theory is merely the means to an end; it lays no claim to being the real thing.

Now as to determining how source quantities enter into the equilibrium equations for a given network, we first make the rather general observation that the insertion of sources into a given passive network is done in either of two ways. One of these is to insert the source into

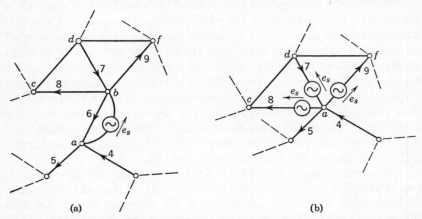

(a)   (b)

Fig. 7. Network graph involving voltage source (constraint) in parallel with a branch (a), and the equivalent revised graph (b) showing disposition of voltage source.

the gap formed by cutting a branch (as with a pliers); the other is to connect the source terminals to a selected node pair (as with a soldering iron). These two methods will be distinguished as the "pliers method" and the "soldering-iron method" respectively. We shall now show that one may consider the pliers method restricted to the insertion of voltage sources and the soldering-iron method to the insertion of current sources. That is to say, the connection of a voltage source across a node pair or the insertion of a current source in series with a branch implies a revision of the network geometry, with the end result that voltage sources again appear only in series with branches and current sources appear only in parallel with branches (or across node pairs).

For example, in part (a) of Fig. 7 is shown a graph in which a voltage source e_s appears in parallel with branch 6 of some network, and in part (b) of this figure is shown the resultant change in the network geometry and source arrangement which this situation reduces to. Thus, in considering the given arrangement in part (a), one should first observe that branch 6 is rendered trivial by having e_s placed in parallel with it since the value of v_6 is thus forced to be equal to e_s and hence (along with j_6) is no longer an unknown. That is to say, the determination of the current in branch 6 is rendered trivially simple and independent of what happens in the rest of the network. Therefore we can remove branch 6 from our thoughts and from the rest of the graph so that e_s alone appears as a connecting link between nodes a and b. Next we observe that the potentials of nodes c, d, f, relative to that of node a are precisely the same in the arrangement of part (b) in Fig. 7 as they are in part (a). For example, the potential of node c with respect to that of node a is $(e_s - v_8)$ as is evident by inspection of either part (a) or part (b) of this figure. Similarly the potential of node d with respect to that of node a is seen to be $(e_s + v_7)$ in the arrangement of part (a) or of part (b). It thus becomes clear that the branch voltages and currents in the graph of part (b) must be the same as in the graph of part (a), except for the omission of the trivial branch 6.

We may conclude that placing a voltage source across a node pair has the same effect upon the network geometry as placing a short circuit across that node pair. Comparing graphs (a) and (b) in Fig. 7, we see, for example, that the voltage source e_s in graph (a) effectively unites nodes a and b in that graph, thus eliminating branch 6, and yielding the revised graph (b). The effect of the voltage source so far as this revised graph is concerned is taken into account through placing identical voltage sources in series with all branches confluent in the original node b. We can alternately place the identical voltage sources in series with the branches originally confluent in node a: that is, in branches 4 and 5 instead of 7, 8, and 9.

It is useful in this connection to regard a voltage source as though it were a sort of generalized short circuit, which indeed it is. Thus, by a short circuit we imply a link or branch for which the potential difference between its terminals is zero independent of the branch current, while for a voltage source the potential difference is e_s independent of the branch current. For $e_s = 0$, the short circuit is identical with the voltage source. Or we may say that a dead voltage source is a short circuit. The preceding discussion shows that the effect of a voltage source upon the network geometry is the same as that of an applied short-circuit constraint.

Analogously, part (a) of Fig. 8 depicts a situation in which a current source i_s appears in series with branch 4 of some network, and part (b) shows the resultant change in geometry and source arrangement which is thereby implied. With reference to the given situation in part (a) it is at once evident that branch 4 becomes trivial since its current is identical with the source current and hence is known. It is also evident that the effect of the current source i_s upon the rest of the network is the same as though there had been no branch linking nodes a and b through which the source is applied. We can, therefore, regard the current source to be bridged across the node pair a–b in a modified graph in which branch 4 is absent.

A further step that results in having all current sources in parallel with branches may be carried out as shown in part (b) of Fig. 8. The equivalence of the four identical current sources i_s bridged across

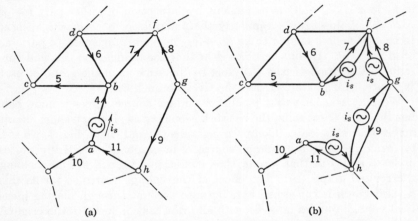

Fig. 8. Network graph involving current source (constraint) in series with a branch (a), and the equivalent revised graph (b) showing disposition of current source.

branches 11, 9, 8, 7, with a single source i_s bridged across the node pair a–b is evident by inspection since the same amount of source current still leaves node a and enters node b, while no net source current enters or leaves the nodes f, g, and h.

We may conclude that inserting a current source in series with a branch has the same effect upon the network geometry as does the open-circuiting or the removal of that branch. In this altered network the source appears bridged across the node pair originally linked by the removed branch, or in the form of several identical sources bridged across a confluent set of branches joining this node pair.

According to these results we may regard a current source as a generalized open circuit. By an open circuit we understand a branch for which the current is zero independent of the branch voltage; and by a current source we understand a branch for which the current is i_s independent of the branch voltage. For $i_s = 0$, the current source is identical with an open circuit; the latter may be regarded as a dead current source.

In summary we may say that, so long as voltage sources appear only in series with branches, and current sources are associated only in parallel with branches or across node pairs, their presence does not disturb the network geometry in the sense that all matters pertaining to that geometry remain unaltered, such as the numbers of independent voltages and currents uniquely characterizing the state of the network, or their algebraic relations to the branch currents and voltages. In a sense, the open-circuit character of a current source and the short-circuit character of a voltage source become evident here as they do in the reasoning of the immediately preceding paragraphs.

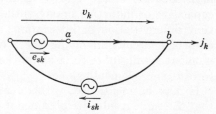

Fig. 9. Passive branch with associated current and voltage source.

On the other hand, we see that the network geometry *is* affected whenever a current source is placed in series with a branch or a voltage source in parallel with one. In both cases the branch in question becomes trivial and can be removed, leaving in its place an open circuit if the inserted source is a current, and a short circuit if the inserted source is a voltage. After this revision in the geometry is carried out, the source appears either as a current in parallel with a branch (or with several branches) or as a voltage in series with a branch (or with several branches). These two source arrangements alone, therefore, are all that need to be considered in the following discussion.

Thus we may regard any branch in a network to have the structure shown in Fig. 9. Here the link $a–b$ represents the passive branch without its associated voltage and current sources; that is to say, when the sources are zero (as they usually are for most of the branches in a network), then the branch reduces to this link $a–b$ alone. However, we shall take the attitude at this point that any or all of the branches in a network may turn out to have the associated sources shown in Fig. 9. The network is thus regarded as a geometrical configuration of active instead of passive branches. This turn of events changes nothing with regard to all that has been said previously except the relations between branch voltages and branch currents [designated as the relations (b) in the summary of Art. 3 regarding the formulation of equilibrium equations].

Since v_k and j_k denote the net voltage drop and the net current in branch k, the voltage drop and current in the passive link $a–b$ (noting the reference arrows in Fig. 9) are $(v_k + e_{sk})$ and $(j_k + i_{sk})$ respectively.

These are the quantities that are related by the passive circuit element which the branch represents. If the functional relationship between voltage drop and current in the passive link is formally denoted by $v = z(j)$ or $j = y(v)$, we have, for the general active branch of Fig. 9,

$$(v_k + e_{sk}) = z(j_k + i_{sk}) \quad \text{or} \quad (j_k + i_{sk}) = y(v_k + e_{sk}) \tag{43}$$

In a resistance branch, the notation $z(j)$ reduces simply to a multiplication of the current j by the branch resistance, and $y(v)$ denotes a multiplication of the voltage drop v by the branch conductance. In capacitive or inductive branches the symbols $z(j)$ and $y(v)$ also involve time differentiation or integration, as will be discussed in detail later on when circuits involving these elements are considered. For the moment it will suffice to visualize the significance of Eqs. 43 with regard to resistance elements alone.

It may be mentioned, with reference to the arrangement in Fig. 9, that the same results are obtained if the current source i_{sk} is assumed to be in parallel with the passive link a–b alone rather than with the series combination of this link and the voltage source e_{sk}. If $i_{sk} = 0$, the link is activated by a series voltage source alone; if $e_{sk} = 0$, one has the representation of a passive branch activated by a current source alone. For $e_{sk} = i_{sk} = 0$, the arrangement reduces to the usual passive branch. Thus the volt-ampere relations 43 are sufficiently general to take care of any functional dependence between net branch voltages and currents that can arise in the present discussions.

The method of including the effect of sources in the derivation of equilibrium equations is now easily stated. Namely, one proceeds precisely as described in the previous articles for the unactivated network except that the relations between branch voltages and branch currents are considered in the form of Eqs. 43, so as to take account of the presence of any voltage or current sources. This statement applies alike to the determination of equilibrium equations on the loop or the node basis. Thus, regardless of the nature and distribution of sources throughout the network, the procedure remains straightforward and is essentially the same as for the unexcited network.

8 Summary of the Procedures for Deriving Equilibrium Equations

At this point it is effective to bring together in compact symbolic form the steps involved in setting up equilibrium equations. Thus we have on the *loop basis*:

(a) The Kirchhoff voltage-law equations in terms of branch voltages:

$$\Sigma \pm v_k = 0 \tag{44}$$

(b) The relations between branch voltages and branch currents (Eqs. 43):

$$v_k = -e_{sk} + z(j_k + i_{sk}) \tag{45}$$

(c) The branch currents in terms of the loop currents:

$$j_k = \Sigma \pm i_r \tag{46}$$

The rows of a tie-set schedule (like 13, for example) place in evidence the Kirchhoff Eqs. 44, while the columns of this schedule yield the branch currents in terms of the loop currents, Eqs. 46. The expressions for the v_k's in terms of the j_k's, Eqs. 45, are obtained from a knowledge of the circuit parameters and the associated voltage and current sources, as illustrated in Fig. 9.

The desired equilibrium equations are the Kirchhoff Eqs. 44 expressed in terms of the loop currents. One accomplishes this end through substituting the j_k's given by Eqs. 46 into Eqs. 45, and the resulting expressions for v_k into Eqs. 44. Noting that the linearity of the network permits one to write $z(j_k + i_{sk}) = z(j_k) + z(i_{sk})$, the result of this substitution among Eqs. 44, 45, 46 leads to

$$\Sigma \pm z(\Sigma \pm i_r) = \Sigma \pm [e_{sk} - z(i_{sk})] = e_{sl} \tag{47}$$

Interpretation of this formidable looking result is aided by pointing out that $z(\Sigma \pm i_r)$ represents the passive voltage drop in any branch k due to the superposition of loop currents i_r in that branch, and that the left-hand side of Eq. 47 is the algebraic summation of such passive branch voltage drops around a typical closed loop l. The right-hand side, which is abbreviated by the symbol e_{sl}, is the net apparent source voltage acting in the same loop. It is given by an algebraic summation of the voltage sources present in the branches comprising this closed contour (tie set) and the additional voltages induced in these branches by current sources that may simultaneously be associated with them. The latter voltages, which are represented by the term $-z(i_{sk})$, must depend upon the circuit parameter relations in the same way as do the passive voltage drops caused by the loop currents, except that their algebraic signs are reversed because they are rises.

Thus the resulting equilibrium Eqs. 47 state the logical fact that the net passive voltage drop on any closed contour must equal the net active voltage rise on that contour. If we imagine that the loops are determined through selecting a tree and identifying the link currents with loop currents, then we can interpret the source voltages e_{sl} as equivalent link voltages in the sense that, if actual voltage sources having these values are placed in the links and all original current and voltage sources are removed, the resulting loop currents remain the same. Or we can say that, if the *negatives* of the voltages e_{sl} are placed in the links, then the effect of all other sources becomes neutralized, and the resulting network response is zero; that is, the loop currents or link currents are zero, the same as they would be if all links were opened.

Hence we have a physical interpretation of the e_{sl} in that they may be regarded as the negatives of the voltages appearing across gaps formed by opening all the links. In many situations to which the simplified procedure discussed in Art. 6 is relevant, this physical interpretation of the net excitation quantities e_{sl} suffices for their determination by inspection of the given network.

An entirely analogous procedure and corresponding process of physical interpretation applies to the derivation of equilibrium equations on the *node basis*. Here one has

(a) The Kirchhoff current-law equations in terms of branch currents:

$$\Sigma \pm j_k = 0 \tag{48}$$

(b) The relations between the branch currents and branch voltages (Eqs. 43):

$$j_k = -i_{sk} + y(v_k + e_{sk}) \tag{49}$$

(c) The branch voltages in terms of the node-pair voltages:

$$v_k = \Sigma \pm e_r \tag{50}$$

The rows of a cut-set schedule (like 20, for example) place in evidence the Kirchhoff Eqs. 48, while the columns of this schedule yield the branch voltages in terms of the node-pair voltages, Eqs. 50. The expressions for the j_k's in terms of the v_k's, Eqs. 49, are obtained from a knowledge of the circuit parameters and the associated voltage and current sources, as illustrated in Fig. 9.

The desired equilibrium equations are the Kirchhoff Eqs. 48 expressed in terms of the node-pair voltages. One obtains this end by substituting the v_k's given by Eqs. 50 into Eqs. 49, and the resulting expressions for j_k into Eqs. 48. Noting that the linearity of the network permits one to write $y(v_k + e_{sk}) = y(v_k) + y(e_{sk})$, the result of this substitution among Eqs. 48, 49, 50 leads to

$$\Sigma \pm y(\Sigma \pm e_r) = \Sigma \pm [i_{sk} - y(e_{sk})] = i_{sn} \tag{51}$$

Interpretation of this formidable looking result is aided through recognizing that $y(\Sigma \pm e_r)$ represents the passive current in any branch k due to the algebraic sum of node-pair voltages e_r acting upon it, and hence the left-hand side of Eq. 51 is the summation of such branch currents in all branches of a typical cut set; for example, the set of branches divergent from a given node n if the node-pair voltages are chosen as a node-to-datum set.

The right-hand side of Eq. 51, which is abbreviated by the symbol i_{sn}, is the net apparent source current for this cut set, for example, it is the net apparent source current entering node n in a node-to-datum situation. The net source current is given by an algebraic summation of the current sources associated with the branches comprising the pertinent cut set and the additional currents induced in these branches by voltage sources that may simultaneously be acting in them. The latter currents, which are represented by the term $-y(e_{sk})$, must depend upon the circuit-parameter relations in the same way as do the passive currents caused by the node-pair voltages except that their algebraic signs are reversed because they represent a flow of charge *into* the cut set rather than out of it.

Thus the resulting equilibrium Eqs. 51 state the logical fact that the net current in the several branches of a cut set must equal the total source current feeding this cut set. If we imagine that the cut sets have been determined through selecting a tree and identifying the tree-branch voltages with node-pair voltages, then we can interpret the source currents i_{sn} as equivalent sources bridged across the tree branches in the sense that, if actual current sources having these values are placed in parallel with the tree branches and all original current and voltage sources are removed, the resulting node-pair voltages remain the same. Or we can say that, if the *negatives* of the currents i_{sn} are placed across the tree branches, then the effect of all other sources becomes neutralized, and the resulting network response is zero; that is, the node-pair voltages or tree-branch voltages are zero, the same as they would be if all tree branches were short-circuited.

Hence we have a physical interpretation of the i_{sn} in that they may be regarded as the negatives of the currents appearing in short circuits placed across all the tree branches. In a node-to-datum choice of node pairs, the i_{sn} may be regarded as the negatives of the currents appearing in a set of short circuits placed across these node pairs, and a node-to-datum set of current sources having these values can be used in place of the original voltage and current sources in computing the desired network response. In many situations to which the simplified procedure discussed in Art. 6 is relevant, this physical interpretation of the net excitation quantities i_{sn} suffices for their determination by inspection of the given network.

9   Examples

The complete procedure for setting up equilibrium equations will now be illustrated for several specific examples: Consider first the resistance

network of Fig. 10.   The element values in part (a) are in ohms, and the
source values are $i_s = 10$ amperes, $e_s = 5$ volts (both constant).   In

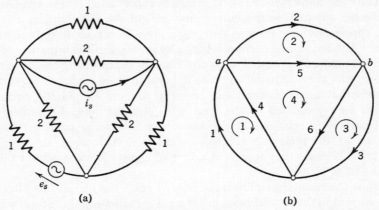

(a)   (b)

FIG. 10.   A resistance network (element values in ohms) and its graph showing the
choice of meshes as loops.

part (b) of the same figure is shown the graph with its branch numbering
and a choice of meshes to define loop currents.

Loop No.	Branch No.					
	1	2	3	4	5	6
1	1	0	0	−1	0	0
2	0	1	0	0	−1	0
3	0	0	1	0	0	−1
4	0	0	0	1	1	1

(52)

The tie-set schedule corresponding to this choice is given in 52.   The
rows give us the voltage-law equations:

$$v_1 - v_4 = 0$$
$$v_2 - v_5 = 0$$
$$v_3 - v_6 = 0$$
$$v_4 + v_5 + v_6 = 0$$

(53)

and the columns yield the branch currents in terms of the loop currents, thus:

$$j_1 = i_1 \qquad j_4 = -i_1 + i_4$$
$$j_2 = i_2 \qquad j_5 = -i_2 + i_4 \qquad (54)$$
$$j_3 = i_3 \qquad j_6 = -i_3 + i_4$$

These correspond respectively to Eqs. 44 and 46 in the above summary.

With regard to Eqs. 45 relating branch voltages to branch currents, we observe that, if we associate the current source with branch 5 (we could alternately associate it with branch 2), then all branches except 1 and 5 are passive and no special comment is needed for them. The net voltage drop in branch 1 is $v_1 = -e_s + j_1$, and the net current in the arrow direction in branch 5 is $j_5 = i_s + (v_5/2)$, the term $(v_5/2)$ being the current in the 2-ohm resistance which is the passive part of this branch. Noting the source values given above, the relations expressing net branch-voltage drops in terms of net branch currents read

$$v_1 = j_1 - 5 \qquad v_4 = 2j_4$$
$$v_2 = j_2 \qquad v_5 = 2j_5 - 20 \qquad (55)$$
$$v_3 = j_3 \qquad v_6 = 2j_6$$

The relations involving the active branches are seen to contain terms that are independent of current.

The desired equilibrium equations are found through substitution of Eqs. 54 into 55, and the resulting expressions for the v's into the voltage-law equations 53. After proper arrangement this gives

$$3i_1 + 0i_2 + 0i_3 - 2i_4 = \quad 5$$
$$0i_1 + 3i_2 + 0i_3 - 2i_4 = -20$$
$$0i_1 + 0i_2 + 3i_3 - 2i_4 = \quad 0 \qquad (56)$$
$$-2i_1 - 2i_2 - 2i_3 + 6i_4 = \quad 20$$

These are readily solved for the loop currents. One finds

$$i_1 = 5, \qquad i_2 = -10/3, \qquad i_3 = 10/3, \qquad i_4 = 5 \qquad (57)$$

whence substitution into Eqs. 54 yields all the branch currents

$$j_1 = 5, \quad j_2 = -10/3, \quad j_3 = 10/3, \quad j_4 = 0, \quad j_5 = 25/3, \quad j_6 = 5/3 \qquad (58)$$

The value of j_5 is the net current in branch 5. That in the passive part of this branch is smaller than j_5 by the value of the source current, and hence is $(25/3) - 10 = -5/3$.

Now let us solve the network given in Fig. 10 by the node method, choosing as node-pair voltages the potentials of nodes a and b respectively, with the bottom node as a reference. The appropriate cut-set schedule is 59. The rows give us the current-law equations,

Node Pair No.	Branch No.					
	1	2	3	4	5	6
1	−1	1	0	−1	1	0
2	0	−1	1	0	−1	1

$$(59)$$

$$-j_1 + j_2 - j_4 + j_5 = 0$$
$$-j_2 + j_3 - j_5 + j_6 = 0$$

$$(60)$$

and the columns yield the branch voltages in terms of the node-pair voltages, thus:

$$v_1 = -e_1 \qquad\qquad v_4 = -e_1$$
$$v_2 = e_1 - e_2 \qquad\quad v_5 = e_1 - e_2$$
$$v_3 = e_2 \qquad\qquad\quad v_6 = e_2$$

$$(61)$$

These correspond respectively to Eqs. 48 and 50 in the above summary.

Regarding Eqs. 49 relating the branch currents to the branch voltages, we note as before that $j_1 = v_1 + e_s$ and $j_5 = i_s + 0.5v_5$, so that the complete set of these equations reads

$$j_1 = v_1 + 5 \qquad\quad j_4 = 0.5v_4$$
$$j_2 = v_2 \qquad\qquad\; j_5 = 0.5v_5 + 10$$
$$j_3 = v_3 \qquad\qquad\; j_6 = 0.5v_6$$

$$(62)$$

which are simply the inverse of Eqs. 55.

The desired equilibrium equations are found through substitution of Eqs. 61 into 62, and the resulting expressions for the j's into the current-law equations 60. After proper arrangement one finds

$$3e_1 - 1.5e_2 = -5$$
$$-1.5e_1 + 3e_2 = \;\; 10$$

$$(63)$$

The solution is readily found to be

$$e_1 = 0, \qquad e_2 = 10/3 \tag{64}$$

and the branch voltages are then computed from Eqs. 61 to be

$$v_1 = 0, \ v_2 = -10/3, \ v_3 = 10/3, \ v_4 = 0, \ v_5 = -10/3, \ v_6 = 10/3 \tag{65}$$

With regard to branch 1 it must be remembered that the value of v_1 is for the total branch, including the voltage source. The drop in the passive part, therefore, is 5 volts.

As a second example we shall consider the network graph shown in Fig. 11(a). The sources in series with the branches are voltages having

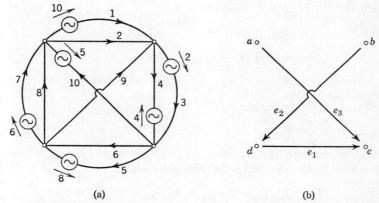

(a)   (b)

FIG. 11. Graph of a resistance network (a) with branch conductance values given by Eqs. 69. Choice of node-pair voltage variables is indicated in (b).

the values indicated. Since for this graph $b = 10$, $n = 3$, and $l = 7$, it will be advantageous to choose the node method. A geometrical specification of node-pair voltages is shown in part (b) of the same figure. In cut-set schedule 66 pertaining to this choice of node pairs a last column

Node Pair No.	Branch No.										Picked-Up Nodes
	1	2	3	4	5	6	7	8	9	10	
1	1	1	−1	−1	1	1	−1	−1	0	0	a, c
2	1	1	−1	−1	0	0	0	0	1	0	a, c, d
3	−1	−1	0	0	0	0	1	1	0	1	b, c, d

(66)

indicating the corresponding "picked-up" nodes is added to facilitate understanding its construction.

According to the rows of this schedule one obtains the Kirchhoff current-law equations,

$$j_1 + j_2 - j_3 - j_4 + j_5 + j_6 - j_7 - j_8 = 0$$

$$j_1 + j_2 - j_3 - j_4 + j_9 = 0 \qquad (67)$$

$$-j_1 - j_2 + j_7 + j_8 + j_{10} = 0$$

while the columns yield the following relations for the branch voltages in terms of the node-pair voltages:

$$
\begin{array}{ll}
v_1 = e_1 + e_2 - e_3 & v_6 = e_1 \\
v_2 = e_1 + e_2 - e_3 & v_7 = -e_1 + e_3 \\
v_3 = -e_1 - e_2 & v_8 = -e_1 + e_3 \qquad (68) \\
v_4 = -e_1 - e_2 & v_9 = e_2 \\
v_5 = e_1 & v_{10} = e_3
\end{array}
$$

The branches are again considered to be resistive. Let us assume for their conductances the following values in mhos:

$$g_1 = 2, \quad g_2 = 2, \quad g_3 = 1, \quad g_4 = 3, \quad g_5 = 4,$$
$$g_6 = 5, \quad g_7 = 1, \quad g_8 = 3, \quad g_9 = 2, \quad g_{10} = 6 \qquad (69)$$

The relations expressing the branch currents in terms of the net branch-voltage drops are then readily found by noting the appropriate expression for the drop in the passive part of each branch and multiplying this by the corresponding conductance. For example, the voltage drop in the passive part of branch 1 is $v_1 + 10$, in branch 3 it is $v_3 + 2$, in branch 5 it is $v_5 - 8$, and so forth. Thus we see that

$$
\begin{array}{ll}
j_1 = 2v_1 + 20 & j_6 = 5v_6 \\
j_2 = 2v_2 & j_7 = v_7 + 6 \\
j_3 = v_3 + 2 & j_8 = 3v_8 \qquad (70) \\
j_4 = 3v_4 - 12 & j_9 = 2v_9 \\
j_5 = 4v_5 - 32 & j_{10} = 6v_{10} - 30
\end{array}
$$

Substitution of the v's from Eqs. 68 into Eqs. 70 and the resulting expressions for the j's into Eqs. 67 gives the desired equilibrium equations.   After proper arrangement these read

$$21e_1 + 8e_2 - 8e_3 = 8$$

$$8e_1 + 10e_2 - 4e_3 = -30 \qquad (71)$$

$$-8e_1 - 4e_2 + 14e_3 = 44$$

Their solution yields

$$e_1 = 3.49, \qquad e_2 = -4.22, \qquad e_3 = 3.93 \qquad (72)$$

from which the net branch-voltage drops may readily be computed using Eqs. 68, and the branch currents are then found from Eqs. 70.

PROBLEMS

1. Regarding the independence of Kirchhoff voltage-law equations, it might be supposed that, if the number of equations equals $l = b - n$, and if collectively they involve all of the branch voltages, then they must form an independent set.   Show that this conclusion is false by constructing a counter example.   Thus, with regard to the accompanying graph, consider equations written for the combined contours of meshes 1 and 2, 2 and 3, 3 and 4, 4 and 1.   Although all branch voltages are involved, show that these equations do not form an independent set.

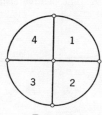

PROB. 1.

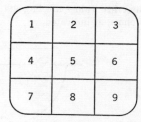

PROB. 3.

2. Prove or disprove the statement: "The number of independent Kirchhoff voltage-law equations equals the smallest number of closed paths that traverse all of the branches."

3. With reference to the graph shown, determine whether a set of voltage-law equations written for the following combined mesh contours is an independent one:

$$(1 + 2 + 3), \quad (4 + 5 + 6), \quad (7 + 8 + 9), \quad (1 + 4 + 7), \quad (2 + 5 + 8),$$

$$(3 + 6 + 9), \quad (1 + 2 + 4 + 5), \quad (2 + 3 + 5 + 6), \quad (5 + 6 + 8 + 9)$$

4. Construct the dual to Prob. 1, and solve it.

5. In Prob. 1 show that voltage-law equations written for the following combined mesh contours do form an independent set $(1 + 2 + 3)$, $(2 + 3 + 4)$, $(3 + 4 + 1)$, $(4 + 1 + 2)$.

Is the following set independent: $(1 - 2)$, $(2 - 3)$, $(3 - 4)$, $(4 - 1)$?

6. In a 5-mesh mappable network, are voltage-law equations written for the following mesh combinations independent:

$$(1 + 2), \quad (2 + 3), \quad (3 + 4), \quad (4 + 5), \quad (5 + 1)?$$

or

$$(1 - 2), \quad (2 - 3), \quad (3 - 4), \quad (4 - 5), \quad (5 - 1)?$$

7. Translate Prob. 6 into its dual. Make appropriate sketches and answer the pertinent questions involved.

8. Prove that voltage-law equations written for the mesh contours in a mappable network always form an independent set by constructing the dual situation and carrying out the corresponding proof. In which situation is the proof more readily obvious?

9. Consider the graph of Prob. 1, Ch. 1, and choose branches 5, 6, **7**, 8 as constituting a tree. For the meshes, which become the closed paths upon which the link currents circulate, write Kirchhoff voltage-law equations, and use these to express the link voltages in terms of the tree-branch voltages. Now write a voltage-law equation for an additional closed path, say, for the mesh combination $(1 + 2 - 3)$ or any other one. In this equation substitute the expressions for the link voltages obtained above, and note that it reduces to the trivial identity $0 \equiv 0$.

10. Construct the dual to the situation described in Prob. 9, and thus give an illustrative example showing that no more than n Kirchhoff current-law equations are independent.

11. In the sketch below, the series source is a voltage, and the parallel one is a current. Numerical values are in volts and amperes. The passive element is a resistance of 3 ohms, as indicated.

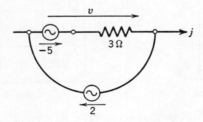

Using the superposition principle which allows us to add separate effects, treating each as though the others did not exist, and remembering that a nonexistent current is an open circuit, demonstrate the correctness of each of the following relations

$$v = 5 + 3 \times 2 + 3 \times j = 3j + 11$$

$$j = -2 - \frac{5}{3} + \frac{v}{3} = \frac{1}{3}v - \frac{11}{3}$$

and check them, using Eq. 43. Thus show that the given active branch is replaceable by either of the following ones:

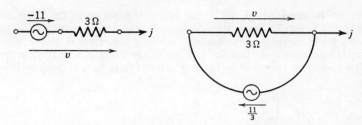

12. Using the ideas brought out in the preceding problem, reduce the following to (a) an equivalent single passive element with a series voltage source, (b) an equivalent single passive element with a parallel current source.

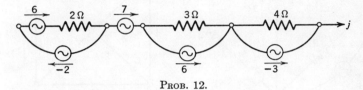

PROB. 12.

13. Apply the statement of Prob. 12 to the following:

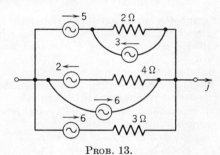

PROB. 13.

14. Apply the statement of Prob. 12 to the arrangement of sources and passive elements shown below.

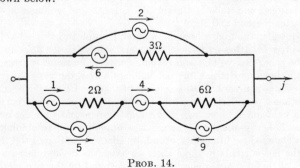

PROB. 14.

15. In the following circuit the central source is a current. The other sources are understood to be voltages or currents, according to their series or parallel association with the pertinent passive element. Element values are in ohms. Through appropriate manipulation, reduce this problem to one involving a single loop current, and, after finding its value, obtain the four currents i_1, i_2, i_3, i_4 in terms of this one.

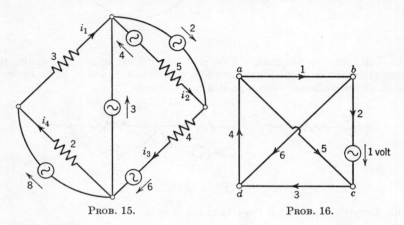

PROB. 15. PROB. 16.

16. In the pertinent graph, the branch numbers may be regarded as also indicating branch conductance values in mhos. Construct two cut-set schedules, one for the choice of node-pair voltages, $e_1 = v_1$, $e_2 = v_2$, $e_3 = v_3$, and the other one for the picked-up nodes, a–c, b–c, d.

Using the first schedule for the definition of variables and the second one for the determination of the Kirchhoff current-law equations, obtain the equilibrium equations (having a nonsymmetrical parameter matrix), and solve. Alternately obtain symmetrical equilibrium equations through use of the first schedule alone. Solve these, and check the previous solutions.

17. Construct the complete dual to Prob. 16 and solve.

18. Consider the 2-, 4-, 5-ohm branches as forming a tree.

(a) Find equivalent voltage sources in the links alone. Set up loop equations, and solve.

(b) Find an equivalent set of current sources across the tree branches alone. Set up node equations, and solve. Obtain all currents and voltages in the passive branches by each method and check.

Find the equivalent voltage sources in (a), first, by replacing the -4-volt and 2-volt sources in the tree branches by respectively equal sources in the links and combining these with the other link-voltage sources and converted current sources; second, by opening all the links and noting the net voltages across the gaps thus formed (the desired link-voltage sources are the negatives of these). Check the results found by these two methods. Similarly in part (b) find the desired equivalent current sources, first, through conversion of voltage to current sources and then replacing current sources across links by equal ones across tree branches and combining these with other sources across these branches; second, by short-circuiting all the tree branches and noting the net currents in these short circuits (the desired current sources are the negatives of these). Again check the results found by the two methods.

Note carefully that the sources in (a) yield the correct loop currents but that the voltages across the tree branches, which are now purely passive, are not the actual net tree-branch voltages. Hence, if we convert the voltage sources in (a) to equivalent current sources and transfer these across the tree branches, we should not expect to check the current sources found in part (b). Similarly, we cannot expect from the results of (b) to find those of (a) through source transformation methods alone. Discuss this aspect of the problem.

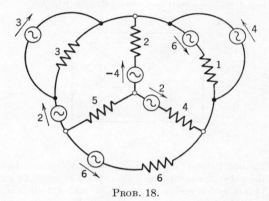

PROB. 18.

19. The sketch below shows the graph of a network consisting of seven 1-ohm branches and a 1-volt source. Find the values of the node potentials e_1, e_2, e_3 with respect to that of the common node at 0. Although any valid method is acceptable, it is suggested that you use the technique of source transformations in order to avoid deriving and solving a set of algebraic equations.

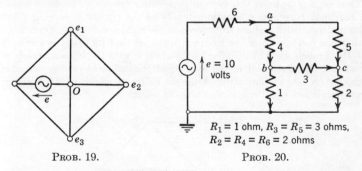

PROB. 19.   PROB. 20.

$R_1 = 1$ ohm, $R_3 = R_5 = 3$ ohms,
$R_2 = R_4 = R_6 = 2$ ohms

20. (a) In the network shown consider branches 1, 3, and 4 as forming a tree. Identify the link currents with the loop currents, and write a tie-set schedule for the network. Write down explicitly the three sets of equations: (1) Kirchhoff's voltage-law equations, (2) the appropriate volt-ampere relations for the branches, (3) the branch currents in terms of the loop currents. Substitute (3) into (2) and then (2) into (1) to obtain the equilibrium equations on a loop basis.

(b) Write down this last set of equations directly, using mesh currents as variables and the simplified procedure discussed in Art. 6.

21. (a) For the network of Prob. 20 consider the node-pair voltages from a, b, and c to ground as an independent set. Write a cut-set schedule for them. Then obtain the three sets of equations: (1) Kirchhoff's current-law equations, (2) the appropriate volt-ampere relations for the branches, (3) the branch voltage drops in terms of the node-pair voltages. By substitution of (3) into (2), and then these into (1), obtain the equilibrium equations on a node basis.

(b) Write down this last set of equations directly, using the same node-pair voltages as variables and the simplified procedure discussed in Art. 6.

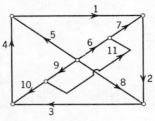

PROB. 22.

22. Choosing the link currents 1, 2, 3, 4, 11, as variables, repeat parts (a) and (b) of Prob. 20 for the network shown here. Branches 1 through 10 are 2-ohm resistances. Branch 11 is a 1-ohm resistance in parallel with a 1-ampere current source.

23. When a branch with its associated sources as shown in Fig. 9 becomes degenerate through having its passive resistance assume an infinite value, then its voltage source is trivial, and its current is constrained by the associated current source to the value $j_k = -i_{sk}$. One way of dealing with this situation is to revise the network geometry and dispose of the current source as shown in Fig. 8. Show, however, that one may alternately meet this situation by treating this branch in the normal manner. Thus on a node basis this type of degeneracy creates no problem since terms in the Kirchhoff current-law equations involving the current $j_k = -i_{sk}$ simply become known quantities and are transposed to the right-hand sides. On a loop basis, show that one can construct the tie-set schedule so that its first $l - 1$ rows do not involve this branch, thus identifying loop current i_l with the known branch current and rendering the first $l - 1$ of the loop equations sufficient for the determination of all unknowns. As an illustration, treat the following circuit in this manner. Let the branch numbers equal resistance values in ohms.

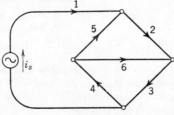

PROB. 23.

24. When a branch with its associated sources as shown in Fig. 9 becomes degenerate through having its passive resistance assume a zero value, then its current source is trivial, and its voltage is constrained by the associated voltage source to the value $v_k = -e_{sk}$. One way of dealing with this situation is to revise the network geometry and dispose of the voltage source in the manner shown in Fig. 7. Show, however, that one may alternately meet this situation by treating this branch in the normal manner. Thus on a loop basis this type of degeneracy creates no problem since terms in the Kirchhoff voltage-law equations involving the voltage $v_k = -e_{sk}$ simply become known quantities and are transposed to the right-hand sides. On a node basis, show that one can construct the cut-set schedule so that its first $n - 1$ rows do not involve this branch, thus identifying node-pair voltage e_n with the known branch voltage and rendering the first $n - 1$ of the node equations sufficient for the determination of all unknowns. As an illustration, treat the following circuit in this manner. Let the branch numbers equal conductance values in mhos.

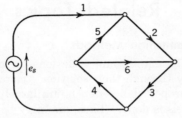

PROB. 24.

25. For the circuit shown in the accompanying sketch, assume the branch numbers to indicate also the resistance values in ohms, and let i_s be one ampere. Choosing branches 1, 2, 3, 4, 5 as links, find a set of link-voltage sources equivalent to the given current source as being the negatives of the voltages appearing at gaps cut simultaneously into all links. With these replacing the current source i_s, write down by

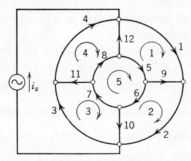

PROB. 25.

inspection the equilibrium equations on a mesh basis using the simplified procedure given in Art. 6 and inserting the net source voltages around meshes as the right-hand members. Alternately obtain these same equations using the procedure described in Prob. 23 in which the current source is treated as a normal branch, and check.

Now replace i_s by identical sources in parallel with branches 3 and 4; convert to voltage sources in series with these branches, and again write mesh equations. Will these yield the same mesh currents as above? Explain in detail.

Methods of Solution
and
Related Topics

1 Systematic Elimination Methods

Having written the equilibrium equations for a given network, the next task is to carry through their solution. Here one may proceed in several ways, the proper choice depending largely upon the objective for which the analysis is done. Thus, one may be interested merely in the numerical solution to a specific situation, or in a more general solution in which some or all of the network parameters enter symbolically. The latter type of problem is actually equivalent to the simultaneous study of an infinity of specific numerical situations and consequently presents greater algebraic difficulties which can be overcome only through the use of correspondingly more general methods of analysis. An effective tool for dealing with such problems is given in the next article. For the moment we shall concern ourselves with the less difficult task of solving a specific numerical case.

Suppose we choose as an example the Eqs. 24 appropriate to the network of Fig. 3 in Ch. 2, with arbitrary nonzero right-hand members, thus:

$$
\begin{aligned}
1.142e_1 - 0.976e_2 + 0.643e_3 + 0.500e_4 &= 1 \\
-0.976e_1 + 2.326e_2 - 1.893e_3 - 0.750e_4 &= 2 \\
0.643e_1 - 1.893e_2 + 2.218e_3 + 0.950e_4 &= 3 \\
0.500e_1 - 0.750e_2 + 0.950e_3 + 1.061e_4 &= 4
\end{aligned}
\tag{1}
$$

The straightforward method of solving a set of simultaneous equations like these consists in systematically eliminating variables until an equation with a single unknown is obtained. After its value is found, an equation involving this and one other variable is used to compute the value of a second unknown, and so forth. Unless the entire process is systematized, however, a considerable amount of lost motion may result. The following procedure is an effective one.

It is clear that only the numerical coefficients enter into the computational procedure. Therefore it is sensible to omit writing the symbols e_1, e_2, $\cdots$ altogether and consider only numerical matrix 2. We now

$$\begin{bmatrix} 1.142 & -0.976 & 0.643 & 0.500 & 1.000 \\ -0.976 & 2.326 & -1.893 & -0.750 & 2.000 \\ 0.643 & -1.893 & 2.218 & 0.950 & 3.000 \\ 0.500 & -0.750 & 0.950 & 1.061 & 4.000 \end{bmatrix} \tag{2}$$

contemplate the detailed manner in which one may carry out the following plan in terms of the Eqs. 1: First, we undertake to eliminate e_1 from all but the first of these equations; this step leaves us with three equations involving e_2, e_3, e_4. From all but the first of these, we now eliminate e_2, so that we have two equations with e_3 and e_4. From one of these we eliminate e_3 and have a single equation in e_4.

Note at this stage that we also have an equation involving e_3 and e_4, one involving e_2, e_3, and e_4, and the first of the original equations involving all four unknowns. We can, therefore, readily solve these equations in sequence and obtain all the unknowns without further difficulty. Specifically, we solve first the equation in e_4 alone. Next, the one involving e_3 and e_4 is solved for e_3. Then, with e_3 and e_4 known, the equation involving e_2, e_3, and e_4 yields the value of e_2, and the first of the original equations, lastly, is used to find e_1.

With reference to matrix 2, the process of eliminating e_1 from all but the first of Eqs. 1 is evidently equivalent to an elimination of the second, third, and fourth elements in the first column. This end is accomplished by operating directly upon the rows of matrix 2 as one would upon the corresponding Eqs. 1. Thus, if we add to the elements of the second row the respective α-multiplied elements of the first row, with $\alpha = 0.976/1.142$, the result reads

$$0.000 \quad 1.492 \quad -1.343 \quad -0.323 \quad 2.855 \tag{3}$$

which we regard as a new second row. Similarly, a new third row is formed by adding to the elements of the present third row the respective α-multiplied elements of the first row with $\alpha = -0.643/1.142$, yielding

$$0.000 \quad -1.343 \quad 1.856 \quad 0.668 \quad 2.437 \tag{4}$$

Finally a new fourth row is analogously formed with $\alpha = -0.500/1.142$, giving

$$0.000 \quad -0.323 \quad 0.668 \quad 0.842 \quad 3.562 \tag{5}$$

These steps are summarized by observing that the original matrix 2 has thus been transformed into the following equivalent one:

$$
\begin{bmatrix}
1.142 & -0.976 & 0.643 & 0.500 & 1.000 \\
0.000 & 1.492 & -1.343 & -0.323 & 2.855 \\
0.000 & -1.343 & 1.856 & 0.668 & 2.437 \\
0.000 & -0.323 & 0.668 & 0.842 & 3.562
\end{bmatrix}
\tag{6}
$$

If we were to write down the equations corresponding to this matrix, it would become clear that the numerical operations just carried out are equivalent to the elimination of e_1 from the last three of the original Eqs. 1.

We now proceed to eliminate e_2 from the last two equations corresponding to matrix 6. To this end we add to the elements of the third row of this matrix the respective α-multiplied elements of the second row with $\alpha = 1.344/1.492$, obtaining the new third row:

$$0.000 \quad 0.000 \quad 0.646 \quad 0.378 \quad 5.008 \tag{7}$$

Next, **multiplying** the elements of the second row in 6 by $\alpha = 0.323/1.492$ **and adding to** the respective elements of the fourth **row gives**

$$0.000 \quad 0.000 \quad 0.378 \quad 0.772 \quad 4.180 \tag{8}$$

The original matrix now has assumed the form

$$
\begin{bmatrix}
1.142 & -0.976 & 0.643 & 0.500 & 1.000 \\
0.000 & 1.492 & -1.343 & -0.323 & 2.855 \\
0.000 & 0.000 & 0.646 & 0.378 & 5.008 \\
0.000 & 0.000 & 0.378 & 0.772 & 4.180
\end{bmatrix}
\tag{9}
$$

corresponding to a set of equations in which e_1 does not appear in the second, while e_1 and e_2 do not appear in the third and fourth.

We now carry out a step equivalent to eliminating e_3 from the last of the set of equations represented by the matrix 9 by adding the α-multiplied elements of the third row to the respective ones of the fourth row, with $\alpha = -0.378/0.646$, giving a final fourth row that reads

$$0.000 \quad 0.000 \quad 0.000 \quad 0.551 \quad 1.251 \tag{10}$$

and the following final form for the matrix:

$$\begin{bmatrix} 1.142 & -0.976 & 0.643 & 0.500 & 1.000 \\ 0.000 & 1.492 & -1.343 & -0.323 & 2.855 \\ 0.000 & 0.000 & 0.646 & 0.378 & 5.008 \\ 0.000 & 0.000 & 0.000 & 0.551 & 1.251 \end{bmatrix} \qquad (11)$$

The last row represents the equation

$$0.551e_4 = 1.251 \qquad (12)$$

from which $\qquad\qquad\qquad e_4 = 2.27 \qquad\qquad\qquad (13)$

The third row in matrix 11 implies the equation

$$0.646e_3 + 0.378e_4 = 5.008 \qquad (14)$$

which, through use of the value 13 for e_4, becomes

$$0.646e_3 = 5.008 - 0.857 = 4.150 \qquad (15)$$

and hence yields $\qquad\qquad e_3 = 6.42 \qquad\qquad\qquad (16)$

From the second row in matrix 11 we next have the equation

$$1.492e_2 - 1.343e_3 - 0.323e_4 = 2.855 \qquad (17)$$

or, in view of the values 13 and 16,

$$1.492e_2 = 2.855 + 8.629 + 0.732 = 12.216 \qquad (18)$$

from which $\qquad\qquad\qquad e_2 = 8.189 \qquad\qquad\qquad (19)$

Finally the first of Eqs. 1, corresponding to the first row in matrix 11, together with the values for e_2, e_3, and e_4 already found, becomes

$$1.142e_1 - 7.992 + 4.130 + 1.135 = 1 \qquad (20)$$

and thus

$$1.142e_1 = 3.727 \quad \text{or} \quad e_1 = 3.264 \qquad (21)$$

The basic process in this systematic elimination method is the transformation of the original matrix 2 into the so-called *triangular form* 11, whence the unknowns are obtained through an obvious recursion process which begins with the computation of the last of the unknowns $e_1 \cdots e_4$ and successively yields all the others. It may readily be seen that this computational procedure involves a minimum of lost motion and hence is the best method to apply in any numerical example.

If some terms in the given equations already have zero coefficients, it may be necessary first to rearrange the equations in order that the elimination method be applicable in precisely the form described above while enabling one to take advantage of the simplifications implied by such missing terms. These modifications in procedure, however, the reader can readily supply for himself as he carries out actual examples, and further pertinent discussion of them will not be given here.

2 Use of Determinants

Although the determinant method of solving simultaneous algebraic equations may be used in numerical examples, the amount of computation involved is usually greater than in the systematic elimination process just described. It does, on the other hand, afford a means for expressing the solutions in a compact symbolic form that enables one to study their functional properties and thus deduce with little effort a number of important and useful general network characteristics, some of which will be pointed out in the latter part of this chapter. Our immediate objective is to discuss briefly some of the more important algebraic properties of determinants.

The so-called *determinant* of the system of equations

$$a_{11}x_1 + a_{12}x_2 + \cdots + a_{1n}x_n = y_1$$

$$a_{21}x_1 + a_{22}x_2 + \cdots + a_{2n}x_n = y_2$$

$$\cdot \quad \cdot \quad \cdot \quad \cdot \quad \cdot \quad \cdot \quad \cdot \quad \cdot \quad \cdot \quad \cdot \quad \cdot \quad \cdot$$

$$a_{n1}x_1 + a_{n2}x_2 + \cdots + a_{nn}x_n = y_n$$

$$(22)$$

is written in the form

$$A = \begin{vmatrix} a_{11} & a_{12} & \cdots & a_{1n} \\ a_{21} & a_{22} & \cdots & a_{2n} \\ \cdot & \cdot & \cdot & \cdot \\ a_{n1} & a_{n2} & \cdots & a_{nn} \end{vmatrix} \tag{23}$$

In appearance it is much like the corresponding matrix (differing only in that the array of coefficients is enclosed between vertical lines instead of square brackets), but in its algebraic significance it is entirely different from the matrix in that it is a *function* of its elements and has a value corresponding to the values of these elements as does any function of several variables. The elements are the coefficients a_{sk} in Eqs. 22. For n equations the determinant has n^2 elements and is said to be of *order n*.

The determinant is a particular kind of function of many variables that was created by mathematicians for the sole purpose of its being useful in the solution of simultaneous equations. Hence it was given those properties that turn out to serve best this objective. These may be summarized in the following three statements:

> *The value of a determinant is unchanged if the elements of any row (or column) are added to the respective ones of another row (or column).* (24)

> *The value of a determinant is multiplied by k if all the elements of any row or column are multiplied by k.* (25)

> *The value of a determinant is unity if the elements on the principal diagonal are unity and all others are zero.* (26)

The last statement may be written in the form

$$A = \begin{vmatrix} 1 & 0 & 0 & \cdots & 0 \\ 0 & 1 & 0 & \cdots & 0 \\ \cdot & \cdot & \cdot & \cdot & \cdot \\ 0 & 0 & \cdots & 0 & 1 \end{vmatrix} = 1 \tag{27}$$

Through combining the properties 24 and 25 it follows that the value of A remains unchanged if the k-multiplied elements of any row (or column) are added to the respective ones of another row (or column). Since k may be numerically negative, this statement includes the subtraction as well as the addition of respective elements. It also follows from these properties that a determinant has the value zero (a) if the elements of any row or column are all zero, or (b) if the elements of any two rows (or columns) are respectively equal or proportional, for a row or column of zeros implies $k = 0$, and a condition of equal or proportional rows (or columns) immediately leads to a row (or column) of zeros through appropriate manipulations of the sort just mentioned.

The value of a numerical determinant may readily be found through use of these properties since, by means of them, one can consecutively reduce to zero all but the diagonal elements (after the fashion that matrix 2 in the previous article is transformed to form 11). Once the determinant has this diagonal form, properties 25 and 26 show that the value equals the product of the diagonal elements. In fact it can be shown that the determinant in triangular form has this same property; that is,

$$A = \begin{vmatrix} a_{11} & a_{12} & a_{13} & \cdots & a_{1n} \\ 0 & a_{22} & a_{23} & \cdots & a_{2n} \\ 0 & 0 & a_{33} & \cdots & a_{3n} \\ \cdot & \cdot & \cdot & \cdot & \cdot \\ 0 & 0 & 0 & \cdots & a_{nn} \end{vmatrix} = a_{11}a_{22} \cdots a_{nn} \tag{28}$$

so that only the elements below the principal diagonal (upper left to lower right) need be reduced to zero through appropriate manipulation.

An alternate method for the evaluation of a determinant is had through its so-called *Laplace development* or *expansion*. Thus the value of a determinant is expressed as the sum of products of the successive elements of any row (or column) and quantities referred to as corresponding *cofactors* (whose construction we shall describe presently). Denoting the respective cofactor of an element a_{sk} by A_{sk} (that is, by the upper-case letter with like indexes), we may indicate the Laplace expansion of A along its first row as

$$A = a_{11}A_{11} + a_{12}A_{12} + \cdots + a_{1n}A_{1n} \tag{29}$$

along its second row as

$$A = a_{21}A_{21} + a_{22}A_{22} + \cdots + a_{2n}A_{2n} \tag{30}$$

or along its first column as

$$A = a_{11}A_{11} + a_{21}A_{21} + \cdots + a_{n1}A_{n1} \tag{31}$$

There are evidently $2n$ different possible expansions of this sort, and each gives the same numerical value, namely the value of A.

The formation of a cofactor A_{sk} consists in canceling (that is, removing) row s and column k from the given determinant A and prefixing the remainder (called a minor determinant of order $n - 1$) by the algebraic sign-controlling factor $(-1)^{s+k}$. Thus the cofactor equals the respective minor determinant except for its algebraic sign, which is *plus* if the sum of indexes referring to the canceled row and column is *even*, and *minus* if this sum of indexes is *odd*. The canceled row and column is that pair that intersects at the position of the element a_{sk} with which the cofactor is associated in each term of the expansion. In numerical examples where the elements of a determinant are mere numbers and hence bear no indexes to identify their row and column positions, the latter must be observed by inspection in determining the algebraic signs of the various terms in the expansion. The same is true of a determinant in symbolic form where the notation for one reason or another fails to convey, in an evident manner, information as to the row and column positions of its elements.

This form of expansion expresses the value of a given determinant of order n in terms of the values of n determinants, each of order $n - 1$. These n minor determinants can separately be expressed in terms of $(n - 1)$ additional minor determinants, each of order $n - 2$. Continuation of the procedure finally yields the desired result when the minor determinants obtained are of order 1. Since the number of terms in the initial step (like that given by Eqs. 29, 30, or 31) is n, and each of these terms yields $(n - 1)$ further terms of which each again yields $(n - 2)$ terms, and so forth, it is readily appreciated that the final evaluation consists of $n!$ terms, each of which is a product of n elements. Clearly, this method of evaluation is computationally very tedious. It is, therefore, not used for numerical evaluation but rather for the purpose of demonstrating a property of determinants that enables one to write down at once (in symbolic form) the solutions to a given set of simultaneous equations. The following discussion now shows how this objective is accomplished.

First, one should observe that the cofactors associated with the elements of a given row (or column) do not depend upon the elements of that row (or column), for the simple reason that this row (or column) is removed in the formation of these cofactors. So far as the values of these cofactors are concerned, the elements in the respective row (or column) could have any values at all. With this thought in mind, suppose we consider an expression like

$$a_{11}A_{21} + a_{12}A_{22} + a_{13}A_{23} + \cdots + a_{1n}A_{2n} \tag{32}$$

which looks like the Laplace development of the determinant A, except that the elements of the *first* row are multiplied respectively by the cofactors associated with the elements of the *second* row. That is to say, in expression 32 the elements a_{11}, a_{12}, $\cdots$, a_{1n} are multiplied by the cofactors of the elements of the wrong row. Since these cofactors do not depend upon the elements of the second row, the entire expression 32 does not depend upon these elements, and hence one can suppose that it is written for a determinant having its second row identical with the first. For this determinant, however, it represents the correct Laplace development along its second row; and, since this determinant has the value zero, it is seen that expression 32, evaluated for any determinant A, has the value zero.

This reasoning shows that the sum of products formed from the elements of any row (or column) of a determinant and the cofactors of the respective elements of *another* row (or column) equals zero. That is to say, if we write down what appears to be the Laplace development of a determinant, but associate the elements of a row (or column) with the respective cofactors of the elements of any other row (or column), the resulting sum is always zero.

Now consider Eqs. 22, and suppose that we multiply the successive ones respectively by the cofactors A_{11}, A_{21}, $\cdots$, A_{n1} (associated with the elements of the first column), and then add all terms, a column at a time. The first column clearly adds to x_1 times a Laplace development of A;

the second column adds to x_2 times one of these pseudodevelopments of A that equals zero; and the same applies to all the other sums of left-hand columns. Thus we get as a result

$$A \cdot x_1 = A_{11}y_1 + A_{21}y_2 + \cdots + A_{n1}y_1 \tag{33}$$

whence

$$x_1 = \frac{A_{11}y_1 + A_{21}y_2 + \cdots + A_{n1}y_1}{A} \tag{34}$$

Any other of the unknowns is obtained in a similar manner. More specifically, if we wish to obtain an expression for the unknown x_k, we suppose that the successive Eqs. 22 are multiplied respectively by the cofactors A_{k1}, A_{k2}, $\cdots$, A_{kn} associated with the elements of the kth column of A. Subsequent addition of all terms yields zeros for the resulting coefficients of all x's except x_k, which has for its coefficient the correct Laplace development of A along its kth column. Hence there results the expression for x_k given below: *

$$x_k = \frac{A_{1k}y_1 + A_{2k}y_2 + \cdots + A_{nk}y_n}{A} \tag{35}$$

More commonly, one finds that only one of the quantities $y_1 \cdots y_n$ is nonzero (the electrical network is excited at only one point). If the nonzero y is y_s, then the corresponding unknown x_k becomes

$$x_k = \frac{A_{sk}}{A} y_s \tag{36}$$

Since the equations are linear, the result when all y's are simultaneously present is simply the sum of the respective results 36 for separate non-zero y's, and so we may interpret the more general result 35 as a super-position of solutions 36 for the y's taken separately.

Equation 36 enables one to set down in compact analytic form the expression for the response (voltage or current) at any desired point in a network in terms of the excitation applied at the same point $(s = k)$ or at some other point $(s \neq k)$. As already mentioned, no advantage is thus gained so far as numerical evaluation is concerned; in fact it is usu-ally a disadvantage in numerical cases to use the determinant method. However, the analytic form of result 36, in conjunction with known determinant properties, enables one to determine by inspection numerous general properties of network solutions and characteristic network functions, as will be seen at various points in our later discussions.

---

* A statement describing this result is known as "Cramer's rule."

3 Methods Applicable to Ladder and Other Special Network Configurations

In examples where the network geometry or distribution of parameter values enables one to achieve short cuts in numerical computation, it is advantageous to maintain a flexible attitude toward the general systematic procedures. The latter are often the only ones applicable in random situations, and, while it is therefore well to be thoroughly fluent in their use, one should not permit such use to become habit-forming to the extent of obscuring one's awareness of computational economies possible in special situations through the use of less conventional procedures of restricted applicability. In this connection it is well also to recognize

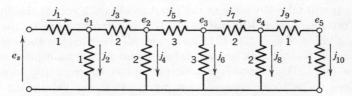

FIG. 1. Example of an unbalanced ladder network.

that the completely random network is more of a theoretical fiction than an actuality. The usual network configurations found in practice are more apt to exhibit a simplicity of structure or a geometric symmetry in form and element values (even as to their mode of excitation) that renders them vulnerable to a judiciously chosen method of attack.

A commonly encountered network configuration of this sort is the so-called *unbalanced ladder* mentioned in Art. 9 of Ch. 1 and illustrated there in Figs. 16 and 17. Figure 1 shows a specific example of such a network having resistance branches with the ohmic values indicated. The bottom conductor (assumed to have zero resistance) serves as a common return for the currents in the various shunt branches and in practice usually takes the form of a common *grounded* return conductor (the network is then spoken of as being "unbalanced with respect to ground"). Suppose a value for the excitation voltage e_s is given, and the resulting currents and voltages in the various branches are wanted. The most direct approach is to ignore the given e_s value to start with but instead assume that e_5, the potential of the right-hand node, is 1 volt, and endeavor to find what value of e_s gives such a result.

To this end we note first that, if $e_5 = 1$, then $j_{10} = j_9 = 1$ ampere, whence $v_9 = 1$ volt and $e_4 = e_5 + v_9 = 2$ volts. Next $j_8 = e_4/2 = 1$ ampere, and so $j_7 = j_8 + j_9 = 2$ amperes. The following relations, which continue the pattern thus established, should be self-evident:

$$v_7 = 2j_7 = 4 \text{ volts} \qquad j_3 = j_4 + j_5 = 13 \text{ amperes}$$

$$e_3 = e_4 + v_7 = 6 \text{ volts} \qquad v_3 = 2j_3 = 26 \text{ volts}$$

$$j_6 = e_3/3 = 2 \text{ amperes} \qquad e_1 = e_2 + v_3 = 44 \text{ volts}$$

$$j_5 = j_6 + j_7 = 4 \text{ amperes} \qquad j_2 = e_1/1 = 44 \text{ amperes} \qquad (37)$$

$$v_5 = 3j_5 = 12 \text{ volts} \qquad j_1 = j_2 + j_3 = 57 \text{ amperes}$$

$$e_2 = e_3 + v_5 = 18 \text{ volts} \qquad v_1 = 57 \text{ volts}$$

$$j_4 = e_2/2 = 9 \text{ amperes} \qquad e_s = e_1 + v_1 = 101 \text{ volts}$$

Thus it will take 101 volts at the input to obtain 1 volt at the output, or the ratio $e_5/e_s = 1/101 = 0.0099$. If e_s is given as 50 volts, then the resulting value of e_5 is (50/101) volts, and all the currents and voltages elsewhere in the network are the values found above, multiplied by the fraction (50/101). Hence it is a simple matter subsequently to adjust all values so as to accommodate a given excitation voltage e_s, while for the essential computations it is easier to assume one volt at the output. The so-called input resistance is $e_s/j_1 = 101/57 = 1.77$ ohms, and is also seen to be readily obtainable by this method, which is far shorter than any loop or node analysis. Wherever ladder networks are involved, one should always follow a simplified procedure of this sort unless one of the conventional methods is indicated for special reasons.

In some cases, symmetry conditions enable one to solve a problem by inspection. An example of this sort is the following. Consider a network graph in which the branches are arranged geometrically as are the 12 edges of a cube. Assume each branch to be a resistance of 1 ohm, and let the problem be that of finding the net resistance (a) between diagonally opposite corners of any side of the cube, (b) between diagonally opposite corners of the cube itself.

This graph may be developed upon a plane surface as shown in Fig. 2. Part (a) of the problem involves finding the net resistance between nodes a and d, whereas in part (b) the net resistance between nodes a and c is called for.

For part (a) assume that a current is injected into node a and retrieved at node d. From the symmetry it is immediately clear that nodes $e, f, g,$ and h must all have the same potential, namely the arithmetic mean of the potentials of nodes a and d. We may conclude, therefore, that the currents in branches 4 and 7 are zero. Removal of these branches leaves three parallel paths between nodes a and d, viz.: a 2-ohm path via node

h, a 2-ohm path via node e, and a 3-ohm path via nodes b and c. The net resistance is thus seen to be

$$R_{ad} = \frac{1}{\frac{1}{2} + \frac{1}{2} + \frac{1}{3}} = \frac{3}{4} \text{ ohm} \tag{38}$$

For part (b) of this problem, we assume that a current is injected into node a and retrieved at node c. Under these conditions the symmetry of the network permits the conclusion that the currents in branches

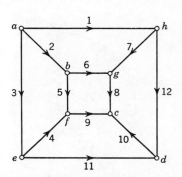

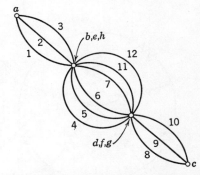

Fig. 2.   Graph corresponding to the edges of a cube.

Fig. 3.   Degenerate form of the graph of Fig. 2 appropriate to computation of the resistance between nodes a and c.

1, 2, 3 are equal, as are those in branches 8, 9, 10. Consequently nodes b, e, h, have the same potential and may be allowed to coincide; and, similarly, nodes d, f, g have equal potentials and may be allowed to coincide. The graph resulting from the superposition of these groups of nodes is shown in Fig. 3. Noting that each branch is a 1-ohm resistance, one can now see by inspection that the desired resistance is given by

$$R_{ac} = \tfrac{1}{3} + \tfrac{1}{6} + \tfrac{1}{3} = \tfrac{5}{6} \text{ ohm} \tag{39}$$

This problem may be made to seem somewhat more complex through inserting additional 1-ohm branches diagonally inside the cube. With reference to Fig. 2 such a procedure amounts to adding a branch from a to c, one from b to d, one from e to g, and one from f to h. The process of finding R_{ac} remains, however, as simple as before. That is to say, the symmetry enables one again to conclude that nodes b, e, h have the same potential, and likewise that nodes d, f, g have the same potential, whence the graph in Fig. 3 again applies, except that we must insert the additional 1-ohm branches. One of these connects a with c; the other three are in parallel with the central group of branches. Hence one has

$$R_{ac} = \cfrac{1}{1 + \cfrac{1}{\frac{1}{3} + \frac{1}{9} + \frac{1}{3}}} = \frac{7}{16} \text{ ohm} \qquad (40)$$

Consider as another example the resistance network shown in Fig. 4(a), in which we shall assume that each branch has a resistance of 1 ohm. Let the central node be chosen as a datum, and let the potentials $e_1 \cdots e_5$

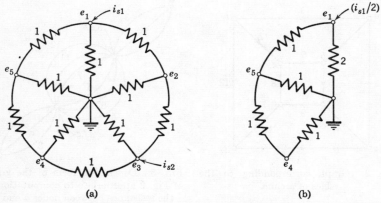

(a)   (b)

FIG. 4. Symmetrical network (a) and its degenerate form (b) when excited by the current i_{s1} alone.

of the rest of the nodes with respect to this datum be unknowns. The excitation is assumed to consist of two current sources i_{s1} and i_{s2} as shown (having a common return through the datum node); their numerical values are for the moment of no interest.

The net response is most expeditiously computed by adding the responses for the sources taken separately. Considering the source i_{s1} alone, it may be seen from the symmetry that no current exists in the bottom branch connecting e_3 and e_4, and so we may consider this branch removed. The remaining network consists of two identical halves, symmetrical about a vertical center line. One such half is shown separately in part (b) of Fig. 4. Note that the resistor between e_1 and the datum must be regarded as being split longitudinally down the middle, thus virtually halving its cross section and doubling its ohmic value; the current source is likewise halved.

The network of Fig. 4(b) is now recognized to be an unbalanced ladder. To compute the voltage distribution along it, we assume the output voltage e_4 to be 1 volt. By inspection we see that e_5 is 2 volts, and, since the current in the branch between e_1 and e_5 is $2 + 1 = 3$ amperes, $e_1 = e_5 + 3 = 5$ volts. The current from e_1 to the datum is $e_1/2 = 5/2$ amperes, and so $(i_{s1}/2) = 3 + (5/2) = 11/2$ amperes. Thus we see that $i_{s1} = 11$ amperes gives $e_1 = 5$, $e_5 = 2$, $e_4 = 1$; or $i_{s1} = 1$ ampere gives $e_1 = 5/11$, $e_5 = 2/11$, $e_4 = 1/11$ volt. Hence, returning our attention to the given network in Fig. 4(a), we can say that

For $i_{s1} = 1$ ampere:

$$e_1 = 5/11, \quad e_2 = e_5 = 2/11, \quad e_3 = e_4 = 1/11 \text{ volt} \qquad (41)$$

The results for the excitation i_{s2} alone are entirely similar, with a shift in the axis of symmetry. One can say at once from the values given in Eqs. 41 that

For $i_{s2} = 1$ ampere:

$$e_3 = 5/11, \quad e_2 = e_4 = 2/11, \quad e_1 = e_5 = 1/11 \text{ volt} \qquad (42)$$

Now suppose we are told that actually $i_{s1} = 5$ amperes, and $i_{s2} = 10$ amperes. The net results are the ones in 41 multiplied by 5 plus the ones in 42 multiplied by 10, or

$$e_1 = 35/11, \quad e_2 = 30/11, \quad e_3 = 55/11, \quad e_4 = 25/11,$$

$$e_5 = 20/11 \text{ volts} \qquad (43)$$

If this network is excited by voltage sources as shown in Fig. 5, the above analysis is still applicable since, as discussed in Art. 8 of Ch. 2, we can readily determine an equivalent set of currents feeding the nodes. Thus we argue that, if we were to place the negatives of such equivalent current sources across the node pairs (in this case a node-to-datum set) while the voltage sources as given are simultaneously present, the net node potentials must be zero (by definition of what the term "equivalent current sources" means). Since the node-pair voltages are all zero, nothing is affected if we assume that short circuits are placed across all node pairs; and, if we now remove the current sources, the state of the network still cannot change because the

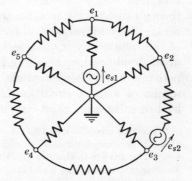

Fig. 5. Network of Fig. 4 excited by voltage sources.

short circuits hold all node-pair voltages at the zero value. The short circuits simply take over the functions previously performed by the current sources in that they carry the currents that these sources were supplying to the node pairs.* Hence one can find the values of the equivalent current sources by computing the negatives of the currents that flow in a set of short circuits (in the node-to-datum direction) with the given voltage sources applied.

In the circuit of Fig. 5, the pertinent short-circuit currents are seen by inspection to be †

$$i_{ss1} = e_{s1}, \quad i_{ss2} = e_{s2}, \quad i_{ss3} = -e_{s2}, \quad i_{ss4} = 0, \quad i_{ss5} = 0 \quad (44)$$

Thus, if the voltage sources are given as $e_{s1} = -10$ volts and $e_{s2} = 15$ volts, we conclude that the same node potentials $e_1 \cdots e_5$ result if current sources are applied to nodes 1, 2, and 3 having the values

$$i_{s1} = 10, \quad i_{s2} = -15, \quad i_{s3} = 15 \text{ amperes} \quad (45)$$

The results of the previous solution involving the situation in Fig. 4 are then immediately applicable.

It is important to observe that the resulting values for the e's thus obtained are the correct ones with reference to the given situation shown in Fig. 5. For example, e_1 in this figure is the potential of the top node with respect to the datum, and the voltage across the 1-ohm resistor in this vertical branch is $e_1 - e_{s1}$. Similarly the voltage across the 1-ohm resistor in the branch connecting e_2 and e_3 is $e_2 - e_3 - e_{s2}$, and so forth.

An important point which these examples illustrate is the simplification that can be brought about in the analysis of certain networks through discovering in some way any branches in which the current is zero. The removal of such trivial branches often reveals the remainder of the solution by inspection. In an analogous way one can capitalize upon simplifications resulting from the discovery that two nodes in the network have like potentials, for their identification (connection by means of a short circuit), which is obviously permitted, can likewise lead to substantial short-cuts in numerical computation.

---

* Someone might ask at this point how it is that a short circuit can do the work of a source when the latter is capable of supplying energy and the short circuit is not. The answer is that, in the situation described here, the current sources are working into zero voltages and hence are not called upon to deliver energy. In this case a short circuit can do as well.

† The negatives of these may alternately be obtained through conversion of voltage sources in series with resistances into current sources in parallel with them (as discussed in Ch. 2 and in Art. 5 below) and subsequently replacing the resulting source between nodes 3 and 2 by one from 3 to datum and another from datum to 2. The reader should thus check the results given in Eqs. 44.

Returning to ladder networks again, it is interesting to see that the simplified procedure discussed above lends itself also to certain kinds of synthesis problems. Suppose one wishes to obtain a stated voltage distribution along a ladder network as indicated in Fig. 6 where the numbers 1, 4, 9, 16, 25 are the desired node potentials (here chosen as the sequence of squared integers). The branch resistances $r_0 \cdots r_8$ are to be found, assuming the excitation to be at the left.

Since there are more unknowns than specified quantities, it is clear that we can choose some resistances arbitrarily and thus arrive at many alternative solutions. To keep things very simple, suppose we choose r_0, r_2, r_4, r_6, r_8, respectively, equal to 1, 4, 9, 16, 25 ohms. This choice

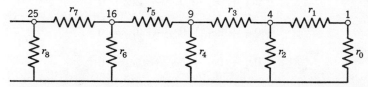

FIG. 6.   Unbalanced ladder with desired values of node potentials specified.

makes all currents in these shunt branches equal to 1 ampere, whence the currents in the series resistors r_1, r_3, r_5, r_7 are immediately seen to have the values 1, 2, 3, 4 amperes respectively. In terms of these branch currents and the known potential differences in these branches we have the values for the remaining resistances, namely, $r_1 = 3$, $r_3 = 5/2$, $r_5 = 7/3$, $r_7 = 9/4$ ohms. The input resistance is seen to be 5 ohms. One can readily continue this network to the left, up to a node potential of n^2 volts. The shunt resistors increase up to n^2 ohms, the input resistance becomes n ohms, and the series resistors settle down to a value very close to 2 ohms.

4   Network Transformations; Wye-Delta (Y-Δ) Equivalents

When the systematic elimination method (discussed in Art. 1) is applied, it is sometimes useful to interpret the successive steps in terms of corresponding simplifications in the associated network geometry. If the given equations represent equilibrium on the mesh basis, the elimination of a variable (mesh current) may, under appropriate circumstances, be interpreted geometrically as equivalent to the elimination of the corresponding mesh from the network graph; and, on a node-to-datum basis, the elimination of a node-potential variable corresponds to the suppression of the associated node. An understanding of the detailed aspects of this correlation between certain analytic manipulations and their geometrical implications is often found useful both as an aid to numerical computation and in the physical interpretation of network properties. A brief discussion of these ideas would seem, therefore, to be in order.

In Fig. 7 is shown a network fragment involving three branches and four nodes. The numbers on the branches indicate the corresponding conductance values in mhos, and the potentials $e_1 \cdots e_4$ are specified with respect to some common datum, not shown.

By the simplified procedure discussed in Art. 6, Ch. 2, one obtains the following equations linking the four voltage variables $e_1 \cdots e_4$, disregarding for the moment the rest of the network in which this fragment is embedded,

$$2e_1 + 0e_2 + 0e_3 - 2e_4 = 0$$

$$0e_1 + 3e_1 + 0e_3 - 3e_4 = 0$$

$$0e_1 + 0e_2 + 5e_3 - 5e_4 = 0 \tag{46}$$

$$-2e_1 - 3e_2 - 5e_3 + 10e_4 = 0$$

with the conductance matrix

$$[G] = \begin{bmatrix} 2 & 0 & 0 & -2 \\ 0 & 3 & 0 & -3 \\ 0 & 0 & 5 & -5 \\ -2 & -3 & -5 & 10 \end{bmatrix} \tag{47}$$

Suppose we decide to eliminate the variable e_4 from these equations. The corresponding manipulations of the matrix $[G]$ are such as will reduce to zero the first three elements in the fourth column. This result is accomplished by adding to the elements of the first row the $(2/10)$-multiplied elements of the fourth row, then adding to the elements of the second row the $(3/10)$-multiplied elements of the fourth row, and finally adding to the elements of the third row the $(5/10)$-multiplied elements of the fourth row. The resulting conductance matrix becomes

$$[G'] = \begin{bmatrix} 1.6 & -0.6 & -1.0 & 0 \\ -0.6 & 2.1 & -1.5 & 0 \\ -1.0 & -1.5 & 2.5 & 0 \\ -2.0 & -3.0 & -5.0 & 10 \end{bmatrix} \tag{48}$$

If we wish, we can subtract the last row from itself and reduce all its elements to zero, but this step is trivial and unnecessary since this row no longer has any significance anyway. The first three rows determine equilibrium equations for a revised network in which node 4 is no longer coupled to nodes 1, 2, and 3. We may say that through the above manipulations, node 4 has been decoupled from the rest of the network, and this decoupling has been accomplished in such a way that the remaining node potentials are unaffected. The network fragment to which the conductance matrix consisting of the first three rows and columns of

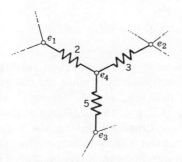

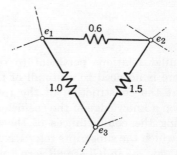

FIG. 7. Configuration known as a *wye* circuit, embedded in a larger network. Element values are in mhos.

FIG. 8. Configuration known as a *delta* circuit, equivalent to the wye in Fig. 7. Element values are in mhos.

48 pertains (in the manner that matrix 47 pertains to the network portion shown in Fig. 7) may thus be regarded as equivalent to that in Fig. 7, in the sense that we may replace one by the other without disturbing the behavior of the entire network in which this fragment is embedded.

The appropriate network geometry is readily seen to be that shown in Fig. 8 in which the numerical values again are conductances in mhos. The correctness of this result is readily checked by writing down, for the network of Fig. 8, the corresponding node-conductance matrix, according to the simplified procedure referred to above, and comparing it with the first three rows and columns of matrix 48.

By careful attention to the manipulative procedure that transforms matrix 47 to form 48, noting the correlation of the latter with the network of Fig. 8, one can formulate a direct procedure for the transformation of the network of Fig. 7 into the equivalent form shown in Fig. 8. Thus, denoting symbolically the elements of $[G]$ by g_{sk} and those of $[G']$ by g'_{sk}, we note that the manipulations leading to the elements of the first row of $[G']$ are expressed by

$$g'_{11} = g_{11} - \frac{g_{14}g_{41}}{g_{44}} = 2 - \frac{4}{10} = 1.6$$

$$g'_{12} = g_{12} - \frac{g_{14}g_{42}}{g_{44}} = 0 - \frac{6}{10} = -0.6$$

$$g'_{13} = g_{13} - \frac{g_{14}g_{43}}{g_{44}} = 0 - \frac{10}{10} = -1.0 \tag{49}$$

$$g'_{14} = g_{14} - \frac{g_{14}g_{44}}{g_{44}} = -2 + 2 = 0.0$$

Similar relations pertinent to the remaining g'_{sk} are evident, and so there is no need to write all of these down, especially since we observe that the construction of the resulting network, Fig. 8, depends only upon a knowledge of the coefficients g'_{12}, g'_{13}, g'_{23}, the negatives of these being the conductances of the respective branches linking the nodes to which the subscripts refer. Noting that the corresponding coefficients g_{12}, g_{13}, g_{23} in $[G]$ are all zero,* we have for the branch conductances in Fig. 8 the values

$$-g'_{12} = \frac{g_{14}g_{42}}{g_{44}} = \frac{2 \cdot 3}{10} = 0.6$$

$$-g'_{13} = \frac{g_{14}g_{43}}{g_{44}} = \frac{2 \cdot 5}{10} = 1.0 \tag{50}$$

$$-g'_{23} = \frac{g_{24}g_{43}}{g_{44}} = \frac{3 \cdot 5}{10} = 1.5$$

An effective pictorial way of summarizing these simple results is shown in Fig. 9 where the given network fragment of Fig. 7 is drawn with full lines and its equivalent (as in Fig. 8) is indicated by dotted lines. The g's with lower-case literal subscripts are conductances in the given network, and those with upper-case literal subscripts refer to the branches of the desired equivalent. Application of the results 50, noting that $g_{44} = g_a + g_b + g_c$, gives

* Considering the rest of the network in which the part considered here lies embedded, these elements may of course have nonzero values. In any case, their values, and the element values of the remaining network structure that they imply, remain superimposed and unaltered throughout these manipulations and hence may for the present be ignored.

$$g_A = \frac{g_a g_b}{g_a + g_b + g_c}$$

$$g_B = \frac{g_b g_c}{g_a + g_b + g_c} \qquad (51)$$

$$g_C = \frac{g_c g_a}{g_a + g_b + g_c}$$

It is customary to refer to the given network as a Y (wye) and to its transformed equivalent as a Δ (delta), for reasons that are self-evident.

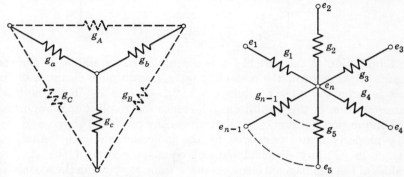

FIG. 9. Pictorial representation of the wye-delta transformation expressed by Eqs. 51.

FIG. 10. The *star*, which is a generalization of the wye circuit.

Expressions 51 are described by saying that any conductance in the equivalent delta equals the product of the two adjacent wye conductances divided by the sum of all three wye conductances. To apply this so-called *wye-delta transformation*, therefore, one need merely follow the procedure indicated in the descriptive phrase: *"the product of the adjacent two, divided by the sum of all three."*

One should not lose sight, however, of the important fact that this transformation is the revision in the network geometry accompanying a step in the systematic elimination procedure whereby one of the variables (node potentials) is suppressed. Thus the elimination of a node potential is equivalent to the elimination of a node. Through a repeated application of the same procedure one can ultimately render the network geometry so simple that the desired response may be seen by inspection.

Although the above example of this type of transformation involves only three branches divergent from the node in question, the same procedure evidently applies, regardless of how many branches are involved. In Fig. 10 is shown a general situation in which $n - 1$ branches are divergent from a given node n that is to be eliminated. In terms of the conductances g_1, g_2, $\cdots$, g_{n-1} of these branches and the node conductance

$$g_{nn} = g_1 + g_2 + \cdots + g_{n-1} \tag{52}$$

pertaining to the nth node, the matrix $[G]$ corresponding to this situation reads

$$[G] = \begin{bmatrix} g_1 & 0 & 0 & 0 & \cdots & -g_1 \\ 0 & g_2 & 0 & 0 & \cdots & -g_2 \\ 0 & 0 & g_3 & 0 & \cdots & -g_3 \\ \cdot & \cdot & \cdot & \cdot & \cdot & \cdot \\ -g_1 & -g_2 & -g_3 & & \cdots & g_{nn} \end{bmatrix} \tag{53}$$

Elimination of the variable e_n is accomplished by adding to the elements of the sth row the respective (g_s/g_{nn})-multiplied elements of the last row, for the integer values $s = 1, 2, \cdots, n - 1$. In the network interpretation of the resulting conductance matrix $[G']$, it is important to observe that the sum of the elements in any row of $[G]$ is zero, and that this property is not destroyed by the indicated row transformations. Hence in $[G']$ any diagonal element equals the sum of the absolute values of the nondiagonal elements in the same row; and in the associated network geometry this fact implies that there are no branches linking the various nodes with the datum node (some node other than any of those shown) as is also true of the given configuration in Fig. 10. That is to say, only the mutual node-conductance parameters g_{sk} in $[G]$ and g'_{sk} in $[G']$ corresponding to $s \neq k$ need be considered in the process of associating a network with either of these matrices. All branches are mutual branches having conductance values equal to $-g_{sk}$ or $-g'_{sk}$ linking nodes to which the subscripts refer.

From the indicated manipulations to which matrix 53 is subjected, it follows that

$$-g'_{sk} = g_s g_k / g_{nn} \tag{54}$$

In the resulting network (equivalent to that shown in Fig. 10) in which the node n is suppressed, each of the remaining nodes to which the potentials e_1, e_2, $\cdots$, e_{n-1} refer, is linked with every other node in this group by a branch having a conductance given by formula 54. The given network of Fig. 10 is spoken of as a *star*, and the resulting one just described is referred to as the equivalent *mesh*. The total elimination procedure is, therefore, called a *star-mesh* transformation, and is the logical generalization of the *wye-delta* transformation discussed above. Since the more general transformation increases the total number of branches involved in the network, it is more of theoretical interest than of practical value and is seldom used, although its application is accomplished by carrying out the same simple pattern pertinent to the three-branch case.

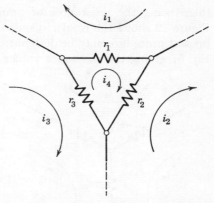

The analogous procedure on a loop basis, namely, that of eliminating a mesh-current from the equilibrium equations and a corresponding mesh from the network, follows an entirely similar pattern, and is in every sense the dual (see Art. 9, Ch. 1) of the procedure just described. Thus Fig. 11 shows a network fragment that corresponds on a

FIG. 11. The delta circuit embedded in a larger network.

mesh basis to the situation depicted in Fig. 7 for the node basis. Letting

$$r_{44} = r_1 + r_2 + r_3 \tag{55}$$

the equilibrium equations relating the four mesh currents involved, have the matrix

$$[R] = \begin{bmatrix} r_1 & 0 & 0 & -r_1 \\ 0 & r_2 & 0 & -r_2 \\ 0 & 0 & r_3 & -r_3 \\ -r_1 & -r_2 & -r_3 & r_{44} \end{bmatrix} \tag{56}$$

Through adding to the elements of the sth row the respective (r_s/r_{44})-multiplied elements of the last row, for $s = 1, 2, 3$, one obtains a matrix $[R']$ in which the first three elements of the fourth column are zeros. To the first three rows of this transformed matrix there correspond three equations involving only the mesh currents i_1, i_2, and i_3; that is to say, i_4 has been eliminated.

Moreover, the rows of $[R']$ like those of $[R]$ have the property that the sum of all elements in a row equals zero, or that the diagonal element equals the sum of the absolute values of the nondiagonal elements. Hence the network corresponding to $[R']$ is found by considering only

its nondiagonal elements

$$-r'_{sk} = r_s r_k / r_{44} \quad \text{for} \quad s \neq k \tag{57}$$

these being the resistances of branches common to meshes s and k. Figure 12 shows the result. Comparison with Fig. 11 suggests that the present procedure may be designated as a *delta-wye* transformation; and Eq. 57 giving the resistance values in the resulting wye indicates that

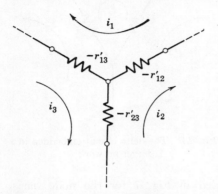

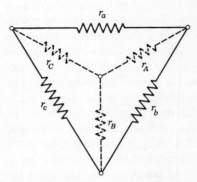

FIG. 12. The wye equivalent of the delta in Fig. 11. Element values are given by Eqs. 55 and 57.

FIG. 13. Pictorial representation of the delta-wye transformation expressed by Eqs. 58.

analytically the pattern is identical with that characterizing the wye-delta transformation, the only difference being that resistance values instead of conductance values are involved.

Figure 13 summarizes the present result after the fashion that Fig. 9 summarizes the significant features of the wye-delta transformation. The accompanying analytic relations are

$$r_A = \frac{r_a r_b}{r_a + r_b + r_c}$$

$$r_B = \frac{r_b r_c}{r_a + r_b + r_c} \tag{58}$$

$$r_C = \frac{r_c r_a}{r_a + r_b + r_c}$$

from which we see that the phrase *"the product of the adjacent two, divided by the sum of all three"* is again applicable.

A generalization of this procedure so as to involve the elimination of a mesh which is surrounded by more than three other meshes (the logical extension of the situation shown in Fig. 11), although straightforward analytically, does not permit a geometrical interpretation for the reason that it is not possible to construct a graph having an arbitrary number of meshes in which each mesh independently has a branch in common with all the others. The truth of this statement may also be seen from the fact that the network resulting from the elimination of the central node in the general star of Fig. 10 is not mappable on a plane and hence (according to the discussion in Art. 9 of Ch. 1) does not possess a dual. Since this dual is the network sought in the generalization of the mesh-elimination procedure, its nonexistence predicts the futility of any attempt to find such a generalization.

In order to enable the reader to appreciate a bit more specifically the essence of this argument, let us consider an example representing the extension of the mesh-elimination procedure from the situation in Fig. 11 involving a total of four meshes to one involving five. Through choosing a sufficiently simple configuration for the rest of the network in which the fragment under consideration is embedded, we find that the elimination procedure still permits a geometrical interpretation, although not in the simple terms that an optimistic attitude might lead us to expect. The result is disappointing and not very practical, but does serve in some measure to illustrate the principles involved.

This example is shown in Fig. 14 where we have included also the corresponding star-mesh transformation which is its dual. Since the latter is geometrically easier to understand, its inclusion in the total picture helps clarify the details of the mesh-star situation. In each sketch, the network in which the transformed portion lies embedded is shown dotted. The star-mesh transformation eliminates node 5, while the mesh-star transformation eliminates mesh 5. As the given network in the mesh-star situation is drawn, mesh 5 is the periphery and hence does not appear to have the simple character that a mesh should have, unless we visualize the network to be drawn on a sphere (as explained in Art. 9, Ch. 1), which the reader is encouraged to do anyway since he then will recognize more easily the mappable character of all the graphs shown in this figure.

The most unexpected feature of the mesh-star transformation is the result that the geometry of the rest of the network does not remain invariant as in the star-mesh transformation. However we do see that the quantity $l = (b - n)$ is one less in the resulting "star" than in the given "mesh," and that the geometry corresponds in every way to the analytic procedure involved in the elimination of mesh current 5. The remaining mesh currents (1, 2, 3, 4) traverse the same fixed branches 1, 2, 3, 4 in the same directions after the transformation is carried out as they do originally.

The resulting branch resistances in the star are given by the logical extension of formula 57; and the duality of these networks with respect to the corresponding ones in the star-mesh example is borne out in this

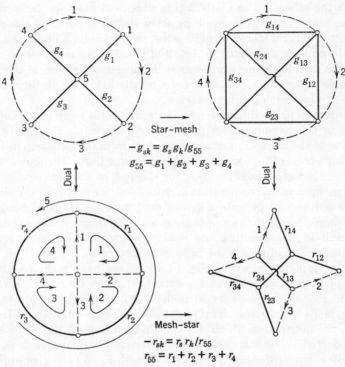

Star-mesh

$$-g_{sk} = g_s g_k / g_{55}$$
$$g_{55} = g_1 + g_2 + g_3 + g_4$$

Mesh-star

$$-r_{sk} = r_s r_k / r_{55}$$
$$r_{55} = r_1 + r_2 + r_3 + r_4$$

Fig. 14.   A star-mesh and mesh-star transformation in which the given star or mesh involves four branches.

detail also since the pertinent formulas are identical except for an interchange of resistance and conductance.

The student might well ask at this point what we gain by all this geometrical interpretation of the systematic elimination procedure discussed in Art. 1. Why not just carry out this procedure numerically and not bother to interpret the steps geometrically, especially since such interpretations lead us in some cases into exceedingly complex and even impossible situations? The answer is that we can gain computational advantages through judicious use of these ideas in appropriate situations. Again it takes some experience to know how and when to use them. Perhaps a simple example will serve best to illustrate these remarks.

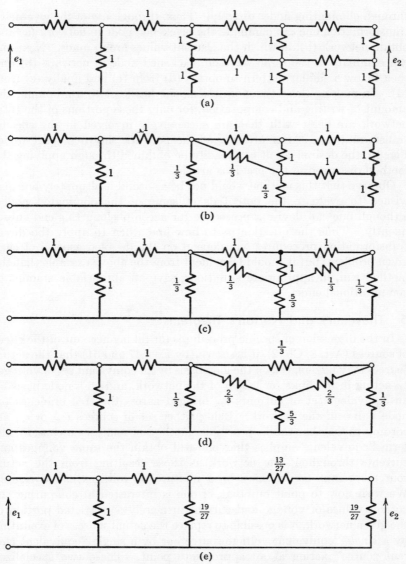

FIG. 15. Succession of steps in the solution of a problem through repeated use of the delta-wye transformation. The darkened node in each sketch is the one that is eliminated. Element values are in mhos.

Network (a) in Fig. 15, let us say, is given, and the voltage ratio e_2/e_1 is sought. Instead of writing the equilibrium equations and systematically eliminating variables, one can save time and writing effort through eliminating nodes directly. Thus, through use of the wye-delta transformation one can eliminate the blackened node in network (a) and obtain network (b), in which the element values are in mhos. Next one can eliminate in the same way the blackened node in network (b) and then follow a similar pattern to obtain (d) from (c) and finally (e) from (d). In making these transformations one has kept to a minimum the amount of writing and computation, for only those portions of the total network are dealt with that are successively involved in the specific transformations. After arriving at the network shown in part (e) of Fig. 15, the desired result can readily be obtained through applying the method discussed in the previous article.

Observe that this method would not be as useful if ultimately one also wished to evaluate the potentials of some of the eliminated nodes, although one can devise a procedure for accomplishing this end subsequently. Thus the question as to how and when to apply the direct transformation procedures will depend on the detailed aspects of each given problem; but it should be evident from the above example that the method can, in appropriate situations, save an appreciable amount of computational effort.

5   Thévenin's and Norton's Theorems

In the discussion of specific procedures for taking account of the effect of sources (Art. 8, Ch. 2), it is shown (by Eqs. 47 and 51) that the actual sources may be replaced on the loop basis by an equivalent set of voltages e_{sl} acting in the links (or loops) of the network, and on a node basis by an equivalent set of currents i_{sn} bridged across the tree branches (or node pairs) of the network. Using either set of sources (e_{sl} or i_{sn} according to whether the loop or node method of analysis is chosen), the term "equivalent" implies that one will obtain the same voltages and currents throughout the network as those resulting from the actual sources present (which may be a mixture of voltages and currents). We wish now to point out that, if one is interested in computing the correct values of voltage and current in merely a restricted portion of the given network, it is possible to replace the actual sources of excitation by a *single* "equivalent voltage source" or by a single "equivalent current source" acting at an appropriate point. These two specialized procedures, which are pertinent, respectively, to the loop and node viewpoints, are known as *Thévenin's and Norton's* theorems. Basically they are methods of source transformation whereby the net effect of many randomly distributed sources of both types is replaced by a single source acting at the point of interest.

Since a restricted kind of source equivalence is implied by this procedure, it is important that we discuss carefully the reasoning involved so that its use may be clearly presented and any misleading interpretations forestalled. Suppose we are interested only in the current in one branch of a network that is excited in a random manner. An additional voltage source inserted into this branch can be adjusted to such a value that the current in it becomes zero; that is to say, the additional voltage source bucks to a standstill the flow of charge through this branch. Under these conditions, the act of removing the additional voltage source and leaving a gap in its place can have no effect upon anything, not even upon the voltage across this gap, which is the same whether the voltage source fills the gap or not. Thus, when the additional voltage source has the particular value that results in zero current in that branch, this source is idle; and, being idle, its presence or absence is immaterial. Through this reasoning we deduce the fact that the voltage appearing at the gap formed by opening any branch equals the particular value of an inserted voltage source that renders the net current in that branch zero.

If we now apply to this situation the additive property of linear networks that permits a resultant current due to the simultaneous presence of several sources to be computed through addition of the currents caused by these sources taken separately, we can interpret the condition of zero current in the branch in question as the sum of two equal but opposing currents, of which one is caused by the original random excitation acting alone, and the other by the additionally inserted voltage source alone. Thus it becomes clear that the current produced in this branch by the random excitation may alternately be produced through inserting into this branch a source voltage equal in value to the negative of the voltage that appears across a gap formed by opening the branch while the original excitation is acting. This open-circuit voltage (the negative of the gap voltage) is called the *equivalent Thévenin source voltage*. It alone replaces the effect of any original random distribution of sources, but only so far as the current in this particular branch is concerned.

The structure of a network may be such that, when the current in the particular branch in question is rendered zero through opening it or through inserting the bucking voltage, currents simultaneously become zero in several other branches of the network. In this case the single equivalent Thévenin source voltage replaces the effect of the original random source distribution for these branches also, and thus turns out ▸ to be a less restricted form of source equivalence. It is important to note, however, that the single Thévenin source voltage is equivalent to the given source distribution only for the computation of those branch currents that become zero when the particular branch in question is opened. In this sense Thévenin's theorem deals with a restricted kind of source equivalence. We may say that it yields an oversimplified replacement for the actual source distribution, that nevertheless gives the correct value of current in a specific branch or network portion. Since this branch may be chosen at will, the method can actually be used to compute all currents, but only through first determining as many different Thévenin source voltages (barring simplifications resulting from a less random character of the given excitation). It, therefore, belongs in the category of "special artifices," but turns out to be one of considerable usefulness, and frequently is chosen to replace the basic procedures both in theoretical as well as in numerical work.

By applying an argument that is dual to the one just given, we can see that the single source replacing the effect of the given distribution of sources may alternately be regarded as a current. Thus, an additional current source placed in parallel with a given branch may be adjusted to a value that causes the voltage drop in that branch to become zero. One can most easily recognize the possibility of accomplishing such a condition through first supposing that the voltage in this branch is forced to be zero by placing a short circuit across it and then replacing the short circuit by a current source having a value equal to the short-circuit current. The current source and the short circuit are in this instance equivalent since they provide the same current; neither supplies any energy because the terminal voltage (branch voltage) is zero.

If we now apply to this situation the additive property of linear networks that permits a resultant voltage due to the simultaneous presence of several sources to be computed through addition of the voltages caused by these sources taken separately, we can interpret the condition of zero voltage in the branch in question as resulting from the sum of two equal but opposing voltages, of which one is caused by the original random excitation acting alone, and the other by the additionally inserted current source alone. Thus it becomes clear that the voltage produced in this branch by the random excitation may alternately be produced by bridging across this branch a source current equal in value to the negative of the current in a short circuit placed across the branch while the original excitation is acting. This single source current replaces the effect of any original random distribution of sources, but only so far as the voltage in this particular branch is concerned unless the structure of the network is such that the voltages in other branches become zero when the branch in question is short-circuited. In this case the single source current is equivalent to the original excitation with respect to these other branches as well.

This dual method of determining a single source equivalent to any random excitation is known as *Norton's theorem*. Further comments relative to it, parallel those already made with respect to Thévenin's theorem.

As an illustrative example, suppose we consider the network shown in Fig. 16 in which the sources are voltages and the parameter values are in

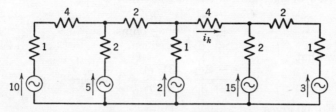

FIG. 16. A problem to be treated by Thévenin's theorem.

ohms. The desired unknown is the current i_k in the 4-ohm branch as indicated. If we wish to apply Thévenin's theorem to the computation of this current, the first step is to determine the voltage e_{oc} at the gap formed by removing this branch, as shown in Fig. 17. Noting that $e_{oc} = e_2 - e_1$, this determination leads us to the two subsidiary problems

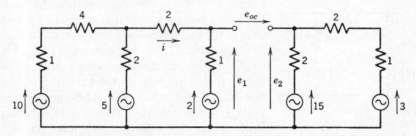

FIG. 17. The open-circuit voltage appropriate to the problem of Fig. 16.

of finding the voltages e_1 and e_2. The latter is readily seen to be given by

$$e_2 = 15 - \left(\frac{15 - 3}{5}\right) 2 = 10.2 \text{ volts} \qquad (59)$$

The voltage e_1, we observe, may be expressed as

$$e_1 = 2 + i \times 1 \qquad (60)$$

where i is the current in the 2-ohm branch as indicated in the left-hand portion of the network of Fig. 17. This current we may likewise compute through use of the reasoning underlying Thévenin's theorem, and to this end we need to determine the voltage e as shown in Fig. 18. By inspection we have

$$e = 5 + \left(\frac{10 - 5}{7}\right) 2 = \frac{45}{7} \text{ volts} \tag{61}$$

Since the net resistance at the terminal pair a–b in Fig. 18 (the voltage sources now being regarded as short circuits) is

$$\frac{1}{\frac{1}{2} + \frac{1}{5}} = \frac{10}{7} \text{ ohms} \tag{62}$$

it follows that

$$i = \frac{e - 2}{\frac{10}{7} + 3} = \frac{(31/7)}{(31/7)} = 1 \text{ ampere} \tag{63}$$

and so Eq. 60 gives

$$e_1 = 3 \text{ volts} \tag{64}$$

Thus we finally get for the open-circuit voltage of Fig. 17 the value

$$e_{oc} = 10.2 - 3 = 7.2 \text{ volts} \tag{65}$$

The original network with the single voltage source equivalent is shown in Fig. 19. Note that this single equivalent voltage source is the

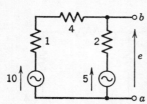

FIG. 18. Portion of the circuit in Fig. 16 needed to compute a contribution to e_{oc} in Fig. 17.

negative of the open-circuit voltage 65 and, therefore, acts in a direction opposite to that shown by the reference arrow for e_{oc} in Fig. 17. It should also be observed that this single equivalent voltage source will yield the correct value only for the current i_k in the one branch for which the Thévenin source voltage is determined. To compute currents in the remaining branches one must first determine the corresponding single source equivalents.

The calculation of the current i_k in Fig. 19 may now be accomplished in a relatively straightforward manner. For example, one can determine the net resistance presented at the terminals of the voltage source (the resistance that the source "looks into"), which is 4 ohms plus the net

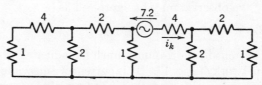

FIG. 19. Thévenin equivalent of the circuit of Fig. 16 for the computation of the current i_k.

resistance presented by the left-hand and right-hand portions of the network. Using the result 62 for the resistance between the terminals a–b of the portion shown in Fig. 18, one sees that the total resistance in question becomes

$$\frac{1}{\dfrac{1}{\frac{10}{7}+2}+1} + 4 + \frac{1}{\frac{1}{2}+\frac{1}{3}} = \frac{24}{31} + 4 + \frac{6}{5} = 5.974 \text{ ohms} \qquad (66)$$

Hence the desired current is

$$i_k = -(7.2/5.974) = -1.205 \text{ amperes} \qquad (67)$$

In comparing the original network of Fig. 16 with the one of Fig. 19, it is important to observe that, when the original excitation is regarded as

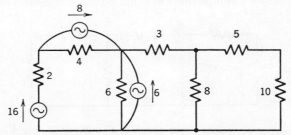

Fig. 20.   A circuit involving both voltage and current sources.

absent, the sources involved become short circuits because zero voltage sources are short circuits, as pointed out in Art. 7 of Ch. 2. When current sources are also involved, one must be reminded of the fact that these become open circuits when their values are zero.

A problem involving both voltage and current sources is given in Fig. 20 where the parameter values again are in ohms, and the sources are understood to be currents (with values in amperes) or voltages (with values in volts) according to their parallel or series association with the respective branches.

Let the desired current be that in the 3-ohm branch. Then the equivalent Thévenin source voltage e_s is that at the open-circuited terminal pair of the network portion shown in Fig. 21 which contains all of the

Fig. 21.   The Thévenin source voltage e_s appropriate to the problem in Fig. 20.

active branches of the original network. A simple way to find this voltage is first to compute the value of the circulatory current i. To this end the following Kirchhoff voltage-law equation suffices, namely,

$$16 - 2i - 4(i - 8) - 6(i + 6) = 0 \qquad (68)$$

whence

$$12 - 12i = 0 \quad \text{or} \quad i = 1 \text{ ampere} \qquad (69)$$

With reference to Fig. 21, e_s is the voltage across the 6-ohm resistor. The current through this resistor in the downward direction is $6 + i$ amperes; hence,

$$e_s = 7 \times 6 = 42 \text{ volts} \qquad (70)$$

With the sources in the network of Fig. 21 dead, there is left a simple configuration having a net resistance of 3 ohms between the terminals to which e_s refers. Hence the Thévenin equivalent of the original net-

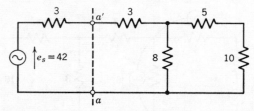

FIG. 22. Thévenin equivalent of the circuit of Fig. 20 for the computation of currents and voltages to the right of a–a'.

work in Fig. 20 becomes that shown in Fig. 22. The portion to the left of the dotted line a–a' replaces the active part of the original network, as shown in Fig. 21. Since the currents in all of the remaining branches become zero when the 3-ohm branch is opened, the resulting circuit of Fig. 22 is equivalent to the original one with respect to all of the network portion to the right of the dotted line a–a'.

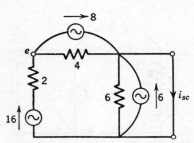

FIG. 23. The short-circuit current appropriate to treatment of the circuit of Fig. 20 by Norton's theorem.

If we wish to apply Norton's theorem to this problem so as to obtain an equivalent with respect to the same group of branches, we can do so by regarding the entire passive portion of the network of Fig. 20 as a single branch, whereupon the short-circuit current in question becomes that indicated in Fig. 23 which, like Fig. 21, shows the active portion of the original network. Clearly this position for the short circuit, rather than across the 3-ohm branch, is appropriate since the voltage in the remaining passive branches would otherwise not also be forced to have zero values.

A Kirchhoff current-law equation applied to the node to which the potential e refers is readily seen to read

$$\frac{e - 16}{2} + \frac{e}{4} + 8 = 0 \tag{71}$$

whence

$$2e - 32 + e + 32 = 0 \quad \text{or} \quad e = 0 \tag{72}$$

The short-circuit current, therefore, is

$$i_{sc} = 8 + 6 = 14 \text{ amperes} \tag{73}$$

and hence the Norton equivalent of the circuit of Fig. 20 becomes that shown in Fig. 24. Again the equivalence holds with respect to the entire

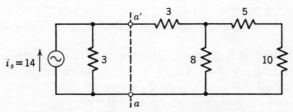

FIG. 24. Norton equivalent of the circuit of Fig. 20 comparable to the Thévenin equivalent in Fig. 22.

portion to the right of the terminal pair a–a', because short-circuiting these terminals renders all currents and voltages in this portion zero.

Comparison of the results shown in Figs. 22 and 24 reveals the equivalence of the voltage source $e_s = 42$ volts in series with the 3-ohm resistance, and the current source $i_s = 14$ amperes in parallel with this resistance, so far as the response in the rest of the network is concerned, a result that we have seen to follow directly from the discussion in Art. 7 of Ch. 2 (as is emphasized by Prob. 11 of that chapter). This equivalence between voltage and current sources together with their associated "internal" resistance is readily demonstrated in an alternate way through use of either Thévenin's or Norton's theorem. Thus we can say that any two sources are equivalent so far as their effect upon an external load is concerned if *either* their open-circuit voltages and internal resistances are alike, *or* if their short-circuit currents and internal conductances are alike. The ideal voltage or current source together with its associated resistance or conductance is here regarded as a source unit for which the terminal voltage is a function of the terminal current or vice versa. It is this source unit to which the idea of equivalence refers.

Inspection of the pair of source arrangements shown in Fig. 25 reveals that they are thus externally equivalent, since the relation between the terminal voltage e_t and current i_t is the same for both, as the reader should verify by substitution of the given equivalence relations $e_s = R i_s$ or $i_s = G e_s$, with $G = R^{-1}$.

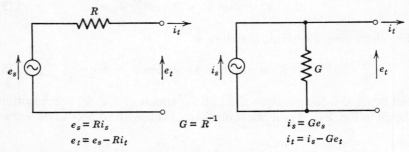

$$e_s = R i_s$$
$$e_t = e_s - R i_t$$

$$G = R^{-1}$$

$$i_s = G e_s$$
$$i_t = i_s - G e_t$$

Fig. 25. Transformation of a voltage into an equivalent current source and vice versa.

It is also obvious from these relations that one may regard any two source units as equivalent if they have the same terminal voltage on open circuit, and the same terminal current on short circuit. Reference to Figs. 22 and 24, moreover, shows that the net resistance of the active portion (the 3-ohm resistance to the left of a–a') is equal to the ratio of the open-circuit voltage to the short-circuit current. Hence a knowledge of these two quantities suffices to characterize the active portion of the original network so far as the determination of voltages and currents in the passive part are concerned.

In using these source conversions one must be mindful of the stated restriction, namely, that the equivalence holds only for currents and voltages computed in other network portions to which the sources may be connected, and that the equivalence specifically does *not* apply to currents or voltages in the associated source resistance R or source conductance G.

In order to illustrate the use of this artifice, let us reconsider the problem of finding the open-circuit voltage e_s in the network of Fig. 21. Since this voltage is *external* to the several sources involved, one is appropriately led to apply the source transformation relations of Fig. 25 to the conversion of the two current sources into equivalent voltage sources, and thus to regard the arrangement of Fig. 21 as being equivalent to that shown in Fig. 26. Here the circulatory current is seen to be given by

$$i = \frac{16 + 32 - 36}{12} = 1 \text{ ampere} \tag{74}$$

a result that checks the previous one given by Eq. 69. The terminal voltage e_s is then readily found from the relation

$$e_s = 36 + 6i = 42 \text{ volts} \tag{75}$$

which Eq. 70 shows to be correct.

From these examples we can conclude that Thévenin's and Norton's theorems are most useful as computational aids if the given excitation is not randomly distributed throughout all of the network but is more or less localized in one portion which may be detached from the rest of the network so as to produce a single terminal pair. Knowledge of the open-circuit voltage and short-circuit current at this terminal pair then suffices to replace the effect of the active portion of the original network by either of the simple source units shown in Fig. 25.

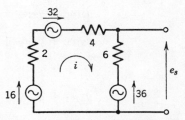

FIG. 26. The circuit of Fig. 21 with its current sources converted into voltage sources.

When the given source distribution is more random so that it becomes necessary to consider in this manner several separate active portions as replaced by their respective simple source units, the computational advantage is proportionately diminished. It obviously ceases to exist when the number of source units needed to replace the given excitation equals the smaller of the two integers l or n characterizing the number of variables on a loop or node basis, for the general methods of analysis have shown (Eqs. 47 and 51 of Art. 8, Ch. 2) that any random excitation is exactly replaceable by that number of equivalent sources. In fact, the computational advantage of making a source replacement probably ceases to exist in a given network with only a moderately random source distribution such as that shown by the network of Fig. 16, and one must have some experience in order to judge beforehand whether to apply the conventional procedure in such a case or to use the method discussed in this article.

6 The Reciprocity Theorem

A useful general property of all linear passive bilateral networks may be described by stating that the ratio of excitation to response, with a single excitation applied at one point and the response observed at another, is invariant to an interchange of the points of excitation and observation. The detailed interpretation of this statement, together with a demonstration of its truth, provides the topic for discussion in this article.

Suppose on a node basis we assume that the network is excited by two current sources i_{s1} and i_{s2}, bridged across node pairs to which the variables e_1 and e_2 pertain, and regard all elements as being pure resistances (resp. conductances) as we have throughout the discussions of this chapter. The equilibrium equations then read

$$g_{11}e_1 + g_{12}e_2 + g_{13}e_3 + \cdots + g_{1n}e_n = i_{s1}$$

$$g_{21}e_1 + g_{22}e_2 + g_{23}e_3 + \cdots + g_{2n}e_n = i_{s2}$$

$$g_{31}e_1 + g_{32}e_2 + g_{33}e_3 + \cdots + g_{3n}e_n = 0 \tag{76}$$

$$\cdots \cdots \cdots \cdots \cdots \cdots \cdots$$

$$g_{n1}e_1 + g_{n2}e_2 + g_{n3}e_3 + \cdots + g_{nn}e_n = 0$$

Since any two node pairs in the given network could be regarded as those corresponding to the voltage variables e_1 and e_2, no restriction is implied by the form of these equations so far as the selection of these node pairs is concerned. We are, however, making the tacit assumption that the node pairs to which the equilibrium equations (i.e. the Kirchhoff current-law equations) refer are the same as those with which the respective node-pair voltages are associated, so that (according to the discussion in Art. 5, Ch. 2) the parameter matrix for these equations is symmetrical; that is, the conductances fulfill the condition $g_{sk} = g_{ks}$.

Let us first consider the simple case for $n = 2$. We then have

$$g_{11}e_1 + g_{12}e_2 = i_{s1}$$
$$g_{21}e_1 + g_{22}e_2 = i_{s2} \tag{77}$$

Setting $i_{s1} = 0$ and solving for e_1, we find

$$\left(\frac{e_1}{i_{s2}}\right)_{i_{s1}=0} = \frac{g_{12}}{(g_{12}g_{21} - g_{11}g_{22})} \tag{78}$$

while setting $i_{s2} = 0$ and solving for e_2 gives

$$\left(\frac{e_2}{i_{s1}}\right)_{i_{s2}=0} = \frac{g_{21}}{(g_{12}g_{21} - g_{11}g_{22})} \tag{79}$$

Since $g_{12} = g_{21}$, we have the result

$$\left(\frac{e_2}{i_{s1}}\right)_{i_{s2}=0} = \left(\frac{e_1}{i_{s2}}\right)_{i_{s1}=0} \tag{80}$$

Because of the assumption yielding symmetry for the parameter matrix, it is clear that e_2 and i_{s2} are associated with the same terminal pair as are e_1 and i_{s1} also. Hence the result expressed by Eq. 80 may be stated by saying that the ratio of voltage response to current excitation makes no distinction as to which of the two terminal pairs is the point of excitation and which is the point at which the response is being observed.

This result, known as the *reciprocity theorem*, may be seen to apply generally through returning now to the Eqs. 76 pertaining to an arbitrary situation. Specifically we shall show that, if we systematically and successively eliminate the variables e_n, e_{n-1}, $\cdots$, e_3, the remaining two equations involving e_1 and e_2 have the form of Eqs. 77 in which the symmetry condition $g_{12} = g_{21}$ holds. That is to say, the symmetry of the parameter matrix in Eqs. 76 is not lost through applying the systematic elimination procedure. To recognize this property of the equations, consider the associated matrix

$$[G] = \begin{bmatrix} g_{11} & g_{12} & g_{13} & \cdots & g_{1n} \\ g_{21} & g_{22} & g_{23} & \cdots & g_{2n} \\ g_{31} & g_{32} & g_{33} & \cdots & g_{3n} \\ \cdot & \cdot & \cdot & \cdot & \cdot \\ g_{n1} & g_{n2} & g_{n3} & \cdots & g_{nn} \end{bmatrix} \tag{81}$$

and carry out the process equivalent to the elimination of e_n, as follows: From the g_{nn}-multiplied sth row, subtract the g_{sn}-multiplied last row, for $s = 1, 2, \cdots, n-1$. The matrix of the resulting equations involving the variables $e_1, e_2, \cdots, e_{n-1}$ then has the form indicated by

$$\begin{bmatrix} (g_{11}g_{nn} - g_{n1}g_{1n}) & (g_{12}g_{nn} - g_{n2}g_{1n}) & (g_{13}g_{nn} - g_{n3}g_{1n}) & \cdots \\ (g_{21}g_{nn} - g_{n1}g_{2n}) & (g_{22}g_{nn} - g_{n2}g_{2n}) & (g_{23}g_{nn} - g_{n3}g_{2n}) & \cdots \\ (g_{31}g_{nn} - g_{n1}g_{3n}) & (g_{32}g_{nn} - g_{n2}g_{3n}) & (g_{33}g_{nn} - g_{n3}g_{3n}) & \cdots \\ \cdot & \cdot & \cdot & \cdot \end{bmatrix} \tag{82}$$

Clearly the symmetry condition $g_{sk} = g_{ks}$ pertaining to the original matrix assures the symmetry of the matrix 82. That is to say, the process of eliminating the variable e_n from Eqs. 76 leaves the symmetry of their parameter-matrix invariant.

Since the subsequent elimination of the variable e_{n-1} follows the same pattern, the resulting matrix for the equations involving $e_1 \cdots e_{n-2}$ will again be symmetrical, and so forth. Hence we shall eventually arrive at a pair of equations involving e_1 and $\dot{e}_2$ that, like Eqs. 77, have a symmetrical parameter matrix; whence the result expressed by Eq. 80 is again seen to apply. We may with complete generality, therefore, make the statement: *In any linear passive bilateral network, a determination of the ratio of voltage produced at one terminal pair to the value of current excitation applied at another involves no distinction between these terminal pairs.*

It is evident that we might equally well start from a set of equilibrium equations on the loop basis. The excitation then is a voltage inserted into one branch and the response a current in another branch. In this situation the ratio of current to voltage turns out to be independent of which of the two branches contains the voltage source.

An alternate method that is commonly used to prove the reciprocity theorem makes use of the compact form for the relation between excitation and response afforded by the use of determinants in the solution of the pertinent equations. Thus, Eq. 36 in Art. 2 expresses a response x_k caused by an excitation y_s in terms of the determinant A and cofactor A_{ks} of the associated Eqs. 22. The indexes s and k may refer to any two meshes if a loop basis is implied, or to any two node pairs if a node basis is involved. In either case, one index characterizes the point of excitation while the other designates the point at which the response is observed.

If the elements a_{sk} in the determinant A, Eq. 23, fulfill the symmetry condition $a_{sk} = a_{ks}$, then determinant theory shows that the cofactors fulfill a similar condition, namely $A_{sk} = A_{ks}$. In Eq. 36 relating excitation y_s with response x_k, one may therefore interchange the indexes s and k without losing the validity of this equation; whereupon the essence of the reciprocity theorem is seen to follow at once.

The method of proof given above, which is based upon showing that the symmetrical property of a group of equations is invariant to the typical cycle in a systematic elimination procedure, is no less general than the one involving determinants, and has the advantage that it requires no particular algebraic background beyond that gained from practice with the solution of numerical examples.

In applying the reciprocity theorem it is significant to observe that both current and voltage are always involved. Thus, of the two quantities, excitation and response, one must be a voltage and the other a current. Except in some very special cases, reciprocity does *not* apply where the excitation and the response are both voltages or both currents. The reason for this restriction is easy to see. Thus, suppose both quantities are voltages. The voltage source (as has frequently been pointed out) is a generalized short circuit, while the observation of a voltage response at some terminal pair implies an open-circuit condition. Hence, the point of excitation is short-circuited while the point of observation is open-circuited. An interchange of the points of excitation and observation is accompanied by an interchange of open- and short-circuit constraints at these terminal pairs, and one cannot under these circum-

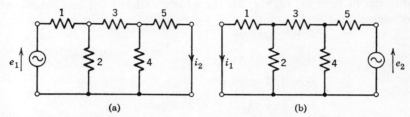

FIG. 27.   Illustration of a situation to which the reciprocity theorem applies.

stances expect the ratio of response to excitation to remain unchanged since the network geometry is altered. Although one may find some special cases in which reciprocity nevertheless still holds, it is in general not applicable.

The same is true if the excitation and response are both currents, for a current source is effectively an open circuit while the observation of a current at some terminal pair implies a short-circuit condition. Hence, an interchange of the points of excitation and observation again necessitates an interchange of open- and short-circuit constraints at both terminal pairs.

When the excitation is a voltage and the response a current, then short-circuit constraints are implied at both terminal pairs; and, when the excitation is a current and the response a voltage, the implied constraints are both open circuits. Hence, in these cases no change in the terminal constraints accompanies shifting the source from one terminal pair to the other. These are the situations to which reciprocity applies in its full generality.

As an illustration consider the network shown in Fig. 27, where, for reasons of simplicity, the numbers on the branches may be regarded as also indicating their resistance values in ohms. Using the procedure applicable to ladder networks, as discussed in Art. 3, one obtains for the situation in part (a) of Fig. 27

$$i_2 = 1 \text{ ampere} \qquad v_2 = 5 + (27/4) = 47/4 \text{ volts}$$

$$v_5 = v_4 = 5 \text{ volts} \qquad j_2 = 47/8 \text{ amperes}$$

$$j_4 = 5/4 \text{ amperes} \qquad j_1 = (47/8) + (9/4) = 65/8 \text{ amperes}$$

$$j_3 = 9/4 \text{ amperes} \qquad e_1 = (65/8) + (47/4) = 159/8 \text{ volts}$$

(83)

Hence,

$$(i_2/e_1) = 8/159 \tag{84}$$

Interchanging the points of excitation and observation yields the situation in part (b) of Fig. 27, for which we have the computational sequence

$$i_1 = 1 \text{ ampere}$$

$$v_1 = v_2 = 1 \text{ volt}$$

$$j_2 = 1/2 \text{ ampere}$$

$$j_3 = 1 + (1/2) = 3/2 \text{ amperes}$$

$$v_4 = 1 + (9/2) = 11/2 \text{ volts}$$

$$j_4 = 11/8 \text{ amperes}$$

$$j_5 = (11/8) + (3/2) = 23/8 \text{ amperes}$$

$$e_2 = (11/2) + (115/8) = 159/8 \text{ volts}$$

(85)

leading to

$$(i_1/e_2) = 8/159 \tag{86}$$

which checks, as it should, with the result 84.

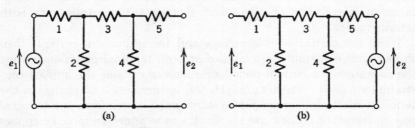

(a)   (b)

FIG. 28. Illustration of a situation to which the reciprocity theorem does not apply.

Now we shall show that reciprocity does not hold for this same network with respect to a voltage-to-voltage ratio. Figure 28 illustrates the corresponding geometry involved. For part (a) we have the computational sequence

$$e_2 = v_4 = 1 \text{ volt}$$

$$j_4 = j_3 = 1/4 \text{ ampere}$$

$$v_2 = 1 + (3/4) = 7/4 \text{ volts}$$

$$j_2 = 7/8 \text{ ampere} \tag{87}$$

$$j_1 = (7/8) + (1/4) = 9/8 \text{ amperes}$$

$$e_1 = (9/8) + (7/4) = 23/8 \text{ volts}$$

Hence,

$$(e_2/e_1) = 8/23 \tag{88}$$

For the situation in part (b) of Fig. 28, on the other hand, we have

$$e_1 = v_2 = 1 \text{ volt}$$

$$j_2 = j_3 = 1/2 \text{ ampere}$$

$$v_4 = 1 + (3/2) = 5/2 \text{ volts}$$

$$j_4 = 5/8 \text{ ampere} \tag{89}$$

$$j_5 = (5/8) + (1/2) = 9/8 \text{ amperes}$$

$$e_2 = (5/2) + (45/8) = 65/8 \text{ volts}$$

whence

$$(e_1/e_2) = 8/65 \tag{90}$$

It is clear that reciprocity does not hold with respect to the ratio of voltages. However, observe from computations 87 that $(e_2/j_1) = 8/9$, and from those given in 89 that $(e_1/j_5) = 8/9$ also. These are situations to which reciprocity again applies, for j_1 and j_5 may be regarded as the values of applied current sources.

As will be appreciated later on, reciprocity is a network property that has many uses. Unfortunately it is frequently misused, for the restrictions pointed out above are not always clearly observed by those who apply network theory to practical problems. The student should reread the rather general statement of the reciprocity theorem as it is given in the opening paragraph of this article and be sure that he can supply the necessary restrictive provisions to establish it on a foolproof basis.

7 Driving-Point and Transfer Functions

Suppose we consider the equilibrium equations on the loop basis for a network in which only a single voltage source is present. If the point of excitation is the contour of the sth loop, the equations have the form

$$r_{11}i_1 + r_{12}i_2 + \cdots + r_{1l}i_l = 0$$

$$\cdots \cdots \cdots \cdots \cdots \cdots$$

$$r_{s1}i_1 + r_{s2}i_2 + \cdots + r_{sl}i_l = e_s \tag{91}$$

$$\cdots \cdots \cdots \cdots \cdots \cdots$$

$$r_{l1}i_1 + r_{l2}i_2 + \cdots + r_{ll}i_l = 0$$

In terms of the determinant

$$R = \begin{vmatrix} r_{11} & r_{12} & \cdots & r_{1l} \\ r_{21} & r_{22} & \cdots & r_{2l} \\ \cdot & \cdot & \cdots & \cdot \\ r_{l1} & r_{l2} & \cdots & r_{ll} \end{vmatrix} \tag{92}$$

and its cofactors R_{sk}, the solution for the current in loop k may, according to the discussion in Art. 2 (Eq. 36), be expressed as

$$i_k = \frac{R_{ks}}{R} e_s \tag{93}$$

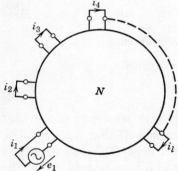

FIG. 29. An l terminal-pair network formed through considering the loops as points of access.

In order to gain a useful interpretation of this result, let us suppose that the loop currents $i_1 \cdots i_l$ are identified with link currents in a given network, and that we are interested in having access to the network only through its links. Hence, the network is completely enclosed in a box N, as shown in Fig. 29, but portions of the links are allowed to protrude so as to have the appearance externally of short-circuited terminal pairs. These terminal pairs are spoken of as the *points of entry* into the network or as its *external terminal pairs*. The network N is referred to as an *l terminal pair*.* The terminal pairs are the network's points of accessibility.

* In writing this designation for a network having a specified number of terminal pairs or points of entry, it should be observed that there is no hyphen between the number or letter (like l above) and the word "terminal" because this form would imply that the network has l terminals, which is not the case. Properly speaking, the network does not have any terminals; it has only *terminal pairs*, and there are l of these.

In Fig. 29 the point of excitation is chosen as being in loop 1 or at terminal pair 1, but could equally well be located at any other terminal pair. Observe that all terminal pairs are short-circuited, even the one at which the excitation is located, for the voltage source is a generalized short circuit.

Considering the result expressed by Eq. 93, the quantities

$$y_{ks} = R_{ks}/R \qquad (94)$$

for all possible combinations of the integers k and s are regarded as *response functions*, since the current response at any terminal pair is obtained through multiplying the excitation by this function for appropriate integers k and s. In the present instance the excitation is a voltage and the response is a current, so that the response function y_{ks} is the ratio of current to voltage, and is denoted as an *admittance*.

When $s = k$, admittance 94 relates current and voltage at the same point and hence is called a *driving-point* admittance, since the point of excitation is also referred to as the driving point. For $s \neq k$, the quantities y_{ks} are called *transfer admittances*. Multiplied by the excitation voltage at the terminal pair s, the quantity y_{ks} yields the short-circuit current at the terminal pair k, all other terminal pairs being simultaneously short-circuited. The complete set of y_{ks} are, therefore, spoken of as the *short-circuit driving-point and transfer admittances* of the l terminal-pair network N.

In an analogous fashion we may consider the equilibrium equations for some network to be the following ones on the node basis:

$$g_{11}e_1 + g_{12}e_2 + \cdots + g_{1n}e_n = 0$$

$$\cdots \cdots \cdots \cdots \cdots \cdots \cdots$$

$$g_{s1}e_1 + g_{s2}e_2 + \cdots + g_{sn}e_n = i_s \qquad (95)$$

$$\cdots \cdots \cdots \cdots \cdots \cdots \cdots$$

$$g_{n1}e_1 + g_{n2}e_2 + \cdots + g_{nn}e_n = 0$$

where again only a single source is assumed to excite the network, and its location is at the sth node pair. In terms of the determinant method of solution, one can write for any node-pair voltage

$$e_k = \frac{G_{ks}}{G} i_s \qquad (96)$$

where the determinant of Eqs. 95 is

$$G = \begin{vmatrix} g_{11} & g_{12} & \cdots & g_{1n} \\ g_{21} & g_{22} & \cdots & g_{2n} \\ \cdot & \cdot & \cdots & \cdot \\ g_{n1} & g_{n2} & \cdots & g_{nn} \end{vmatrix} \tag{97}$$

and G_{sk} are its cofactors.

In this situation we may likewise think of the network as being enclosed in a box, as shown in Fig. 30, with terminal pairs brought out from the node pairs to which the voltages $e_1 \cdots e_n$ refer. In contrast to the network shown in Fig. 29, the terminal pairs in the present representation are all open-circuited, even the one at the driving point, for the current source is a generalized open circuit. The quantities

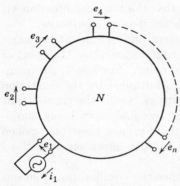

$$z_{ks} = G_{ks}/G \tag{98}$$

are the response functions in this case, since the voltage response at any terminal pair is obtained by multiplying the excitation by z_{ks} with appropriate integers k and s. For $k = s$ we refer to quantity 98 as a driving-point function, while for $k \neq s$ it is referred to as a transfer function. Since it represents the ratio of voltage to current, it is called an *impedance* (this being the traditional name given to such a ratio). Multiplied by the excitation current at the terminal pair s, the quantity z_{ks} yields the open-circuit voltage at the terminal pair k, all other terminal pairs being simultaneously open-circuited. The complete set of z_{ks} are, therefore, spoken of as the *open-circuit driving-point and transfer impedances* of the n terminal-pair network N.

FIG. 30. An n terminal-pair network formed through considering the node pairs as points of access.

The admittances y_{ks}, Eq. 94, may be seen to have the dimensions of mhos (reciprocal ohms) by noting that the terms in the complete expansion of R are products of l elements r_{sk} while those in the expansion of R_{ks} are products of $(l-1)$ such elements. In like manner, the z_{ks} of Eq. 98 may be seen to have the dimensions of ohms (reciprocal mhos) by noting that the terms in the complete expansion of G are products of n elements g_{sk} while those in the expansion of G_{ks} are products of $(n-1)$ such elements. Although dimensionally the z_{ks} and y_{ks} are reciprocal, it should not be inferred that they are numerically reciprocal, as attention to their mode of derivation will readily reveal.

It is a property of determinants that, if the elements, like the r_{sk} in 92, fulfill the symmetry condition $r_{sk} = r_{ks}$, then so do the cofactors; that is, $R_{sk} = R_{ks}$. Hence, if equilibrium Eqs. 91 for the loop basis and 95 for the node basis have symmetrical matrices, then we have from Eqs. 94 and 98

$$y_{ks} = y_{sk} \quad \text{and} \quad z_{ks} = z_{sk} \tag{99}$$

From the interpretations given above for these quantities, we recognize that this result is again a verification of the network property referred to as the reciprocity theorem and substantiated more carefully in the foregoing article.

It is seldom that one is interested in the currents in all the loops of a network or in the voltages at all of its node pairs. Specifically, with reference to Eqs. 91 and the network representation shown in Fig. 29, one may be interested only in regarding say $i_1, i_2, \cdots, i_p$ as accessible currents. In the representation of Fig. 29 this situation is readily taken care of by bringing out only the terminal pairs $1 \cdots p$, while analytically this attitude is dealt with by applying to Eqs. 91 the systematic elimination procedure so as to eliminate the variables $i_{p+1} \cdots i_l$. The resulting equations linking the remaining variables $i_1 \cdots i_p$ are then related to a corresponding p terminal-pair network in the same fashion that Eqs. 91 are related to the l terminal-pair network of Fig. 29.

Analogously one may abridge the n terminal-pair network of Fig. 30 to a p terminal-pair one, by eliminating from Eqs. 95 those variables whose accessibility is not called for. Thus one may obtain the set of admittances y_{sk} or impedances z_{sk} for any network whose points of access have independently been chosen as to number and location.

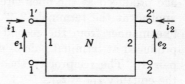

FIG. 31. A two terminal-pair network showing the conventional current and voltage reference directions.

We shall now discuss in further detail the most commonly encountered situation of this sort for which the number of accessible points is two. Such a so-called *two terminal-pair network* is represented by the sketch in Fig. 31. The pertinent relations between the currents and voltages may be regarded as derived either from a set of node equations like 95 written for two nonzero current sources i_1 and i_2, or from a set of loop equations like 91 written for two nonzero voltage sources e_1 and e_2. After elimination of all but the first two dependent variables, one obtains the desired relations either in the form

$$y_{11}e_1 + y_{12}e_2 = i_1$$
$$y_{21}e_1 + y_{22}e_2 = i_2$$

(100)

or

$$z_{11}i_1 + z_{12}i_2 = e_1$$
$$z_{21}i_1 + z_{22}i_2 = e_2$$

(101)

which must, of course, be inverse pairs of equations since they pertain to the same network.

Physically, y_{11} is the admittance at the terminal pair 1 when terminal pair 2 is short-circuited as may be seen from the first Eq. 100 by noting that y_{11} equals i_1/e_1 for $e_2 = 0$. Similarly, y_{22} is the admittance at terminal pair 2 with terminal pair 1 short-circuited. The short-circuit transfer admittance y_{21} is in a like manner interpreted as the ratio of i_2 at the short-circuited terminal pair 2, to an excitation e_1 at terminal pair 1, and y_{12} as the ratio of i_1 at the short-circuited terminal pair 1, to an excitation e_2 applied to the terminal pair 2. By the reciprocity theorem these two ratios are equal ($y_{12} = y_{21}$).

In an analogous manner one may interpret physically the z_{sk} in Eqs. 101. Thus z_{11} and z_{22} are seen to be the impedances at the terminal pairs 1 and 2 respectively under open-circuit conditions. For example, the first of Eqs. 101 reveals z_{11} to be equal to e_1/i_1 for $i_2 = 0$ (open-circuit condition at terminal pair 2). Similarly, this same equation shows that z_{12} equals e_1/i_2 for $i_1 = 0$; that is to say, it equals the voltage produced at the open-circuit terminals 1–1' per ampere of current applied at the terminals 2–2'. The impedance z_{21} is interpreted in a like manner from the second of Eqs. 101 as the open-circuit voltage produced at terminal pair 2, per ampere of current applied to terminal pair 1. The reciprocity theorem again lends physical significance to the equality $z_{12} = z_{21}$.

In applying these physical interpretations to specific examples (as is done in the next article), the reader is cautioned to give careful attention to the reference arrows shown in Fig. 31, which are chosen in a symmetrical manner so as to deal with the question of "input" and "output" in an impartial manner.

Solution of set 100 so as to obtain relations like those in Eqs. 101, yields the following connection between the z's and y's,

$$z_{11} = \frac{y_{22}}{|y|}, \qquad z_{22} = \frac{y_{11}}{|y|}, \qquad z_{12} = \frac{-y_{12}}{|y|}$$

(102)

where the determinant of the Eqs. 100 is denoted by

$$| y | = y_{11}y_{22} - y_{12}{}^2 \tag{103}$$

the symmetry condition $y_{12} = y_{21}$ being tacitly assumed. The converse procedure yields the y's in terms of the z's, thus

$$y_{11} = \frac{z_{22}}{| z |}, \qquad y_{22} = \frac{z_{11}}{| z |}, \qquad y_{12} = \frac{-z_{12}}{| z |} \tag{104}$$

where the determinant of Eqs. 101 is

$$| z | = z_{11}z_{22} - z_{12}{}^2 \tag{105}$$

and the symmetry condition $z_{12} = z_{21}$ holds. The determinants $| y |$ and $| z |$, of course, have reciprocal values; that is,

$$| y | = | z |^{-1} \tag{106}$$

as is clear, incidentally, from a comparison of relations 102 and 104.

These results contain the interesting and useful relationship expressed by

$$y_{11}z_{11} = y_{22}z_{22} \tag{107}$$

A simple example will illustrate the unusual character of this result. With reference to the network of Fig. 32 in which the element values are in ohms, we note that z_{11} is the resistance of the series combination of the two branches, while y_{11} is the conductance of the 2-ohm branch alone. Hence

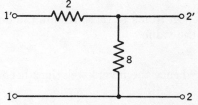

FIG. 32. A simple example of a dissymmetrical two terminal-pair network for which the property expressed by Eq. 107 is illustrated.

$$y_{11} = 1/2, \qquad z_{11} = 10 \tag{108}$$

At the opposite end of this two terminal pair we observe that z_{22} is given by the 8-ohm resistance alone while y_{22} is the conductance of the two branches in parallel. Thus we have

$$y_{22} = 5/8, \qquad z_{22} = 8 \tag{109}$$

Physically and numerically the pairs of quantities 108 and 109 seem unrelated; yet it is clear that they do fulfill the condition expressed by Eq. 107, as indeed they must, since this relationship holds for any two terminal-pair network.

Returning to Fig. 31 again, it is often useful to express the quantities e_1, i_1 in terms of e_2, i_2 or vice versa. Such relations are readily obtained through an appropriate manipulation of Eqs. 100 or 101. It is customary to write them as

$$e_1 = Ae_2 - Bi_2$$
$$i_1 = Ce_2 - Di_2 \tag{110}$$

It is a simple matter to determine the coefficients A, B, C, D, called the *general circuit parameters*, in terms of the y's or the z's. The following relations are self-explanatory, and make use of Eqs. 100, 101, and Eqs. 102 and 104 relating the y's and z's.

$$A = \left(\frac{e_1}{e_2}\right)_{i_2=0} = \frac{z_{11}}{z_{12}} = -\frac{y_{22}}{y_{12}} \tag{111}$$

$$B = \left(\frac{e_1}{-i_2}\right)_{e_2=0} = -\frac{1}{y_{12}} = \frac{|z|}{z_{12}} \tag{112}$$

$$C = \left(\frac{i_1}{e_2}\right)_{i_2=0} = \frac{1}{z_{12}} = -\frac{|y|}{y_{12}} \tag{113}$$

$$D = \left(\frac{i_1}{-i_2}\right)_{e_2=0} = -\frac{y_{11}}{y_{12}} = \frac{z_{22}}{z_{12}} \tag{114}$$

In terms of these results the determinant of Eqs. 110 is seen to have the value

$$BC - AD = -1 \tag{115}$$

whence the inverse relations become

$$e_2 = De_1 - Bi_1$$
$$i_2 = Ce_1 - Ai_1 \tag{116}$$

Since only three quantities (like the three y's or the three z's) are needed to characterize the two terminal pair, it is to be expected that the four parameters A, B, C, D must bear some relation to one another. This relation turns out to be the simple one expressed by Eq. 115; and, as a result, one finds that Eqs. 116, inverse to Eqs. 110, have coefficients that again are simply the quantities A, B, C, D, and that these two inverse relations are identical in form except for an interchange in the roles played by the coefficients A and D.

A useful application of these relations involving the parameters $ABCD$ is the problem of expressing the *input impedance* Z_1 of a two terminal-pair network (Fig. 33) in terms of its load impedance Z_2. Since $Z_1 = e_1/i_1$ and $Z_2 = e_2/(-i_2)$, where the voltage and current reference directions in Fig. 31 are noted, we see that division of the first of the Eqs. 110 by the second one yields

$$Z_1 = \frac{AZ_2 + B}{CZ_2 + D} \tag{117}$$

In mathematical function theory, this relationship between the quantities Z_1 and Z_2 is known as a *linear fractional transformation*. Physically we regard the network N in Fig. 33 as literally transforming Z_2 into the value Z_1. One of the uses of two terminal-pair networks in practice is to effect such a transformation. Relation 117 has many uses, and it will be referred to frequently in later discussions.

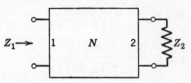

FIG. 33.   A situation illustrating impedance transformation 117.

8   Common Network Configurations and Their Equivalence Relations

Several specific configurations for two terminal-pair networks occur sufficiently often in subsequent discussions to justify their individual consideration at this time in order that their separate characterizations and their interrelationships may appropriately be emphasized.

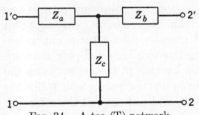

FIG. 34.   A tee (T) network.

Figure 34 shows the so-called tee (T) network in which the boxes labeled Z_a, Z_b, Z_c are for their own part the driving-point impedances of any two-terminal networks. That is to say, the boxes may contain single elements or any geometrical configuration of elements having one accessible terminal pair. The open-circuit driving-point and transfer impedances of the two terminal-pair network given by this tee are seen by inspection to be

$$z_{11} = Z_a + Z_c = (Y_a + Y_c)/Y_aY_c \tag{118}$$

$$z_{22} = Z_b + Z_c = (Y_b + Y_c)/Y_bY_c \tag{119}$$

$$z_{12} = Z_c = 1/Y_c \tag{120}$$

in which Y_a, Y_b, Y_c are the admittances corresponding to the impedances Z_a, Z_b, Z_c.

The z determinant is thus seen to be

$$|z| = z_{11}z_{22} - z_{12}{}^2 = Z_aZ_b + Z_aZ_c + Z_bZ_c$$

$$= \frac{Y_a + Y_b + Y_c}{Y_aY_bY_c} \tag{121}$$

so that, according to Eqs. 104, the short-circuit driving-point and transfer admittances become

$$y_{11} = \frac{z_{22}}{|z|} = \frac{Y_a(Y_b + Y_c)}{Y_a + Y_b + Y_c} = \frac{Y_aY_b}{Y_a + Y_b + Y_c} + \frac{Y_aY_c}{Y_a + Y_b + Y_c} \tag{122}$$

$$y_{22} = \frac{z_{11}}{z|} = \frac{Y_b(Y_a + Y_c)}{Y_a + Y_b + Y_c} = \frac{Y_aY_b}{Y_a + Y_b + Y_c} + \frac{Y_bY_c}{Y_a + Y_b + Y_c} \tag{123}$$

$$y_{12} = \frac{-z_{12}}{|z|} = \frac{-Y_aY_b}{Y_a + Y_b + Y_c} \tag{124}$$

It is interesting to compare these results with those found for the so-called pi (π) network shown in Fig. 35, which is more appropriately characterized in terms of admittances than impedances. Thus, in terms of the driving-point admittances Y_1, Y_2, Y_3, one may write down by inspection the following expressions for the short-circuit driving-point and transfer admittances characterizing the two terminal-pair network given by this pi structure (using the

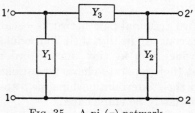

FIG. 35.   A pi (π) network.

physical interpretations of the y_{sk} given in the paragraph following Eqs. 100 and 101 in the previous article, and noting well the reference arrows as shown in Fig. 31).

$$y_{11} = Y_1 + Y_3 = (Z_1 + Z_3)/Z_1Z_3 \tag{125}$$

$$y_{22} = Y_2 + Y_3 = (Z_2 + Z_3)/Z_2Z_3 \tag{126}$$

$$y_{12} = -Y_3 = -1/Z_3 \tag{127}$$

in which Z_1, Z_2, Z_3 are the impedances corresponding to the admittances Y_1, Y_2, Y_3.

The y determinant is thus seen to be

$$|y| = y_{11}y_{22} - y_{12}{}^2 = Y_1Y_2 + Y_1Y_3 + Y_2Y_3$$

$$= \frac{Z_1 + Z_2 + Z_3}{Z_1Z_2Z_3} \tag{128}$$

so that, according to Eqs. 102, the open-circuit driving-point and transfer impedances for this same pi network become

$$z_{11} = \frac{y_{22}}{|y|} = \frac{Z_1(Z_2 + Z_3)}{Z_1 + Z_2 + Z_3} = \frac{Z_1 Z_2}{Z_1 + Z_2 + Z_3} + \frac{Z_1 Z_3}{Z_1 + Z_2 + Z_3} \quad (129)$$

$$z_{22} = \frac{y_{11}}{|y|} = \frac{Z_2(Z_1 + Z_3)}{Z_1 + Z_2 + Z_3} = \frac{Z_1 Z_2}{Z_1 + Z_2 + Z_3} + \frac{Z_2 Z_3}{Z_1 + Z_2 + Z_3} \quad (130)$$

$$z_{12} = \frac{-y_{12}}{|y|} = \frac{Z_1 Z_2}{Z_1 + Z_2 + Z_3} \quad (131)$$

The dual character of the tee and pi structures should be rather clear from this comparison of the relationships characterizing them. The conditions for which they become equivalent are readily seen from an inspection of the equations giving the respective y_{sk} and z_{sk}. Thus, from a comparison of Eqs. 118, 119, 120 with Eqs. 129, 130, 131 we see that the impedances of the tee in terms of those of the pi are given by

$$Z_c = \frac{Z_1 Z_2}{Z_1 + Z_2 + Z_3}, \qquad Z_b = \frac{Z_2 Z_3}{Z_1 + Z_2 + Z_3}$$

$$Z_a = \frac{Z_1 Z_3}{Z_1 + Z_2 + Z_3} \quad (132)$$

while a comparison of Eqs. 122, 123, 124 with Eqs. 125, 126, 127 yields the following expressions for the admittances of the pi in terms of the admittances of the tee:

$$Y_3 = \frac{Y_a Y_b}{Y_a + Y_b + Y_c}, \qquad Y_2 = \frac{Y_b Y_c}{Y_a + Y_b + Y_c}$$

$$Y_1 = \frac{Y_a Y_c}{Y_a + Y_b + Y_c} \quad (133)$$

Again the duality of the situation is in evidence, since the transformation from pi to tee (Eqs. 132) on an impedance basis is identical in form with the transformation from tee to pi (Eqs. 133) on an admittance basis.

The reader should observe also that the tee and pi networks discussed here are structurally the same as the wye and delta configurations (respectively) discussed in Art. 4, and that the delta-wye transformation Eqs. 58 are equivalent to the pi-tee transformation Eqs. 132 above, while the wye-delta transformation Eqs. 51 are equivalent to the tee-pi transformation Eqs. 133. Thus the phrase "product of the two adjacent divided by the sum of all three" is seen to be a compact way of expressing what is essential to the results given by Eqs. 132 and 133. To add clarity and emphasis to these remarks the reader should make sketches involving the tee and pi networks that are analogous to Figs. 9 and 13 in Art. 4. In applying the above phrase to obtain Eqs. 132 and 133, he should notice that the pertinent sums $Z_1 + Z_2 + Z_3$ and $Y_a + Y_b + Y_c$ have the simple physical significance of being, respectively, the total impedance around the mesh of the pi (Fig. 35) and the total admittance confluent in the central node of the tee (Fig. 34), whereas the two incorrect sums $Y_1 + Y_2 + Y_3$ and $Z_a + Z_b + Z_c$

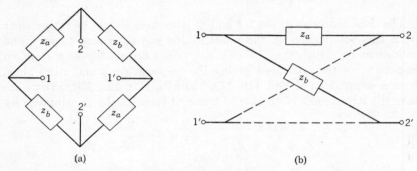

(a)   (b)

FIG. 36.   The symmetrical lattice (b) and its "bridge" circuit equivalent (a).

(which he might erroneously be tempted to use) have no such simple physical counterparts with reference to the circuits involved.

When, in the tee of Fig. 34, $Z_a = Z_b$, or, in the pi of Fig. 35, $Y_1 = Y_2$, these networks are said to be *symmetrical* with respect to their input and output terminal pairs, for an interchange of these terminal pairs then has no influence upon the electrical behavior of the larger network in which the tee or pi may be embedded. A symmetrical structure that is found to play an important part in network theory is the *lattice* or *bridge* shown in Fig. 36. In part (a) of this figure the network is completely drawn in the familiar form of a Wheatstone bridge; in part (b) the same circuit is redrawn as a lattice, using the convention of drawing dotted lines rather than repeating the boxes z_a and z_b.

In order to recognize the equivalence of the bridge and the lattice, the reader should imagine taking hold of the lower right-hand box z_a in the bridge and turning it over (end for end) longitudinally so that the boxes z_b cross over each other. The terminals 1–1' will then be at the lower left of the figure and the terminals 2–2' will be at the upper right. The impedances z_a of the lattice are thus sometimes referred to as the "series arms" and the impedances z_b as the "cross-arms." Notice, however, that, if one twists *either* terminal pair 1–1' *or* 2–2' (not both), then the z_a boxes become crossed and the z_b boxes become uncrossed. Hence the symmetrical lattice has the property that an interchange of its component impedances z_a and z_b is equivalent to a twist of either terminal pair.

It should be observed that the lattice, unlike the tee or pi networks considered above, possesses symmetry with respect to a horizontal centerline (not to be confused with its symmetry about a vertical centerline which yields symmetry with respect to the two terminal pairs). Since a horizontal centerline is usually taken to be at a reference or ground potential, the symmetrical lattice is spoken of as being "balanced with respect to ground." The symmetrical tee or pi structure in contrast is referred to as being "unbalanced with respect to ground" or more briefly as being an "unbalanced network." Thus the terms "balanced" and "unbalanced" are used to refer to symmetry or assymmetry about a horizontal centerline, while the terms "symmetrical" and "dissymmetrical," when used in conjunction with a two terminal pair, refer to its symmetry or dissymmetry about a vertical centerline.

The open-circuit driving-point and transfer impedances of the symmetrical lattice (Fig. 36) are readily found by inspection. Thus, with terminals 2–2' open, we note that the circuit between 1 and 1' consists of two parallel paths, each being a series connection of z_a and z_b. Hence it is clear that

$$z_{11} = z_{22} = \tfrac{1}{2}(z_b + z_a) \tag{134}$$

To evaluate the open-circuit transfer impedance according to the physical interpretations given in the previous article, let us suppose that 1 ampere is injected into terminal 1 and withdrawn from terminal 1'. The impedance z_{12} then is the resulting voltage rise from terminal 2' to terminal 2. Noting that the two parallel paths joining terminals 1–1' are identical, it is clear that $\tfrac{1}{2}$ ampere traverses each path. Either route from 2' to 2 traverses z_a in a direction confluent with the current (yielding a voltage drop) and z_b in a counterfluent direction (yielding a voltage rise). Hence we have

$$z_{12} = \tfrac{1}{2}(z_b - z_a) \tag{135}$$

This last relation makes it clear that $z_{12} = 0$ for $z_a = z_b$, which is recognized as the condition for which the bridge is balanced.

From results 134 and 135 the z determinant is readily seen to have the value

$$|z| = z_{11}{}^2 - z_{12}{}^2 = z_a z_b \tag{136}$$

and Eqs. 104 then give for the short-circuit driving-point and transfer admittances

$$y_{11} = y_{22} = \tfrac{1}{2}(y_b + y_a) \tag{137}$$

$$y_{12} = \tfrac{1}{2}(y_b - y_a) \tag{138}$$

where $y_a = 1/z_a$ and $y_b = 1/z_b$ are the lattice admittances. These relations are, except for an interchange of the letters y and z, identical respectively with Eqs. 134 and 135, thus showing that the symmetrical lattice is its own dual.

We can readily obtain the equivalence relations between the lattice and the symmetrical tee (Fig. 34 with $Z_a = Z_b$) by comparison of Eqs. 118, 119, 120 with Eqs. 134 and 135. Thus we see that

$$Z_a = Z_b = z_a, \qquad Z_c = \tfrac{1}{2}(z_b - z_a) \tag{139}$$

or conversely

$$z_a = Z_a = Z_b, \qquad z_b = Z_a + 2Z_c \tag{140}$$

Similarly we can obtain the equivalence relations between the lattice and the symmetrical pi (Fig. 35 with $Y_1 = Y_2$) by comparison of Eqs. 125, 126, 127 with Eqs. 137 and 138. Thus we have

$$Y_1 = Y_2 = y_b, \qquad Y_3 = \tfrac{1}{2}(y_a - y_b) \tag{141}$$

or conversely

$$y_b = Y_1 = Y_2, \qquad y_a = Y_1 + 2Y_3 \tag{142}$$

Since Eqs. 139 and 141 (representing the conversion of a lattice to an equivalent tee or pi structure) contain minus signs, it is clear that a physical lattice (one with positive resistances in its branches) does not

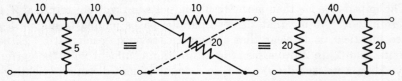

FIG. 37. Example of a tee-pi transformation via the lattice. Element values are in ohms.

necessarily possess a physical equivalent tee or pi. A physical symmetrical tee or pi, on the other hand, always possesses a physical equivalent lattice, since the conversion relations 140 and 142 involve only plus signs.

A simple example involving these equivalence relations is shown in Fig. 37. The given network is the symmetrical tee at the left. Through use of Eqs. 140 it is readily converted into the lattice, and the latter is seen to be equivalent to the pi circuit on the right according to the conversion relations 141 (noting that one must now reason in terms of mhos since Eqs. 141 involve admittances).

A somewhat more elaborate series of transformations is shown in Fig. 38. Here we begin with the so-called "bridged T" at the left, which is the symmetrical tee of Fig. 37 with a 20-ohm resistance bridged across the top. The first step in the conversion process consists of redrawing this bridged tee as a parallel connection of two networks, one of which is the tee and the other might be regarded as a pi that has lost

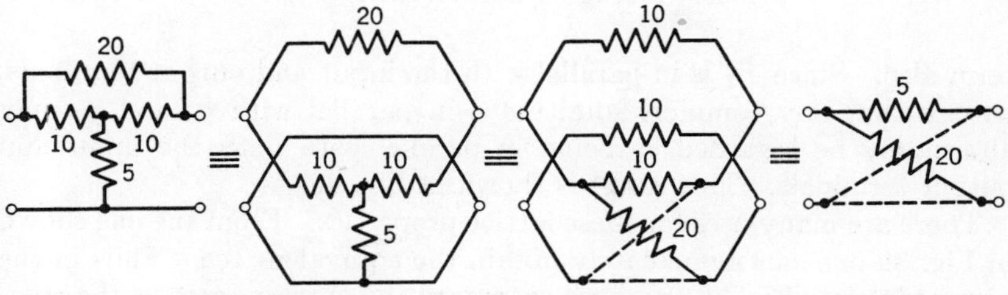

FIG. 38.   A bridged-tee to lattice transformation via the parallel combination of simpler networks.   Element values are in ohms.

its shunt branches. In the next step, each network is transformed to a balanced structure; the tee is transformed into a lattice and the 20-ohm resistor is split into two 10-ohm resistors in series. The latter network may be regarded as a lattice that has lost its cross-arms. In the final step, the two networks are again combined into one, this being again a lattice. The z_a arm of this resultant lattice is obviously the parallel combination of the two 10-ohm resistances, and the z_b arm is the same as the cross-arm in the lattice of the previous step.

Thus, the conversion of a bridged tee to an equivalent lattice is readily carried out, and the subsequent conversion of the lattice into a resultant tee or pi can, if desired, be done as in the previous example. Through manipulations in the reverse direction, one may convert from· a tee or pi to a bridged tee; and this conversion can be done with many variations, since the division of one resistance into two parallel ones can be accomplished in an infinite variety of ways.

Additional manipulative flexibility is had through noting the following properties of the lattice. Equations 140 show that, if z_a and z_b have a common additive term, then Z_a of the equivalent symmetrical tee has this additive term also. Since Z_a is in series with the input and output terminals, we see that any common impedance in series with z_a

and z_b may alternately be regarded as being in series with both the input and output terminals. This result is illustrated in Fig. 39.

Analogously, Eqs. 142 show that, if y_a and y_b have a common additive term, then Y_1 of the equivalent symmetrical pi has this additive

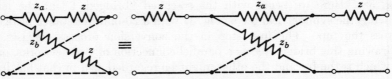

FIG. 39.   Illustrating a useful lattice property.

term also. Since Y_1 is in parallel with the input and output terminals, we see that any common admittance in parallel with y_a and y_b may alternately be regarded as being in parallel with both the input and output terminals. This result is shown in Fig. 40.

There are many uses for these lattice properties. From the one shown in Fig. 39 one can immediately obtain the equivalent tee. Thus in the normal lattice (Fig. 36) suppose we regard the entire z_a arm as the common additive term. Its removal as in Fig. 39 leaves a remaining lattice with short circuits for the series arms and an impedance $(z_b - z_a)$ for

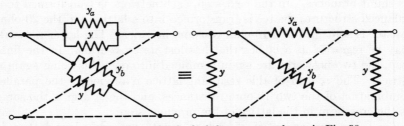

FIG. 40.   Illustrating the dual of the property shown in Fig. 39.

each cross-arm. Since the two cross-arms are thus placed in parallel, we recognize that the resulting structure is a tee with its series and shunt impedances given by Eq. 139. In an analogous manner one can use the property shown in Fig. 40 to obtain at once the equivalent pi for any given lattice.

Through regarding only a fraction of the given lattice resistances or conductances as a common additive term, and applying the properties illustrated in Figs. 39 and 40 alternately in a continuing sequence, one can develop the lattice into an equivalent ladder. Figure 41 shows an example of this process where the method of Fig. 39 is first applied, and that of Fig. 40 is then used to complete the development (which could alternatively be carried through a larger number of steps, if desired).

Conversely, one can use this process to convert a symmetrical ladder into a single lattice and thence into an equivalent tee or pi.

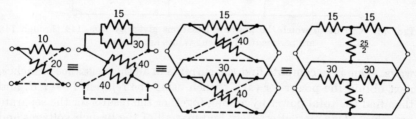

FIG. 41.   Ladder development of the lattice, using the properties shown in Figs. 39 and 40.   Element values are in ohms.

An example illustrating the decomposition of a single lattice into the parallel combination of two, and the subsequent transformation of these into tee circuits is shown in Fig. 42.   The resultant structure on the right consists of two tees in parallel, an arrangement that is commonly referred to as a "twin T."   The lattice is readily convertible into a twin

FIG. 42.   Lattice to twin-tee transformation.   Element values are in ohms.

tee, or the latter into an equivalent lattice, through use of artifices of the sort we are here discussing.   In fact, an endless variety of additional equivalent forms are readily obtainable, as the reader may now demonstrate for himself.

9   Power Relations, and Transformations under Which They Remain Invariant

If a single resistance of R ohms conducts a current of i amperes, the potential difference across R is $e = Ri$ volts, and the power delivered to R, or the time rate of energy dissipation in R, is

$$P = ei = e^2/R = i^2R \text{ joules per second or watts} \qquad (143)$$

The source furnishing this power may be the voltage e (an impedanceless voltage generator) or it may be the current i (an admittanceless current generator); the expression 143 for the power delivered or consumed is correct in either case. Significant is the result that, if the source is a voltage, the power varies inversely as the resistance (that is, proportional to the conductance $G = 1/R$), whereas, if the source is a current, the power varies proportional to the resistance. In both cases the power is proportional to the *square* of the source intensity.

Of the four quantities, P, R, e, i, a knowledge of any *two* uniquely fixes the other two, as is clear from the consideration that there are two independent relations linking these four quantities, viz.: $P = ei$, and $e = Ri$.

In a network consisting of a random interconnection of various resistances, one may compute the total power consumed in several different

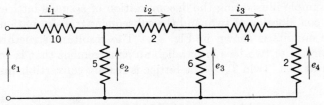

FIG. 43.   Circuit to which the power calculations given by Eqs. 144 through 148 are pertinent.   Element values are in ohms.

ways. One is to compute first the currents in all the resistance branches, next obtain the power for each branch using the relation $P = i^2R$, and then find the total power by adding together the results for the separate branches. One may alternately find first all of the branch voltages and thus obtain the power absorbed by each branch; and there are obviously many combinations of these schemes for computing separately the power in each branch.

When there is a source at one point only, it may be simpler to compute first the net resistance at the terminals of this source and then obtain the total power as that supplied to this net resistance as though the entire network were replaced by a single resistance having this value. In fact, the so-called net resistance or driving-point resistance may be regarded physically as a resistance of such a value that the power absorption from the source becomes identical with that absorbed by the given network. Since the computations involved in the determination of the driving-point resistance are usually about as extensive as those required for the computation of the voltages or currents in the various branches of the network, this alternative way of finding the total power is not necessarily computationally simpler. Experience and judgment alone can indicate the best method to use in a given example. Usually there is not enough difference to render the decision of any great moment. Let us illustrate with a simple example.

The network of Fig. 43 is assumed to be driven at the left-hand end. Nevertheless, suppose we begin by assuming, for e_4, 1 volt. Then the following sequence of calculations are self-evident.

$$e_4 = 1 \text{ volt}$$
$$i_3 = 1/2 \text{ ampere}$$
$$e_3 = 1 + (4/2) = 3 \text{ volts}$$
$$i_2 = (1/2) + (3/6) = 1 \text{ ampere} \tag{144}$$
$$e_2 = 3 + 2 = 5 \text{ volts}$$
$$i_1 = 1 + 1 = 2 \text{ amperes}$$
$$e_1 = 5 + 20 = 25 \text{ volts}$$

The total power supplied by the source may be calculated by adding the values of power absorbed by the separate branches. Since either the current or voltage for each branch is known from calculations 144, the power absorbed by any branch is obtained by use of the appropriate relation given in Eq. 143. Beginning at the right-hand end, this process yields the following

$$P = (1/2) + (4/4) + (9/6) + 2 + (25/5) + 10 \times 4 = 50 \text{ watts} \tag{145}$$

Instead, we can find the driving-point resistance as

$$R_{11} = e_1/i_1 = 25/2 = 12.5 \text{ ohms} \tag{146}$$

and compute the input power as the single term

$$P = e_1{}^2/R_{11} = 25^2/12.5 = 25 \times 2 = 50 \text{ watts} \tag{147}$$

or, in terms of the input current

$$P = i_1{}^2 R_{11} = 4 \times 12.5 = 50 \text{ watts} \tag{148}$$

Now suppose e_1 is given as 1 volt instead of 25 volts. Then all the voltages and currents in the calculations 144 are $\frac{1}{25}$th as large, all terms in Eq. 145 are $\frac{1}{625}$th as large, and the net power input is $\frac{1}{625}$th as large or $\frac{2}{25} = 0.08$ watt. On the other hand, if e_1 were given as 100 volts, that is, 4 times larger than it turns out to be in the calculations 144, then all values in these calculations are 4 times larger, and the power absorbed by any branch as well as the total power is 16 times larger.

When there is more than one driving point in the network, corresponding to the simultaneous application of several sources, then one must be careful to make an appropriate extension of the above procedures. The total power is in any case expressible as a sum of the values for power absorbed by the separate branches, and the power taken by any branch is computed from the pertinent branch current or branch voltage in the same way, irrespective of whether these currents and voltages are caused by a single source or by several sources acting simultaneously. However, when several sources are present, we have seen that it is effective to compute the current or voltage in a particular branch by considering the contributions due to each source acting separately and adding these to get the net value. For n sources, this approach would yield for the current in a particular branch an expression of the form $i = (i_1 + i_2 + \cdots + i_n)$ where each term is the result produced by a single source acting alone. If the pertinent branch resistance is R ohms, then the net power absorbed by that branch is

$$p = i^2 R = (i_1 + i_2 + \cdots + i_n)^2 R \tag{149}$$

which is R multiplied by

$$i^2 = i_1{}^2 + 2i_1 i_2 + 2i_1 i_3 + \cdots + 2i_1 i_n \tag{150}$$
$$+ i_2{}^2 + 2i_2 i_3 + \cdots + 2i_2 i_n$$
$$+ i_3{}^2 + \cdots + 2i_3 i_n$$
$$+ \cdots + i_n{}^2$$

From this result we see that what we cannot do, but might be tempted to do, is compute the net power absorbed by this branch through adding together the values of power dissipated in it owing to the current components for each source taken separately. This sum, which is equal to R multiplied by $i_1{}^2 + i_2{}^2 + \cdots + i_n{}^2$ evidently falls short of the correct value 149 by the contributions coming from the double product terms in 150. It thus becomes clear that we *cannot* compute the net power taken by a network fed from several sources by computing the power delivered by each source separately and adding these. *The rule of simple addition or superposition that applies to the computation of voltages or currents does not apply to the computation of power!*

We can appreciate the reason for this conclusion from several additional points of view. First of all, we should be reminded of the fact that the simple additive property applies only so long as the analytic relations involved are *linear*. Only systems or situations governed by linear equations have the additive property or permit the superposition of solutions. The relations expressing power, as given above, are *quad-*

ratic, not linear. Hence we should expect the superposability of solutions to fail, as indeed the preceding discussions show.

Still another point of view is helpful here. Considering the several sources involved, it must certainly be true that the net power supplied equals the sum of the various values of power supplied by the separate sources; but observe that this statement is correct only if we compute the power supplied by each source *while all the others are simultaneously acting*—not while the one source in question alone is acting. The important point is that the amount of power that a given source supplies equals the product of its terminal voltage and current; if the source is a voltage, then its current depends not only upon this voltage, but in an equal manner upon the intensities of the other sources, and, if the source is a current, then its voltage depends jointly upon the intensities of all the sources. Thus the power supplied by an individual source can vary widely, according to whether it is acting alone or in the presence of other sources, either at the same point or at other points in the network.

A safe way of treating a situation of this sort is to compute the net currents and voltages at all the sources, using superposition to do this if we wish, for the additive property does apply to the calculation of voltages and currents. From the net values of source voltage and current we can compute the net power supplied by each source and through addition obtain the total power. Alternately we can compute the net currents or voltages in the separate branches, again using for this purpose the principle of superposition if we find it expedient to do so. From the net branch quantities we can then readily compute the net power absorbed by each branch and through addition get the total power.

An interesting expression for the total power is obtained by starting from the equilibrium equations on the loop basis

$$r_{11}i_1 + r_{12}i_2 + \cdots + r_{1l}i_l = e_1$$
$$r_{21}i_1 + r_{22}i_2 + \cdots + r_{2l}i_l = e_2$$

$$\cdots \cdots \cdots \cdots \cdots \cdots \quad (151)$$

$$r_{l1}i_1 + r_{l2}i_2 + \cdots + r_{ll}i_l = e_l$$

in which $i_1 \cdots i_l$ are the loop currents, $e_1 \cdots e_l$ are the source voltages acting in the respective loops, and

$$[R] = \begin{bmatrix} r_{11} & r_{12} & \cdots & r_{1l} \\ r_{21} & r_{22} & \cdots & r_{2l} \\ & \cdots & \cdots & \\ r_{l1} & r_{l2} & \cdots & r_{ll} \end{bmatrix} \quad (152)$$

is the resistance parameter matrix on the loop basis. Since the total power delivered to the network is given by

$$P = e_1 i_1 + e_2 i_2 + \cdots + e_l i_l \tag{153}$$

we see that the power absorbed by the network is obtained through multiplying Eqs. 151 successively by $i_1, i_2, \cdots, i_l$ and adding the results. One obtains

$$\begin{aligned}
P = {}& r_{11} i_1{}^2 + r_{12} i_1 i_2 + \cdots + r_{1l} i_1 i_l \\
& + r_{21} i_2 i_1 + r_{22} i_2{}^2 + \cdots + r_{2l} i_2 i_l \\
& + \cdot \cdot \cdot \cdot \cdot \cdot \cdot \cdot \cdot \cdot \cdot \cdot \\
& + r_{l1} i_l i_1 + r_{l2} i_l i_2 + \cdots + r_{ll} i_l{}^2
\end{aligned} \tag{154}$$

This expression, which is homogeneous and quadratic in the variables $i_1 \cdots i_l$, is known as a *quadratic form*, and $[R]$ in Eq. 152 is the matrix of its coefficients. No matter what real values (positive or negative) may be substituted for the variables $i_1 \cdots i_l$, this quadratic form must yield a positive value, for the power absorbed by a passive network cannot be negative. A quadratic form having this property is called *positive definite*. If the coefficient matrix $[R]$ arises from a given passive network, it will always yield a positive definite quadratic form; conversely, if an R matrix is specified and a corresponding passive network is to be found (synthesis problem), then a solution can exist only if $[R]$ is the matrix of a positive definite quadratic form. Later on, when we shall be concerned with this kind of problem, we will show how a given matrix $[R]$ may be tested to see whether it meets this condition so that one can tell beforehand whether or not a corresponding passive network exists. The power relation 154 is thus seen to be useful in other ways than merely that of affording a means for computing power.

Another useful result can readily be obtained from expression 154. Observing that a particular loop current i_k is a factor of the kth row and of the kth column, and is contained in no other terms of this expression, it follows that the value of P is unaffected if we replace the variable i_k by

$$i^*{}_k = i_k/a \tag{155}$$

and simultaneously multiply the kth row and the kth column in $[R]$ by the factor a. Stated in another way, we can say that, if the parameter matrix $[R]$ is changed through having its kth row and column multiplied by a factor a, and the loop current i_k is divided by this same factor, then the expression 154 for the total power remains unchanged. Reference to the relation 153 for the power reveals that these manipulations imply a simultaneous replacement of e_k by

$$e^*_k = ae_k \tag{156}$$

but that all other voltages and currents in the network remain unaltered.

If the kth loop contains no voltage source, then a change in the network parameters corresponding to the multiplication of the kth row and column of $[R]$ by a factor a leaves the power relations invariant and has no effect upon any of the voltages or currents except that the current in the kth loop is changed by the factor $1/a$ as expressed by Eq. 155.

The same results may also be seen directly from equilibrium Eqs. 151. Thus, suppose we multiply all terms in the kth equation by the

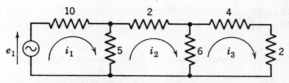

FIG. 44.   Example illustrating the transformations that leave power relations invariant (Eqs. 157 through 161).   Element values are in ohms.

factor a, then multiply all coefficients in the kth column by a, and replace i_k by i_k/a as in Eq. 155.   The last two operations cancel each other because they amount to multiplying all terms in the kth column first by a and then by $1/a$; while the multiplication of any equation by a factor has obviously no effect upon the solutions.   However, the kth row and column in R are multiplied by a, and only the voltage and current in the kth loop are affected as shown by Eqs. 155 and 156.   Since $e^*_k i^*_k = e_k i_k$, it follows that the power relationships have not been affected.

Now let us see how we can apply these results in specific situations. In Fig. 44 the circuit of Fig. 43 is redrawn indicating the mesh currents as variables (which, however, are evidently identical with the like numbered branch currents shown in Fig. 43).   By inspection one may write down the pertinent parameter matrix

$$[R] = \begin{bmatrix} 15 & -5 & 0 \\ -5 & 13 & -6 \\ 0 & -6 & 12 \end{bmatrix} \tag{157}$$

and the equilibrium equations

$$15i_1 - 5i_2 + 0i_3 = e_1$$
$$-5i_1 + 13i_2 - 6i_3 = 0 \tag{158}$$
$$0i_1 - 6i_2 + 12i_3 = 0$$

Their solution for $e_1 = 1$ volt is readily found to yield

$$i_1 = 2/25, \qquad i_2 = 1/25, \qquad i_3 = 1/50 \text{ ampere} \qquad (159)$$

Now suppose we multiply the second row and column of $[R]$ by the factor $3/2$ as indicated in the following

$$\begin{bmatrix} 15 & -5 & 0 \\ -5 & 13 & -6 \\ 0 & -6 & 12 \end{bmatrix}_{\substack{\leftarrow \, 3\!/\!2 \\ \uparrow \, 3\!/\!2}} = \begin{bmatrix} 15 & -\frac{15}{2} & 0 \\ -\frac{15}{2} & \frac{117}{4} & -9 \\ 0 & -9 & 12 \end{bmatrix} = [R'] \qquad 160)$$

To this matrix there corresponds the same circuit configuration as the one in Fig. 44 but with the element values shown in Fig. 45, as the

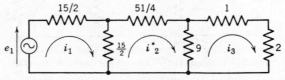

FIG. 45. Result of subjecting the circuit of Fig. 44 to an internal impedance level transformation expressed by the matrix Eq. 160. Element values are in ohms.

reader may readily verify by inspection. Solution of the corresponding equilibrium equations for $e_1 = 1$ volt is seen to give

$$i_1 = 2/25, \qquad i^*_2 = 2/75 = (2/3)i_2, \qquad i_3 = 1/50 \text{ ampere} \qquad (161)$$

showing that only i_2 is changed by a factor $2/3$. The driving-point and transfer ratios e_1/i_1 and e_1/i_3 are the same for the circuit of Fig. 45 as they are for the one shown in Fig. 44. The transfer ratio e_1/i^*_2 is $3/2$ times the ratio e_1/i_2.

If we were to shift the voltage source into mesh 2, with the value e_2 in the circuit of Fig. 44 and the value $e^*_2 = (3/2)e_2$ in the circuit of Fig. 45, then the ratios e^*_2/i_1 and e^*_2/i_3 would turn out to be $3/2$ times the ratios e_2/i_1 and e_2/i_3, respectively, while the ratio e^*_2/i^*_2 would be $(3/2)^2$ times the ratio e_2/i_2.

In short, the complete set of driving-point and transfer impedances are the same for the two circuits except that the driving-point impedance of mesh 2 is $(3/2)^2$ times as large in the circuit of Fig. 45, and any transfer impedance involving either the current or the voltage of mesh 2 (like e^*_2/i_1 or e_1/i^*_2) is $3/2$ times as large. The operation upon the parameter matrix as carried out in transformation 160 is, therefore, referred to as *raising the impedance level of mesh 2* by the factor $(3/2)^2$; it is spoken of as an *impedance-level transformation*. Its effect upon the circuit whose matrix $[R]$ is involved is readily seen, as in the above example. Its effect upon the voltage and current relations in the circuit can be predicted beforehand, and its effect upon the power relationships is nil.

As a further example, suppose we drop the impedance level of mesh 3 in the circuit of Fig. 44 by the factor $(2/3)^2$ as indicated in the following transformation of its resistance matrix

$$[R''] = \begin{bmatrix} 15 & -5 & 0 \\ -5 & 13 & -6 \\ 0 & -6 & 12 \end{bmatrix} \underset{\substack{\leftarrow \\ \uparrow 2/3}}{\overset{2/3}{\longrightarrow}} \begin{bmatrix} 15 & -5 & 0 \\ -5 & 13 & -4 \\ 0 & -4 & \frac{16}{3} \end{bmatrix} \qquad (162)$$

The resulting network is shown in Fig. 46. The corresponding equi-

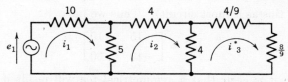

FIG. 46. Result of lowering the impedance level in mesh 3 of the circuit in Fig. 44 by the factor $(2/3)^2$ according to the matrix manipulation 162. Element values are in ohms.

librium equations written for $e_1 = 1$ volt yield the following solutions,

$$i_1 = 2/25, \qquad i_2 = 1/25, \qquad i{*}_3 = 3/100 = (3/2)i_3 \text{ ampere} \qquad (163)$$

as the reader can readily verify. The final resistor at the right of the circuit (which may be regarded as a load) is $(8/9) = (2/3)^2 \times 2$ ohms, consistent with the lowering of the impedance level at the output by the factor $(2/3)^2$. The voltage across this load is now $(2/3)$ times its former value; the power delivered to the load is unchanged.

As the reader may readily demonstrate for himself, one cannot change impedance levels by any desired factors without running the risk of obtaining corresponding networks involving some negative resistance values. Theoretically these are still passive networks, for they have the same power relationships as the original one, but they are not physically realizable in simple terms. Therefore, one should avoid using multiplying factors which lead to such results.

With reference to the tee and pi circuits discussed in the previous article, we can now recognize that a dissymmetrical tee or pi is equivalent to a symmetrical one with an impedance transformation applied to its input or output side. Stated in another way, we can say: Except for an impedance-level transformation, a dissymmetrical tee or pi circuit is no more general than a symmetrical one.†

† This statement is accurately true only for resistance circuits. The extent to which it is generally true will be seen in later discussions.

Consider, for example, the dissymmetrical tee of part (a) in Fig. 47. In writing its resistance matrix we can ignore the presence of the 40-ohm

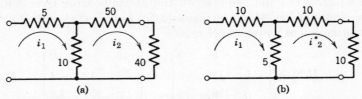

FIG. 47. The dissymmetrical tee (a) subjected to a transformation lowering its output impedance level by the factor 1/4 yields the symmetrical tee (b) with appropriately reduced load resistance. Element values are in ohms.

load (treat this as a short circuit). Thus we have

$$[R] = \begin{bmatrix} 15 & -10 \\ -10 & 60 \end{bmatrix} \tag{164}$$

from which it is clear that a symmetrical tee will result if we depress the impedance level at the output by the factor $60/15 = 4$, as is done in the transformation

$$[R^*] = \begin{bmatrix} 15 & -10 \\ -10 & 60 \end{bmatrix} \underset{\underset{\frac{1}{2}}{\uparrow\frac{1}{2}}}{\rightarrow} \begin{bmatrix} 15 & -5 \\ -5 & 15 \end{bmatrix} \tag{165}$$

yielding the circuit shown in part (b) of Fig. 47 in which the appropriate load resistance is $(1/4) \times 40 = 10$ ohms. For equal input voltages, $i^*_2 = 2i_2$; the voltage across the 10-ohm load is 1/2 the voltage across the 40-ohm load; the power delivered to the load is the same for both circuits.

It may incidentally be of interest to note that we can also make wye-delta or tee-pi transformations with this method. This is more easily done using the node method, and so in part (a) of Fig. 48 we have redrawn the tee of Fig. 47(a) indicating the element values in mhos, numbering the relevant nodes, and emphasizing the choice of datum through shading. The pertinent node-conductance matrix is

$$[G] = \begin{bmatrix} \frac{10}{50} & -\frac{10}{50} & 0 \\ -\frac{10}{50} & \frac{16}{50} & -\frac{1}{50} \\ 0 & -\frac{1}{50} & \frac{1}{50} \end{bmatrix} \tag{166}$$

If we multiply the second row and column by a factor which is the ratio of the sum of the nondiagonal elements to the diagonal element (the ratio of $\frac{10}{50} + \frac{1}{50}$ to $\frac{16}{50}$ or 11/16), then the resulting matrix has the property that its diagonal term equals the sum of the nondiagonal ones, as may be seen from the following:

$$[G^*] = \begin{bmatrix} \frac{10}{50} & -\frac{10}{50} & 0 \\ -\frac{10}{50} & \frac{16}{50} & -\frac{1}{50} \\ 0 & -\frac{1}{50} & \frac{1}{50} \end{bmatrix} \overset{\leftarrow}{{}_{1\frac{1}{10}}} = \begin{bmatrix} \frac{10}{50} & -\frac{110}{800} & 0 \\ -\frac{110}{800} & \frac{121}{800} & -\frac{11}{800} \\ 0 & -\frac{11}{800} & \frac{1}{50} \end{bmatrix} \quad (167)$$

$\uparrow 1\frac{1}{10}$

The corresponding network is that shown in part (b) of Fig. 48 (element values in mhos) in which the significant feature is that there is

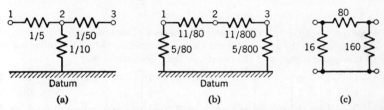

FIG. 48. A tee-pi (wye-delta) transformation effected through use of the impedance-level transformation technique. Element values in parts (a) and (b) are expressed in mhos; in part (c) they are expressed in ohms.

no branch connecting node 2 with the datum. Changing to resistance values in ohms and combining the series branches yields the pi circuit in part (c) of the same figure.

The delta-wye or pi-tee transformation is best done on a loop basis, as the reader may prove to himself as an exercise. This method of carrying out these transformations has no particular advantage but is of some collateral interest.

Later on we will see that these impedance-level transformations can equally well be applied to circuits involving inductance and capacitance as well as resistance elements, and their usefulness in providing a simple means for revising circuit-element values without affecting certain desired input or transfer relations will be found to give us an invaluable tool in circuit design or synthesis. In the immediately following chapters our objective is to acquaint the reader with the most important effects of inductive and capacitive elements upon circuit properties and circuit behavior.

PROBLEMS

1. Solve the following equations by the systematic elimination method:

$$x_1 + 2x_2 + 3x_3 = 14 \qquad 2x_1 - 4x_2 + 5x_3 + 6x_4 = 33$$

$$4x_1 + 5x_2 + 6x_3 = 32 \qquad -4x_1 + 10x_2 + 7x_3 - 8x_4 = 5$$

$$7x_1 + 8x_2 + 9x_3 = 50 \qquad 5x_1 + 7x_2 + 2x_3 - 10x_4 = -15$$

$$6x_4 - 8x_2 - 10x_3 + 12x_4 = 8$$

2. By systematic elimination, solve the following three equation sets:

$$14x_1 + 12x_2 + 3x_3 = 1, \quad 14x_1 + 12x_2 + 3x_3 = 0, \quad 14x_1 + 12x_2 + 3x_3 = 0$$

$$12x_1 + 11x_2 + 3x_3 = 0, \quad 12x_1 + 11x_2 + 3x_3 = 1, \quad 12x_1 + 11x_2 + 3x_3 = 0$$

$$3x_1 + 3x_2 + x_3 = 0, \quad 3x_1 + 3x_2 + x_3 = 0, \quad 3x_1 + 3x_2 + x_3 = 1$$

and then write down the expressions for the x's in the more general equations:

$$14x_1 + 12x_2 + 3x_3 = y_1$$

$$12x_1 + 11x_2 + 3x_3 = y_2$$

$$3x_1 + 3x_2 + x_3 = y_3$$

3. Solve the examples in Probs. 1 and 2 by means of determinants.

4. Through use of the systematic elimination technique, reduce the following matrices to triangular forms, and thus evaluate their determinants:

$$\begin{bmatrix} 2 & -1 & -1 & 0 \\ -1 & 1 & 0 & 1 \\ -1 & 0 & 1 & -1 \\ 0 & 1 & -1 & 2 \end{bmatrix} \quad \begin{bmatrix} 3 & -1 & -1 & 1 \\ -1 & 2 & 1 & 1 \\ -1 & 1 & 2 & -1 \\ 1 & 1 & -1 & 3 \end{bmatrix} \quad \begin{bmatrix} 3 & -1 & -1 & 1 \\ -1 & 1 & 0 & 1 \\ -1 & 0 & 1 & -1 \\ 1 & 1 & -1 & 3 \end{bmatrix}$$

5. For the following ladder networks compute the voltage and current distributions with $e_s = 1$ volt. What do the answers become if the source is a current of 1 ampere?

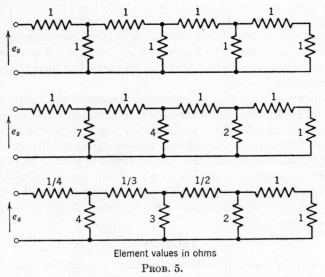

Element values in ohms

PROB. 5.

6. Show that the unbalanced ladder in sketch (b) is equivalent to the balanced ladder in sketch (a) so far as the determination of mesh currents is concerned (since both ladders have the same resistance parameter matrix on a mesh basis). By first obtaining the mesh currents in the unbalanced ladder pertinent to having 1 volt at

the output, find the potentials of all the nodes in the balanced ladder in sketch (a) if node n is at zero potential and node m has a potential of 100 volts.

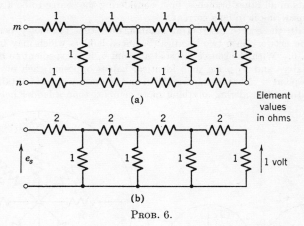

(a)

Element values in ohms

(b)

PROB. 6.

7. Assume $e_{10} = 1$ volt; $e_9 = x$ volts. Then, starting at the right-hand end, find successively the currents in all branches and the voltages at all nodes except node 1 as a function of x. From the equations

$$e_1 = e_3 + i_{13} = e_2 + i_{12}$$

determine x and e_1; and then find all the voltages and currents explicitly, including

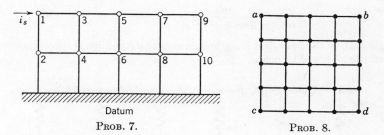

All branches are 1-ohm resistances

Datum

PROB. 7.

PROB. 8.

the source current i_s. Now take $i_s = 1$ ampere, and revise all voltages and currents accordingly.

8. In the uniform rectangular grid shown here, each branch is a resistance of 1 ohm. Find the currents in all branches and the potentials of all nodes as well as the net input resistance when one ampere is applied at the following terminal pairs: (a) nodes a and c, (b) a joined to b and c joined to d, (c) a joined to d and b joined to c, (d) nodes a and d.

Hint: Apply symmetry conditions and the results of Prob. 7 to get (a); then construct the other situations as superpositions of appropriate ones of type (a).

9. In the graphs shown in the following sketches, each branch is a resistance of 1 ohm.   If a source is inserted at one of the points a, or b, determine the voltages and currents in all other branches, first, considering the source to be a voltage, and, second, considering it to be a current.

Hint: With the source inserted at point a, note that symmetry permits one to separate the network into two identical balanced ladders which may be dealt with as in Prob. 6.   With the source inserted at point b, it is expedient to divide it into identical halves and to place such identical halves opposing each other (equal to nothing) at point c.   Now use superposition and symmetry so as to obtain the desired solution without considering anything more complex than a ladder network.

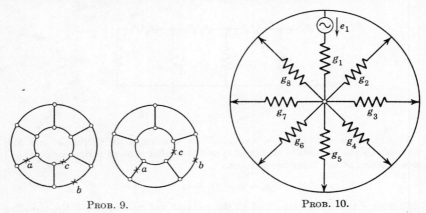

PROB. 9.   PROB. 10.

10. With reference to the circuit shown here (in which the circular conductor is a common node), show first by independent reasoning and then by use of the star-mesh transformation that

$$\frac{i_k}{e_1} = \frac{g_1 g_k}{g_1 + g_2 + \cdots + g_k} \quad \text{for} \quad k = 2, \cdots, 8$$

Hint: Draw the equivalent mesh, and, in view of the position of the voltage source, eliminate all trivial branches.

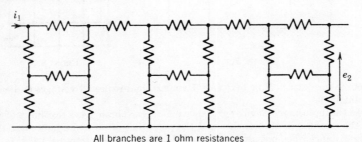

All branches are 1 ohm resistances

PROB. 11.

11. Through appropriate star-delta transformations, reduce the circuit shown in the above sketch to an unbalanced ladder, and solve for the ratio e_2/i_1.

12. In the circuit shown below in which all branches are 1-ohm resistances, solve for the ratio e_5/i_1:

(a) By making wye-delta transformations appropriate to the suppression of nodes 2, 3, 4, thus leaving the resulting circuit in the form of a π.

(b) By writing down the conductance matrix on a node-to-datum basis and systematically carrying out operations analogous to those expressed by Eqs. 49 corresponding to the successive elimination of nodes 2, 3, 4. Thus begin by adding to

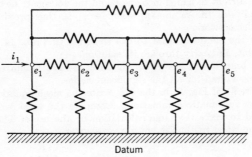

Datum

PROB. 12.

the elements of rows 1, 3, 4, 5 the respective α-multiplied elements of the second row so as to reduce to zero all elements in column 2 except the one on the principal diagonal. At this point node 2 is decoupled from the rest of the network and row 2 may be dropped from the matrix as may also the remaining column 2 which consists entirely of zeros. We now have a symmetrical four-by-four matrix whose columns relate respectively to the node potentials e_1, e_3, e_4, e_5. Treat this matrix in precisely the same manner as just described for the original one, and obtain a symmetrical three-by-three matrix whose columns relate respectively to the node potentials e_1, e_4, e_5. Finally obtain a two-by-two matrix appropriate to the pi network found by procedure (a) above and check.

13. With reference to the circuit of Prob. 8, use Thévenin's theorem to compute the current through a 5-ohm resistor placed across nodes b–c when 1 volt is applied at a–d. Again for the resistor placed across b–d with the voltage applied across a–c.

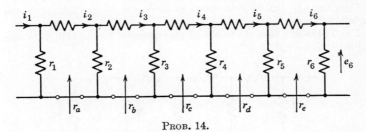

PROB. 14.

14. In the circuit shown here, the quantities denoted by r_a, r_b, $\cdots$ are the net resistances that one would obtain at terminal pairs created by cutting (as with a pair of pliers) into the respective meshes in succession, each time leaving the previous

cuts open. Through reasoning in terms of Thévenin's theorem, show that

$$\frac{i_2}{i_1} = \frac{r_1}{r_a}, \quad \frac{i_3}{i_2} = \frac{r_2}{r_b}, \quad \frac{i_4}{i_3} = \frac{r_3}{r_c}, \quad \text{etc.}$$

and hence that

$$\frac{e_6}{i_1} = \frac{r_1}{r_a} \times \frac{r_2}{r_b} \times \frac{r_3}{r_c} \times \frac{r_4}{r_d} \times \frac{r_5}{r_e} \times r_6$$

Now assume the current to be fed into end 6 and the voltage to be observed at end 1; show that one obtains the same expression for e_1/i_6, thus proving the reciprocity theorem for ladder networks.

15. Construct the complete dual to the situation in Prob. 14. Write the dual problem statement, and carry through its solution.

16. If all the branches in the circuit of Prob. 14 are 1-ohm resistances, obtain values for $r_a, \cdots, r_e$ and for all the significant ratios.

17. For the circuit of Fig. 16 in the text write the mesh equations, and solve for the current i_k by systematic elimination. Compare the total computational effort with that needed to make the same calculation by the use of Thévenin's theorem, and note that the latter method is not always shorter.

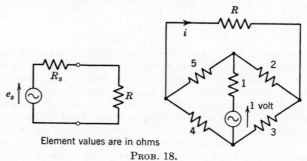

Element values are in ohms

Prob. 18.

18. For the circuit shown above, compute the Thévenin equivalent voltage e_s and the resistance R_s such that the left-hand circuit is an equivalent one so far as the calculation of the current i through the resistance R is concerned. In the computation of R_s, a wye-delta transformation is convenient.

19. Construct the dual of Prob. 18 as an exercise in Norton's theorem, and carry through its solution.

20. Use Thévenin's theorem to obtain an expression for the ratio e_2/i_1 as a function of the resistance R.

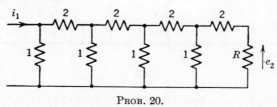

Prob. 20.

21. In the circuit of the previous problem, apply the current i_1 at the right-hand end, and observe the voltage e_2 at the left-hand end. Show that the same expression for e_2/i_1 results, and thus verify the reciprocity theorem in this instance.

22. For the ladder network shown, compute the open-circuit driving-point and transfer impedances by the method discussed for ladder networks, and thus obtain

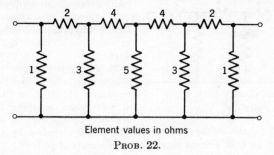

Element values in ohms

PROB. 22.

the equivalent symmetrical tee circuit. Alternately obtain the same result through wye-delta transformations. Contrast the total computations involved in the two methods.

23. Consider the ladder network of the preceding problem with a 2-ohm resistance bridged across the top. Find the equivalent tee, pi, and symmetrical-lattice networks.

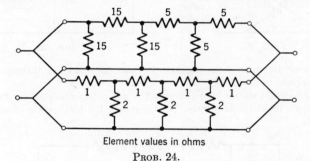

Element values in ohms

PROB. 24.

24. Convert the two terminal pair shown into (a) an equivalent tee, (b) an equivalent pi, (c) an equivalent symmetrical lattice. Compute values of the open-circuit driving-point and transfer impedances, the short-circuit driving-point and transfer admittances, and the general circuit parameters.

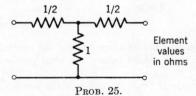

Element values in ohms

PROB. 25.

25. Compute the general circuit parameters of two cascaded two terminal-pair networks whose individual parameters are A_1, B_1, C_1, D_1 and A_2, B_2, C_2, D_2. Write down the particular form of this result when (a) the two networks are identical, (b) the two networks are identical and individually symmetrical. Using the latter result, find the over-all parameters for a cascade of ten identical tee sections as shown above.

26. Show that the physically dissymmetrical network given here is nevertheless electrically symmetrical, and find a physically symmetrical equivalent.

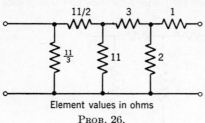

Element values in ohms

PROB. 26.

27. Develop the symmetrical lattice shown into a uniform unbalanced ladder in which each branch is a 1-ohm resistance.

28. A current source and a voltage source in parallel furnish power to a load resistance R. If $i_s = 10$ amperes and $e_s = 50$ volts, compute (a) the power supplied by the current source, (b) the power supplied by the voltage source, (c) the power absorbed by the load. For what value of R do both sources supply equal amounts of power?

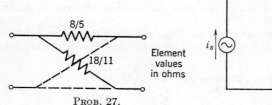

Element values in ohms

PROB. 27.

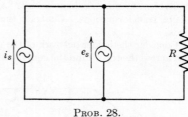

PROB. 28.

29. Construct the dual of the situation in Prob. 28, and carry through the corresponding analysis.

30. For the circuit shown here compute the net power absorbed by first finding the net currents in all the branches. Next compute the total power absorbed separately for the voltage sources acting alone and for the current sources acting alone.

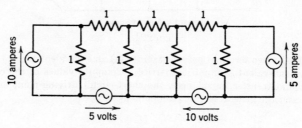

PROB. 30.

rately for the voltage sources acting alone and for the current sources acting alone. Note that the sum of these values equals the total power for all sources acting simultaneously!

31. Continuing the study of Prob. 30, compute the power supplied by the current sources, with and without the voltage sources simultaneously acting, and note the difference in the supplied power due to an insertion of the voltage sources.

Analogously, compute the power supplied by the voltage sources, with and without the current sources simultaneously acting, and note the difference in the supplied power due to an application of the current sources. What can you conclude as to the superposition of power due to voltage and current sources?

32. Consider the uniform ladder network of Prob. 30 with the voltage sources and the right-hand current source removed. Compute the ratio of voltage at the right to current at the left, and the value of current in the central mesh.

Now transform to a ladder for which the impedance level of the central mesh is twice as large. Again compute the transfer voltage-to-current ratio and the current in the central mesh. Compute the power input in both cases. What conclusions do you draw from these results?

33. Through symmetry considerations show that the schematic representation of three interconnected balanced transmission lines with associated sources and loads

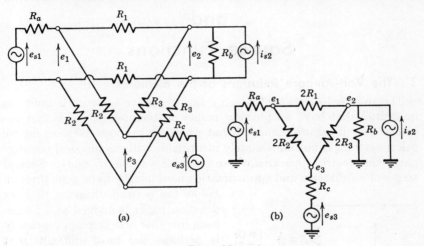

(a)   (b)

PROB. 33.

shown in sketch (a) may be replaced by the so-called single-line diagram in sketch (b) so far as the determination of the voltages e_1, e_2, e_3, and the currents in the resistances R_a, R_b, R_c are concerned. The common datum (ground) is indicated by shading.

34. The sketch below shows a single-line diagram of the sort discussed in the previous problem. All resistances are 1 ohm, and the voltages are fixed by sources at all but one node. Through appropriate source manipulations determine directly a single equation yielding the node potential e. Then find all branch and source currents, and compute the power supplied by each source.

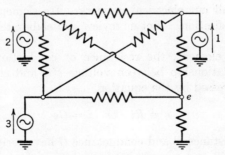

PROB. 34.

Circuit Elements
and
Source Functions

1 The Volt-Ampere Relations of the Elements

The so-called *elements* of which a linear passive network is built are quantities that have no physical reality in themselves. This fact becomes clear if we are reminded that what, for purposes of analysis, we call a network is not immediately identifiable with its physical counterpart—the electric apparatus whose behavior we wish to study. Several stages of idealization and approximation need usually to be gone through before the network diagram that we draw on paper is arrived at. To accomplish this first step appropriately is perhaps the most difficult part of our entire problem and one that requires not only a sizable knowledge of network theory but skill and judgment as well. Suffice it to say at this point that it is almost always possible to find some schematic network configuration which, for purposes of analysis, represents the behavior of the physical apparatus with acceptable tolerances. This schematic representation of the actual apparatus we call our electrical network. Its elements exist only by mathematical definition. Let us review and elaborate upon these definitions.

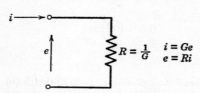

FIG. 1.   Resistance element R in ohms or conductance G in mhos.

The simplest element, the resistance or conductance, is shown in Fig. 1. The relationship between voltage $e(t)$ and current $i(t)$ at its terminals is expressed by the equation

$$e = Ri \quad \text{or} \quad i = Ge \tag{1}$$

in which the resistance R and conductance G have reciprocal values.

The voltage $e(t)$ and current $i(t)$ are arbitrary functions of the time, except that they are related to each other by Eq. 1. Since R or G is a constant, these functions are simply proportional to each other; that is to say, they are represented by curves of exactly the same shape when plotted graphically. They may both be accommodated by the same plotted curve by assigning to its ordinates appropriate scale factors as determined by R or G. Thus, if $e(t)$ is a constant, $i(t)$ is a constant; if $e(t)$ is a sinusoid, $i(t)$ is a sinusoid; if $e(t)$ is a funny-looking wave, then $i(t)$ is the same funny-looking wave. Moreover, it makes no difference whether $e(t)$ is an applied source and $i(t)$ the resulting current, or the other way about. The linkage between $e(t)$ and $i(t)$ is rigidly fixed by the relation 1.

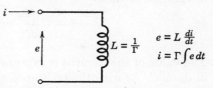

Fig. 2.   Inductance element L in henrys or reciprocal inductance Γ in reciprocal henrys.

The inductance element together with its volt-ampere characteristic is shown in Fig. 2. Here

$$e = L\frac{di}{dt} \quad \text{or} \quad i = \Gamma \int e\,dt \tag{2}$$

It is unfortunate that there exists no established symbol or name for reciprocal inductance.*

Here again $e(t)$ and $i(t)$ are arbitrary time functions except for the stated relation between them. This relation is not one of simple proportion as it is for the resistive element, but involves differentiation or integration. Thus, if $e(t)$ is a rectangular pulse, as shown in Fig. 3, then $i(t)$ is constant before and after this pulse, and linearly increasing during the pulse interval as is also shown in the same figure. Except for the proportionality constant L or L^{-1} respectively, the function $e(t)$ shown here is the derivative of $i(t)$, and, conversely, $i(t)$ is the integral of $e(t)$, as called for by relation 2. The shapes of these curves could be anything else, except that $e(t)$ would always have to be proportional to the derivative of $i(t)$ with L equal to the constant

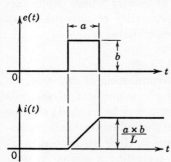

Fig. 3.   Voltage and current functions at the terminals of an inductance.

* The symbol used in this text is an upside down L as in Eq. 2.

of proportionality; and this relationship remains the same whether $e(t)$ is an excitation and $i(t)$ the response or vice versa.

The third element—the capacitance—is shown in Fig. 4. Here also, the volt-ampere characteristic is expressed through differentiation or integration; that is,

$$i = C \frac{de}{dt} \quad \text{or} \quad e = S \int i\, dt \tag{3}$$

The value of the element is expressed either in terms of C in farads or S in darafs. As with the resistance element, established names and symbols are available for both the capacitance C and its reciprocal, the elastance S.

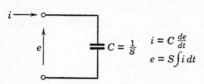

Fig. 4.   Capacitance element C in farads or elastance S in darafs.

Detailed comments in the case of the volt-ampere characteristic determined by the capacitance element are entirely similar to those just given for the inductance element, with the essential difference that the identities of current and voltage are interchanged.

Careful attention to the relations expressed in Eqs. 1, 2, and 3 reveals an interesting fact, namely, that as a group they remain unaltered if one interchanges e with i, R with G, and L with C (or L^{-1} with S). This invariant property will be made use of extensively later on. It forms the basis for the so-called *principle of duality* which capitalizes on the fact that more general invariant properties of networks may readily be derived from the simple ones revealed here.

2   Voltage and Current Sources

Linear passive networks are built by interconnecting in any way the basic elements R, L, and C. Before we have a problem of analysis before us, however, the network must in some way be excited; that is, a source of some sort must be present. Since the inductance and capacitance elements are capable of storing energy in their associated magnetic or electric fields, an effective way of regarding a source in connection with our present studies is to consider it as a device that inserts electromagnetic energy into one or more of the storage elements L or C (the element R, not being capable of energy storage, plays no part in this phase of the discussion). As in the consideration of resistive networks, the device serving to supply energy is regarded as being one of two possible types—a voltage source or a current source. These are illustrated schematically in Fig. 5. Both are fictitious since they exist only by definition; but as in the case of the network elements they suffice, together with appropriate elements, for the representation of actual physical sources.

The voltage source produces at its terminals the voltage $e_s(t)$ which may be whatever function it is appropriate to consider in view of the problem in hand. Since the terminal voltage is $e_s(t)$ by *definition*, it cannot be altered through any circumstances of environment in which the source may find itself. That is to say, the terminal voltage remains precisely $e_s(t)$ regardless of what may be placed across these terminals

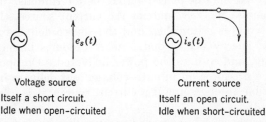

Voltage source
Itself a short circuit.
Idle when open-circuited

Current source
Itself an open circuit.
Idle when short-circuited

FIG. 5. Voltage and current sources or constraints.

If a conductance G is placed across the terminals of the voltage source, then a current equal to Ge_s amperes is established, and the source delivers $Ge_s{}^2$ watts or $Ge_s{}^2$ joules of energy per second. As G becomes larger, the current becomes larger and so does the power delivered. If a short circuit is placed across the source, then an infinite current exists and infinite power is delivered, but the terminal voltage remains unshakably $e_s(t)$. It is not sensible to short-circuit a voltage source; it is idle when open-circuited. Nevertheless, if we imagine the terminals short-circuited and an infinite current existing in the closed loop formed by the source in series with the short-circuiting path, then we realize that the source itself must be a short circuit, otherwise the finite voltage $e_s(t)$ acting in the closed loop could not be producing infinite current. This fact is very significant: namely, that the voltage source itself is a short circuit. Its presence in a network inserts a voltage $e_s(t)$ and nothing else. If a voltage source is bridged across two points in a network, then, except for the voltage $e_s(t)$ existing between them, these points are short-circuited.

Another way of looking at the voltage source is to regard it as a peculiar kind of circuit element for which the volt-ampere relation is such that the voltage has the same value regardless of the current, namely the value $e_s(t)$. If we specify that $e_s(t) = 0$, then the voltage source is identical with a short circuit, for a short circuit is a device whose terminal voltage is zero regardless of the current. Like a short circuit, the voltage source is a constraint; but it is more general in that it constrains the voltage at its terminals to any desired value. In this sense one may say that a voltage source is a generalized short circuit.

In precisely an analogous manner the current source of Fig. 5 is regarded as a device that provides a stated current $i_s(t)$ at its terminals. Since the terminal current is $i_s(t)$ *by definition*, it cannot be altered through any circumstances of environment in which the source may find itself. That is to say, the terminal current remains precisely $i_s(t)$, regardless of what may be placed across these terminals. If a resistance R is placed across the terminals of the current source, then a voltage equal to Ri_s volts is established and the source delivers Ri_s^2 watts or Ri_s^2 joules of energy per second. As R becomes larger, the voltage becomes larger, and so does the power delivered. On open circuit, the current source produces an infinite voltage and delivers infinite power. It is not sensible to open-circuit a current source; it is idle when short-circuited.

A current source may be regarded as a peculiar kind of circuit element whose volt-ampere relation specifies that the current is independent of the voltage. For the value $i_s(t) = 0$, the current source is identical with an open circuit, for an open circuit is a device that forces the current to be zero regardless of the terminal voltage. Like an open circuit, the current source is a constraint; but it is more general in that it constrains the current at its terminals to any desired value. In this sense one may say that a current source is a generalized open circuit.

A current source may be used to deliver charge to a capacitance, this situation being crudely similar to the process of filling a tumbler with water from a pitcher, the latter playing the role of "source" and the tumbler resembling the capacitance. The water is regarded as analogous to charge, and its velocity is the analogue of current. If the velocity is high, the tumbler fills rapidly. Just so, for a large source current $i_s(t)$ the voltage across the capacitance to which it connects mounts rapidly.

To fill a tumbler with water in the normal manner requires a finite time, but it is conceivable that we could have the water packaged beforehand and toss it into the tumbler—"kerplunk." In this case the tumbler is filled instantly—or substantially so. Analogously we might conceive of a current source delivering a packaged amount of charge instantaneously to a capacitance and raising its voltage from nothing to something in zero time. Such a kind of source function is called an *impulse*. It plays a very useful role in our later work, and it is worth while looking into its properties more carefully.

A kind of current source function that delivers a finite amount of total charge is shown in part (a) of Fig. 6. The charge $q(t)$, which is the time integral of the current, is shown in part (b) of the same figure. The total time of delivery is δ seconds. The source current is constant at the value I_s during this interval, and zero otherwise. The charge $q(t)$ rises linearly during the interval δ, reaching the final value $I_s \times \delta$, this being the area under the current function. The latter is referred to as a rectangular pulse. Its integral $q(t)$ is called a *linear ramp*. The pulse is the derivative of the ramp, and the latter is the integral of the pulse. Graphically, these mutual relations between the two functions are clearly visualizable.

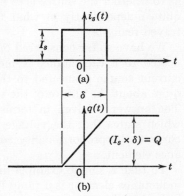

What has been said about the pair of functions shown in Fig. 6 is true for any nonzero value of δ, however small. Suppose we stipulate that $I_s \times \delta$, the area under the current pulse, or the net charge delivered, is fixed at say Q coulombs. Then, if δ is assumed to be very small, the current pulse is tall and

FIG. 6. A current source function $i_s(t)$ and its associated charge $q(t)$.

slim, and the charge rises from zero to the value Q at a rapid rate. As δ becomes smaller and smaller, the current pulse approaches closer and closer to an impulse. In the limit $\delta \to 0$ the source current is zero everywhere except at $t = 0$ where it is infinite; nevertheless in this limiting form the current pulse (which is then called an impulse) is still regarded as enclosing the same area Q. The linear ramp function $q(t)$ is in the limit referred to as a *step function*.

If the enclosed area Q is unity, the limiting current function is called a *unit* impulse and the limiting charge function a *unit* step. Otherwise these are referred to respectively as an impulse *of value Q* and a step *of value Q*.

It is of utmost significance to note that $i_s(t)$ remains the derivative of $q(t)$, and $q(t)$ the integral of $i_s(t)$ at any stage in the limiting process indicated by $\delta \to 0$, and that one is permitted to apply this interpretation regarding the mutual relationship between $i_s(t)$ and $q(t)$ *even in the limit*. Thus the derivative of a step function of value Q is an impulse of value Q; and the integral of an impulse of value Q is a step function of value Q. One has thus gained a useful and mathematically usable interpretation for the derivative of a function at a point of discontinuity.

Although the basic thoughts involved in the concepts of "pulse function," "ramp function, "impulse," and "step" have been presented in terms of a current source, they may equally well be applied to a voltage source. Thus we may at times find it appropriate to consider a voltage source $e_s(t)$ to be a pulse, or a ramp, or an impulse, or a step. As the following discussion shows, however, one usually has a choice as to whether the source is to be considered as a voltage or as a current, quite independently of what the actual physical situation to be portrayed really is.*

We have so far considered only the situation of a current source connected to a capacitance element. Suppose, instead, we consider the current source connected to the inductance element of Fig. 2, and inquire about the nature of the voltage developed across this inductance. The answer is given in terms of the pertinent volt-ampere relation, which states that the voltage is proportional to the derivative of the current, the proportionality constant being the value L of the inductance element.

To take a simple example first, suppose the current $i_s(t)$ feeding the inductance element is a ramp function like $q(t)$ in Fig. 6. It is clear at once that the voltage $e(t)$ developed across the inductance has the form of the rectangular pulse in part (a) of Fig. 6. If the ramp $i_s(t)$ has a final value I_s and a rise time δ, then the voltage pulse $e(t)$ has a height LI_s/δ and a duration δ. These matters are clear by inspection of the simple geometry involved and the basic notion that the derivative of a graphical function is its slope. The slope of the linear ramp is a nonzero constant during the rise interval, and zero otherwise. Note that the area under the rectangular pulse $e(t)$ is (height) $\times$ (duration) $= (LI_s/\delta) \times \delta = LI_s$, a value independent of δ. Therefore, if we now consider the limiting process $\delta \to 0$, the current function $i_s(t)$ approaches a step of the value I_s and $e(t)$ approaches an impulse of the value LI_s.

In arriving at this result we supposed that the current is the applied source or "cause," and the voltage is the network response or "effect." Mathematically the volt-ampere relationship determined by the inductance element is true regardless of which quantity, e or i, is the "cause" and which is the "effect." We are permitted to conclude, therefore, that a source-voltage impulse applied to an inductance element produces a current step-function response. In the above considerations the voltage impulse has the value LI_s and the associated current step

* The detailed mechanism whereby this flexibility in viewpoint is achieved, is that discussed for resistive circuits in Art. 5 of Ch. 3, and will be given in more general form in Art. 3 of Ch. 5.

has the value I_s. If both of these values are multiplied by the same constant, the relationship between voltage and current or cause and effect is unchanged. Such an operation is always permitted in a linear system. Therefore we can state that, if a unit-voltage impulse (considered as a source) is applied to an inductance L, the response is a step-function current of the value $1/L$ amperes.

We now have two interesting results that we wish to compare. A unit current impulse applied to a capacitance, instantaneously places a charge of 1 coulomb in that capacitance; a unit voltage impulse applied to an inductance instantaneously creates a finite current in that inductance. The parallelism between these two statements may be made more complete through the following physical considerations. If the inductance is regarded as a coil, then the voltage at its terminals is appropriately thought of as due to a rate of change of flux linkages; that is, $e(t) = n\, d\phi/dt$, n being the number of turns in the coil and ϕ the flux linking it. Since by definition $L = n\phi/i$, we note that a current of the value $1/L$ corresponds to a flux linkage $n\phi$ of unity. The statement in the second sentence of this paragraph may now be made more precise: A unit current impulse applied to a capacitance instantaneously places unit charge (1 coulomb) in that capacitance; a unit voltage impulse applied to an inductance instantaneously places unit flux linkage (1 weber-turn) in that inductance.

These two statements, one about a current impulse and the other about a voltage impulse, are identical except for an interchange of quantities in the pairs: e and i, C and L, charge and flux linkage. Or we may say that only one statement is made, and that this one remains true upon interchange of the dual quantities in the pairs mentioned. Here again we have an example of the principle of duality which we shall elaborate further as our discussions continue.

The sudden introduction of electric charge into a capacitance represents the sudden addition of a finite amount of energy to the system of which that capacitance is a part. Q coulombs in C farads represents an energy of $Q^2/2C$ joules, which may alternatively be written $CE_c^2/2$ if $E_c = Q/C$ denotes the voltage produced in the capacitance by the charge Q. Similarly, the sudden introduction of flux linkage into an inductance represents the addition of energy to the network of which that inductance is a part. $n\phi$ weber-turns in L henrys represents an energy of $(n\phi)^2/2L$ joules, which may alternatively be written $LI_L^2/2$ if $I_L = n\phi/L$ denotes the current produced in the inductance by the flux linkage $n\phi$.

A remark somewhat apart from the present topic but nevertheless appropriate at this point is to the effect that some readers may not like the statement about flux linkage producing current. They may feel that it is quite the other way about, that current produces flux linkage. While it is true that teachers of electricity and magnetism have consistently presented the situation in this way for as long as the subject has been taught, there is actually more reason based upon physical interpretation (if "physical" interpretation of such purely mathematical fictions as electric and magnetic fields makes any sense at all) to adhere to the view that the electromagnetic field produces voltage and current rather than that the reverse is true. For purposes of analysis it does not matter one jot how we interpret the mathematical relationships. It is best to take a very flexible view of such things and be ready to accept either interpretation, whichever is consistent with the tenor of reasoning at the moment.

To summarize the statements about current or voltage impulses and the energy they impart to network elements we may say: A unit current impulse applied to a capacitance of C farads establishes instantly a charge of 1 coulomb and inserts $1/2C$ joules of energy; a unit voltage impulse applied to an inductance of L henrys establishes instantly a flux linkage of 1 weber-turn (hence a current of $1/L$ amperes) and inserts $1/2L$ joules of energy.

3 The Family of Singularity Functions; Some Physical Interpretations

The impulse and step functions introduced in the previous article are found to be practically useful because many actual excitation functions can be represented in terms of them. In this regard, the step function is probably the most widely known of the two, for it has been discussed and employed in the literature on circuit theory for many years, having been introduced through the writings of Oliver Heaviside during the latter part of the nineteenth century.

In order to appreciate the usefulness of such a concept as the step function, consider the commonly occurring situation pictured in part (a) of Fig. 7 where some passive network (shown by the box) is assumed to be connected to a battery with the constant value of E volts through the switch S. The problem usually is to study the network response that takes place following closure of the switch, with the assumption that rest conditions obtain before this time.

If the principal interest is in the network response long after the instant of switch closure, then the excitation function is regarded as a constant voltage having the value E. However, if the interest lies chiefly in the behavior of the network immediately following the switch closure, then it is obviously not appropriate to regard the excitation as a constant, for it is the *discontinuity* in this function occurring at the switching instant that is its outstanding characteristic. That is to say, it is the sudden *change* in the excitation from the zero value prior to the switching instant to its nonzero constant value afterward that characterizes the nature of the network response near this time instant.

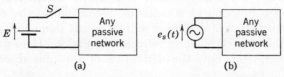

(a)   (b)

FIG. 7. Application of a constant voltage E through closure of switch S at the instant $t = t_0$ may alternately be represented without reference to a switching operation by definition of $e_s(t)$ as the step function shown in Fig. 8.

This view of the situation, which places the discontinuous nature of the excitation in evidence, is enhanced through redrawing the physical situation as shown in part (b) of Fig. 7 where the network is regarded as excited by some voltage source function $e_s(t)$, and describing this function graphically as shown in Fig. 8 where the *jump* in $e_s(t)$ occurring at $t = t_0$ is its principal feature.

The reason it is necessary to describe this $e_s(t)$ by showing a picture of it is that one does not have an analytic way of indicating such a function because functions that jump are not analytic. Heaviside overcame this difficulty by inventing a symbol that represents the step function by definition. Normalizing the value E at 1 volt and the time of occurrence at $t_0 = 0$ seconds (as can usually be done with-

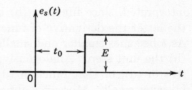

FIG. 8. A voltage step function of value E occurring at $t = t_0$.

out inconvenience), he called the function the *unit step*, and indicated it analytically by the symbol $1(t)$.

At the time Heaviside proposed these ideas, mathematicians were reluctant to accept them because functions possessing discontinuities were considered improper for respectable mathematicians to associate with. A discontinuity was regarded as a blemish or even worse—a sort of mark of degenerateness that absolutely barred its possessor from association with the society of genteel functions whose behavior made them acceptable to mathematicians. The game of mathematics was played according to a very strict code in those days.

Gradually, however, this ultraconservative attitude has worn off, with marked advantage to all who are primarily interested in the usefulness of mathematical tools and concepts, and with no loss in the rigor through which such use is justified. Thus we not only accept today such functions as the unit step, but we have gone farther in that a simple, rigorous, and usable interpretation is given to the derivative of this function—the unit impulse. Once this essential hurdle has been passed, namely, the establishment of a simple interpretation for the derivative of a function at a point of discontinuity, the way is open for the interpretation of all higher derivatives at this point.

This statement is clarified by reference to Fig. 9. Here parts (a) and (b) show once more how the derivative of the unit discontinuity is

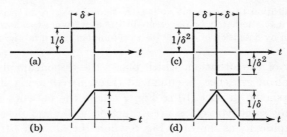

FIG. 9. Functions (a) and (d) both approach the unit impulse as $\delta \to 0$, while (b) and (c) represent respectively the integral and the derivative of this function.

interpreted, since function (b) is clearly the integral of function (a) or the latter the derivative of function (b) for any finite δ, however small. As δ becomes smaller and smaller, (a) approaches the unit impulse and (b) the unit step. Analogously, we see that function (c) is the derivative of (d), or that function (d) is the integral of (c) for any finite δ, however small. Moreover, functions (a) and (d) both enclose unit area and in character approach each other as δ becomes small. Thus, with $\delta \to 0$, function (b) approaches the unit step, functions (a) and (d) approach the unit impulse, and function (c) approaches what can be interpreted as the derivative of the unit impulse. Since, for very small δ, function (c) consists of two oppositely directed very tall spikes that are extremely close together, the function in the limit is called a unit *doublet*. It is similar in nature to a *couple* used in mechanics to indicate the application of a torque at some point.

Essentially the technique used to circumvent the difficulty imposed by the presence of a discontinuity is to replace it by a gradual rise of very short duration. Theoretically we then regard the rise interval as becoming infinitely short. So long as the rise interval is not actually zero, there can be no question as to the rigor or appropriateness of these interpretive methods; and whether or not they are still rigorous in the limit $\delta = 0$ does not even matter to us, for practically speaking we can always be content with a sufficiently small *nonzero* δ, since in nature there is no such thing as an absolutely abrupt change, and the engineer deals only with things that occur in nature.

It should be clear that one can similarly interpret the derivative of the unit doublet (called a unit triplet), and that one can theoretically continue to differentiate each function successively obtained.

The successive differentiation can be undone through successive integration. Thus, as we have seen, the integral of the unit impulse is the unit step; its integral is the unit ramp which is simply a linear rise with unit slope. Another integration yields a parabolic rise, etc.

(a)   (b)

FIG. 10. The charge and subsequent discharge of a capacitance C into a network may more simply be represented through assuming the excitation to be a current impulse.

We thus have an infinite family of functions that are related one to the other through differentiation or integration. This family is spoken of as the *singularity functions* since, in the light of conservative mathematics, their behavior is rather singular. Any one of these functions is denoted by the symbol $u_n(t)$ in which the subscript n is referred to as the *order* of the singularity function, and successive functions are related as indicated by

$$u_{n+1}(t) = du_n/dt \tag{4}$$

The unit impulse is chosen as the central function of this family and designated as $u_0(t)$, or as the singularity function of zero order. The unit step becomes $u_{-1}(t)$, the unit ramp $u_{-2}(t)$, the unit doublet $u_1(t)$, etc. Thus $u_{-1}(t)$ supersedes the old Heaviside notation $1(t)$.

In all of these functions the instant of occurrence is tacitly assumed to be $t = 0$. A function occurring at $t = t_0$ is written $u_n(t - t_0)$.

Usefulness of the singularity functions as typical kinds of excitation or source functions is partially recognized by the preceding discussion showing that we can simulate actual physical situations through the appropriate choice of singularity functions as applied voltages or currents. This theme we wish further to illustrate. Thus we might encounter the situation pictured in Fig. 10(a). Here the capacitance C may be charged by the battery voltage E by closing switch S_1 for an appropriate interval and opening it again. If now switch S_2 is closed, the capacitance is discharged into the passive network inside the box. This situation may be simulated as shown in part (b) of Fig. 10 where the circuit arrangement involves no switches, and the capacitance C is bridged by a current source equal to an impulse of value EC. At $t = 0$, when this impulse occurs, a charge of EC coulombs is suddenly injected into the capacitance, after which the discharge conditions are precisely the same as in the circuit arrangement of part (a) following closure of S_2.

Not only does one save drawing switches and describing their sequence of opening and closing, but also additional advantages having to do

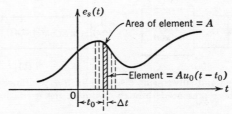

FIG. 11. An arbitrary time function may be regarded as a sum of rectangular elements which become impulses as their common width Δt is chosen to be sufficiently small.

with the method of obtaining the discharge phenomenon accrue from replacing the actual situation in Fig. 10(a) by the fictitious one in part (b) of this figure. This latter feature is discussed in the next chapter.

It might be thought that the singularity functions are very special in form and that only a restricted class of actual problems can be treated by their use. On the contrary, one readily appreciates that an arbitrary function can be expressed in terms of appropriately selected singularity functions. Thus the impulse is essentially a narrow rectangular pulse, especially if we have not bothered to let δ in the sketches of Fig. 9 become zero. As Fig. 11 illustrates, it is possible to represent any time function as the sum of a succession of these elementary narrow rectangular pulses with appropriately varying altitude. Since the value of each quasi-impulse equals its enclosed area, we can vary the height of any pulse by varying the value of the impulse it represents, having chosen a fixed width Δt for all rectangular pulses. Although we shall not employ this artifice until somewhat later in these discussions, it is well even now to see in a general way the important fact that through adding only impulse responses one can construct the response of any linear network to an arbitrary applied disturbance.

Another important artifice in adapting singularity functions to the description of more general types of excitation may be appreciated by consideration of the voltage function shown in Fig. 12, which has several constant values throughout finite intervals and is discontinuous at the transition points. Thus, for $t < 0$, $e_s(t) = 0$; from $t = 0$ to $t = t_1$ it equals $+2$; from $t = t_1$ to $t = t_2$ it equals -1; and for $t > t_2$ it is zero.

It is not difficult to see that we may write this function as

$$e_s(t) = 2u_{-1}(t) - 3u_{-1}(t - t_1) + u_{-1}(t - t_2) \qquad (5)$$

The first term is zero for $t < 0$ and 2 for $t > 0$; the second term is zero for $t < t_1$ and -3 for $t > t_1$; and the third term is zero for $t < t_2$ and 1 for $t > t_2$. The superposition of these three step functions yields the resultant function shown in Fig. 12, as the reader will readily see by making a rough sketch.

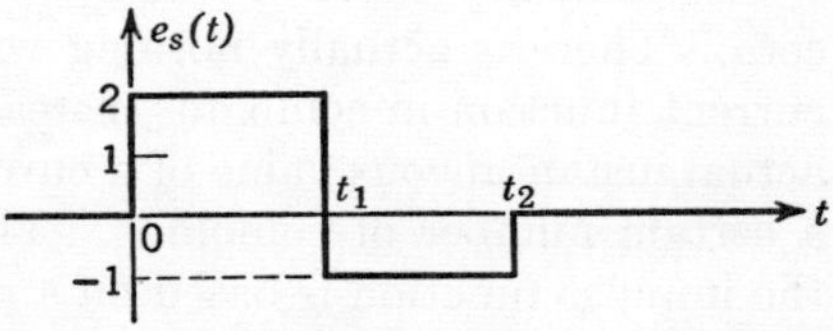

Since any form of function may be approximated by a step curve,

FIG. 12. Resultant time function equal to the sum of step functions given by Eq. 5.

it is easily appreciated that the unit step may likewise be used as a building block for the construction of arbitrary functions.

In connection with the impulse it has been pointed out that the enclosed area is used as a measure of the "value" of this function. Again we have to think of this situation for a nonzero δ since for $\delta = 0$ it is somewhat difficult to visualize what we mean by the term "enclosed area." Ordinarily one uses the term "value of a function" to designate its amplitude or something that is characteristic about its amplitude. For example, the function $f(t) = 10 \sin t$ is said to be a sinusoid of value 10 or amplitude 10. Similarly the function $f(t) = 3u_{-1}(t)$ is a step function of value 3, and 3 is the amount of its discontinuity; that is, it is the amount by which the amplitude of the function jumps.

In considering the impulse, it is manifestly not possible to base the "value" upon amplitude since the latter is infinite. Nevertheless, one must distinguish between impulses of various sizes because the rectangles from which they are derived through an appropriate limiting process can enclose various amounts of area. It is this area that appears to be the logical quantity on which to base the distinction between impulses of different intensity. In the case of a current impulse applied to a capacitance we have seen that the value of the impulse equals the charge in coulombs that is injected into the capacitance. Clearly, one must distinguish between impulses of different value, for their effect upon a network is linearly proportional to this index of intensity.

The disturbing feature about this situation is that it appears to get us into difficulty dimensionally. Thus the time integral of current is charge; that is, area under a current-versus-time curve is charge. Consequently, the "value" of a current impulse dimensionally is a charge, and its units are coulombs. We thus express the value of a current impulse in coulombs, whereas we would naturally expect the value of a current function to be expressed in amperes. Similarly, the value of a voltage impulse is expressed, not in volts, but in weber-turns because it is a flux linkage.

The difficulty expressed here is fortunately not of fundamental concern. There is actually nothing wrong with expressing the value of a current function in coulombs instead of amperes so long as it is not the actual instantaneous value of a current that we are referring to as being a certain number of coulombs. The term "value" in connection with the impulse function is based on a rather special definition which unfortunately does not preserve the dimensions of the physical quantity involved. Although it is well to be aware of this situation so as not to be perplexed by its possible consequences in dimensional reasoning, it is best not to allow one's thinking to be annoyed by it since it can be ignored entirely in all other respects.

Another point of some importance is the question of how an impulse may be indicated in the graphical representation of an excitation function. Since the instantaneous value of an impulse is either nothing or everything, one will have to adopt some conventional method for its

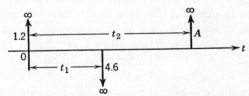

FIG. 13. Graphical representation for the function given in Eq. 6.

representation. The scheme used in the present text is illustrated in Fig. 13, which depicts the function

$$f(t) = 1.2u_0(t) - 4.6u_0(t - t_1) + Au_0(t - t_2) \tag{6}$$

An impulse is indicated by a vertical arrow with the infinity sign (∞) over it; its value (enclosed area) is expressed by the number or symbol written beside the arrow. A negative impulse is drawn as an arrow pointing in the downward direction; or one could alternatively indicate this quality by assigning a negative algebraic sign to the associated value. Thus the central arrow in Fig. 13 could alternatively be drawn upward and its value written −4.6.

It would be possible, of course, to let the height of the arrow, according to a scale of ordinates, indicate the value of the impulse. However, since the value of an impulse is dimensionally not the same as the ordinates of the physical function it represents, it seems better to draw all arrows as having the same length and to indicate values by placing the appropriate numbers or symbols adjacent to them.

Singularity functions of higher order than the impulse are used so infrequently that it is not essential to formulate appropriate graphical representations for them at this time.

4 Single-Element Combinations

In the foregoing chapters, detailed discussion was given for networks consisting of resistance elements alone. Analogously one may encounter networks or portions of networks consisting of capacitance elements alone or of inductance elements alone. We refer to networks of this sort as *single-element* types. The method of determining the voltage and current distribution throughout such a single-element network is essentially the same whether it be resistive, capacitive, or inductive in nature. Therefore, the discussion given in the previous chapters with regard to resistance networks applies in essentially unaltered form to capacitance networks or to inductance networks as well. A few comments regarding characteristic differences in certain specific details, however, are in order.

Suppose we consider a network consisting of capacitances alone and accordingly turn our attention to the pertinent volt-ampere relation 3. The essential difference between this volt-ampere relation and the one pertaining to the resistance element, as given by 1, lies in the fact that the capacitance element injects the operations of differentiation and integration. We can remove this difference in either of two ways. One of these is to use, instead of current, the associated charge defined by

$$q(t) = \int i(t)\, dt \quad \text{or} \quad i(t) = dq/dt \tag{7}$$

so that Eqs. 3 become

$$q = Ce, \qquad e = Sq \tag{8}$$

Alternatively, one can achieve a similar effect by using, instead of voltage, the associated derivative function

$$e'(t) = de/dt \quad \text{or} \quad e(t) = \int e'(t)\, dt \tag{9}$$

whence Eqs. 3 read

$$i = Ce', \qquad e' = Si \tag{10}$$

If we use relations 8 instead of relations 3 to characterize the capacitance element, we are representing the properties of this element in terms of its voltage-charge rather than its volt-ampere (or voltage-current) relation. Instead of finding the current distribution throughout a capacitance network we find the charge distribution. If we subsequently prefer to know the current rather than the charge in a certain branch, we need merely to differentiate the appropriate charge (Eq. 7). Knowledge of the charge distribution is in every respect as useful as a knowledge of the current distribution; and to find it we need to employ only relations 8 which, like relations 1 characterizing the resistance element, do not involve differentiation or integration.

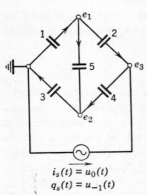

FIG. 14. Capacitance network excited by a current impulse. Element values are in farads.

Alternatively relations 10 can be used to characterize the capacitance element. In this case one finds the distribution of a voltage-derivative function instead of the distribution of voltage throughout the network. The voltage in any branch can then be found by integrating the derivative function. Again one is dealing in the network problem with relations that involve no derivative or integral signs, and hence this part of the analysis is entirely similar to the treatment of a pure resistance network.

As an example consider the network of Fig. 14. Here the numbers associated with the branches serve to indicate the branch numbering and may also be regarded as indicating the capacitance element values in farads. The source is assumed to be a unit current impulse, or expressed as a charge it is a unit step.

For purposes of analysis, the node basis is chosen and the voltage variables are defined as a node-to-datum set as indicated, the left-hand node being the datum. Using relations 8 we can write for the various branch charges

$$q_1 = -e_1$$

$$q_2 = 2(e_1 - e_3)$$

$$q_3 = 3e_2 \tag{11}$$

$$q_4 = 4(e_3 - e_2)$$

$$q_5 = 5(e_1 - e_2)$$

The Kirchhoff current-law equations are written directly in terms of charges (current integrals). As pointed out in Ch. 2, Art. 1, these equations are based upon the principle of the conservation of charge and hence apply in unaltered form to the charges as well as to the currents (the time derivatives of the charges). With reference to Fig. 14 it is clear that

$$-q_1 + q_2 + q_5 = 0$$

$$q_3 - q_4 - q_5 = 0 \tag{12}$$

$$- q_2 + q_4 = q_s$$

Substitution of Eqs. 11 into 12 yields after appropriate arrangement

$$8e_1 - 5e_2 - 2e_3 = 0$$

$$-5e_1 + 12e_2 - 4e_3 = 0 \tag{13}$$

$$-2e_1 - 4e_2 + 6e_3 = q_s$$

with the capacitance matrix

$$[C] = \begin{bmatrix} 8 & -5 & -2 \\ -5 & 12 & -4 \\ -2 & -4 & 6 \end{bmatrix} \tag{14}$$

It should be evident after careful examination of these results that matrix 14 and the set of Eqs. 13 could have been written down by inspection of Fig. 14 following the pattern established in Ch. 2, Art. 6 for the analysis of resistance networks on the node basis. The situation here is precisely the same except that we deal with capacitances instead of with conductances (we get a capacitance matrix $[C]$ instead of a conductance matrix $[G]$); and the excitation function is a charge instead of a current.

Solution of Eqs. 13 may proceed through regarding the first two of these equations by themselves in the form

$$8e_1 - 5e_2 = 2e_3$$
$$-5e_1 + 12e_2 = 4e_3$$

$$(15)$$

yielding

$$e_1 = \tfrac{44}{71}e_3 \quad \text{and} \quad e_2 = \tfrac{42}{71}e_3 \qquad (16)$$

Substitution into the third of Eqs. 13 then gives

$$e_3 = \tfrac{71}{170}q_s \qquad (17)$$

whence one obtains from 16

$$e_1 = \tfrac{44}{170}q_s \quad \text{and} \quad e_2 = \tfrac{42}{170}q_s \qquad (18)$$

Since $q_s(t)$ is assumed to be a unit step, it follows that e_1, e_2, e_3 are likewise step functions, their values being the appropriate fractions given in Eqs. 17 and 18. If $q_s(t)$ were some other time function, then the e's would all be this other time function except for the scale factors evident in the results expressed by Eqs. 17 and 18.

From the potentials e_1, e_2, e_3 one can readily compute the voltage across any single capacitance; and from this voltage and the pertinent capacitance value one can compute the associated charge. Or one can compute these charges directly from relations 11.

If the excitation impressed between the datum and node 3 is a voltage instead of a current (resp. charge) then the potential e_3 is this voltage excitation. Equations 16 then yield the solution immediately.

In terms of the expression 17 for e_3 as a function of q_s, one has the net capacitance between node 3 and datum; namely, this capacitance is 170/71 farads.

It should be observed that the voltages in the various branches in this capacitance network are precisely the same as they would be if each capacitance were replaced by a conductance with the same value in mhos as the capacitance value in farads, and if the excitation were a unit *current* step. If in this analogous resistive network one computes the net conductance in mhos between any two nodes, the result is the same as the net capacitance in farads between the same two nodes in the capacitance network. The analogous resistance network may in this sense be regarded as a sort of reference network, since the voltage and current distribution for it is numerically identical with the voltage and charge distribution for the actual capacitance network.

It might be well to emphasize again that all of the voltages in the capacitance network are given by the source charge $q_s(t)$ multiplied by a real constant. These voltages as time functions are precisely the same as the time function $q_s(t)$. In this example $q_s(t)$ is a unit step because $i_s(t)$ was assumed to be a unit impulse. Thus, when a capacitance network is excited at some point by a current impulse, the voltages in *all* parts of that network are step functions. If the excitation were a current step (the integral of the impulse), then all voltages would be ramp functions (the integral of the step). The capacitance network, however complex its geometry may be, has for its driving-point and transfer volt-ampere relations the same fundamental mathematical relationship as is expressed for the single capacitance element by Eqs. 3.

It may be additionally useful to point out that the units implied in the numerical specification of capacitance values need not be considered in carrying through the solution to a capacitance network such as the one in Fig. 14 so long as all values are specified in the same units. For reasons of numerical simplicity, the given numerical values were assumed to be in farads. Someone might suggest that we are being unrealistic about things since 1-, 2-, 3-, 4-, and 5-farad capacitances are larger than are found in ordinary circuits. This circumstance is rather trivial, however, since the solutions we have obtained above are readily adjusted to suit any uniform change in capacitance values. Thus if we were to change these values to 1, 2, 3, 4, and 5 microfarads, all voltages for the same applied current or charge become 10^6 times larger; or all voltages remain the same for an applied current equal to one-millionth of a unit impulse.

It is certainly much more sensible to assume the capacitance values to be in farads during the course of the solution and insert appropriate factors afterward than it would be to write the factor 10^{-6} about fifty times all through the process of numerical solution, to say nothing of encountering factors like $10^{-6} \times 10^{-6} = 10^{-12}$ etc. when carrying out an elimination process between pairs of equations. Being realistic about capacitance values is just plain foolishness.

In an analogous manner it is seen that the problem of finding the distribution of voltage or current throughout a network consisting of *inductances* alone is essentially the same as it is for a resistance network. One way of recognizing this fact is to use, instead of voltage, the associated flux linkage defined by

$$\psi(t) = \int e\, dt \quad \text{or} \quad e(t) = d\psi/dt \tag{19}$$

so that Eqs. 2 become

$$\psi = Li, \qquad i = L^{-1}\psi \tag{20}$$

Alternatively one can achieve the desired result through using, instead of current, the associated derivative function

$$i'(t) = di/dt \quad \text{or} \quad i(t) = \int i'(t) \, dt \tag{21}$$

whereupon Eqs. 2 again are converted to a form in which differentiation or integration is absent, namely,

$$e = Li', \qquad i' = L^{-1}e \tag{22}$$

In Eqs. 20 we are representing the characteristics of the inductance element in terms of its flux linkage–current relation instead of its volt-

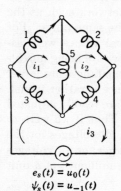

$$e_s(t) = u_0(t)$$
$$\psi_s(t) = u_{-1}(t)$$

FIG. 15. Inductance network excited by a voltage impulse. Element values are in henrys.

ampere relation. In Eqs. 22 it is a voltage-(current derivative) relation rather than the conventional voltage-current relation that is used to characterize the inductance element. Either trick gets rid of the derivative and integral signs, and hence opens the way for an analysis procedure that is entirely analogous to that used with resistance networks.

Further details are best illustrated by means of an example. Thus consider the inductance network of Fig. 15 in which the branch numbering at the same time indicates the element values in henrys. The source is assumed to be a unit voltage impulse or a flux linkage equal to a unit step. The entire situation is like that in Fig. 14 with capacitance replaced by inductance and current excitation replaced by the same kind of voltage excitation.

For purposes of analysis the loop basis is chosen, and the current variables are defined as a set of mesh currents as indicated. Using relation 20 we can write for the various branch flux linkages (those pertaining to the separate inductances)

$$\psi_1 = i_1$$

$$\psi_2 = 2i_2$$

$$\psi_3 = 3(i_1 - i_3) \tag{23}$$

$$\psi_4 = 4(i_2 - i_3)$$

$$\psi_5 = 5(i_1 - i_2)$$

The Kirchhoff voltage-law equations which normally are written in terms of branch voltages are instead written directly in terms of the time integrals of these voltages; that is, in terms of the branch flux linkages. Thus we have

$$\psi_1 + \psi_3 + \psi_5 = 0$$
$$\psi_2 + \psi_4 - \psi_5 = 0 \tag{24}$$
$$-\psi_3 - \psi_4 = -\psi_s$$

Substitution of relations 23 into 24 yields after appropriate arrangement

$$9i_1 - 5i_2 - 3i_3 = 0$$
$$-5i_1 + 11i_2 - 4i_3 = 0 \tag{25}$$
$$-3i_1 - 4i_2 + 7i_3 = -\psi_s$$

with the inductance matrix

$$[L] = \begin{bmatrix} 9 & -5 & -3 \\ -5 & 11 & -4 \\ -3 & -4 & 7 \end{bmatrix} \tag{26}$$

This is the loop-inductance matrix that could have been written by inspection of the network in Fig. 15.

Solving the first two equations in set 25 for i_1 and i_2 in terms of i_3, one obtains

$$i_1 = \tfrac{53}{74}i_3 \quad \text{and} \quad i_2 = \tfrac{51}{74}i_3 \tag{27}$$

Substitution into the third of Eqs. 25 then yields

$$i_3 = -\tfrac{74}{155}\psi_s \tag{28}$$

so that Eqs. 27 give

$$i_1 = -\tfrac{53}{155}\psi_s \quad \text{and} \quad i_2 = -\tfrac{51}{155}\psi_s \tag{29}$$

Since $\psi_s(t)$ is assumed to be a unit step, all the currents are step functions. Thus the applied voltage impulse produces current step functions in all branches of the inductance network the same as it would in a single inductance. If $e_s(t)$ were any other time function, then all the currents would be the integral of this time function multiplied by the factors in Eqs. 28 and 29.

From Eq. 28 one obtains the value of the net inductance between the points ab in Fig. 15, namely,

$$L_{ab} = \tfrac{155}{74} \text{ henrys} \tag{30}$$

It should be clear that, if the inductances in this network were replaced by resistances with values in ohms equal to the pertinent inductance values in henrys, and if the voltage excitation were a unit step instead of a unit impulse, the equilibrium equations would be identical with those given by 25, and all the resulting current values would be the same. The net inductance of the network of Fig. 15 between any node pair is numerically the same as the net resistance between the same node pair in this analogous resistance network.

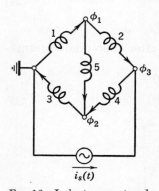

With regard to a uniform change in the units used to express inductance, remarks similar to those given for the capacitance network apply. Thus, if the above inductance values are microhenrys instead of henrys, the currents for the same applied voltage become 10^6 times larger, or they remain the same if the applied voltage is assumed to be 10^6 times smaller.

FIG. 16. Inductance network excited by a current source. Element values are in reciprocal henrys. Analysis on node basis becomes analogous to that pertaining to the capacitance network of Fig. 14.

It is instructive to note that, if we had designated the elements in the network of Fig. 15 as *reciprocal* inductances with the same numerical values in reciprocal henrys, then the equations on the node basis would be identical with the node Eqs. 13 for the capacitance network of Fig. 14. With reference to Fig. 16, in which these changes are incorporated, the quantities ϕ_1, ϕ_2, ϕ_3 are the time integrals of the node potentials e_1, e_2, e_3; that is to say, they are node flux linkages. Denoting the branch currents as usual by $j_1, j_2, \cdots, j_5$, we have according to the relations between current and flux linkage in an inductance element (as given in Eq. 20)

$$j_1 = -\phi_1$$
$$j_2 = 2(\phi_1 - \phi_3)$$
$$j_3 = 3\phi_2 \qquad (31)$$
$$j_4 = 4(\phi_3 - \phi_2)$$
$$j_5 = 5(\phi_1 - \phi_2)$$

while the Kirchhoff current-law equations read

$$-j_1 + j_2 + j_5 = 0$$
$$j_3 - j_4 - j_5 = 0 \qquad (32)$$
$$-j_2 + j_4 = i_s$$

Substitution of Eqs. 31 into Eqs. 32 yields the desired node equations

$$8\phi_1 - 5\phi_2 - 2\phi_3 = 0$$

$$-5\phi_1 + 12\phi_2 - 4\phi_3 = 0 \tag{33}$$

$$-2\phi_1 - 4\phi_2 + 6\phi_3 = i_s$$

with the reciprocal-inductance matrix

$$[\Gamma] = \begin{bmatrix} 8 & -5 & -2 \\ -5 & 12 & -4 \\ -2 & -4 & 6 \end{bmatrix} \tag{34}$$

Note the exact parallelism between Eqs. 11, 12, 13, and 14 pertaining to the capacitance network of Fig. 14 and Eqs. 31, 32, 33, and 34 pertaining to the reciprocal-inductance network of Fig. 16.

Similarly, if in the network of Fig. 14, the element values were regarded as elastances in darafs instead of capacitances in farads, and if the equilibrium of this network were expressed on the loop basis assuming the excitation function to be a voltage, the results would be numerically identical with those expressed by Eqs. 23, 24, 25, and 26 with reference to the inductance network of Fig. 15.

These results are further evidence of the principle of duality pointed out at various times in the preceding discussions. We see that the same numerical equations can represent the equilibrium of a resistance, or inductance, or capacitance network with appropriate interpretation of its coefficients and excitation terms. The principal conclusion of value to be drawn from this situation at the moment is the fact that any problem involving the determination of voltages or currents in a capacitance network or inductance network can be found through considering the analogous situation in an appropriately chosen resistance network. Or one may say that the single-element network analysis problem is essentially the same regardless of which of the three kinds of circuit elements is involved.

APPROXIMATE FORMULAS FOR PARAMETERS OF SIMPLE GEOMETRICAL CONFIGURATION

Resistance Parameter

The resistance R of a longitudinally uniform conductor of length l and cross section A is given by

$$R = \rho \frac{l}{A} \text{ ohms} \tag{1}$$

where ρ is the resistivity of the material. For annealed copper at room temperature $\rho = 1.724 \times 10^{-8}$ in mks units.

Inductance Parameter

The inductance per unit length of a (theoretically infinitely) long solenoid is given by

$$L = \mu A n^2 \text{ henrys per meter of solenoid length} \qquad (2)$$

where μ is the permeability of the assumed uniform isotropic medium in which the solenoid is immersed, A is the cross-sectional area (assumed large compared with the wire diameter), and n equals the turns per meter. For free space $\mu = 4\pi \times 10^{-7}$ in mks units. Then

$$L = 0.4\pi n^2 A \text{ microhenrys per meter} \qquad (3)$$

The formula yields only fair results unless the length of the solenoid is at least several times its diameter.

For single loops of arbitrary shape it is best to proceed from the following relationships:

$$L = \frac{\phi}{i} \qquad (4)$$

$$\phi = \oint A_p \, ds_p \qquad (5)$$

$$A_p = \frac{\mu i}{4\pi} \oint \frac{ds_q \cos \theta_{pq}}{\delta_{pq}} \qquad (6)$$

Here ϕ, the flux linking the loop, is computed by integrating a quantity $A(s)$—known as the magnetic vector potential—around the loop. This quantity, which is a function of distance s measured along the loop, may be computed for any point p on the loop by means of the integral 6 involving the element of path length ds_q at a variable point q, the angle θ_{pq} between the tangents to the loop at the points p and q, and the distance δ_{pq} between these two points.

In any specific example the integrals may readily be evaluated approximately since they depend solely upon the geometry involved. We shall illustrate with examples presently, but first observe that substitution among Eqs. 4, 5, 6 yields

$$L = \frac{\mu}{4\pi} \oint ds_p \oint \frac{ds_q \cos \theta_{pq}}{\delta_{pq}} \qquad (7)$$

from which it is more obvious that the inductance parameter, as just mentioned, is purely a geometrical constant, and (assuming μ to be a dimensionless constant which it is in the electromagnetic system of units) has the dimension of a length. Thus the unit of inductance is fixed through choosing for it some characteristic length. The practical unit—the *henry*—is thus fixed by choosing it equal to the length of the earth's quadrant which is 10,000 kilometers, or 10^7 meters, or 10^9 centimeters.* In the rationalized mks system of units in which $\mu = 4\pi \times 10^{-7}$ formula 7 reads

$$L = 10^{-7} \oint ds_p \oint \frac{ds_q \cos \theta_{pq}}{\delta_{pq}} \text{ henry} \qquad (8)$$

which yields 1 henry when the double integral equals 10^7 meters—the length of the earth's quadrant.

Interpretation of the integral in Eq. 6 (the first one to be computed in an évaluation of formula 8) is facilitated through reference to Fig. 1

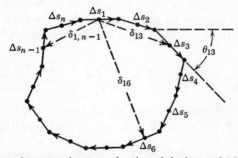

FIG. 1. Pertinent to the approximate evaluation of the integral 6 by the finite sum 9.

where the path increments are regarded as finite, and the fixed increment ds_p, from which the distances δ_{pq} are measured and to which the angles θ_{pq} are referred, is chosen in the horizontal position and labeled Δs_1. The integral is thus approximated by a finite sum which yields sufficiently close results for most practical cases. Note that the angle θ_{1q} for $q = 1, 2, \cdots, n$ varies from zero to substantially 360° so that $\cos \theta_{1q}$ has negative as well as positive values.

The integral in question is thus evaluated approximately by

$$\oint \frac{ds_q \cos \theta_{pq}}{\delta_{pq}} \approx \Delta s \sum_{q=1, 2 \cdots}^{n} \frac{\cos \theta_{1q}}{\delta_{1q}} \qquad (9)$$

in which Δs is the fixed uniform path increment. The term for $q = 1$ which reads $\Delta s/\delta_{11}$ evidently requires special interpretation as to the

* In absolute emu, the unit of inductance is the centimeter which is equivalent to 10^{-9} henry.

distance δ_{11} of the element Δs_1 from itself, which is not zero as might be our first guess. A proper evaluation needs to consider the finite thickness of the wire forming the loop and involves an integration extending over the cross section of the wire as well as an integration over the length Δs of the element. It turns out from such an evaluation that (very nearly, for $\Delta s/r \gg 1$)

$$\Delta s/\delta_{11} = 1 + 2 \ln (\Delta s/r) \tag{10}$$

in which ln denotes the natural logarithm and r is the wire radius (i.e., $2r$ equals the wire diameter or thickness). The integral 9 written for any $\Delta s_1 = \Delta s_p$ then reads

$$\oint \frac{ds_q \cos \theta_{pq}}{\delta_{pq}} \approx 1 + 2 \ln \left(\frac{\Delta s}{r}\right) + \sum_{q=p+1}^{q=p+n-1} \frac{\Delta s \cos \theta_{pq}}{\delta_{pq}} \tag{11}$$

and the double integral in Eq. 8 is obtained through multiplication by Δs and summation over all typical Δs_p. For the first term in Eq. 11 this step amounts to multiplication by the total path length $l = n \, \Delta s$. Hence we have

$$L = 10^{-7} l \left[1 + 2 \ln \left(\frac{\Delta s}{r}\right) + \frac{1}{n} \sum_{p, \, q=1}^{n} \frac{\cos \theta_{pq}}{\delta_{pq}/\Delta s} \right] \tag{12}$$

where the double summation involves all terms for $q = 1, \cdots, n$ except the one for $q = p$, with each $p = 1, \cdots, n$, making altogether $n(n-1)$ terms.

In the special case for which Fig. 1 is a regular polygon (the approximation to a circular loop) all sums over q for $p = 1, 2, \cdots, n$ are identical, so that the double sum is then equal to n times the sum for a single integer p. For the *circular loop* we thus have

$$L = 10^{-7} l \left[1 + 2 \ln \left(\frac{\Delta s}{r}\right) + \sum_{q=2}^{n} \frac{\cos \theta_{1q}}{\delta_{1q}/\Delta s} \right] \tag{13}$$

As an illustrative example, let us compute the inductance of a circular loop of wire through approximating it geometrically by an inscribed regular polygon. Consider first an inscribed square as shown in Fig. 2 for which $\Delta s = R\sqrt{2}$, and suppose we choose the thickness of the wire such that $R/r = 50$. Then $\Delta s/r = 50\sqrt{2}$, and the first term in the bracket of Eq. 13 has the value

$$1 + 2 \ln 50\sqrt{2} = 9.52 \tag{14}$$

Of the three terms in the sum which is the second term in Eq. 13, two are zero because the pertinent cosines are zero, and the third equals

-1 because $\delta_{1q} = \Delta s$ and $\cos \theta_{1q} = -1$. Hence formula 13 yields

$$L = 10^{-7}l(9.52 - 1) = 10^{-7}l \times 8.52 \text{ henry} \qquad (15)$$

where l equals the perimeter of the square.

Next let us use the inscribed hexagon as shown in Fig. 3.   Here

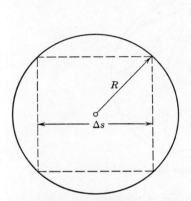

FIG. 2.   Approximation of a circular loop by an inscribed square.

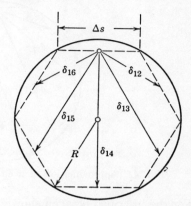

FIG. 3.   Approximation of a circular loop by an inscribed hexagon.

$\Delta s = R$, so that with $R/r = 50$ as before we now have for the first term in the bracket of Eq. 13

$$1 + 2 \ln 50 = 8.83 \qquad (16)$$

The sum contains five terms involving

$$\delta_{12}/\Delta s = \sqrt{3}/2, \qquad \cos \theta_{12} = \quad 1/2$$
$$\delta_{13}/\Delta s = \quad 3/2, \qquad \cos \theta_{13} = -1/2$$
$$\delta_{14}/\Delta s = \sqrt{3}, \qquad \cos \theta_{14} = -1$$
$$\delta_{15}/\Delta s = \quad 3/2, \qquad \cos \theta_{15} = -1/2$$
$$\delta_{16}/\Delta s = \sqrt{3}/2, \qquad \cos \theta_{16} = \quad 1/2$$

This sum thus yields

$$\frac{1}{\sqrt{3}} - \frac{1}{3} - \frac{1}{\sqrt{3}} - \frac{1}{3} + \frac{1}{\sqrt{3}} = -0.089 \approx -0.09$$

so that we have altogether

$$L = 10^{-7}l(8.83 - 0.09) = 10^{-7}l \times 8.74 \qquad (17)$$

which is slightly larger than the value 15 not only in the ratio 8.74/8.52 but also because the perimeter of the inscribed hexagon is larger than that of the inscribed square.

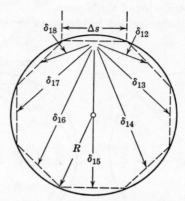

Fig. 4.   Approximation of a circular loop by an inscribed octagon.

For the inscribed octagon shown in Fig. 4 we have

$$\delta_{12}/\Delta s = \delta_{18}/\Delta s = 0.924, \quad \cos \theta_{12} = \quad 0.707, \quad \cos \theta_{18} = \quad 0.707$$

$$\delta_{13}/\Delta s = \delta_{17}/\Delta s = 1.707, \quad \cos \theta_{13} = \quad 0.0, \quad \cos \theta_{17} = \quad 0.0$$

$$\delta_{14}/\Delta s = \delta_{16}/\Delta s = 2.231, \quad \cos \theta_{14} = \quad -0.707, \quad \cos \theta_{16} = \quad -0.707$$

$$\delta_{15}/\Delta s = \quad\quad\quad 2.414, \quad \cos \theta_{15} = \quad -1$$

so that the sum in this case yields

$$\frac{0.707}{0.924} + \frac{0.0}{1.707} - \frac{0.707}{2.231} - \frac{1.0}{2.414} - \frac{0.707}{2.231} + \frac{0.0}{1.707} + \frac{0.707}{0.924} = 0.48 \quad (18)$$

Since $\Delta s/R = 2 \sin 22.5° = 0.765$, the ratio $R/r = 50$ corresponds to $\Delta s/r = 38.3$, giving for the first term in the bracket of Eq. 13

$$1 + 2 \ln 38.3 = 8.29$$

so that we have for the inductance in this case

$$L = 10^{-7}l(8.29 + 0.48) = 10^{-7}l \times 8.77 \quad (19)$$

For most practical problems this result is near enough to the inductance of the circular loop. In fact many cases will permit an even rougher approximation. In this regard it should be noticed in all three of the above examples that the sum involved in Eq. 13 contributes a relatively minor amount to the value of the loop inductance, so that a good estimate is had from the approximate formula

$$L \approx 10^{-7}l\,[1 + 2 \ln (\Delta s/r)] \text{ henrys} \tag{20}$$

or

$$L \approx 0.1\,[1 + 2 \ln (\Delta s/r)] \text{ microhenrys per meter} \tag{21}$$

The following table gives some numerical values. Since the logarithm

$\Delta s/r$	$\ln (\Delta s/r)$	L in μh/meter
50	3.91	0.882
250	5.52	1.204
500	6.21	1.342

is such a lazy function, the inductance is not excitingly dependent upon the ratio $(\Delta s/r)$. One might almost say that any old fair-sized wire has about 1 microhenry inductance per meter, and the shape has roughly no great influence either. Extreme cases must, of course, be excluded; and it is well to know the origin of the approximate formula 21 (as given in the preceding discussion), for it serves as a valuable guide in its use.

Capacitance Parameter

The capacitance of a pair of parallel plates having a separation d is

$$C = \frac{\epsilon}{d} \text{ farads per unit of plate area} \tag{22}$$

where ϵ is the permittivity of the assumed uniform isotropic medium in which the plates are immersed. Like the solenoid formula for L this one for C assumes that the plates are infinite in their dimensions. For a finite plate area A the formula yields only approximate results, but these are very good if the smallest dimension entering into A is still large compared with d (usually fulfilled in practical cases). For free space $\epsilon = 1/4\pi 9 \times 10^9$ in mks units, and so one finds

$$C = \frac{8.84A}{d} \text{ micromicrofarads} \tag{23}$$

(A is in square meters and d in meters.) For a pair of concentric spheres of radii $R_1 < R_2$, one finds (in this case exactly)

$$C = \frac{4\pi\epsilon}{\left(\dfrac{1}{R_1} - \dfrac{1}{R_2}\right)} \rightarrow \frac{4\pi R^2 \epsilon}{d} = \frac{\epsilon A}{d} \tag{24}$$

for $R_1 \approx R_2 = R$ and $R_2 - R_1 = d$, which checks the parallel plate formula.   In another important case $R_2 \rightarrow \infty$, $R_1 = R$, one has

$$C = 4\pi\epsilon R = 111.1R \text{ micromicrofarads} \tag{25}$$

PROBLEMS

1. Given the accompanying sketches of a function $f(x)$, (a) draw the curve $\int_0^x f(x)\,dx$, (b) draw the curve $df(x)/dx$.

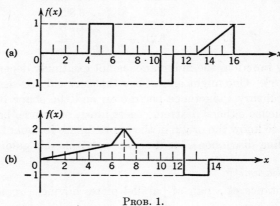

PROB. 1.

2. An inductance of 100 microhenrys is to be constructed out of copper tubing 1 centimeter in outside diameter wound into the shape of a helix with a pitch of about 3 centimeters and a diameter of 30 centimeters.   Approximately how long a piece of tubing will be needed and how long will the helix be?

If the wall thickness of the tubing is 2 millimeters, compute the approximate resistance of this coil and determine its time constant in seconds.

3. A single-layer solenoid is wound on a 5-centimeter-diameter cylindrical core with enameled copper wire of about 1 millimeter diameter closely spaced from turn to turn.   Compute the approximate inductance, resistance, and time constant of this coil if its length is 30 centimeters.

4. A circular multiturn coil is wound out of enameled copper wire of about 1 millimeter thickness with all the turns packed together so that the resultant shape is that of a doughnut.   The mean diameter of the doughnut is 20 centimeters and the coil contains 100 turns.   Compute the approximate inductance, resistance, and time constant.

5. The chassis of a piece of communication apparatus is wired with enameled copper wire having a diameter of about 0.5 millimeter.   In completing the job, about 10 meters of wire were used altogether.   Estimate the order of magnitude of total parasitic inductance inserted into the circuitry by the lead wires.

6. An air condenser is to be constructed of a number of dovetailed parallel plates 10 x 10 centimeters with a common separation of 1 millimeter.   About how many plates will be needed to obtain a capacitance of 0.005 microfarad?   If each plate has a thickness of 2 millimeters, what will be the approximate outside dimensions of this condenser?

7. The spherical electrode of some piece of electrical apparatus has a diameter of 1.5 meters. It is situated approximately in the center of a cubically shaped room, the walls of which are covered with a grounded netting. If the common dimension of the room is 10 meters, compute the approximate capacitance of the electrode. If this electrode is raised to a potential of 5×10^6 volts above ground, compute the charge in coulombs and the energy stored in joules. If this energy could be released uniformly to light a 10-watt bulb at normal incandescence, how long would the bulb remain lighted?

8. An inductance L structurally consists of a parallel combination of L_1, L_2, and L_3. If $L_1 = 10$, $L_2 = 50$, and L is to be 5 (all values in microhenrys), what must be the value of L_3?

9. Capacitances of 1, 2, 3, 4, 5 microfarads respectively are connected in series to a 1-volt d-c source. Compute the potential drop across each capacitance, the charge in each, the net charge, the net energy stored, and the distribution of this energy throughout the various capacitances. Suppose the given capacitance values are farads instead of microfarads, what changes do you make in the above answers?

10. Inductances of 1, 2, 3, 4, 5 millihenrys respectively are connected in parallel to a 1-ampere d-c source. Compute the current taken by each inductance, the flux linkage in each, the net flux linkage, the net stored energy, and its distribution throughout the various inductances. Suppose the given inductance values are henrys instead of millihenrys, what changes do you make in the above answers?

11. Reconsider Prob. 9 for a unit current impulse applied.

12. Reconsider Prob. 10 for a unit voltage impulse applied.

13. Knowing that a unit voltage impulse applied to an inductance L instantly establishes a current of $1/L$ amperes, what value of current is established by this voltage impulse in a circuit consisting of R and L in series? Again, for a circuit consisting of R, L, and C in series?

14. Knowing that a unit current impulse applied to a capacitance C instantly establishes a potential of $1/C$ volts, what value of potential is established by this current impulse in a circuit consisting of R and C in parallel? Again, for a circuit consisting of R, L, and C in parallel?

15. If a unit voltage step is applied to a circuit consisting of R, L, and C in series, show that the net effect, so far as the resultant current is concerned, may be regarded as equivalent to suddenly charging the capacitance to 1 volt and thereafter leaving the circuit, short-circuited upon itself, to perform whatever natural behavior results from the discharge of the capacitance.

16. If a unit current step is applied to a circuit consisting of R, L, and C in parallel, show that the net effect, so far as the resultant voltage is concerned, may be regarded as equivalent to suddenly establishing in the inductance a current of 1 ampere and thereafter leaving the parallel-connected elements to perform whatever natural behavior results from the discharge of the inductance.

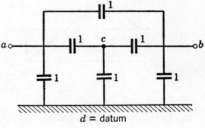

d = datum

Prob. 17.

17. In the accompanying sketch the capacitance values are in microfarads. Compute the net capacitance between the terminals a and b. Repeat for the terminal

pair c–d. If a d-c potential of 1 volt is applied to the terminals c–d, compute the steady voltage across each capacitance and the charge on each. Compute the energy stored in each condenser, and through the addition of these results get the total stored energy. Check the latter value through computing the net energy from the net capacitance between c and d. If the applied voltage is raised to 316, how do the values of charge change? How do the values of energy change?

18. If the capacitances in the network of Prob. 17 are replaced by inductances whose values in millihenrys are the same, and if a steady direct current of 1 ampere is applied to the terminal pair c–d, what are the currents in the various branches? What are the stored energies in the various inductances, and what is the total stored energy of the system? How do these values change if the applied current is changed to 1000 amperes?

19. If a unit step voltage is applied to the terminal pair c–d in the network of Prob. 17, what is the resulting terminal current in nature and value? Ditto for all the separate currents in the various branches.

20. If a unit current impulse is applied to the terminal pair c–d of Prob. 17, what is the resulting voltage in nature and value for all the various branches as well as at the driving point? What is the total energy supplied, and how is it distributed?

21. For the network configuration of Prob. 17 with capacitances replaced by inductances as pointed out in Prob. 18, a unit voltage impulse is applied to the terminal pair c–d. Determine the nature and value of the resulting current in each branch as well as the driving-point current. Compute the energy stored in each branch and the total energy.

22. A series combination of $R = 1$ ohm, $L = 10^{-3}$ henry, $C = 10^{-6}$ farad has applied to it a voltage step of the value 1000. For the initial instant, compute values of the current through the inductance, its rate of increase, the voltage across the capacitance, and its first and second derivatives.

23. In the circuit configuration of Prob. 17, all the capacitances are replaced by 1-ohm resistances except the one across terminals a–c which is 2 ohms, and the one directly across terminals a–b which is replaced by an inductance of 1 millihenry. A voltage step of 1000 is applied to the terminal pair c–d. Compute the initial rate of change of current through the inductance.

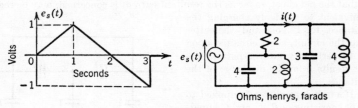

PROB. 24.

24. In the circuit shown above, the voltage source as a function of time is sketched at the left. Compute and plot the current $i(t)$, showing separately the component currents in the 3-farad capacitance and in the 4-henry inductance.

25. The current function $i_s(t)$ shown below is impressed upon a capacitance C. What should be the value A of the impulse so that the voltage across C becomes zero for $t > 5$ seconds?

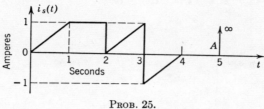

PROB. 25.

26. If the current source function of Prob. 25 is involved in the accompanying circuit, compute and plot $e(t)$.

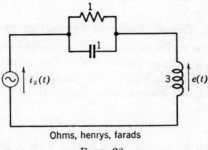

Ohms, henrys, farads

PROB. 26.

27. Given the following sources and the results they produce in a single circuit element, deduce the type of element and its value in henrys, farads, or ohms, as the case may be:

Current or Voltage Source	Resultant Current or Voltage
$i_s(t) = 5u_0(t)$	$10u_{-1}(t)$
$i_s(t) = 5u_{-1}(t)$	$3u_0(t)$
$e_s(t) = 10u_{-1}(t)$	$5u_0(t)$
$i_s(t) = (3/2)u_0(t)$	$(9/4)u_0(t)$
$e_s(t) = (1/3)u_0(t)$	$3u_{-1}(t)$

28. Application of a source current $i_s(t) = \sin t$ to the terminals of a box containing an unknown linear passive network produces a steady voltage at the terminals given by $e(t) = 10 \sin (t + 30°)$. What can you deduce as to the contents of the box? How does the answer to this question change if $e(t) = 10 \sin (t - 30°)$?

Impulse and Step-Function Response
of Simple Circuits

1 The Series RL Circuit; General Properties of the Solution

Figure 1 shows a series combination of resistance and inductance, excited by a known voltage source $e_s(t)$. The resulting current $i(t)$ is to be found. According to Kirchhoff's voltage law and the volt-ampere relations for the circuit elements as discussed in Ch. 4, we have the equilibrium equation

$$L \, (di/dt) + Ri = e_s(t) \tag{1}$$

This equation is to be solved for $i = i(t)$ with a given $e_s(t)$. Before choosing a specific $e_s(t)$, or proceeding with the formulation of a solution,

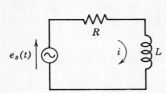

FIG. 1. Series RL circuit excited by a voltage source.

let us pause for a moment and look carefully at the kind of equation we have before us, and see if we can discover some of the properties our solution will have before we even attempt to find one. Some folks may think this is a silly thing to contemplate doing; in fact they may even go so far as to exclaim: "How can you tell anything about the properties of a solution you haven't yet found?" We shall see.

One important property of our solution will result as a consequence of the *linearity* of Eq. 1: that is, the fact that $e_s(t)$, $i(t)$, and its derivative do not appear raised to any power other than unity, or that there are no terms involving the product e_s and i. Because of this property of the equilibrium equation we can say at once that, if $e_s(t)$ were replaced by $Ae_s(t)$, where A is any constant, then $i(t)$ becomes replaced by $Ai(t)$. One recognizes the truth of this statement through considering each term in Eq. 1 multiplied by the same constant A as in

$$L \frac{d}{dt} (Ai) + R(Ai) = Ae_s(t) \tag{2}$$

222

whence it is obvious that, if $e'_s(t) = Ae_s(t)$ be a new value for the excitation, then $i'(t) = Ai(t)$ becomes the corresponding new value for the current response. Note that this conclusion would not be permissible if $i(t)$, in one or more terms, entered with the square power or any power other than unity, or if the equation contained terms involving the product $e_s \times i$.

As a result of the property just mentioned we see that in choosing the excitation function $e_s(t)$ we shall be free to consider any scale factor for ordinates that we please, since the solution for any other scale factor is the same except for a multiplication by this factor. Specifically, once we know the solution for say a step function of 1 volt, we know that the solution for a step function of 673.596 volts is simply 673.596 times what it is for 1 volt. We, therefore, never need to bother in our analysis with any particular number of volts. No matter what the actual voltage of the source is, we shall always get the response *per volt* first and then multiply by a specific value afterward. We call this process *normalization* of the excitation function. We shall see that such a normalization is always possible, no matter what our network looks like, so long as the circuit elements R, L, and C are constant, for then the equilibrium equations, like Eq. 1, are linear.

A second property that follows because of the linearity of the equation is this: If, for an excitation $e_1(t)$, we have found a solution $i_1(t)$, and, for a second excitation $e_2(t)$, we have found the solution to be given by $i_2(t)$, then we may say that, if we were to consider the excitation $e(t) = e_1(t) + e_2(t)$, the solution would be given by $i(t) = i_1(t) + i_2(t)$. That is to say, solutions are superposable, or additive. In some physical problem we might encounter an excitation function that consists of several additive parts like $e_1(t)$, $e_2(t)$, etc. We can then obtain the complete solution by first considering each part of the excitation as determining a separate problem. The corresponding separate solutions may then simply be added together to form the complete solution. The truth of these statements is readily verified through direct substitution in the given equation, again observing that its linear character is the feature that permits this simplified way of dealing with an otherwise complex problem.

We can determine another important property of our solution just by looking at Eq. 1, and this one also follows because of the linearity, and is generally true no matter how complex the network may otherwise become. Suppose we differentiate each term in Eq. 1 with respect to the time t, thus:

$$L\frac{d^2i}{dt^2} + R\frac{di}{dt} = \frac{de_s}{dt} \tag{3}$$

Now let us write

$$i' = di/dt \quad \text{and} \quad e'_s = de_s/dt \qquad (4)$$

Then Eq. 3 becomes

$$L\frac{di'}{dt} + Ri' = e'_s(t) \qquad (5)$$

which looks like Eq. 1 again except that $e_s(t)$ and $i(t)$ appear primed. Physically this result tells us that the relation between $e'_s(t)$ and $i'(t)$ as determined by the network of Fig. 1 is precisely the same as is the relation between $e_s(t)$ and $i(t)$. To illustrate with a specific example, suppose we originally had considered $e_s(t)$ to be a unit step. Then $i(t)$, assuming that we had found it, would be the corresponding step-function response of our simple series RL network. Now $e'_s(t)$, being the derivative of $e_s(t)$, is a unit voltage impulse, and, since $i'(t)$ is the response corresponding to the excitation $e'_s(t)$, we have the important result that the *impulse response* of our network can be had by finding the step-function response and differentiating it.

Since integration cancels differentiation, and vice versa, we may alternatively say that the step-function response could be found through first obtaining the impulse response and then integrating the result. Quite generally we can express what we have found out about the relationship between $e_s(t)$ and $i(t)$ by saying that once we have found $i(t)$ for a given $e_s(t)$ we can regard these two functions as a *pair* (as *mates* if you like) whose mutual relationship has once and for all been fixed by the physical nature of the network which, after all, is the only thing that binds them together. What happens to one function in this pair must happen to the other; if one is differentiated, the other one becomes differentiated; if one is integrated, the other becomes integrated; if differentiation is repeated twice on one, it is repeated twice on the other, etc.

We can also see from this way of looking at the problem, that it is immaterial which of the two functions, $e_s(t)$ or $i(t)$, we regard as excitation and which as response. This state of affairs was pointed out previously when we were considering the volt-ampere relationships for the single elements R, L, and C. In Fig. 1 we have a combination of R and L in series, and Eq. 1 is nothing more than the volt-ampere relation at the terminals of this series combination. The volt-ampere relation expressed by Eq. 1 is correct; and this fact has nothing to do with whether we know $e_s(t)$ and are searching for $i(t)$ or whether we happen to know $i(t)$ and are searching for $e_s(t)$. Let us now discuss the solution of Eq. 1 for a specific choice of $e_s(t)$.

Suppose we assume that $e_s(t)$ is a unit impulse. We found previously that a unit voltage impulse, applied to an inductance L alone, instantly establishes in that inductance a current of $1/L$ amperes. A bit of reflection reveals that this situation is not in the least altered by the presence of a series resistance because the finite current of $1/L$ amperes produces in this resistance only a finite voltage drop of R/L volts. Compared with the infinite value of $e_s(t)$ at the instant at which this impulse happens (let us call this instant $t = 0$), any finite voltage drop is negligible. Therefore the value of current, which the voltage impulse instantly establishes in the circuit at the moment it hits, is the same for R and L in series as it is for L alone.

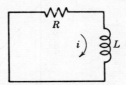

FIG. 2. Series RL circuit under force-free condition.

Since the voltage source $e_s(t)$ is zero for all time after $t = 0$, it is actually just a short circuit all the time except that, at $t = 0$, it suddenly creates a current of $1/L$ amperes. Therefore our problem is synonymous with that of finding how the current $i(t)$ in the closed circuit of Fig. 2 behaves for $t > 0$, knowing that at $t = 0$ it has the value $1/L$. The equilibrium for this situation is expressed by the homogeneous equation

$$L\frac{di}{dt} + Ri = 0 \tag{6}$$

It is readily seen that the following time function

$$i(t) = Ae^{pt} \tag{7}$$

satisfies this differential equation, since

$$di/dt = Ape^{pt} = pi(t) \tag{8}$$

so that substitution into Eq. 6 gives

$$(Lp + R)i(t) = 0 \tag{9}$$

This relation can be satisfied for a nonzero $i(t)$ through setting

$$Lp + R = 0 \tag{10}$$

from which

$$p = -R/L \tag{11}$$

Hence we see that the solution expressed by Eq. 7 reads more specifically

$$i(t) = Ae^{-Rt/L} \tag{12}$$

in which A is a constant of integration which is determined from the condition that $i(t) = 1/L$ for $t = 0$. Writing this condition, one obtains

$$A = 1/L \tag{13}$$

and hence

$$i(t) = (1/L)e^{-Rt/L} \tag{14}$$

This is the current in the circuit of Fig. 1 that results when $e_s(t)$ is a unit impulse. It has the form of a simple decaying exponential as shown

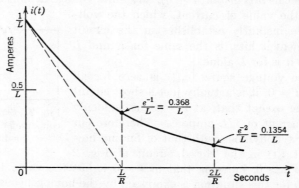

FIG. 3.   Illustrating the natural behavior of the series RL circuit.

in Fig. 3.   The quantity R/L which determines the rate of decay is called the *damping constant*. Its reciprocal L/R has the dimension of time, and is called the *time constant*. It is that length of time in which the current drops to $1/e = 0.368$ of its initial value. It is also that time in which the current would reach the value zero if it continued to de-

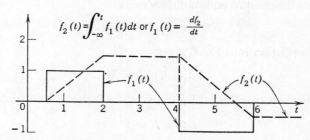

FIG. 4.   Illustrating the integration or differentiation of time functions.

crease at its initial rate, as is shown by the fact that the tangent to the curve at $t = 0$ intersects the zero axis at $t = L/R$. At $t = 2L/R$, that is, after a lapse of time equal to twice the time constant, the current has decayed to $1/e^2 = 0.1354$ of its initial value, etc. The time constant is a convenient unit to choose when plotting a curve such as that shown in Fig. 3.

If we would like to know the response of the circuit of Fig. 1 for $e_s(t)$ equal to a unit step, we have but to integrate the present result as given by Eq. 14. In order to be sure that the details of such a process of integration are clearly understood, let us review a few typical examples, illustrating graphically the essential features involved. In Fig. 4 the function $f_1(t)$ is nonzero only during the intervals $\frac{1}{2} < t < 2$ and $4 < t < 6$; there it has the constant values 1 and -1 respectively. What we wish to consider is the integral of this function; more specifically

$$f_2(t) = \int_{-\infty}^{t} f_1(t)\, dt \tag{15}$$

The function $f_2(t)$, which we refer to simply as the integral of $f_1(t)$, may be visualized as the accumulated area under the curve $f_1(t)$ from $-\infty$ to any variable time t, the upper limit in the integration. As this upper limit varies, the accumulated area varies. It is this variation of the total accumulated area with the time t that the function $f_2(t)$ is supposed to depict.

In Fig. 4 the function $f_2(t)$, according to these ideas, is shown by the dotted curve. Obviously $f_2(t)$ must be zero for all time until the beginning of the first rectangular pulse in $f_1(t)$ occurring at $t = \frac{1}{2}$. At this moment $f_2(t)$ begins to grow at unit rate because $f_1(t) = 1$. The same rate of growth continues throughout the interval $\frac{1}{2} < t < 2$ and ceases abruptly at $t = 2$, when the accumulated area (value of f_2) equals 1.5. This value of $f_2(t)$ remains unchanged from $t = 2$ until $t = 4$ since $f_1(t)$ is zero there and hence cannot cause a contribution to the net area. At $t = 4$ the area suddenly begins to decrease at unit rate and continues to do so until $t = 6$, at which time the net accumulated area equals $-\frac{1}{2}$. For all time after $t = 6$, $f_2(t)$ remains at this final value $-\frac{1}{2}$.

It is essential that the reader develop a facility for sketching graphically the integral of another graphically given curve, such as sketching $f_2(t)$ in Fig. 4 when $f_1(t)$ is drawn. With the same facility he should be able to carry through the reverse process, recognizing at once that the pulse function $f_1(t)$ is the derivative of the trapezoidal function $f_2(t)$.

Another pair of functions related in this manner are shown in Fig. 5. Here $f_1(t)$ is a triangular pulse with a discontinuity at its leading edge. $f_2(t)$, depicting the accumulated area under $f_1(t)$, exhibits a parabolic rise during the interval from $t = 0.5$ to $t = 1.5$. The reader should carefully check all detailed characteristics involved in this example, such as noting that the initial rate of rise in $f_2(t)$ equals 6, wherefore the tangent to $f_2(t)$ at $t = 0.5$ reaches the value 6 at $t = 1.5$ but that the value of $f_2(t)$ there is only half as great; further, that the rising portion of $f_2(t)$ is an inverted parabola with its apex at the point where this function has reached its maximum value. He should observe that $f_2(t)$ has a discontinuous derivative at $t = 0.5$ equal to the discontinuity of $f_1(t)$ at this point, but that the parabolic rise in $f_2(t)$ ahead of the point $t = 1.5$ runs smoothly into the constant value beyond; that is, there is no discontinuity in the derivative of $f_2(t)$ at $t = 1.5$, as is clear from the fact that $f_1(t)$ (equal to the derivative of f_2) is continuous at $t = 1.5$.

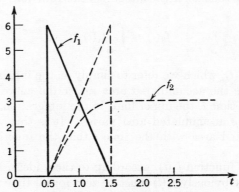

FIG. 5.   The function f_2 is the integral of f_1.

Thus we can obtain a fair idea of what the step-function response of the circuit of Fig. 1 will look like by concentrating our attention upon the impulse-response curve of Fig. 3 and visualizing the process of integration, knowing that the integral of a function is given graphically by the area under the corresponding plotted curve. Since $i(t)$ in Fig. 3 is zero for $t < 0$, it is clear that the integral will be zero for this interval also. At $t = 0$ the area under the curve suddenly begins to grow with time, the rate of growth being $1/L$. After $t = 0$, the rate of growth of area is at any t given by the ordinate of the curve of Fig. 3 for that t, since any function is simply the rate of growth of its integral, according to the elementary notions about "derivative" and "integral."

With these ideas in mind we can say—looking carefully at Fig. 3— that its integral starts from zero at $t = 0$, increases initially at the rate $1/L$, and tapers off in its rate of growth precisely as the curve of Fig. 3 falls off, the rate of growth eventually becoming zero. Thus the integral when plotted should be a curve that rises from zero and monotonically flattens out to an asymptote which equals the total area under the function of Fig. 3 from $t = 0$ to $t = \infty$.

Now that we have a pretty good idea of what the answer should look like, let us integrate Eq. 14 analytically. The formal integration yields

$$-(1/R)e^{-Rt/L} + \text{constant} \tag{16}$$

The constant is determined from the fact that this expression must be

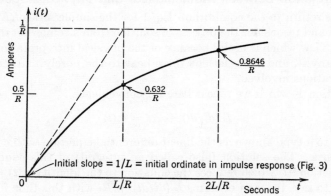

FIG. 6.   Integral of the time function shown in Fig. 3.

zero for $t = 0$ as pointed out above. Thus we find

$$\text{Constant} = 1/R \tag{17}$$

and so the response of the circuit of Fig. 1 to an applied unit voltage step is

$$i(t) = \frac{1}{R}(1 - e^{-Rt/L}) \tag{18}$$

This result is shown plotted in Fig. 6 and bears out what was anticipated above on the basis of purely graphical reasoning.

Since the asymptote in Fig. 6 is approached exponentially, the current actually never reaches this value at any finite time. In practice we find however that time constants are usually very small—a very small fraction of a second—and in extreme cases not more than 1 or 2 seconds. Hence for all practical purposes the current, in a circuit of this sort, equals its asymptotic value in a rather short time, after which the value of the current is determined by the resistance parameter R alone.

The inductance is effective in influencing the nature of the response only during the initial "buildup" period extending essentially over an interval of time equal to two or three time constants. This interval is commonly referred to as the "transient interval" or also as the "interval of signal formation." The asymptotic behavior is called the "steady state" or "stationary state" or "permanent state." In many practical problems one is interested only in the permanent state, in which case a more direct method of solution is possible, as will amply be discussed later on.

2 Correlation between Mathematical and Physical Aspects

Let us return to the equilibrium Eq. 1 for the simple series RL circuit of Fig. 1 and reconsider the process of solution from a somewhat different point of view which is useful because of the physical interpretations that accompany it, and the relations these bear to the purely mathematical considerations involved.

Equation 1, which we repeat here for convenience,

$$L \, (di/dt) + Ri = e_s(t) \tag{19}$$

belongs to a type known as the linear differential equation with constant coefficients. The solution (also called an integral) of this equation is that function $i(t)$ which reduces the equation to the identity $e_s(t) \equiv e_s(t)$. That is to say, the sum of terms $L \, (di/dt) + Ri$ with this time function substituted for $i(t)$ are converted into the function $e_s(t)$. It is reasonable to expect that the time function $i(t)$ that accomplishes this result depends upon the nature of $e_s(t)$ and will differ for different e_s functions. It is thus a very special or particular function $i(t)$ that suits the nature of $e_s(t)$, and for this reason it is called the *particular integral* of Eq. 19. Let us denote this time function by $i_p(t)$.

Although this time function constitutes a solution in the sense that it satisfies the given equation, we can show that it is only part of a more general time function which likewise satisfies the same equation. This fact may be seen if we consider, in addition to Eq. 19, the one

$$L \, (di/dt) + Ri = 0 \tag{20}$$

in which the right-hand member is zero. A solution to this equation is such a time function for $i(t)$ that makes the left-hand terms add to zero for all values of t. In a sense it is a particular integral for $e_s(t) = 0$. Suppose we denote this time function by $i_0(t)$. Then it is easily appreciated that the sum

$$i(t) = i_p(t) + i_0(t) \tag{21}$$

satisfies Eq. 19 because it makes the terms $L \, (di/dt) + Ri$ add to $e_s(t) + 0$, which obviously is the same as $e_s(t)$.

The function $i_0(t)$ which satisfies Eq. 20 is called the *complementary function*. The sum of the particular integral and complementary function, as in Eq. 21, is referred to as the *complete* solution to the differential

Eq. 19. The particular integral reflects only the nature of $e_s(t)$; the complementary function, on the other hand, contains the appropriate integration constants through which the complete solution achieves the flexibility needed to meet arbitrary conditions that may be specified at a particular instant (usually chosen as $t = 0$). The following discussion elaborates upon this item and gives a physical interpretation to the purely mathematical steps presented above.

In a physical problem, $e_s(t)$ very often represents some steady excitation voltage like the constant value of a battery or d-c generator, or the steady repetitive pattern of a sinusoidally time-varying voltage with constant amplitude. However, as indicated in Fig. 7, this steady excitation may not always have been connected to the circuit; that is to say, the switch S may be moved from an open to a closed position during the interval in which the circuit behavior is contemplated. The particular integral $i_p(t)$, on the other hand, recognizes by definition solely the steady pattern of $e_s(t)$, and therefore

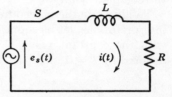

Fig. 7. Pertinent to the physical interpretation of a switching transient.

represents physically what the network response *would be* if the switch *S had been* closed for all time in the past and remains closed during the interval of contemplation. Or we may say that $i_p(t)$ represents the physical behavior of the circuit at a sufficiently long time after an initial switch closure so that the pattern of this behavior is substantially controlled by the nature of $e_s(t)$ alone. According to what is pointed out in the closing paragraph of the preceding article, the particular integral $i_p(t)$ is thus identified with what we refer to physically as the steady-state behavior. Since this part of the solution reflects the nature of the excitation function $e_s(t)$, we also speak of it as representing the *forced* behavior of the network. It is logically sensible that the ultimate behavior of a circuit following the sudden application of a driving force should emulate the character of that force function alone.

It is likewise logical and sensible to expect that the steady pattern of this ultimate behavior is not necessarily established instantly after the driving force is inserted into the network. Thus one may think of the network as initially resisting the dictatorial demands of the applied excitation, but, being passive and therefore having no source of energy with which to sustain such countermeasures, it is gradually beaten into complete submission. The intensity and duration of the initial struggle depends essentially upon the degree to which the behavior pattern imposed by the driving force differs from that which is characteristic of the network itself. The latter, which we call the *natural behavior* of the network, is an expression of what the network chooses to do when left to itself. In this unexcited, or force-free, state the network behavior is governed by Eq. 20; and so we see that the complementary function $i_0(t)$ represents physically the natural behavior of the network.

The resultant behavior emerges as a superposition of the forced and and the force-free behavior patterns of the network. The forced behavior or steady-state response corresponds mathematically to the particular integral; the force-free behavior or natural response is identified with the complementary function. Their sum yields the resultant behavior or the complete solution.

To illustrate the procedure for obtaining a solution according to these interpretations, let us suppose that the source $e_s(t)$ in Fig. 7 is a battery with the constant value E volts. If the instant of switch closure is denoted by $t = 0$, then the differential Eq. 19 for $t > 0$ reads

$$L\ (di/dt) + Ri = E \tag{22}$$

It is logical to assume that the particular integral or steady-state value of i is a constant, thus:

$$i_p(t) = I = \text{constant} \tag{23}$$

Direct substitution into Eq. 22 gives

$$RI = E \tag{24}$$

or

$$I = E/R = i_p(t) \tag{25}$$

The natural behavior of the circuit is determined by the equation

$$L\ (di/dt) + Ri = 0 \tag{26}$$

A solution to this type of differential equation is given by an exponential function of the form

$$i_0(t) = Ae^{pt} \tag{27}$$

in which A and p are constants. Since

$$di_0/dt = pAe^{pt} = p \times i_0(t) \tag{28}$$

substitution into Eq. 26 yields

$$(Lp + R) \times i_0(t) = 0 \tag{29}$$

For a nontrivial solution ($i_0 \neq 0$), it follows that

$$Lp + R = 0 \tag{30}$$

or

$$p = -R/L \tag{31}$$

whence the assumed solution 27 may be written more explicitly as

$$i_0(t) = Ae^{-Rt/L} \tag{32}$$

The complete solution is given by the sum of Eqs. 25 and 32, thus:

$$i(t) = i_p(t) + i_0(t) = \frac{E}{R} + Ae^{-Rt/L} \tag{33}$$

The amplitude A of the exponential part of the solution plays the part of an integration constant. It provides the solution with the necessary flexibility to meet an arbitrary initial condition. Thus the current in the circuit at the initial instant $t = 0$ may, through some more elaborate switching arrangement, be left with a nonzero value $i(0)$. Equation 33 for $t = 0$ then reads

$$i(0) = \frac{E}{R} + A \tag{34}$$

whence

$$A = i(0) - \frac{E}{R} \tag{35}$$

Substitution of this value for A into Eq. 33 thus gives the final result

$$i(t) = \frac{E}{R}(1 - e^{-Rt/L}) + i(0)e^{-Rt/L} \tag{36}$$

The first term for $E = 1$ volt checks Eq. 18 representing the unit step response of this same circuit. The second term involving $i(0)$ shows the effect of some previous disturbance responsible for the nonzero value of the current at $t = 0$. This effect evidently proceeds independently of the step response, owing to the sudden application of the voltage E; the two simply add to give the net response. If the circuit is initially at rest, $i(0) = 0$, and the second term in Eq. 36 drops out.

The function of the natural behavior of the circuit in relation to the net response may clearly be seen from Eq. 32 for $i_0(t)$ and Eq. 35 for the amplitude of this function. Thus the amplitude A of the natural behavior equals the difference between the current available in the circuit at $t = 0$ and that demanded by the excitation. The larger this discrepancy is, the larger will be the amplitude of $i_0(t)$. The latter function may be regarded as playing the role of a buffer or shock absorber, since it absorbs whatever initial discrepancy may exist between the available current and that demanded by the steady-state response, and gradually diminishes this discrepancy so that the net response smoothly approaches the forced behavior.

Since the natural behavior decays exponentially, its effect upon the net response is significant only during a relatively short interval following the switching operation. For this reason it is also called the *transient* part of the complete solution. It comes into existence through the sudden demands made by the driving force at the switching instant, and in intensity equals the disparity between these demands and the available resources of the circuit. In initiating a transient, the circuit is asserting its desire to avoid a sudden change of state which the application of an excitation is trying to force upon it. In resisting the change, it effects a smooth transition to the new order of things.

The transient is absent if no initial discrepancy exists, or if this discrepancy is canceled through some other means such as the application of an impulse whose function it is to establish the appropriate initial state.

The same general philosophy regarding transient response of linear networks applies in all cases regardless of their degrees of complexity; and the mathematical procedure applies also in appropriately extended form. The differential equation linking current $i(t)$ in some part of a network with an excitation $e_s(t)$ at the same point or anywhere else is always of the form

$$a_n \frac{d^n i}{dt^n} + a_{n-1} \frac{d^{n-1} i}{dt^{n-1}} + \cdots + a_1 \frac{di}{dt} + a_0 i$$

$$= b_m \frac{d^m e_s}{dt^m} + b_{m-1} \frac{d^{m-1} e_s}{dt^{m-1}} + \cdots + b_1 \frac{de_s}{dt} + b_0 e_s \quad (37)$$

in which $a_n \cdots a_0$ and $b_m \cdots b_0$ are real constants (the a's are always positive but the b's are not necessarily so).

It is clear that Eq. 19 is a simple example of this type. The complete solution consists of the sum of a particular integral $i_p(t)$ reflecting the nature of the excitation, and a complementary function $i_0(t)$ expressing the force-free behavior of the network. The latter is described by Eq. 37 with $e_s = 0$; and a solution to this equation may always be found through assuming the exponential form

$$i_0(t) = A e^{pt} \quad (38)$$

Since

$$\frac{d^k i_0}{dt^k} = p^k A e^{pt} = p^k \times i_0(t) \quad (39)$$

substitution of Eq. 38 into Eq. 37 yields, for $e_s = 0$,

$$(a_n p^n + a_{n-1} p^{n-1} + \cdots + a_1 p + a_0) i_0(t) = 0 \quad (40)$$

We are not interested in the trivial solution $i_0 = 0$, so we must have

$$a_n p^n + a_{n-1} p^{n-1} + \cdots + a_1 p + a_0 = 0 \qquad (41)$$

This familiar algebraic equation possesses n roots (p values) which we can denote as $p_1, p_2, \cdots, p_n$. Any one of these substituted for p in Eq. 38 yields a possible i_0 function; hence the most general i_0 function is seen to have the form

$$i_0(t) = A_1 e^{p_1 t} + A_2 e^{p_2 t} + \cdots + A_n e^{p_n t} \qquad (42)$$

Since $i_0(t)$ expresses a behavior that is characteristic of the network (i.e. peculiar to its own natural tendencies), Eq. 41 is referred to as the *characteristic equation* and the $p_1, p_2, \cdots, p_n$ as the *characteristic values* (later on we shall introduce the term *complex natural frequencies*) pertaining to the network.

These matters will all be discussed and illustrated in greater detail later on.* We wish at the moment merely to call attention to the fact that the network response always has the form $i_p(t) + i_0(t)$ in which $i_p(t)$ fits the excitation $e_s(t)$ [for example, if $e_s(t)$ is a constant, $i_p(t)$ is a constant; if $e_s(t)$ is a sinusoid, $i_p(t)$ is a sinusoid], and the transient part $i_0(t)$ always has the form given in Eq. 42. The quantities $A_1 \cdots A_n$ are integration constants; their values depend upon the discrepancies existing between the available charges in capacitances and currents in inductances at $t = 0$ (usually chosen as the switching instant) and those demanded by the steady-state functions for these quantities. If just the right values of charges and currents are somehow present at $t = 0$, all A's become zero, and there is no transient. In any case, the transient expresses the network's reaction to the demands of the suddenly applied excitation and acts as a buffer in effecting a smooth transition from the initial to the ultimate steady-state response.

3 Source Transformations; Thévenin's and Norton's Theorems and Their Uses

The results obtained so far may readily be extended to a number of modified forms of the present RL circuit with the help of Thévenin's theorem (see Art. 5, Ch. 3) which we shall here establish in a form particularly suited to our present needs. With reference to part (a) of Fig. 8, the box A is assumed to contain a perfectly arbitrary linear network and various voltage and current sources. The pair of terminals labeled 1–2 are brought out at random. Because the box A contains

* See Chapter 9.

sources, a nonzero voltage labeled e_{oc} will be found to appear at these terminals.

In part (b) of the figure this same box A has connected across the terminals 1–2 and through the switch S a second box B which also contains an arbitrary linear network but no sources. An external source $e_s(t)$ acts in series with both boxes as shown. With the switch S closed, the voltage rise at the terminals 1–2 is not the same as the open-circuit voltage $e_{oc}(t)$ shown in part (a) of the figure unless the current $i(t)$ is caused to be zero through a particular choice of the voltage $e_s(t)$. Such a special condition can always be brought about; in fact it is rather obvious that $i(t)$ will become zero if $e_s(t) = e_{oc}(t)$ for then the voltage

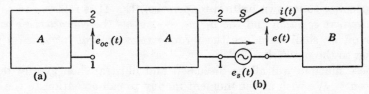

(a)   (b)

FIG. 8.   Pertinent to the discussion of Thévenin's theorem.

across the switch S, when it is open, is $e_{oc}(t) - e_s(t) = 0$ so that $i(t) = 0$ regardless of whether the switch S is open or closed; no current enters the box B.

The current $i(t)$ may, however, be thought of as the algebraic sum of two currents: the one that would exist for $e_s(t) = 0$, and the one that would result if all the sources in the box A became zero but $e_s(t)$ were other than zero. Because of the linearity of all network equations, such separate solutions for $i(t)$ can simply be added together to give the correct $i(t)$ in the presence of all sources [including $e_s(t)$] acting simultaneously, as already mentioned. Since for $e_s(t) = e_{oc}(t)$ the net current is zero, the two currents whose algebraic sum equals this net current can differ in direction (that is in algebraic sign) only. Therefore, the current that exists for $e_s(t) = 0$ may alternatively be calculated by setting all the sources in box A equal to zero and inserting a voltage $e_s(t) = -e_{oc}(t)$ externally to both boxes.

In effect this result represents a rather general source transformation inasmuch as box A may have been the embodiment of an elaborate type of source with terminals 1–2 to which an external source-free (also called "passive") network—the box B—is attached. What we have just demonstrated is the fact that, so far as the current entering box B is concerned (and hence so far as the complete behavior of the network in box B is concerned), we may consider the excitation to be lumped at one point *external* to both boxes.

The external source $e_s(t) = -e_{oc}(t)$ is to be regarded as a fictitious equivalent of all the various sources within the box A initially responsible for the appearance of the voltage $e_{oc}(t)$, which is referred to as an "open-circuit" voltage (hence the subscripts oc) because it is the voltage originally appearing at the terminals 1–2 when these are free. When this equivalent voltage is inserted, the original sources in the box A are to be regarded as dead; and it should be recalled at this time that a dead voltage source is identical with a short circuit while a dead current source is identical with an open circuit. These latter considerations are important because they have a vital bearing upon the geometrical structure

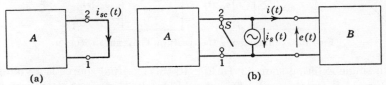

Fig. 9. Pertinent to the discussion of Norton's theorem.

of the resulting passive network in box A that remains after the sources have been set equal to zero (as will be seen from examples later on).

If we wish we may use an equivalent external current source instead of a voltage source to replace the active character of the box A. Figure 9 illustrates the relevant features of this type of source conversion. Here we consider the terminals 1–2 of the original box A by itself [part (a) of the figure] to be short-circuited, yielding the current $i_{sc}(t)$. When box B is placed across the terminals 1–2, as shown in part (b) of the same figure (the short-circuiting switch S being open) a current source $i_s(t)$ is bridged across these terminals also. The current through the terminals 1–2 of box A is then not the same as the short-circuit current $i_{sc}(t)$ shown in part (a) of the figure unless the voltage $e(t)$ is caused to be zero through a particular choice of the current $i_s(t)$. Such a special condition can always be brought about; in fact it is rather obvious that $e(t)$ will become zero if $i_s(t) = i_{sc}(t)$, for then the current through the switch S, when it is closed, is $i_{sc}(t) - i_s(t) = 0$ so that $e(t) = 0$ regardless of whether the switch S is closed or open; no voltage appears across the terminals of box B.

This voltage $e(t)$ may, however, be thought of as the algebraic sum of two voltages: the one that would exist for $i_s(t) = 0$, and the one that would result if all the sources in the box A became zero but $i_s(t)$ were other than zero. Because of the linearity of all network equations, such separate solutions for $e(t)$ can simply be added together to give the correct $e(t)$ in the presence of all sources [including $i_s(t)$] acting simul-

taneously. Since for $i_s(t) = i_{sc}(t)$ the net voltage is zero, the two voltages whose algebraic sum equals this net voltage can differ in direction
(that is, in algebraic sign) only. Therefore, the voltage that exists for
$i_s(t) = 0$ may alternatively be calculated through setting all the sources
in box A equal to zero and inserting a current $i_s(t) = -i_{sc}(t)$ externally
to both boxes.

These results are summarized in Figs. 10 and 11 which show the alternate ways in which the active character of a network may be replaced

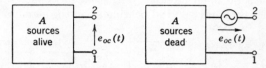

FIG. 10.   Summarizing the result of Thévenin's theorem.

by a single external source. In Fig. 10 this external source is a voltage;
in Fig. 11 it is a current. One should clearly observe that the equivalence in either case refers to what happens to a second passive circuit
that is connected across the terminals 1–2 and *not* to what happens inside the box A. The resultant voltages and currents inside the box A
are, of course, not the same for the single external source as they are
for the original internal sources (although one can determine in any
specific case how they differ). The replacement indicated in either Fig.

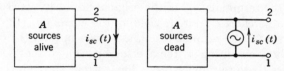

FIG. 11.   Summarizing the result of Norton's theorem.

10 or 11, therefore, is usually sensible only when the interest lies in the
resultant behavior external to the box A.

The equivalence indicated in Fig. 10 is commonly known as *Thévenin's
theorem;* that in Fig. 11, which is its dual, as *Norton's theorem.*

The simplest example of the equivalence of voltage and current
sources according to these ideas is shown in Fig. 12, where a voltage
source $e_s(t)$ in series with a resistance R is presented as being the equivalent of a current source $i_s(t)$ in parallel with the same resistance R if
$e_s(t) = Ri_s(t)$, the truth of this statement being evident upon recognition
that both sources yield the same terminal voltage on open circuit and
the same terminal current on short circuit, and otherwise present the
same passive element between these terminals (again the short-circuit

character of the voltage source and the open-circuit character of the current source are important).

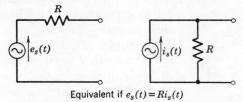

Equivalent if $e_s(t) = Ri_s(t)$

FIG. 12.   Source transformation involving a resistance element.

Further simple examples of this sort of equivalence, involving a single passive element, are shown in Figs. 13 and 14.   In Fig. 13 the passive element is an inductance L.   Here the equivalence demands that (except for the constant multiplier L) the voltage be the derivative of the current

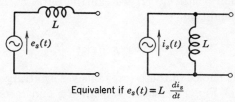

Equivalent if $e_s(t) = L \dfrac{di_s}{dt}$

FIG. 13.   Source transformation involving an inductance element.

or the latter the integral of the former.   Thus, for example, if $e_s(t)$ in this figure is an impulse, then $i_s(t)$ is a step function.

In Fig. 14 the passive element is a capacitance.   Again the current and voltage functions are related by differentiation or integration but

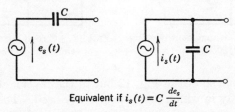

Equivalent if $i_s(t) = C \dfrac{de_s}{dt}$

FIG. 14.   Source transformation involving a capacitance element.

this time with the reference to current and voltage reversed.   That is, if here $i_s(t)$ is an impulse, $e_s(t)$ is a step function.

With these ideas in mind suppose we return to the consideration of the simple circuit of Fig. 1 and apply to the voltage source in series with R, the equivalence relationship given in Fig. 12.   We then obtain the circuit of Fig. 15 and know that the current $i(t)$ through the inductance element here will be precisely the same as in Fig. 1 if $i_s(t)$ is set equal to $1/R$ times $e_s(t)$. For example, if $i_s(t)$ is $(1/R)$th of a unit impulse, then

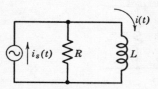

$i(t)$ is given by Eq. 14. Hence, if $i_s(t)$ is a unit impulse, then $i(t)$ is R times the expression given by Eq. 14.

On the other hand, if $i_s(t)$ in Fig. 15 is $(1/R)$th of a unit step, then $i(t)$ is given by Eq. 18; or, if $i_s(t)$ is a unit step, then $i(t)$ equals R times the expression in Eq. 18. Thus the solutions to the previous problem involving a voltage source immediately yield solutions to new situations. Further examples of this useful scheme are the following.

FIG. 15.   Parallel RL circuit excited by a current.

Suppose in Fig. 15 we divide the resistance R into two parallel parts whose combination is still R. If we call the parts R_1 and R_2, then we must fulfill the condition

$$R_1 R_2/(R_1 + R_2) = R \tag{43}$$

but otherwise the choice of these resistances is arbitrary. Now consider the source $i_s(t)$ of Fig. 15 associated with R_1, and reconvert this combination to the form of a voltage source in series with R_1, using again

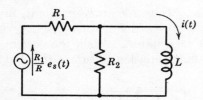
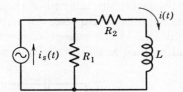

FIG. 16.   Circuit arrangement yielding the same $i(t)$ as in Fig. 15.

FIG. 17.   Circuit arrangement yielding the same $i(t)$ as in Fig. 1.

the same principle shown in Fig. 12 but in the reverse direction as contrasted to the way in which it was previously used. The voltage source becomes $R_1 i_s(t)$, but, remembering that $i_s(t) = e_s(t)/R$, in which $e_s(t)$ is the original voltage source of Fig. 1, we end up with the situation pictured in Fig. 16 in which the current $i(t)$ through the inductance, for a given $e_s(t)$ is the same as in the situation of Fig. 1. We see by these simple and effortless maneuvers (effortless because no difficult calculations or new processes of solution are involved) that the solution to what might otherwise seem to be a more complex network problem is represented through an almost trivial variation in the known solution to a simpler one.

Again, suppose we reconsider the problem of Fig. 1 but this time split the resistance R into series components R_1 and R_2 leaving $R_1 + R_2 = R$. Then, converting the voltage source $e_s(t)$ in series with R_1 into an equivalent current source $i_s(t) = e_s(t)/R_1$ in parallel with R_1, we get the network shown in Fig. 17, in which $i(t)$ is still the same [for a given $e_s(t)$] as found previously when considering the situation of Fig. 1.

It should be clear to the reader that such transformations can be carried on indefinitely (one can apply to R_1 in Fig. 17 the same process that was applied to R in Fig. 15, etc.), and that the procedure can be varied by working on L instead of on R. Further exploitation is left as exercises for the student.

4   The Dual of the Series RL Circuit

We turn our attention now to the circuit of Fig. 18. Here we have the parallel combination of a capacitance C and a conductance G fed by a current source $i_s(t)$, and the voltage $e(t)$ appearing across this parallel arrangement is regarded as the desired response. Equilibrium in this case is an equilibrium of currents, and is expressed by the equation

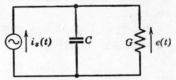

$$C\frac{de}{dt} + Ge = i_s(t) \qquad (44)$$

FIG. 18.   This circuit and that of Fig. 1 are duals.

If we compare this equation with Eq. 1 expressing the equilibrium of the circuit of Fig. 1, we see at once that the two are identical in form. Specifically, Eq. 44 becomes interchanged with Eq. 1 if one interchanges the following quantities in pairs:

$$e(t) \quad \text{with} \quad i(t)$$

$$i_s(t) \quad \text{with} \quad e_s(t)$$

$$C \quad \text{with} \quad L \qquad (45)$$

$$G \quad \text{with} \quad R$$

What we are observing here is further evidence of the principle of duality already mentioned. We refer to the configurations of Figs. 1 and 18 as being the duals of each other, and the reason they are duals is that their equilibrium equations follow one from the other upon interchanging the quantities or concepts

Voltage   and   current

C and L

G and R

$$(46)$$

Series connection   and   parallel connection

Since Eq. 44 has the same form as Eq. 1, we can write down the solution at once. For instance, if we let $i_s(t)$ be a unit impulse (it then has the effect of suddenly, at $t = 0$ say, filling the capacitance C with 1 coulomb, thus raising its voltage to the initial value $1/C$ volts), then the solution for $e(t)$ follows from Eq. 14 as being

$$e(t) = \frac{1}{C} e^{-Gt/C} \qquad (47)$$

When plotted, this function looks like the curve of Fig. 3 with the initial value $1/C$ and abscissa units equal to C/G instead of L/R. The damping constant of the parallel CG circuit is G/C; its time constant is C/G seconds.

If $i_s(t)$ in Fig. 18 is a unit step, the solution has the form of Eq. 18. Specifically, we get

$$e(t) = \frac{1}{G} (1 - e^{-Gt/C}) \qquad (48)$$

which has the form of the curve in Fig. 6 with $1/G$ as the asymptotic value.

We may now maneuver this circuit into a variety of other forms, some of which the reader can work out for himself. Suppose we show how we get other circuit situations through manipulating the capacitance C in Fig. 18. First split this capacitance into two parallel parts C_1 and C_2, keeping $C_1 + C_2 = C$. Consider C_1 nearest the current source $i_s(t)$, and convert this combination into an equivalent voltage source according to the equivalence shown in Fig. 14. We arrive at the circuit of Fig. 19 in which

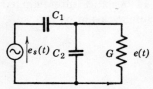

FIG. 19.   Circuit arrangement yielding the same $e(t)$ as in Fig. 18.

$$e_s(t) = \frac{1}{C_1} \int i_s(t) \, dt \qquad (49)$$

if the voltage $e(t)$ is to be the same as in the circuit of Fig. 18 for any

$i_s(t)$. If the latter is a unit impulse, then $e_s(t)$ is a step function of the value $1/C_1$. Since Eq. 47 gives $e(t)$ for a unit impulse $i_s(t)$, we can say that the unit step response of the circuit of Fig. 19 reads

$$e(t) = \frac{C_1}{C} e^{-Gt/C}, \qquad (C = C_1 + C_2) \qquad (50)$$

5   The Series RLC Circuit

Let us now turn our attention to the next problem in order of difficulty. This is the circuit containing all three kinds of elements: R, L, and C.

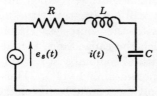
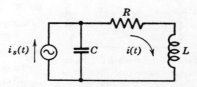

FIG. 20.   The series RLC circuit with voltage excitation.

FIG. 21.   Equivalent circuit arrangement to that in Fig. 20, which is found through making a source transformation as depicted in Fig. 14.

Suppose we consider their series arrangement, fed by a voltage source, Fig. 20.   The voltage equilibrium equation reads

$$L \frac{di}{dt} + Ri + \frac{1}{C} \int i \, dt = e_s(t) \qquad (51)$$

For the excitation function let us choose a unit step.   This situation may be treated most effectively through considering the source transformation illustrated in Fig. 14 where a voltage source in series with a capacitance is converted into an equivalent current source in parallel with this capacitance.   In our present problem we have a choice of considering the voltage source in series with any one of the three elements R, L, or C.   Since the voltage has been assumed to be a step function, the source transformation involving the capacitance turns out to be very effective as the reader will see in a moment (he can then try out the other possibilities for himself if he doesn't agree that our choice is a good one).

At all events, if we associate the capacitance C with the source $e_s(t)$ and then apply the transformation shown in Fig. 14, we get the situation illustrated in Fig. 21 in which the current source is C times the derivative of $e_s(t)$ and, therefore, an impulse of value C.   Now it should be remembered from the discussion in Ch. 4 that a current impulse applied to a capacitance instantly places a finite charge in that capacitance. In our case we also have the associated elements R and L, but their presence is readily seen to have no influence upon this instantaneous happening because the voltage rise across the capacitance is only finite, and hence the current through the RL path will certainly have to be finite. This finite current cannot lower the capacitance voltage in zero time, and so what happens at the initial instant when the current impulse impinges upon the circuit is, as stated above, not influenced by the presence of R and L.

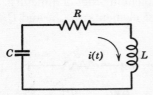

FIG. 22.   Series RLC circuit under force-free condition.

After the impulse strikes (which instant we shall again call $t = 0$), this situation is synonymous with the sourceless circuit of Fig. 22 in which the capacitance C finds itself charged with C coulombs at $t = 0$ (that is, raised to a potential of 1 volt). Thus the problem of applying a unit step voltage to the series circuit of Fig. 20 is reduced to the problem of the simple capacitance discharge in a series RLC circuit, the charge being such as to bring the capacitance initially to 1 volt.

The equilibrium equation for this simplified version of our problem reads

$$L \frac{di}{dt} + Ri + \frac{1}{C} \int i \, dt = 0 \tag{52}$$

We again assume an exponential solution, and try tentatively

$$i(t) = A e^{pt} \tag{53}$$

Since

$$\frac{di}{dt} = pi(t) \quad \text{and} \quad \int i \, dt = \frac{i(t)}{p} \tag{54}$$

substitution into Eq. 52 yields

$$\left(Lp + R + \frac{1}{Cp} \right) i(t) = 0 \tag{55}$$

For a nontrivial solution it is clear that

$$Lp + R + \frac{1}{Cp} = 0 \tag{56}$$

which is satisfied by two p values which for the moment we shall call p_1 and p_2. Since each p value determines an independent solution of the form given by Eq. 53, we recognize that their sum is a more general solution. It may be written

$$i(t) = A_1 e^{p_1 t} + A_2 e^{p_2 t} \tag{57}$$

in which A_1 and A_2 are to be regarded as integration constants. These are needed in order to be able to make the solution 57 fit the conditions that obtain at $t = 0$.

At this instant the capacitance appears charged to 1 volt; that is, with a charge of C coulombs. The current at this moment is still zero since a discontinuous current through the inductance would require an infinite voltage which is not present. The charge in the capacitance is the integral of $i(t)$ as given by Eq. 57. Denoting the charge by $q(t)$, we find

$$q(t) = \frac{A_1}{p_1} e^{p_1 t} + \frac{A_2}{p_2} e^{p_2 t} \tag{58}$$

For $t = 0$ we have * $q = -C$ and $i = 0$. Writing Eqs. 57 and 58 for these conditions gives

$$A_1 + A_2 = 0, \qquad \frac{A_1}{p_1} + \frac{A_2}{p_2} = -C \tag{59}$$

from which the constants A_1 and A_2 are determined. One readily finds

$$A_1 = \frac{p_1 p_2 C}{p_1 - p_2}, \qquad A_2 = \frac{p_1 p_2 C}{p_2 - p_1} \tag{60}$$

Substitution of these values into Eq. 57 yields the formal solution to our problem, noting that the p values are found from Eq. 56.

The detailed character of the solution thus found depends very definitely upon the nature of the p values, or roots of the algebraic Eq. 56, which for this reason is called the "characteristic equation," the p values sometimes being referred to as "characteristic values." Primarily the nature of these roots is determined by the value of the resistance parameter R appearing in Eq. 56. To illustrate this point, let us consider certain specific values of R and, to begin with that value leading to the simplest and most significant case, choose $R = 0$.

---

* The initial charge is such as to make the top plate of the capacitance in Fig. 21 positive, while the reference arrow for the current is such as to make the bottom plate positive.

Equation 56 then reads

$$Lp + 1/Cp = 0 \quad \text{or} \quad p^2 = -1/LC \tag{61}$$

Denoting $1/LC$ by ω_0^2 we have

$$p = \pm j\omega_0 \quad \text{or say} \quad p_1 = j\omega_0, \quad p_2 = -j\omega_0 \tag{62}$$

The roots in this case are a pair of conjugate pure imaginaries. From Eq. 60 one has

$$A_1 = -A_2 = C\omega_0/2j \tag{63}$$

whence Eq. 57 becomes

$$i(t) = C\omega_0 \left(\frac{e^{j\omega_0 t} - e^{-j\omega_0 t}}{2j} \right) = C\omega_0 \sin \omega_0 t \tag{64}$$

which can also be written

$$i(t) = \sin \omega_0 t / L\omega_0 \tag{65}$$

since, by the definition of ω_0, $L\omega_0 = 1/C\omega_0$.

The solution in this case is a simple steady sinusoid with angular frequency ω_0 radians per second determined by the LC product, since $\omega_0 = 1/\sqrt{LC}$. Writing the solution 64 or 65 in the form

$$i(t) = \sqrt{C/L} \sin \omega_0 t \tag{66}$$

makes it clear that the amplitude of the sinusoidal response is determined from the L/C ratio. Thus the two circuit constants L and C determine the two significant things about the sinusoidal response, namely, its amplitude and frequency.

The radian frequency ω_0 is referred to as the *natural* frequency of the physical system described by the LC circuit. As shown by Eq. 62 this natural frequency is determined from the roots of the characteristic equation.

The sinusoidal oscillation is undamped (that is, it persists indefinitely) in this case because the resistance parameter R, which is the dissipative element, is assumed zero. In any practical circuit there will always be some unavoidable resistance. Hence the present example for $R = 0$ is one that represents an unattainable limiting situation. Nevertheless, it is of definite interest because it emphasizes the most significant character of the simple RLC circuit, which is its oscillatory tendency. We shall now assume $R \neq 0$ and return to the characteristic Eq. 56 in this more general case.

For purposes of compactness of notation it is expedient, in addition to writing ω_0^2 for $1/LC$, to let

$$\alpha = R/2L \tag{67}$$

Then Eq. 56 may be written

$$p^2 + 2\alpha p + \omega_0^2 = 0 \tag{68}$$

which yields

$$p = -\alpha \pm \sqrt{\alpha^2 - \omega_0^2} \tag{69}$$

Three distinct possibilities can now occur, depending upon the following relative values of α and ω_0:

(a) *The aperiodic case* which results if

$$\alpha > \omega_0 \tag{70}$$

(b) *The critically damped case*, defined by

$$\alpha = \omega_0 \qquad \text{and} \tag{71}$$

(c) *The damped oscillatory case*, if $\alpha \neq 0$ but

$$\alpha < \omega_0 \tag{72}$$

Of these three cases * the last is by far the most important practically, and our further detailed discussions will be substantially confined to it. It is then more effective to write Eq. 69 in the form

$$p = -\alpha \pm j\sqrt{\omega_0^2 - \alpha^2} \tag{73}$$

Specifically, one may define the roots as

$$p_1 = -\alpha + j\omega_d \quad \text{and} \quad p_2 = -\alpha - j\omega_d \tag{74}$$

where

$$\omega_d = \sqrt{\omega_0^2 - \alpha^2} \tag{75}$$

is referred to as the *damped* natural angular frequency, in distinction to ω_0 which we saw previously to be the *undamped* natural frequency. It is interesting and useful to note from Eq. 75 that the relation among the

* These three cases are also referred to respectively as "overdamped," "critically damped," and "underdamped."

three quantities ω_0, α, ω_d is identical with that relating the three sides of a right triangle, Fig. 23. If ω_0 is regarded as fixed and α is thought of as variable (since Eq. 67 shows that it varies with the resistance R) one obtains a compact and clear picture of how the damped natural frequency ω_d differs from the undamped value ω_0 for varying amounts of "damping" as determined by the value of α.

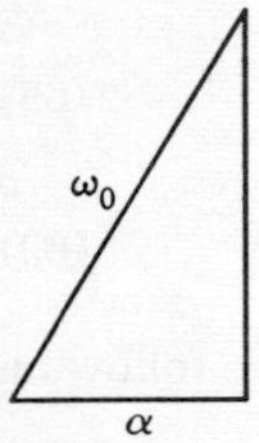

With the values 74 for p_1 and p_2, the constants A_1 and A_2 according to Eqs. 60 become

$$A_1 = -A_2 = C\omega_0^2/2j\omega_d \tag{76}$$

in which Eq. 75 is used to show that $p_1 p_2 = \alpha^2 + \omega_d^2 = \omega_0^2$. Substitution into the formal solution 57 gives

$$i(t) = C\omega_0 \times (\omega_0/\omega_d) \times e^{-\alpha t}\sin\omega_d t \tag{77}$$

Fig. 23. Geometric relationship among the undamped radian frequency ω_0, the damped radian frequency ω_d, and the damping constant α.

or

$$i(t) = \frac{1}{L\omega_0} \times \frac{\omega_0}{\omega_d} \times e^{-\alpha t}\sin\omega_d t \tag{78}$$

or

$$i(t) = \sqrt{\frac{C}{L}} \times \frac{\omega_0}{\omega_d} \times e^{-\alpha t}\sin\omega_d t \tag{79}$$

The result is essentially the same as for the previously considered case except that the sinusoidal oscillation is now exponentially damped because of the factor $e^{-\alpha t}$, and the frequency of oscillation is somewhat decreased as a result of the damping effect ($\omega_d \leq \omega_0$), as shown in Fig. 23. The quantity α, given by Eq. 67, is called the *damping factor;* its reciprocal is again a time constant. Namely, in $1/\alpha$ seconds the amplitude of the sinusoidal oscillation decays to the fraction $1/e = 0.368$ of its initial value; in $2/\alpha$ seconds it decays to $1/e^2 = 0.1354$ of its initial value, etc. This situation may more clearly be appreciated if one visualizes the curve for $e^{-\alpha t}$—essentially that shown in Fig. 3—as forming an envelope for the oscillatory function given by the rest of the expression in Eq. 78.

One should not be misled by Eq. 67 into thinking that the damping factor α depends only upon R and L, and not upon C, for the actual state of affairs may be quite otherwise, depending upon what else (such as ω_0, for instance) one is tacitly thinking of as being held constant while α varies. For example, since $\omega_0^2 = 1/LC$, or $L = 1/C\omega_0^2$, one can rewrite Eq. 67 as

$$\alpha = (RC/2)\omega_0^2 \tag{80}$$

whence, for a constant value of ω_0, α is seen to vary as the product of

R and C. Again from Eq. 75 one would get

$$\alpha = \sqrt{(1/LC) - \omega_d{}^2} \tag{81}$$

from which it is clear that, for a constant value of ω_d, α depends upon the product of L and C.

Returning to our damped oscillatory solution as portrayed by any one of the three expressions 77, 78, or 79, it is sometimes of interest to observe the amount of decay that takes place during one cycle or period, which is given by

$$\tau_d = 2\pi/\omega_d \text{ seconds} \tag{82}$$

The ratio of the amplitude of oscillation at the beginning of any period to that at the end of this period is given by the factor

$$e^{\alpha \tau_d} = e^{2\pi\alpha/\omega_d} \tag{83}$$

The natural logarithm of this factor, which is

$$\Delta = 2\pi\alpha/\omega_d = 2\pi\alpha/\sqrt{\omega_0{}^2 - \alpha^2} \tag{84}$$

is called the "logarithmic decrement" or sometimes just "the decrement" of the circuit. It is useful to observe that $1/\Delta$ equals the number of cycles (or periods) in which the oscillations decay by the factor $1/e = 0.368$.

If $\alpha \ll \omega_0$, the circuit is said to be "highly" oscillatory or "slightly damped." In many communications applications this situation is of special interest, the "quality" of the circuit being regarded as higher the smaller the amount of damping present. In the slightly damped case $\omega_d \approx \omega_0$, and the logarithmic decrement may be written

$$\Delta \approx 2\pi\alpha/\omega_0 = \pi R/L\omega_0 = \pi R\sqrt{C/L} \tag{85}$$

The quantity

$$Q = \frac{L\omega_0}{R} = \frac{1}{R}\sqrt{\frac{L}{C}} \tag{86}$$

commonly referred to as the Q of the circuit is a measure of its quality as an oscillatory system. In terms of Q the logarithmic decrement reads

$$\Delta = \pi/Q \tag{87}$$

There are practical instances in which a nonoscillatory or substantially nonoscillatory discharge is desired but with a premium upon the rapidity of the discharge under certain other fixed conditions such as a given capacitance or inductance. A case in point is the ballistic galvanometer which is essentially a torsion pendulum and hence a mechanical analogue of the type of electric circuit we are studying here. Although the critically damped case (referred to above) is more or less the solution to this optimum discharge problem, it is found that an adjustment which theoretically corresponds to an oscillatory condition but very near to the critically damped state is a more satisfactory answer.

In this connection it may be worth pointing out that the solutions corresponding to the aperiodic and critically damped cases are readily obtained from the results stated by Eqs. 77, 78, or 79. Thus, when $\alpha > \omega_0$, the expression for ω_d as given by Eq. 75 becomes imaginary, and it is appropriate to write

$$\omega_d = j\sqrt{\alpha^2 - \omega_0^2} = j\beta \tag{88}$$

Noting that

$$\sin j\beta t = j \sinh \beta t \tag{89}$$

one obtains from Eq. 79 (either of the two preceding equations could also be used) the result pertinent to the aperiodic case, namely,

$$i(t) = \sqrt{C/L} \times (\omega_0/\beta) \times e^{-\alpha t} \sinh \beta t \tag{90}$$

Since the hyperbolic sine is nonoscillatory, this time function has the appearance of a unidirectional pulse.

In the critically damped case β becomes zero. Noting that, for small βt, $\sinh \beta t \to \beta t$, the result for this case is immediately obtained from Eq. 90, thus:

$$i(t) = \sqrt{C/L}\, \omega_0 t \times e^{-\alpha t} \tag{91}$$

Again it may be pointed out that a variety of modifications of the circuit arrangement of Fig. 21 may be carried out without affecting the nature of the response, through use of one or more of the source transformations shown in Figs. 12, 13, and 14. Thus, if the capacitance C in Fig. 21 is split into $C_1 + C_2 = C$ and the transformation of Fig. 14 applied to $i_s(t)$ and C_1 in parallel to convert this combination into a voltage source $e_s(t) = 1/C_1$ times the integral of $i_s(t)$, one arrives at the circuit of Fig. 24. If $e_s(t)$ here is a step function of the value C/C_1, the current $i(t)$ is precisely the same as just determined.

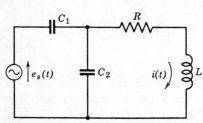

FIG. 24. Circuit arrangement yielding the same $i(t)$ as in Figs. 20 and 21.

If we return to Fig. 20, associate the voltage source with the inductance L, convert to a current source arrangement according to the equivalence in Fig. 13, then split $1/L$ into the additive parts $1/L_1 + 1/L_2$, associate L_1 with the source, and convert back to a voltage, the result has the appearance shown in Fig. 25 in which the current $i(t)$ is again the same function that we have already found, for $e_s(t)$ equal to a step function of the value L_1/L (which incidentally is a factor *larger* than unity). Much time can be saved and greater cir-cumspection gained through use

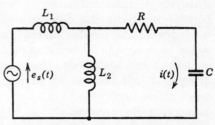

FIG. 25. Alternate circuit arrangement yielding the same $i(t)$ as in Figs. 20 and 21.

of methods of this sort in common with the principle of duality which we shall further illustrate in the following article.

6   The Dual of the Series RLC Circuit

The so-called complete dual of the situation given in Fig. 20 is the circuit arrangement shown in Fig. 26. Instead of R, L, and C in *series* we have their respective duals (G, C, and L) in *parallel*. Instead of

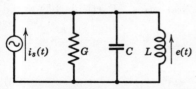

FIG. 26. This circuit and that in Fig. 20 are duals.

exciting by means of a *voltage* source in *series*, the excitation is a *current* source in *parallel*. Instead of being interested in the resulting current in the series loop, we are calling the response a voltage across the parallel combination. The final evidence that the situation of Fig. 26 actually is the complete dual of that shown in Fig. 20 of the previous article is revealed in the equilibrium equation (which incidentally is a current equilibrium as contrastd to the voltage equilibrium expressed by Eq. 51)

$$C\frac{de}{dt} + Ge + \frac{1}{L}\int e\,dt = i_s(t) \qquad (92)$$

Except for an interchange of the dual quantities in the pairs—voltage and current, resistance and conductance, inductance and capacitance—this equilibrium equation has precisely the form of Eq. 51 expressing the equilibrium of the circuit in Fig. 20.

The student should note carefully, in regard to duality, that this property is strictly a *mutual* one. That is to say, it is every bit as appropriate to say that the network of Fig. 20 is the dual of that in Fig. 26. Either network may be regarded as the given one or as the dual of the other one. We happened in the discussions of this chapter to begin with things connected in series, whence the dual things connected in parallel represent the dual situation. We might equally well have started with the parallel arrangement, whence the series arrangement would have been pointed out as being the dual one. In other words, the student should not fall into the habit of thinking that dual means things in parallel just because we happened to start our discussions with a series connection (we couldn't very well have started with both types of connection simultaneously).

Recognition of the duality existing between the two networks in question enables one to write down the solution to the present problem at once, in view of the detailed discussion given in the preceding article. For example, we see that the characteristic values of this system are given by

$$p = -\alpha \pm \sqrt{\alpha^2 - \omega_0{}^2} \tag{93}$$

with

$$\omega_0{}^2 = 1/LC, \qquad \alpha = G/2C \tag{94}$$

and again we have the possibility of overdamped ($\alpha > \omega_0$), critically damped ($\alpha = \omega_0$), and oscillatory ($\alpha < \omega_0$) cases. Particularly for the last we write, as before

$$p = -\alpha \pm j\omega_d \tag{95}$$

with

$$\omega_d = \sqrt{\omega_0{}^2 - \alpha^2} \tag{96}$$

The time function $e(t)$ for this case, assuming $i_s(t)$ to be a unit step, follows directly from Eqs. 77, 78, or 79, and reads

$$e(t) = \sqrt{L/C} \times (\omega_0/\omega_d) \times e^{-\alpha t} \sin \omega_d t \tag{97}$$

Further detailed discussion is identical with that already given and need not be repeated.

The same form of solution may be recognized as applying to numerous additional circuit arrangements derivable from the one shown in Fig. 26 through the source transformations as illustrated before. For example, the arrangement in Fig. 27 yields the same $e(t)$ as that in Fig. 26 for $e_s(t) = L \, di_s/dt$. Thus, if $e_s(t)$ is an impulse of value L, the solution given by Eq. 97 applies directly; if $e_s(t)$ is a unit impulse, then $e(t)$ is the expression given in Eq. 97, multiplied by $1/L$; that is

$$e(t) = \frac{\omega_0^2 \times e^{-\alpha t} \sin \omega_d t}{\omega_d} \qquad (98)$$

If the inductance L in Fig. 26 is first split into the parallel components L_1 and L_2, and the same source conversion applied to $i_s(t)$ in combination with L_1, the result is that shown in Fig. 28 in which $e(t)$ is again given

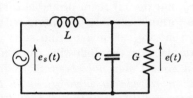

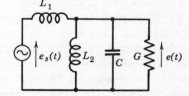

FIG. 27.   Circuit arrangement yielding the same $e(t)$ as in Fig. 26.

FIG. 28.   Alternate circuit arrangement yielding the same $e(t)$ as in Fig. 26.

by Eq. 97 if $e_s(t)$ is an impulse of value L_1.   Further exploitation of these methods is suggested as exercises for the student.

7   Consideration of Arbitrary Initial Conditions

In the preceding discussion of the response of several simple circuits following some kind of voltage or current stimulus, it is tacitly assumed that there is no charge in the capacitance and no current in the inductance just before the occurrence of this excitation.   Since the instant of occurrence of the considered excitation is commonly referred to as the "initial instant," we may say that in our preceding analyses we tacitly assume initial "rest conditions," or that the circuit to which the given excitation is applied is initially at rest.   In practice it sometimes is necessary to consider the response of a circuit that is not at rest when the given excitation is applied.   We wish to say a few words now about the way in which such a situation may be dealt with.

When we encounter a circuit that is not at rest, we may infer that it is in the process of responding to some previous disturbance.   That is to say, when we deal with a condition of initial unrest, we are dealing with a circuit that is in the process of completing some "unfinished business." If a fresh excitation is applied while the circuit is thus in the midst of some other response, it follows, because of the linearity of the differential equation describing the network's equilibrium, that the net behavior is obtained through simply adding together the "unfinished business" and the response due to the fresh excitation, the latter computed as though the circuit were initially at rest.* It thus is merely necessary to discuss how one goes about describing more specifically the "unfinished business."

In this regard one has the off-hand impression that it is necessary to know the entire previous history of the circuit in order to be in a position to compute its behavior after some specified "initial instant"; and, since this "previous history" may in some cases have been rather complex both in nature and extent, one does not contemplate these computations in a particularly cheerful frame of mind, nor does it seem probable that it will be possible to obtain one simple formula capable of dealing with all situations. It turns out, however, that we can in fact find such a simple and yet perfectly general formula, for the following reason: *Any previous history to which the given circuit may have been subjected prior to the considered "initial instant" is completely summarized by a knowledge of the charges in the capacitances and the currents in the inductances at this instant.*

The truth of this statement follows from the fact that the behavior of a network following an initial instant is completely and uniquely determined from the values of the capacitance charges and inductance currents at this instant. Thus the foregoing discussion has shown that the behavior of the series RL circuit (Fig. 2) for $t > 0$ is fixed by the value of the current for $t = 0$ (Eq. 14 is the result for $i(0) = 1/L$). Similarly the behavior of the series RC circuit for $t > 0$ is fixed by the value of the charge for $t = 0$ (in Eq. 47 the capacitance voltage is given for $t > 0$ when the initial charge is 1 coulomb). The series RLC circuit has a definite behavior for $t > 0$ in terms of known values of charge and current at $t = 0$ (as will be shown in further detail presently).

That is to say, the state of the network at $t = 0$ is adequately described by the values of the initial charges and currents; *it is not necessary to know how these values came about!* Although a *given* set of values may have come about as a result of many completely different behavior patterns before the initial instant, the behavior that this set determines for $t > 0$ can have only *one* pattern because the solution to the pertinent differential equation of equilibrium involves as many integration constants as there are independent initial charges and currents, so that the latter determine these constants uniquely, and nothing else can exert an influence on the resulting solution. This point is now further illustrated for the series RLC circuit discussed in Art. 5.

Let us return to the point in the discussion of the RLC circuit where the formal solutions for current and charge (Eqs. 57 and 58) are obtained from the differential Eq. 52. The reason we refer to these as

* See Eq. 36 for a specific example of this sort.

"formal" solutions is that they are not yet explicit relations for the current and charge but merely represent these quantities in functional form because the integration constants A_1 and A_2 appearing in them are as yet not fixed. Since only two unknown constants are involved, two special conditions suffice to render the formal solutions explicit.

For these conditions we may choose two arbitrarily specified values of the current at selected instants of time, or two values of the charge at chosen instants; or, what is more commonly done, we may specify values for the current and the charge at $t = 0$. We call these values the "initial conditions" since they determine the state of the network at $t = 0$. Thus, through considering Eqs. 57 and 58 for $t = 0$, we have for the determination of the integration constants (in place of Eqs. 59)

$$A_1 + A_2 = i(0), \qquad \frac{A_1}{p_1} + \frac{A_2}{p_2} = q(0) \tag{99}$$

Solving these we have

$$A_1 = \frac{p_1 i(0) - p_1 p_2 q(0)}{p_1 - p_2}, \qquad A_2 = \frac{p_2 i(0) - p_2 p_1 q(0)}{p_2 - p_1} \tag{100}$$

Since the characteristic values p_1 and p_2 are conjugate complex, we see that the A's are conjugate complex. By Eqs. 74 and 75 we find

$$p_1 = -\alpha + j\omega_d = j(\omega_d + j\alpha) = j\omega_0 e^{j\phi}$$
$$p_2 = -\alpha - j\omega_d = -j(\omega_d - j\alpha) = -j\omega_0 e^{-j\phi} \tag{101}$$

where

$$\phi = \tan^{-1}(\alpha/\omega_d) = \cos^{-1}(\omega_d/\omega_0) \tag{102}$$

Thus, for the further evaluation of Eqs. 100, we have

$$p_1 p_2 = \omega_0^2, \qquad p_1 - p_2 = j2\omega_d$$

$$\frac{p_1 p_2}{p_1 - p_2} = \frac{\omega_0^2}{j2\omega_d}, \qquad \frac{p_1}{p_1 - p_2} = \frac{\omega_0}{2\omega_d} e^{j\phi} \tag{103}$$

so that

$$2A_1 = \frac{\omega_0}{\omega_d}[e^{j\phi}i(0) + j\omega_0 q(0)] \tag{104}$$

and

$$\frac{2A_1}{p_1} = \frac{\omega_0}{\omega_d}\left[e^{-j\phi}q(0) + \frac{i(0)}{j\omega_0}\right] \tag{105}$$

Equations 57 and 58 then give

$$i(t) = \text{Re}[2A_1 e^{p_1 t}] = \frac{\omega_0}{\omega_d}[i(0) \cos(\omega_d t + \phi) - \omega_0 q(0) \sin \omega_d t]e^{-\alpha t}$$

$$(106)$$

$$q(t) = \text{Re}\left[\frac{2A_1}{p_1} e^{p_1 t}\right] = \frac{\omega_0}{\omega_d}\left[q(0) \cos(\omega_d t - \phi) + \frac{i(0)}{\omega_0} \sin \omega_d t\right] e^{-\alpha t}$$

$$(107)$$

In this evaluation we have made use of the fact that the terms in Eqs. 57 and 58 are conjugate complex; whence their sum is expressible as twice the real part of either one. The student should verify the expressions 106 and 107 through substitution of the results 104 and 105 in order to gain familiarity with the manipulation of complex quantities, more particularly the exponential function with complex exponent.

Equations 106 and 107 yield explicitly the current and charge in a series RLC circuit for $t > 0$ in terms of their values at $t = 0$. Thus, for example, they reduce to the identities $i(0) = i(0)$ and $q(0) = q(0)$, upon substituting zero for t, it being clear from Eq. 102 that $\cos \phi = \omega_d/\omega_0$. These relations are useful in that they are the representation for any unfinished business that the RLC circuit may find itself in the process of carrying out if at $t = 0$ a fresh excitation is applied to it. Thus, for the completion of this unfinished business, one writes Eqs. 106 and 107 with $i(0)$ and $q(0)$ equal to the appropriate values (these must be part of the given data), and then adds the response due to the fresh excitation (for tacitly assumed rest conditions) to obtain the complete behavior for $t > 0$.

It is interesting also to note that Eqs. 106 and 107 give the response of the series RLC circuit for a number of special excitation functions. For example, if we want the response of this circuit to an applied unit voltage impulse, we observe according to the discussion given earlier that this excitation instantly establishes a current in the inductance of the value $1/L$. Hence we need merely consider Eqs. 106 and 107 for $i(0) = 1/L$ and $q(0) = 0$ to have the response appropriate to this excitation. In Art. 5 it is shown (through consideration of Figs. 20 and 21) that an applied unit step voltage is equivalent to starting from an initial capacitance charge $q(0) = -C$ coulombs. Hence Eqs. 106 and 107 for $i(0) = 0$ and $q(0) = -C$ yield results appropriate to this case, as may be verified by comparison with Eq. 77.

These considerations lead us to recognize that the process of taking arbitrary initial conditions into account in a transient-network problem may be done in an alternate way. Thus the existence of a current in an inductance at $t = 0$ is equivalent to inserting a voltage impulse (of appropriate value and occurring at $t = 0$) in series with this inductance, while the existence of a charge in a capacitance at $t = 0$ is equivalent to bridging a current impulse (of appropriate value and occurring at $t = 0$) across this capacitance. In other words, any set of arbitrary initial currents and charges may be replaced by an appropriate set of voltage and current impulse sources connected into the network. Superposition of their individually produced responses and that due to some specific excitation, all computed for initial rest conditions, yields the desired net response.

Thus it may be seen that a discussion of network response that tacitly considers only initial rest conditions is nevertheless sufficient to deal with problems involving arbitrary initial conditions.

SUMMARY REGARDING THE TRANSIENT RESPONSE OF ONE-, TWO-, AND THREE-ELEMENT COMBINATIONS

A   *Single Elements*

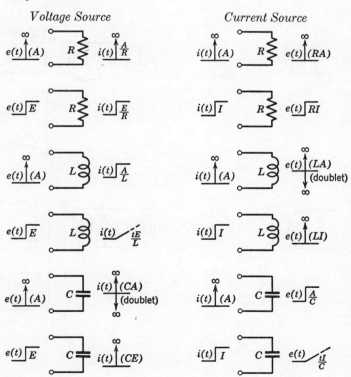

B Two Elements—R, L

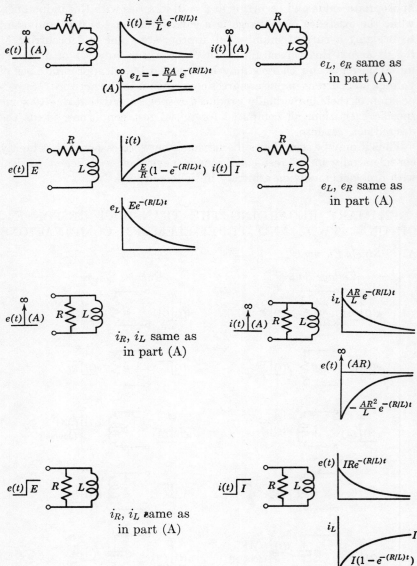

$$i(t) = \frac{A}{L} e^{-(R/L)t}$$

$$e_L = -\frac{RA}{L} e^{-(R/L)t}$$

e_L, e_R same as in part (A)

$$\frac{E}{R}(1 - e^{-(R/L)t})$$

$$Ee^{-(R/L)t}$$

e_L, e_R same as in part (A)

i_R, i_L same as in part (A)

$$\frac{AR}{L} e^{-(R/L)t}$$

$$-\frac{AR^2}{L} e^{-(R/L)t}$$

i_R, i_L same as in part (A)

$$IRe^{-(R/L)t}$$

$$I(1 - e^{-(R/L)t})$$

C   *Two Elements—R, C*

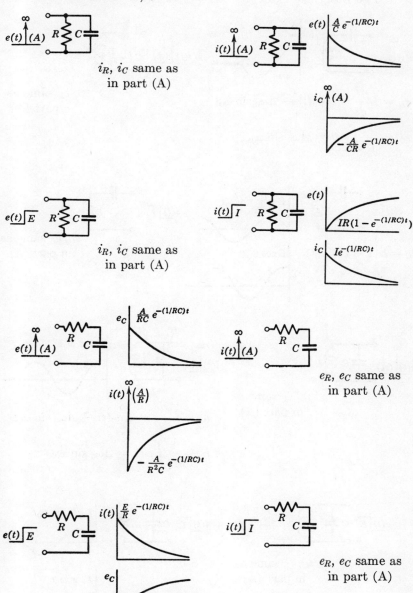

i_R, i_C same as
in part (A)

$e(t)$ $\frac{A}{C}e^{-(1/RC)t}$

i_C $-\frac{A}{CR}e^{-(1/RC)t}$

i_R, i_C same as
in part (A)

$e(t)$ $IR(1 - e^{-(1/RC)t})$

i_C $Ie^{-(1/RC)t}$

e_C $\frac{A}{RC}e^{-(1/RC)t}$

$i(t)$ $\left(\frac{A}{R}\right)$ $-\frac{A}{R^2C}e^{-(1/RC)t}$

e_R, e_C same as
in part (A)

$i(t)$ $\frac{E}{R}e^{-(1/RC)t}$

e_C $E(1 - e^{-(1/RC)t})$

e_R, e_C same as
in part (A)

D   *Two Elements—L, C* $\omega_0 = 1/\sqrt{LC}$

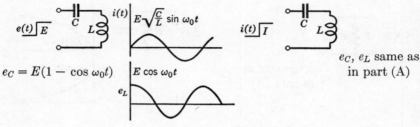

$$e_L = L\frac{di}{dt} = Au_0(t) - A\omega_0 \sin \omega_0 t$$

$$e_C = \frac{1}{C}\int i\,dt = A\omega_0 \sin \omega_0 t$$

e_C, e_L same as
in part (A)

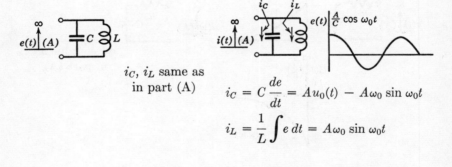

$$e_C = E(1 - \cos \omega_0 t)$$

e_C, e_L same as
in part (A)

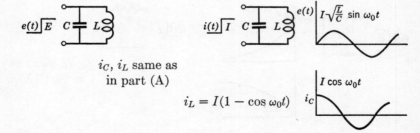

i_C, i_L same as
in part (A)

$$i_C = C\frac{de}{dt} = Au_0(t) - A\omega_0 \sin \omega_0 t$$

$$i_L = \frac{1}{L}\int e\,dt = A\omega_0 \sin \omega_0 t$$

i_C, i_L same as
in part (A)

$$i_L = I(1 - \cos \omega_0 t)$$

E   *Three Elements—R, L, C or G, C, L*
     $(\omega_0 > \alpha)$

$$\omega_0 = \frac{1}{\sqrt{LC}} \qquad \alpha = \frac{R}{2L} \quad \text{or} \quad \frac{G}{2C} \qquad \omega_d = \sqrt{\omega_0{}^2 - \alpha^2}$$

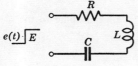   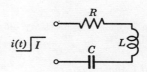

$$i(t) = E \sqrt{\frac{C}{L}} \frac{\omega_0}{\omega_d} e^{-\alpha t} \sin \omega_d t$$

e_L, e_R, e_C as shown
in part (A)

when $\alpha \ll \omega_0$

$$i(t) \approx E \sqrt{\frac{C}{L}} e^{-\alpha t} \sin \omega_0 t$$

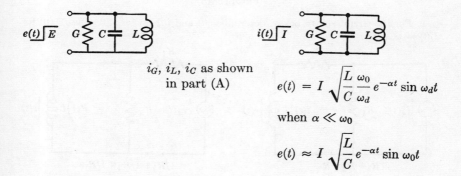

$$i(t) = \frac{A}{L} \frac{\omega_0}{\omega_d} e^{-\alpha t} \cos \left(\omega_d t + \cos^{-1} \frac{\omega_d}{\omega_0} \right)$$

e_L, e_R, e_C as shown
in part (A)

when $\alpha \ll \omega_0$; $i(t) \approx \dfrac{A}{L} e^{-\alpha t} \cos \omega_0 t$

i_G, i_L, i_C as shown
in part (A)

$$e(t) = I \sqrt{\frac{L}{C}} \frac{\omega_0}{\omega_d} e^{-\alpha t} \sin \omega_d t$$

when $\alpha \ll \omega_0$

$$e(t) \approx I \sqrt{\frac{L}{C}} e^{-\alpha t} \sin \omega_0 t$$

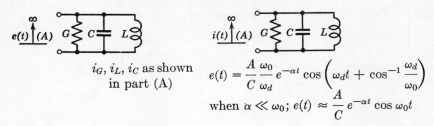

i_G, i_L, i_C as shown in part (A)

$$e(t) = \frac{A}{C}\frac{\omega_0}{\omega_d} e^{-\alpha t} \cos\left(\omega_d t + \cos^{-1}\frac{\omega_d}{\omega_0}\right)$$

when $\alpha \ll \omega_0$; $e(t) \approx \dfrac{A}{C} e^{-\alpha t} \cos \omega_0 t$

Note: When $\alpha \ll \omega_0$, it is necessary only to insert $e^{-\alpha t}$ as a multiplier to the results of part (D).

F   *Initial Conditions*

1   *Initial voltages on condensers*

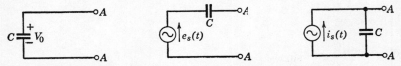

Charged condenser $e_s(t) = V_0 u_{-1}(t)$ in series $i_s(t) = CV_0 u_0(t)$ in parallel

2   *Initial currents in coils*

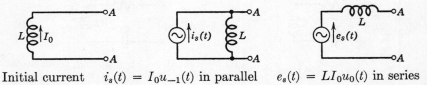

Initial current $i_s(t) = I_0 u_{-1}(t)$ in parallel $e_s(t) = LI_0 u_0(t)$ in series

If other sources are present in the circuit solve by superposition.

PROBLEMS

1. For the circuit shown below, determine $e(t)$ and $i(t)$ (a) for $i_s(t) = u_0(t)$, (b) for $i_s(t) = u_{-1}(t)$.

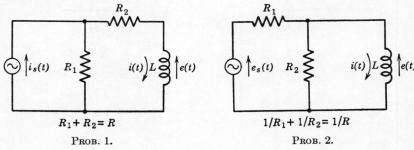

$R_1 + R_2 = R$ $1/R_1 + 1/R_2 = 1/R$

PROB. 1.   PROB. 2.

2. For the circuit shown above, determine $e(t)$ and $i(t)$ (a) for $e_s(t) = u_0(t)$, (b) for $e_s(t) = u_{-1}(t)$.

3. Given $i_s(t) = u_{-1}(t)$. Determine $e(t)$ and $i(t)$.

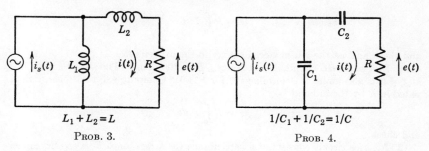

$L_1 + L_2 = L$

PROB. 3.

$1/C_1 + 1/C_2 = 1/C$

PROB. 4.

4. Given $i_s(t) = u_0(t)$. Determine $e(t)$ and $i(t)$.
5. Given $e_s(t) = u_0(t)$. Determine $e(t)$ and $i(t)$.

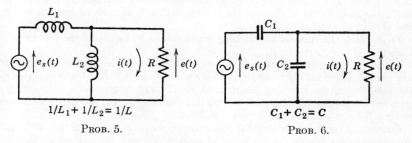

$1/L_1 + 1/L_2 = 1/L$

PROB. 5.

$C_1 + C_2 = C$

PROB. 6.

6. Given $e_s(t) = u_{-1}(t)$. Determine $e(t)$ and $i(t)$.

7. For the circuit shown below, R_1 represents the leakage resistance of the condenser of capacitance C. What is the equation for the charge on the condenser as a function of time after the switch K is closed?

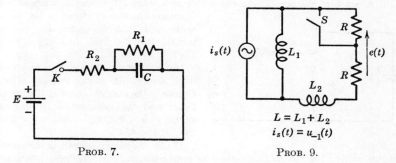

PROB. 7.

$L = L_1 + L_2$
$i_s(t) = u_{-1}(t)$

PROB. 9.

8. Which pairs of the circuits in Probs. 1 to 6 inclusive are potential duals? Using this information, check your answers to these problems.

9. Switch S is closed for $0 < t < L/R$ and is open during the interval $L/R < t < \infty$. Find analytic expressions for the voltage $e(t)$ valid for $0 < t < L/R$ and again for $L/R < t < \infty$.

10. A capacitance C, initially charged to E volts, is suddenly shunted by a resistance R at $t = 0$. From the known solution for the current $i(t)$, compute the total energy dissipated in R from the integral

$$w = R \int_0^\infty i^2 \, dt$$

and check against the initial stored energy in the capacitance.

11. In a series RL circuit, $L = 1$ henry. $R = 100$ ohms. The stored energy in L at $t = 0$ is 450 joules. Determine $i(t)$ for $t > 0$. Compute the total energy dissipated in R by the integral

$$w = R \int_0^\infty i^2 \, dt$$

and check.

12. A series circuit consists of a capacitance C_1, a resistance R, a second capacitance C_2, and a switch. With the switch open, C_1 is charged to 1 volt. The switch closes at $t = 0$. Determine the current $i(t)$ in the circuit and the voltage $e_2(t)$ across C_2 for $t > 0$. Let $1/C = 1/C_1 + 1/C_2$. Determine the initial and the final energy in C_1, the final energy in C_2, and the energy lost in R from an integration of $i^2 R$, and check.

13. In Prob. 12 consider the limiting process $R \to 0$, and state the energy relations that obtain in this limit.

14. In the use of an oscilloscope for the recording of transients it is necessary that one pair of deflecting plates be supplied with a voltage that is a linear function of the time during the recording interval. A simple way of generating a reasonably good approximation to this type of voltage function is essentially the circuit described in Prob. 12 in which $e_2(t)$ is the voltage in question.

Concerning the degree of linearity required, suppose it is stipulated that $e_2(t)$ shall deviate from its tangent at $t = 0$ by at most 5 per cent throughout an interval $0 < t < \tau$ seconds. $C_2 = 10^{-8}$ farad, and C_1 is at least 100 times larger. Sensitivity requirements of the oscilloscope indicate that $e_2(t)$ should vary from zero to 10 volts. Determine the appropriate value of the resistance R in terms of the interval τ and the necessary initial voltage of the capacitance C_1.

15. A constant voltage E is impressed upon a series RL circuit initially at rest. Compute the energy stored in the inductance and that dissipated for the intervals: $0 < t < L/R$, $L/R < t < 2L/R$, $2L/R < t < 3L/R$.

16. A constant voltage E is impressed upon a series RC circuit initially at rest. Compute the energy stored in the capacitance and that dissipated for the intervals: $0 < t < RC$, $RC < t < 2RC$, $2RC < t < 3RC$.

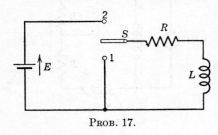

PROB. 17.

17. In the circuit shown in the accompanying sketch the switch S is caused to snap back and forth between positions 1 and 2 at regular intervals equal to the time constant, thus alternately impressing the constant voltage E and leaving the circuit closed upon itself. (a) Determine and plot the ultimate periodic behavior. (b) Starting from rest conditions, suppose the switch is first thrown to position 2 for the interval $L/R + \delta$ seconds, and then snapped

back and forth as described above. What should be the time increment δ in order
that the periodic behavior ensues after the
second throw of the switch?

18. In Prob. 17 compute the energy supplied by the source E per period, and check
against that dissipated in R.

19. A unit voltage step is applied to a series LC circuit. If the resultant current
oscillation is to have an amplitude of 10
amperes and a frequency of 10^6 cycles per
second, determine the values of L and C.

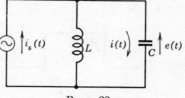

PROB. 20.

What are the peak values of voltage occurring across L and C separately? Sketch
these voltages and the current (neatly) for several cycles.

20. Given $i_s(t) = u_0(t)$. Determine $e(t)$ and $i(t)$.

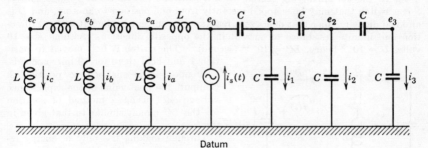

Datum

PROB. 21.

21. The quantities e_0, e_1, e_a, e_2, $\cdots$ are potentials of the indicated nodes with respect to the common datum. Utilizing the results of Prob. 20, determine all indicated voltages and currents for $i_s = u_0(t)$.

22. Repeat Prob. 21 for the source i_s impressed between datum and any of the
other nodes. Do this for several widely separated nodes, and note particularly the
distribution of the sinusoidal components of voltage and current in each case. Can
you infer a general network property?

23. In the circuit shown here, the current source is impressed across a fraction a
of the total turns n in the inductance L. If $i_s = u_{-1}(t)$, determine $e_1(t)$, $e_c(t)$, $i(t)$ for
$t > 0$. Assume that the coil flux links all turns.

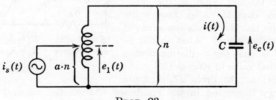

PROB. 23.

24. A voltage source in series with elements L and C has the form of a rectangular
pulse as shown below. Determine and plot the resultant current (a) for δ equal to

one-half a period of the resultant oscillation, (b) for δ equal to a whole period. Let $t = 0$ refer to the beginning of the pulse, and extend your plots over the interval $0 < t < 2\delta$.

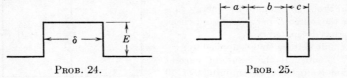

PROB. 24.   PROB. 25.

25. In the circuit of Prob. 24, suppose the voltage source has the form of the pulse train shown above. Assuming equal pulse amplitudes, state some combinations of the intervals a, b, and c that will yield a maximum oscillation after the pulse train. Give some combinations that will yield a rest condition after the pulse train.

26. In the accompanying sketch, E is a constant resistanceless voltage source, S is a switch that may be snapped instantly from one position to another, and D is an ideal diode rectifier that offers zero resistance to current in the left-to-right direction and infinite resistance to current in the opposite direction. Assume $E = 10$ volts, $L = 10^{-5}$ henry, $LC = 10^{-14}$ (second)^2. The switch is first moved to position 1 and held there for 10 microseconds, whereupon it is snapped to position 2. Compute the final value of the capacitance voltage $e_c(t)$, using a method of solution for the LC circuit similar to that given in the text.

Through making use only of energy relations, determine the ratio e_c/E (where e_c is the final value) as a function of L, C, and the time interval τ that the switch is held in position 1 before snapping it into position 2. Discuss the feasibility of this method of transforming a direct voltage from a low to a high value.

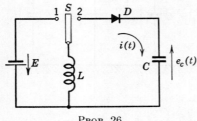

PROB. 26.

27. Let the diode D in the circuit of Prob. 26 be replaced by a resistance R of 1 ohm. Under the same conditions as those stated in the first paragraph of Prob. 26, compute and plot the resulting current $i(t)$ and the voltage $e_c(t)$ across the capacitance. The plot should extend over a time interval of at least 5 periods of the oscillatory response.

What is the Q, and what is the "decrement" of this circuit? After how many periods or cycles has the oscillation decayed to $1/e$ of its initial value? What should be the value of R so that the oscillation decays to $1/e$ of its initial value in 10 cycles?

28. With reference to Prob. 27, compute the total energy dissipated in the resistance R from the integral

$E = 10$ volts $R_1 = R_2 = R_5 = 2$ ohms
$L = 2$ henrys $R_3 = R_4 = 4$ ohms

PROB. 29.

$$w = R \int_0^\infty i^2 \, dt$$

and check against the energy initially stored in the inductance L.

29. At $t = 0$ switch K is closed. Find the value of C necessary for critical damping of the resultant transient. Compute the transient current in the LC branch.

30. In the accompanying circuit, the switch K is suddenly opened at $t = 0$ when the current $i(t)$ equals 2 amperes and di/dt equals 1 ampere per second. Find the values of i_L, i_C, i_R, and $e(t)$ immediately before and again immediately after the instant $t = 0$.

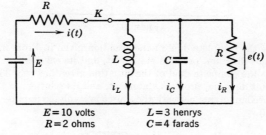

$E = 10$ volts $\qquad L = 3$ henrys
$R = 2$ ohms $\qquad C = 4$ farads

PROB. 30.

31. In the following circuit assume first that i_{s2} and e_s are both zero, but that i_{s1} is a unit step, and determine the ultimate steady values of current and voltage in the circuit elements.

Now determine appropriate values for the excitation functions i_{s2} and e_s such that the steady values found above are immediately established; that is to say, determine those conditions that will cause the transient response initiated by i_{s1} to be absent.

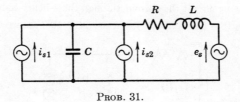

PROB. 31.

32. The circuit is initially at rest, and the switch closes at $t = 0$. What must i_s be so that the steady state ensues immediately, and what is this steady state?

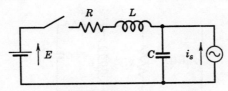

PROB. 32.

33. In the accompanying circuit, both switches are initially open and the capacitance C is without charge. S_1 closes, and $i(t)$ begins to increase. At an instant $t = 0$ when $i(t)$ has the value $i_0 < E/R$, S_2 closes. Find $e(t)$ for $t > 0$ in terms of i_0 as a parameter. Plot $e(t)$ and also the current $i_L(t)$ through the inductance from the

time S_1 closes until some time after S_2 closes, showing all significant values and characteristics of these functions.

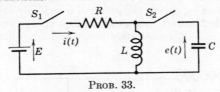

PROB. 33.

34. Formulate the complete dual of the situation given in Prob. 32 including the appropriate circuit diagram, problem statement, and its solution.

35. Formulate the complete dual of the situation given in Prob. 33, including the appropriate circuit diagram, problem statement, and its solution.

36. If in the accompanying network the source is a voltage impulse $e_s(t) = 10u_0(t)$, find $i_1(t)$ and $i_2(t)$.

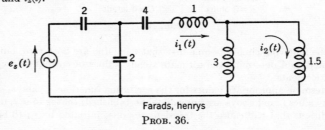

Farads, henrys

PROB. 36.

37. In the following circuit the current through the 4-henry inductance is

$$i_1(t) = 5 \sin (6t + 7°) + 8 \cos (9t + 10°) \text{ amperes}$$

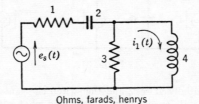

Ohms, farads, henrys

The dual of this network is shown below.

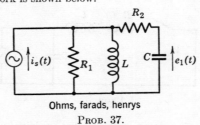

Ohms, farads, henrys

PROB. 37.

The current source $i_s(t)$ (in amperes) of the dual is numerically equal to the voltage source $e_s(t)$ (in volts) of the original network. (a) Give the numerical values (in ohms, farads, and henrys) of all the circuit elements shown in the dual network. (b) Find $e_1(t)$, the voltage across C. (c) Find the current through the resistance R_2.

38. In the network shown the voltage source is a unit step, $e_s(t) = u_{-1}(t)$. The initial conditions at time $t = 0$ are: no charge on the capacitance, but a current I_0 = 5 amperes through the inductance in the direction indicated. Find $i(t)$.

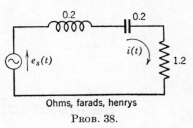

Ohms, farads, henrys

PROB. 38.

39. Solve the series RLC circuit of Fig. 20 for a unit step voltage excitation directly from equilibrium Eq. 51 by noting that the permanent state $i_p(t) = 0$ and hence the complete solution is given by the complementary function 57 satisfying the force-free equilibrium Eq. 52. Instead of solving for A_1 and A_2 from Eq. 57 and its integral 58, consider Eq. 57 and its *derivative* for $t = 0$, obtaining the value of (di/dt) for $t = 0$ from the original equilibrium Eq. 51 by noting that, immediately after $t = 0$, $e_s = 1$ while the current and condenser charge are still zero. Thus, with the help of Eqs. 74 and 75, check the values given for A_1 and A_2 by Eq. 60.

40. Considering the previous problem, observe that the successive derivatives of the equilibrium Eq. 51 considered at the instant immediately after $t = 0$ will yield the values of any number of higher initial derivatives for the current $i(t)$ so that one may write down any number of terms in a Maclaurin expansion of this function. Thus obtain the first five terms in the Maclaurin expansion of $i(t)$, and check against the appropriate expansion of Eq. 78. Contrast this method of obtaining the function $i(t)$ with that involving conventional solution of the differential equation plus evaluation of integration constants.

41. Solve the RLC circuit of Fig. 20 for a unit step voltage excitation through considering the mesh charge $q(t)$ rather than the mesh current $i(t)$ to be the unknown. That is to say, proceed from the equilibrium equation

$$L \frac{d^2q}{dt^2} + R \frac{dq}{dt} + \frac{q}{C} = u_{-1}(t)$$

for which the particular integral is *not* zero but equals a constant, as does the excitation in the permanent state. The total solution consisting of a nonzero particular integral and a complementary function involves two constants of integration as before, which are evaluated from stated initial values of charge and current following the usual pattern. Assuming initial rest conditions, obtain the complete solution for the mesh charge. Differentiate it to find the mesh current, and check your result against Eq. 78.

42. In the circuit, $e_s(t)$ is a unit step. For initial rest conditions, find $e(t)$ through an appropriate adaptation of the result given by Eq. 97 for the step response of the circuit shown in Fig. 26.

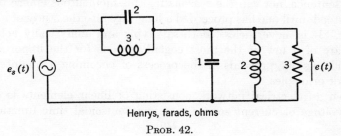

Henrys, farads, ohms

PROB. 42.

C H A P T E R   S I X

Behavior of Simple Circuits
in the Sinusoidal Steady State

1 Why Sinusoids Play Such a Predominant Part in the Study of Electrical Networks

In the practical exploitation of electrical phenomena, the earliest sources of electric energy (apart from various electrostatic generators which played no significant role) were batteries of one sort or another. These represented voltage sources of substantially constant value. When the rotating machine was introduced as a more copious and reliable source, it also was devised to produce an essentially constant voltage at its terminals. Thus our earliest experience with electrical network response deals with constant excitation functions; and, since the resulting currents are likewise constant, such circuits are referred to as *direct current* circuits, or more briefly as d-c circuits. The discussion of their behavior is still item number one on the agenda of most electrical engineering curricula for the reason that the mathematical process of computing network response (so long as we restrict our attention to the stationary state) is simplest when the exciting force is a constant.

As the electrical art progressed, we find that the constant (which is the simplest form of mathematical time function) was gradually discarded in favor of another time function, namely, the *sinusoid*. We may well ask why, out of an infinite possible array of time functions, the sinusoid was singled out as the *one* that shall forever be king and ruler within the realm of network theory. The answer cannot be given in a single sentence, nor can the reasons for this momentous choice be fully understood until one has proceeded a long way into the study of network theory. It is, nevertheless, both satisfying and analytically helpful to be aware of a few of the most cogent reasons for the importance of sinusoids, as one proceeds in the process of becoming acquainted with network principles.

When an electrical network consisting of linear elements is excited by a voltage or current source that is a sinusoidal time function, the resulting stationary voltages and currents in all parts of the network are likewise sinusoidal time functions, differing from each other and from the excitation function at most in their respective amplitudes and time phases.   The network may have a structure of unlimited complexity; it may consist of several complex lumped structures, geographically separated by great distances, and interconnected by transmission lines and cables of various sorts; still the voltages and currents everywhere in this entire system are time functions which in essence are identical in form, namely, sinusoidal.   *No other periodic time function can claim such distinction!*

It is not difficult to demonstrate the truth of this statement once one has seen that the equilibrium of an electrical network is described by a linear differential equation with constant coefficients or by a set of simultaneous equations of this sort, for it is readily appreciated that the particular integral of such an equation is a sinusoid when the right-hand member (physically the excitation function) is sinusoidal.   These details will be supplied later on.   Meanwhile it is more useful to point out other distinctive features of the sinusoidal function.

There is something very peculiar—yes, almost uncanny—about the sinusoidal waveform that gives it the property of remaining unaltered when another sinusoid having the same period but any amplitude and random phase is added to it.   That is to say, if one adds together (or superimposes) two sinusoidal functions having arbitrarily different amplitudes and time phases, the resulting function has the same sinusoidal form as either constituent provided only that their periods are alike.   It follows at once that the sum of any number of sinusoids of like period but random amplitudes and phases yields again a sinusoid of the same period.   The amplitude and phase of this resultant sinusoid will, of course, depend upon the various amplitudes and phases of the component sinusoids entering into the summation, but the shape of the resultant function is still sinusoidal.   No other periodic function can lay claim to this property either.

The shape of a sinusoid has further unique characteristics.   The derivative—that is, the slope—of a sinusoid is again sinusoidal in form; and, therefore, so is the integral.   In fact one may differentiate or integrate a sinusoid arbitrarily often; the result still has the same shape as the function one started with.   Anyone who has some experience with the graphical representation of functions and their derivatives and integrals knows that in general the process of differentiation tends to accentuate any irregularities in the form of a given function while integration has the opposite effect of smoothing out the function.   The sinusoid is unique in that its shape is invariant to integration or differentiation, no matter how often either operation may be repeated.

The properties mentioned in the last two paragraphs are indeed the ones responsible for the fact that the response of a network to a sinusoidal excitation must likewise be sinusoidal, for the sum of terms in a linear differential equation with constant coefficients yields a sinusoid when each variable is a sinusoid of the same period.

A further contributing reason for the importance of the sinusoidal function in network theory is due to the existence of a theorem, first announced by the mathematician Fourier, to the effect that any periodic function (subject to certain limitations that are not important at the moment) may be approximated with a finite but arbitrarily small tolerance through the linear superposition of a finite number of sinusoidal functions alone. This approximating function is known as the partial sum of a *Fourier series*. Through the simple artifice of regarding the period of the given function to be arbitrarily large, one is able to apply essentially the same type of representation to functions that do not exhibit periodicity, and thus obtain the important result that *any* time function that we shall ever have to deal with in our practical network considerations (transient or steady state) can be represented as a sum of sinusoids. In essence this statement means that the sinusoid is the building block from which anything else can be constructed, and that we can find the response of a network to any form of excitation function once we know its sinusoidal response.

In determining the network response to nonsinusoidal excitation functions in specific instances we may or may not avail ourselves of the possibilities of this important result, for it is sometimes computationally simpler to obtain a solution by other means. Nevertheless, the existence of the result stated is of inestimable theoretical importance since, in effect, it permits one to regard the investigation of linear-network behavior in the sinusoidal steady state as no less general than would be a study of linear network behavior with perfectly arbitrary excitation functions.

Finally, with regard to the significance of sinusoidal functions, it is well to recognize that the sinusoid is nature's building block also. Thus the natural behavior of the simplest physical system capable of sustained oscillation is the sinusoid. The simple pendulum (except for minor perturbations) executes simple harmonic or sinusoidal motion. The simplest electric circuit capable of oscillation (the combination of an inductance and a capacitance) executes sinusoidal behavior. The natural behavior of any linear network, however complicated, is described by a superposition of sinusoids or exponentially damped sinusoids.

Since the sinusoid is thus revealed to play a dominant role in our network studies, it is fitting that we acquaint ourselves inordinately well with its detailed characteristics and the manifold ways in which it may mathematically be represented. The following article elaborates upon this theme.

2   Complex Representation of Sinusoids

In dealing with the analysis of electrical networks, complex forms are frequently more convenient than the equivalent trigonometric ones for expressing sinusoidal steady-state functions such as voltages and currents. Moreover, they naturally lead to the expression of impedances and admittances in complex form and, therefore, to a more compact and circumspect method of expressing the properties of the circuits themselves.

The basis for complex notation * is expressed by the identity

$$e^{\pm jx} = \cos x \pm j \sin x \tag{1}$$

from which it follows that

$$\cos x = \frac{1}{2}(e^{jx} + e^{-jx}), \qquad \sin x = \frac{1}{2j}(e^{jx} - e^{-jx}) \tag{2}$$

Suppose a voltage is given as

$$e(t) = |E| \cos(\omega t + \psi) \tag{3}$$

Letting $x = \omega t + \psi$ in Eq. 2 one has

$$\begin{aligned}
\cos(\omega t + \psi) &= \tfrac{1}{2}[e^{j(\omega t + \psi)} + e^{-j(\omega t + \psi)}] \\
&= \tfrac{1}{2}(e^{j\psi}e^{j\omega t} + e^{-j\psi}e^{-j\omega t})
\end{aligned} \tag{4}$$

Thus, if we define a *complex* voltage amplitude as

$$E = |E| e^{j\psi} \tag{5}$$

and its conjugate as

$$\bar{E} = |E| e^{-j\psi} \tag{6}$$

Equation 3 may be written

$$e(t) = \tfrac{1}{2}(Ee^{j\omega t} + \bar{E}e^{-j\omega t}) \tag{7}$$

* The letter j is here used as a symbol for $\sqrt{-1}$. The reader is expected to be familiar with the elements of complex numbers and with functions of a complex argument.

Here the second term is, at every instant, the conjugate of the first. Hence, if the symbol Re is used to indicate that only the real part of the following complex quantity is to be taken, one may write

$$e(t) = \text{Re}[Ee^{j\omega t}] \tag{8}$$

The phase angle ψ of this voltage function is contained in the expression 8 by virtue of the complex character of the amplitude E as shown in Eq. 5.

Equations 3, 7, and 8 are thus seen to be alternative expressions for the same function. It should be observed in connection with the form 7 that the complex constituents $Ee^{j\omega t}$ and $\bar{E}e^{-j\omega t}$ separately have no physical significance. It is only their sum that is capable of representing a physical voltage. Nevertheless one may inquire as to what the network response would be if a "voltage" function given by say the constituent $Ee^{j\omega t}$ were impressed upon a circuit. To illustrate with a specific example, let the circuit be a resistance R in series with an inductance L. The voltage equilibrium reads

$$L\frac{di}{dt} + Ri = Ee^{j\omega t} \tag{9}$$

in which the current $i = i(t)$ is the response sought.

It is readily appreciated that a function of the form

$$i(t) = Ie^{j\omega t} \tag{10}$$

satisfies Eq. 9, since direct substitution yields

$$(Lj\omega + R)Ie^{j\omega t} = Ee^{j\omega t} \tag{11}$$

which is satisfied through setting

$$I = \frac{E}{R + j\omega L} = \frac{E}{Z} \tag{12}$$

Here the complex quantity

$$Z = R + j\omega L \tag{13}$$

represents the so-called impedance of the circuit.

In an exactly analogous fashion one finds that, if the complex constituent $\bar{E}e^{-j\omega t}$ is substituted into Eq. 9 in place of $Ee^{j\omega t}$, then Eqs. 10 and 11 are replaced by

$$i(t) = \bar{I}e^{-j\omega t} \tag{14}$$

and

$$(-Lj\omega + R)\bar{I}e^{-j\omega t} = \bar{E}e^{-j\omega t} \tag{15}$$

whence

$$\bar{I} = \frac{\bar{E}}{R - j\omega L} = \frac{\bar{E}}{\bar{Z}} \tag{16}$$

This is the conjugate of 12.

Employing the principle of superposition which states that, since the equilibrium Eq. 9 is linear, separate solutions are superposable, one may conclude that, if the right-hand side of Eq. 9 is replaced by the voltage function 7, then the resulting current (a physical current this time) is given by one-half the sum of expressions 10 and 14, that is,

$$i(t) = \tfrac{1}{2}(Ie^{j\omega t} + \bar{I}e^{-j\omega t}) \tag{17}$$

in which I and $\bar{I}$ are respectively given by Eqs. 12 and 16.

Since Eq. 17 may alternatively be written as

$$i(t) = \mathrm{Re}[Ie^{j\omega t}] \tag{18}$$

it is observed that the resulting current for the physical voltage function as expressed by any of the Eqs. 3, 7, or 8 may be obtained through consideration of the complex constituent $Ee^{j\omega t}$ alone, and subsequently taking only the real part of the resulting complex current (Eq. 10).

So long as it is tacitly understood that only the real parts of the indicated complex expressions are to be considered, it is permissible to simplify the entire manipulations by writing for the voltage and current functions only the corresponding complex constituents, thus,

$$\begin{aligned} e(t) &= Ee^{j\omega t} \\ i(t) &= Ie^{j\omega t} \end{aligned} \tag{19}$$

in which the complex current and voltage amplitudes are related through Eq. 12. Since this relationship is physically determined by the circuit, the properties of the latter are, incidentally, observed to be completely expressed by the complex impedance Z as given in this simple example by Eq. 13.

By analogy to the equivalent forms 3 and 8, it is seen that Eq. 18 may be alternatively be written in the trigonometric form

$$i(t) = |I| \cos(\omega t + \phi) \tag{20}$$

with

$$I = |I|e^{j\phi} \tag{21}$$

Hence, if the polar form

$$Z = |Z|e^{j\theta} \tag{22}$$

is adopted for the impedance, one has

$$|I| = \frac{|E|}{|Z|} \tag{23}$$

and

$$\phi = \psi - \theta \tag{24}$$

It is clear, therefore, that the phase angle of the resulting current is contained in expression 18 by virtue of the complex character of the current amplitude I.

In dealing with sinusoidal steady-state behavior only, it is ordinarily not necessary to retain the exponential factor $e^{j\omega t}$. The only significant

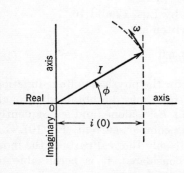

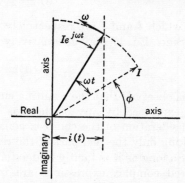

FIG. 1.   Relevant to the geometrical interpretation of Eq. 18 showing the position of the complex current vector for $t = 0$.

FIG. 2.   The complex current vector in Eq. 18 at a time $t > 0$.

quantities are E, I, and Z, which are simply related by the complex equivalent of Ohm's law,

$$E = IZ \tag{25}$$

A contributing reason for the effectiveness of the complex notation for sinusoids lies in the circumspection with which one may deal with the addition of sinusoids of like frequency that differ in their amplitudes and time-phase angles. This circumspection stems from the fact that the desired addition is accomplished through a vectorial addition of their complex amplitudes.

To appreciate how this is done, it is essential first to grasp the so-called vectorial interpretation of a single sinusoid. Here the sketches in Figs. 1 and 2 are helpful, illustrating the interpretation of Eq. 18 in the complex plane. Figure 1 shows the complex function $Ie^{j\omega t}$ for $t = 0$, while in Fig. 2 this same function is drawn as it appears at a slightly later instant when $\omega t = \pi/6$ radians. Thus I is this complex function at $t = 0$, whereas at any subsequent instant the function is this same complex I vector rotated through an angle of ωt radians in the counter-clockwise (positive) direction. To indicate that the vector I rotates with time at the angular velocity ω radians per second, it is customary to attach at the tip of the I vector a small arrow labeled ω, pointing in the direction of rotation.

The instantaneous sinusoidal function $i(t)$ is at any moment equal to the real part of the rotating I vector; that is, $i(t)$ equals the projection of this complex function $Ie^{j\omega t}$ upon the real axis of the associated com-

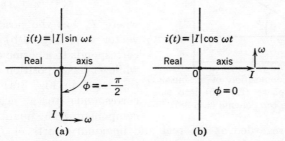

FIG. 3. The geometric interpretation of Fig. 1 pertinent (a) to the sine function and (b) to the cosine.

plex plane. This fact is likewise indicated in the two figures. It is clear that the phase angle ϕ, the angle of the complex amplitude I (Eq. 21), governs the value of $i(t)$ at $t = 0$.

Parts (a) and (b) of Fig. 3 show the complex representation of Fig. 1 for two particular values of ϕ that are of special interest because they correspond respectively to $i(t)$ being a sine or a cosine function. The sine function is zero for $t = 0$, and becomes positive immediately there-after. Hence the corresponding position of the vector I must be such that it has no projection upon the real axis, but will have a positive projection as it starts to rotate. The position shown in Fig. 3(a) fulfills these conditions. The cosine function has its maximum positive value for $t = 0$, wherefore the corresponding vector I is seen to coincide with the positive real axis, as shown in Fig. 3(b).

These particular results are helpful in the interpretation of the general case (Fig. 1), since they suggest that the latter may be regarded as a linear combination of sine and cosine components, and thus they yield a graphical interpretation for the familiar trigonometric identity applied to Eq. 20 which reads

$$i(t) = \left| I \right| \cos (\omega t + \phi) = \left| I \right| \cos \phi \cos \omega t - \left| I \right| \sin \phi \sin \omega t \quad (26)$$

Letting

$$A = |I| \cos \phi, \qquad B = |I| \sin \phi \qquad (27)$$

permits us to write

$$i(t) = A \cos \omega t - B \sin \omega t \qquad (28)$$

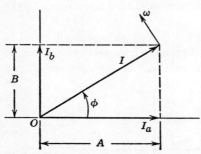

FIG. 4. Decomposition of a sinusoid of arbitrary phase (Eq. 26) into sine and cosine components (Eq. 28).

The corresponding graphical interpretation is shown in Fig. 4. The complex amplitude I is seen to be given by the vector sum

$$I = I_a + I_b \qquad (29)$$

where I_a has the position of the vector I in Fig. 3(b) and hence corresponds to a cosine component, while I_b has a position opposite to that of I in Fig. 3(a) and hence corresponds to a negative sine component. The quantities A and B may be regarded as the real and imaginary parts of I, as is expressed by the relation

$$I = A + jB \qquad (30)$$

From Eq. 27 one has

$$|I| = \sqrt{A^2 + B^2}, \qquad \tan \phi = B/A \qquad (31)$$

which serve to determine the magnitude and angle of the vector I from a representation of $i(t)$ in the form 28.

It is now a simple matter to indicate how the addition of sinusoids of like frequency may be carried out. Suppose we have

$$i_1(t) = \operatorname{Re}[I_1 e^{j\omega t}] = |I_1| \cos (\omega t + \phi_1) \qquad (32)$$

$$i_2(t) = \operatorname{Re}[I_2 e^{j\omega t}] = |I_2| \cos (\omega t + \phi_2) \qquad (33)$$

and wish to evaluate their sum

$$i(t) = i_1(t) + i_2(t) = \operatorname{Re}[I e^{j\omega t}] = |I| \cos (\omega t + \phi) \qquad (34)$$

Since the sum of real parts equals the real part of the sum of two complex quantities, it follows that

$$\operatorname{Re}[I e^{j\omega t}] = \operatorname{Re}[(I_1 + I_2)e^{j\omega t}] \qquad (35)$$

whence

$$I = I_1 + I_2 \qquad (36)$$

wherein complex or vectorial addition is, of course, implied.

More specifically, if each of the sinusoids in Eqs. 32 and 33 is written, according to the pattern of Eq. 28, as

$$i_1(t) = A_1 \cos \omega t - B_1 \sin \omega t$$
$$i_2(t) = A_2 \cos \omega t - B_2 \sin \omega t \tag{37}$$

so that (like Eq. 30) we have

$$I_1 = A_1 + jB_1, \qquad I_2 = A_2 + jB_2 \tag{38}$$

then Eqs. 30 and 36 give

$$A = A_1 + A_2, \qquad B = B_1 + B_2 \tag{39}$$

for the real and imaginary parts of the resultant complex amplitude.

Figure 5 illustrates the vectorial addition implied in Eq. 36. One may carry it out through adding together corresponding components of the separate vectors I_1 and I_2 so as to form the components of the resultant I, as indicated in Eq. 39, or one may carry it out geometrically through constructing I as the diagonal of a parallelogram whose sides are I_1 and I_2, as in the addition of force vectors in mechanics.

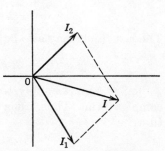

FIG. 5. Pertinent to the addition of sinusoids as expressed analytically by Eqs. 32 through 36.

It should carefully be observed, however, that the superposition principle, which is essential to the foregoing reasoning, is valid only in connection with linear relations. Hence the use of complex notation as just outlined is restricted to linear operations such as addition, subtraction, differentiation, and integration—which are the operations encountered in the solution of linear differential equations with constant coefficients. To state the matter in another way we may say that, since the four above-named operations, when performed upon complex expressions, are commutative with respect to the operation of taking the real part (as, for example, the sum of real parts equals the real part of the sum, or the derivative of a real part equals the real part of the derivative of a complex expression), one may work with the complex expressions while solving the differential equations and take the real parts afterward.

In dealing with power or energy relationships which involve quadratic expressions, a similar procedure is not possible since it is not true that the real part of the square of a complex expression is equal to the square of its real part. That is to say, it is *not* correct to assume in connection with Eq. 8 for instance that

$$e^2(t) \;=\; \mathrm{Re}[Ee^{j\omega t}]^2 \tag{40}$$

may be written in place of

$$e^2(t) \;=\; [\mathrm{Re}(Ee^{j\omega t})]^2 \tag{41}$$

In other words the operation of *squaring* is not commutable with taking the real part as are the linear operations mentioned above.

It is permissible, however, to square the entire right-hand side as in Eq. 41 or, using the equivalent form 7, to write

$$e^2(t) \;=\; \tfrac{1}{4}(Ee^{j\omega t} + \bar{E}e^{-j\omega t})^2 \tag{42}$$

which yields

$$e^2(t) \;=\; \tfrac{1}{4}(E^2 e^{j2\omega t} + \bar{E}^2 e^{-j2\omega t} + 2E\bar{E}) \tag{43}$$

or

$$e^2(t) \;=\; \tfrac{1}{2}\big| E \big|^2 + \tfrac{1}{2}\mathrm{Re}[E^2 e^{j2\omega t}] \tag{44}$$

The last result may also be written (through use of Eq. 5)

$$e^2(t) \;=\; \tfrac{1}{2}\big| E \big|^2 + \tfrac{1}{2}\big| E \big|^2 \cos{(2\omega t + 2\psi)} \tag{45}$$

Similar remarks apply to the product of a voltage and a current in complex form. Thus, using the simplified notation in 19, it is *not* correct to write

$$e(t) \cdot i(t) \;=\; EIe^{j2\omega t} \tag{46}$$

for this is *not* the equivalent of

$$\mathrm{Re}[Ee^{j\omega t}] \times \mathrm{Re}[Ie^{j\omega t}] \tag{47}$$

even though the real part of the expression 46 be taken.

Although the simplified notation in Eqs. 19 is useful in dealing with many aspects of circuit theory, the student should not lose sight of the reasoning that underlies its use, or the restrictions that are thus implied.

Since manipulations with complex expressions will become more involved as we proceed with the use of complex notation, a few additional remarks may well be brought to the student's attention at this time. Following the usual procedure, given the complex number

$$n \;=\; M + jN \tag{48}$$

the magnitude is

$$\big| n \big| \;=\; \sqrt{M^2 + N^2} \tag{49}$$

Hence, if one is given the form

$$n = \frac{a + jb}{c + jd} \tag{50}$$

and the magnitude is asked for, a tendency is first to put this given expression into form 48 and then apply 49: that is, through rationalizing the denominator obtain from 50

$$n = \frac{(a + jb)(c - jd)}{(c + jd)(c - jd)} = \frac{ac + bd + j(bc - ad)}{c^2 + d^2} \tag{51}$$

and then have according to Eq. 49

$$|n| = \frac{\sqrt{(ac + bd)^2 + (bc - ad)^2}}{c^2 + d^2} \tag{52}$$

Although correct, this procedure is needlessly long. It is more expedient to recall that the magnitude of the quotient of two complex numbers is equal to the quotient of their magnitudes. Thus the magnitude of the expression 50 is written down at once as

$$|n| = \sqrt{\frac{a^2 + b^2}{c^2 + d^2}} \tag{53}$$

The results given by Eqs. 52 and 53 are entirely equivalent. The method leading to Eq. 52 not only incurs a waste of time and effort, but frequently obliterates the characteristics of the resultant function and makes its interpretation needlessly difficult.

Similar remarks apply to the formation of the magnitude of a product such as

$$n = (a + jb)(c + jd) = (ac - bd) + j(ad + bc) \tag{54}$$

which may be written

$$|n| = \sqrt{(a^2 + b^2)(c^2 + d^2)} \tag{55}$$

or as

$$|n| = \sqrt{(ac - bd)^2 + (ad + bc)^2} \tag{56}$$

Again, the first of these is usually preferable and more easily formed.

The same principle should be employed in more complicated situations. For instance, if

$$n = \frac{(a + jb)jc(d - je)}{(f + jg)e^{jq}} \tag{57}$$

the magnitude is written down at once as the square root of

$$| n |^2 = \frac{(a^2 + b^2)c^2(d^2 + e^2)}{(f^2 + g^2) \times 1} \tag{58}$$

In forming the conjugate of a complex expression it is likewise unnecessary first to obtain the standard form 48. Thus the conjugate of the expression 57, for example, is simply

$$\bar{n} = \frac{(a - jb)(-jc)(d + je)}{(f - jg)e^{-jq}} \tag{59}$$

3 Elaborations upon the Impedance Concept

Consider the simple circuit of Fig. 6 which consists of a sinusoidal voltage source $e_s(t)$ in series with the elements R and L. The problem is to find the current $i(t)$ on the assumption that the source has been acting in the circuit for a sufficiently long time so that the transient initiated by its original insertion has subsided to a negligible value. It is only the permanent state or steady state that is of interest.

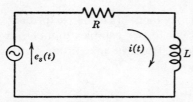

FIG. 6. The series RL circuit excited by a sinusoidal voltage.

To illustrate the relative effectiveness of complex notation in dealing with sinusoids we will solve the present problem first without the use of this notation, and then with it. Thus suppose we write

$$e_s(t) = E \cos \omega t \tag{60}$$

in which E is a real constant and $\omega = 2\pi f$ is the radian frequency of this source. The differential equation of the circuit reads

$$L \frac{di}{dt} + Ri = E \cos \omega t \tag{61}$$

Physical reasoning suggests that the ultimate behavior of the current will be described by

$$i(t) = I \cos (\omega t + \phi) \tag{62}$$

since it is only reasonable to suppose that the response, like the source causing it, should be sinusoidal, although its amplitude I and time phase ϕ relative to the excitation may have other values. From Eq. 62 we have

$$di/dt = -I\omega \sin (\omega t + \phi) \tag{63}$$

so that substitution into Eq. 61 gives

$$[-L\omega \sin (\omega t + \phi) + R \cos (\omega t + \phi)]I = E \cos \omega t \tag{64}$$

This equation is now to be solved for the values of I and ϕ. A procedure for doing this is first to apply the trigonometric identities

$$\sin (\omega t + \phi) = \sin \omega t \cos \phi + \cos \omega t \sin \phi$$
$$\cos (\omega t + \phi) = \cos \omega t \cos \phi - \sin \omega t \sin \phi \tag{65}$$

whence Eq. 64 may be written

$$I(R \cos \phi - L\omega \sin \phi) \cos \omega t - I(R \sin \phi + L\omega \cos \phi) \sin \omega t = E \cos \omega t \tag{66}$$

or

$$[I(R \cos \phi - L\omega \sin \phi) - E] \cos \omega t - I(R \sin \phi + L\omega \cos \phi) \sin \omega t = 0 \tag{67}$$

This equation has the form

$$A \cos \omega t + B \sin \omega t = 0 \tag{68}$$

which can be satisfied for all values of the time t only if both coefficients A and B are zero. Thus we have from Eq. 67

$$I(R \cos \phi - L\omega \sin \phi) = E \tag{69}$$

$$I(R \sin \phi + L\omega \cos \phi) = 0 \tag{70}$$

The last of these equations yields

$$\tan \phi = -L\omega/R \tag{71}$$

or

$$\phi = -\tan^{-1} (L\omega/R) \tag{72}$$

from which the time phase of the current is determined.

Using Eq. 71, together with well-known trigonometric relations, one has

$$\cos \phi = \frac{R}{\sqrt{R^2 + L^2\omega^2}} \tag{73}$$

$$\sin \phi = \frac{-L\omega}{\sqrt{R^2 + L^2\omega^2}} \tag{74}$$

whence Eq. 69 becomes

$$I\sqrt{R^2 + L^2\omega^2} = E \tag{75}$$

from which we have the amplitude of the current

$$I = \frac{E}{\sqrt{R^2 + L^2\omega^2}} \tag{76}$$

Equations 62, 72, and 76 constitute the solution to our problem.

Now let us solve the same problem using complex notation, writing for the voltage source

$$e_s(t) = Ee^{j\omega t} \tag{77}$$

in which the real part is implied, and E may be real so as to have the expression 77 correspond to 60; or E may be complex if we wish for some reason to leave the time phase of the source arbitrary. Since phase angles do not appear explicitly in complex notation it is just as easy to include them.

The equilibrium equation reads

$$L\frac{di}{dt} + Ri = Ee^{j\omega t} \tag{78}$$

Again assuming on physical grounds that the steady-state current will also be a sinusoid, we write

$$i(t) = Ie^{j\omega t} \tag{79}$$

where the implied complex character of I now contains the time phase angle without further explicit mention thereof. Differentiating 79 we have

$$\frac{di}{dt} = j\omega Ie^{j\omega t} \tag{80}$$

so that substitution of the assumed solution 79 into 78 yields after some simple factoring

$$(R + j\omega L)Ie^{j\omega t} = Ee^{j\omega t} \tag{81}$$

Here we may cancel the factor $e^{j\omega t}$ appearing on both sides of the equation and solve at once for I, getting

$$I = \frac{E}{R + j\omega L} \tag{82}$$

Writing I in its polar form as

$$I = |I|e^{j\phi}$$

and assuming E in Eq. 82 to be real (so as to match the situation previously treated by trigonometric methods), we have

$$|I| = \frac{E}{\sqrt{R^2 + L^2\omega^2}} \tag{83}$$

and

$$\phi = -\tan^{-1}(L\omega/R) \tag{84}$$

which check with Eqs. 76 and 72 respectively.

The compact and circumspect nature of the complex method as contrasted to the trigonometric one is striking, even in this very simple example. As one considers more elaborate networks, the complex method preserves its compact and algebraically straightforward character, while the trigonometric method rapidly becomes so involved as to make the evaluation of solutions in terms of it practically impossible. In addition, the complex method permits an interpretation of our solution which reveals its essential similarity to the solution of d-c circuits involving pure resistances. Thus, if we define the quantity

$$Z = R + j\omega L \tag{85}$$

as the *impedance* of our series RL circuit, Eq. 82 reads

$$I = E/Z \tag{86}$$

which has the simple character of Ohm's law relating voltage and current for a resistance element. The series RL circuit obeys essentially the same simple law relative to its volt-ampere relation in the sinusoidal steady state, with the one detailed refinement that the quantities E, I, and Z entering into the Ohm's law relation are complex quantities instead of real ones, thus taking account of the important circumstance that our sinusoidal current and voltage may in general be displaced in time phase.

If we write the impedance 85 in its polar form as

$$Z = |Z|e^{j\theta} \tag{87}$$

we have

$$|Z| = \sqrt{R^2 + L^2\omega^2} \tag{88}$$

and

$$\theta = \tan^{-1}(L\omega/R) \tag{89}$$

The solution as expressed by Eqs. 83 and 84 may then be written

$$|I| = \frac{E}{|Z|} \quad \text{and} \quad \phi = -\theta \tag{90}$$

More generally, if we regard the source voltage as having an arbitrary phase also, through writing its amplitude E as

$$E = |E|e^{j\psi} \tag{91}$$

these results are modified only in the manner indicated by

$$|I| = \frac{|E|}{|Z|} \quad \text{and} \quad \phi = \psi - \theta \tag{92}$$

Thus the current magnitude is the voltage magnitude divided by the impedance magnitude, while the current phase is the voltage phase minus the impedance angle. This simple rule holds for all networks, however complicated. The only thing that changes as we proceed to the consideration of other circuits is the detailed form of the impedance in its dependence upon circuit parameters and upon the frequency. In this respect we can further exploit the circumspect nature of the complex method through an effective graphical interpretation, as is discussed in the following article.

4   Interpretation of Impedance in the Complex Frequency Plane

Let us pause for a moment at this point in our discussions and reflect upon the physical significance of the steady-state solution that we are now discussing in contrast to the transient behavior dealt with in the previous chapter. It will be recalled in the consideration of transient response that we were studying the manner in which a circuit behaves when, following some initial stimulus such as heaving a packaged charge into a capacitance, the circuit is left to its own devices; that is to say, when it is permitted to execute its own *natural* behavior—a behavior that is characteristically its own. It was observed that this natural behavior assumes different forms, depending upon the geometry of the network and the kinds of elements (R, L, or C) that are contained in it. In the RL and RC circuits, the natural behavior was seen to be a simple exponential decay; in the RLC circuit it takes the form of a decaying oscillation which may degenerate into a nonoscillatory character for unfavorable parameter values.

In any case the natural behavior is described analytically by one or more additive terms of the form Ae^{pt}, in which the nature of the p values or characteristic values is pre-eminent in setting the pattern of this behavior. Thus a negative real value, such as $-R/L$ in the case of the RL circuit, leads to a simple decay; a pair of conjugate imaginary values, as those given by Eq. 62 of Ch. 5 in the discussion of the LC circuit, lead to an undamped oscillation; a pair of conjugate complex values, as those given by Eq. 74 of Ch. 5 for the RLC circuit, lead to a damped oscillatory behavior. Note, incidentally, that real p values and real parts of complex p values always are *negative*, thus yielding exponential time functions that tend toward zero with increasing time. This circumstance is characteristic of *passive* circuits (such with no internal energy sources), since p's with positive real parts would produce time functions that continuously increase with time—a condition that clearly is precluded on the grounds of physical reasoning.

Although we shall for the time being not consider the transient or natural behavior of more complex circuits (involving elaborate geometrical configurations with random distributions of R, L, and C elements), it is pertinent to recall from the discussion in Art. 2 of Ch. 5 that this behavior is in all cases described by a sum of terms of the form Ae^{pt}; the more complicated networks merely require a larger number of such terms with appropriate A values and p values.* Thus we may say quite generally that the natural behavior of any linear passive network may be described as a simple addition of decaying oscillations with appropriate frequencies, rates of decay, initial magnitudes, and time phases. The frequencies and rates of decay are determined by the pertinent p values (which in general are complex), while the initial magnitudes and time phases are determined by the pertinent A values (which likewise are in general complex, but unlike the p values depend upon the initial state of the network and its mode of excitation).

It is appropriate to regard all characteristic p values as complex, and look upon purely real ones or purely imaginary ones as degenerate forms. Having done this, it is found additionally helpful to accept the notion of a *complex frequency* and regard the p values as such. The imaginary part of a complex frequency is thus the actual radian frequency of the pertinent natural oscillation, and the real part is its damping constant. In degenerate cases such as those represented by RL or RC circuits, the "complex frequencies" to be sure have zero imaginary parts, and the damped natural "oscillations" may not oscillate at all, but it is nevertheless still appropriate to refer to such characteristic values as complex frequencies since their degenerateness affects only their particular values; generically they are the same as the ones that have complex values, and the role they play in regard to network behavior is the same.

The important feature that the present discussion is leading up to is a recognition of the fact that these complex natural frequencies or characteristic values of a network not only play a dominant role in fixing the pattern of its natural behavior, but also determine the character of its sinusoidal steady-state behavior. In fact, as our study of network theory progresses, it becomes increasingly evident that the complex

---

* Detailed discussion of these matters is given in Ch. 9.

natural frequencies of a linear system completely characterize that system's behavior under transient and steady-state conditions alike (except for some less important scale factors whose independent adjustment is always possible), and that transient behavior and sinusoidal steady-state behavior can therefore be uniquely related, one to the other—a circumstance of inestimable value in problems of analysis and of synthesis.

In regard to the sinusoidal steady-state behavior it should first of all be recognized that it is *completely* characterized by a single quantity—the *impedance* of the circuit in question. Thus in a sinusoidal steady-state problem we have a given excitation, say a voltage of fixed amplitude, frequency, and phase, and we seek the current that is *forced* to exist as a result of this applied voltage. Observe that the character or nature of the circuit response is here being dictated by the source; the circuit has no choice but to obey the wishes of this dictator. The source is a sinusoid of a given frequency, and so the response must be a sinusoid of the same frequency. This much follows from the linear character of the differential equation governing the equilibrium of the circuit. The only effect that the circuit can exert upon the response is to control its amplitude and time phase relative to the amplitude and phase of the excitation, and this control is completely and compactly effected through the circuit impedance (refer to Eqs. 85 and 86 of the previous article for evidence of this fact in the case of the simple RL circuit).

Although in the sinusoidal steady state, the nature of the response is forced upon the network by the excitation, the circuit is seen to inject its individuality into the response through the effect it has upon the impedance. The latter is the "go-between" as it were that placates the source on the one hand and the network on the other, and mutually satisfies both. What should be more natural, then, than to find that the value of an impedance depends partly upon something that is characteristic of the source and partly upon something that is characteristic of the network. These "somethings" are (as the reader may guess from what has been said) the complex frequencies of the source and of the network. The "complex frequency" of the source is a pure imaginary value $j\omega$ (see Eq. 77) since this device is called upon to produce an undamped sinusoid. The complex natural frequencies of the network are restricted only by the requirement that they have negative real parts. The impedance, which is revealed to be a function of all of these complex frequencies, is itself a complex quantity which, as in Eq. 86, relates the complex voltage and current amplitudes characterizing the steady-state behavior.

Visualization of these matters is greatly enhanced through graphical representation. To this end one introduces the notion of a *complex frequency plane* which serves as a means for displaying all the complex frequencies involved and also as a potent means for recognizing by inspection many of the essential characteristics of the impedance as a function of these frequencies. Detailed illustrations of these matters will now be given in terms of the RL circuit treated in the preceding article and the other simple circuits whose transient behavior is discussed in Ch. 5.

5 Impedance and Admittance Functions for Simple Circuits

Regarding the impedance of the series RL circuit, Eq. 85, which we repeat here for convenience

$$Z = R + j\omega L \tag{93}$$

suppose we introduce the notation

$$s = j\omega \tag{94}$$

$$s_1 = -R/L \tag{95}$$

and write

$$Z = L(s - s_1) \tag{96}$$

Here the lower-case letter s is used as a symbol for any complex frequency; in particular, the complex frequency of the source is $s = j\omega$, that characteristic of the series RL circuit is $s_1 = -R/L$. The result

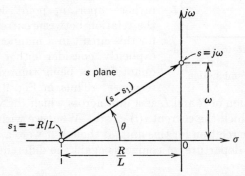

Fig. 7. Graphical interpretation of the frequency factor in the impedance 96 through its representation as a vector in the complex frequency plane.

expressed by Eq. 96 shows that the impedance Z is proportional to the difference between the source frequency s and the natural frequency s_1 of the RL circuit.

The significance of this result may easily be visualized with the help of graphical representation in the complex frequency plane referred to above, as is done in Fig. 7. In this s plane any complex value of $s = \sigma$

$+ j\omega$ is represented as a point. The horizontal axis or σ axis is also referred to as the "real" axis or "axis of reals"; the vertical axis is the "axis of imaginaries" or "j axis." The complex frequency of the undamped sinusoidal source corresponds to some point on the j axis; the natural frequency of the RL circuit is represented by the point s_1 on the negative real axis. Except for the constant multiplier L, the impedance Z is the vector $(s - s_1)$ which emanates from the point s_1 and terminates upon the point $s = j\omega$ on the j axis.

If one is interested in noting how the impedance changes with different values of the radian frequency ω of the source, the diagram of Fig. 7 is particularly helpful, since one need merely regard the point $s = j\omega$ on the j axis as moving along this axis. Thus the tip of the Z vector moves along the j axis with varying ω while the base of this vector remains fixed at the point s_1. The variation of both the magnitude and the angle of the Z vector are thus clearly portrayed.

Although in the derivation of the impedance of this series RL circuit the voltage is regarded as the applied disturbance or source and the current as the response, the relation between the complex current and

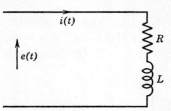

voltage vectors, as given in terms of the impedance by the Ohm's law expression 86, is valid, regardless of which quantity, E or I, is the excitation and which is the response. In order to appreciate this rather important point, let us rederive the relation between current and voltage for this circuit in a manner that does not explicitly consider either one of these quantities as being the excitation or the response. Thus in Fig. 8 we regard the

Fig. 8. Pertinent to the sinusoidal volt-ampere relation for the series RL combination.

series combination of R and L as a unit across which the voltage $e(t)$ appears and in which the current $i(t)$ exists. What we wish to establish is the volt-ampere relation for this unit, as though it were a single element.

The point of departure, of course, is again the differential equation

$$L\frac{di}{dt} + Ri = e \tag{97}$$

In order to indicate that we are interested only in the steady state for both current and voltage functions we write

$$e = Ee^{st} \quad \text{and} \quad i = Ie^{st} \tag{98}$$

With these expressions we must now satisfy Eq. 97. Since

$$di/dt = Ise^{st} = si(t) \tag{99}$$

substitution yields

$$(Ls + R)Ie^{st} = Ee^{st} \tag{100}$$

whence, after cancelation of the factor e^{st}, we have

$$(Ls + R)I = E \tag{101}$$

or

$$I = E/Z \tag{102}$$

with

$$Z = R + Ls = L(s - s_1) \tag{103}$$

where

$$s_1 = -R/L \tag{104}$$

These results evidently check the previous ones; yet here it is manifestly clear that Eq. 102 together with 103 represents the volt-ampere relation for the series RL unit, with no implication as to which quantity, the voltage or the current, is the excitation.

Through defining the so-called *admittance* as the reciprocal of the impedance, thus,

$$Y = \frac{1}{Z} = \frac{1}{L(s - s_1)} \tag{105}$$

the volt-ampere relations for the series RL unit may be written in symmetrical fashion as the mutually inverse pair

$$\begin{aligned} E &= ZI \\ I &= YE \end{aligned} \tag{106}$$

with Y and Z given by Eqs. 103 and 105.

The first of these two relations is more convenient to use when I is given (excitation) and E is to be found, the second when E is given and I is to be found. The relations 106 also suggest that one may regard the impedance Z as the voltage per unit of applied current, and the admittance as the resulting current per unit applied voltage. Thus, in Fig. 7, the vector $(s - s_1)$ may be regarded as the voltage vector E when the applied current I is $1/L$ amperes. If I differs from this value by any constant multiplier A, then E differs from $(s - s_1)$ by the same constant multiplier.

The relations 106 are observed to have precisely the form of volt-ampere relations for pure resistance networks, with the difference that Z appears instead of the resistance R and Y in the place of conductance

$G = 1/R$. Because of this fact, one is permitted to conclude that the volt-ampere relations for more extensive combinations of circuit elements may be found in terms of the impedances or admittances of the elements through dealing with these in precisely the same manner that resistance and conductance elements are dealt with when numerous such elements are interconnected in various ways.

This procedure, which essentially reduces the study of sinusoidal steady-state network behavior to d-c circuit manipulations (except for the final interpretation of the complex quantities as time functions), begins with a consideration of the complex volt-ampere relations of the three basic circuit elements. Thus for the resistance

$$e = Ri, \qquad i = Ge \qquad (107)$$

the inductance

$$e = L\frac{di}{dt}, \qquad i = \frac{1}{L}\int e\,dt \qquad (108)$$

and the capacitance

$$e = \frac{1}{C}\int i\,dt \qquad i = C\frac{de}{dt} \qquad (109)$$

we have with

$$e = Ee^{st}, \qquad i = Ie^{st} \qquad (110)$$

the respective results

$$E = IR, \qquad I = EG \qquad (111)$$

$$E = ILs, \qquad I = E/Ls \qquad (112)$$

$$E = I/Cs, \qquad I = ECs \qquad (113)$$

The last three equations are the complex volt-ampere relations for the resistance, inductance, and capacitance elements, respectively. That is to say, for a resistance alone the impedance Z is R and the admittance Y is G; for an inductance element the impedance Z is Ls and the admittance Y is $1/Ls$; for a capacitance element the impedance Z is $1/Cs$ and the admittance Y is Cs.

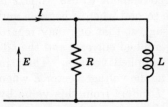

Fig. 9. Pertinent to the complex volt-ampere relation for the parallel RL circuit.

When components are connected in series, the resultant impedance is the sum of the impedances of the separate components; when connected in parallel, the resultant admittance is formed by adding the admittances of the components. Thus the impedance concept is a useful one when components appear in series, the admittance concept being appropriate to parallel combinations. In dealing with a more elaborate circuit geometry one may need to convert repeatedly from an impedance basis to an admittance basis, and vice versa.

Let us now consider the impedances of a number of additional simple element combinations. For the parallel combination of R and L shown in Fig. 9 we have

$$I = \left(\frac{1}{R} + \frac{1}{Ls}\right) E \tag{114}$$

from which

$$Y = \frac{1}{R} + \frac{1}{Ls} = \frac{R + Ls}{RLs} \tag{115}$$

Again letting $s_1 = -R/L$ we may write

$$Y = \frac{(s - s_1)}{Rs}, \qquad Z = \frac{Rs}{(s - s_1)} \tag{116}$$

These functions may be portrayed in the complex frequency plane as shown in Fig. 10. In this case the impedance is not represented by just a single vector in this plane, but by the ratio of two. Thus the factor s

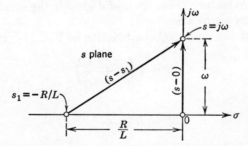

Fig. 10. Complex frequency plane representation of the frequency factors in the impedance 116 for the parallel RL circuit of Fig. 9.

in the numerator of Z may be regarded as $(s - 0)$; that is to say, as similar to the factor $(s - s_1)$ except that for this factor the s_1 value is zero. In Fig. 10 this factor is given by the vertical arrow (vector) emanating from the origin and terminating upon the point $s = j\omega$. The denominator factor $(s - s_1)$ is interpreted vectorially just as in Fig. 7. Except for the multiplier R, the impedance is given by the ratio of the two vectors $(s - 0)$ and $(s - s_1)$ as shown. Again one may visualize how Z changes in value as the point $s = j\omega$ assumes various positions on the j axis. Thus the magnitude of Z is always equal to R times the ratio of the lengths of the vectors $(s - 0)$ and $(s - s_1)$, while the angle θ of Z equals the angle of $(s - 0)$ which is $\pi/2$ radians, minus the angle of $(s - s_1)$ which is $\tan^{-1} (L\omega/R)$. It is clear that, as ω increases from zero, the magnitude of Z increases from zero and approaches unity times R, while the angle θ of Z starts from $\pi/2$ and approaches zero.

The admittance Y, being the reciprocal of Z, has infinite magnitude and a negative angle of $\pi/2$ radians for $\omega = 0$ and approaches the magnitude $1/R$ with the angle zero as ω increases continuously.

In any case the interpretation in the complex s plane is an important aid in visualizing the values of Y or of Z for various values of ω. For

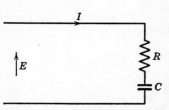

example, if someone wanted the phase displacement between voltage and current in this circuit to be 45° or 30° or some such angle, one can see at once from an obvious graphical construction what the frequency $s = j\omega$ would have to be for a fixed R/L, or what R/L would have to be for a given frequency $s = j\omega$, etc. It is also clear that the complex natural frequency $s_1 = -R/L$ charac-terizes the whole steady-state picture

Fig. 11. Pertinent to the com-plex volt-ampere relation for the series RC circuit.

except for a scale factor. These are useful ideas in the solution of analysis and synthesis problems alike.

Consider next the series RC combination of Fig. 11. Here

$$E = I\left(R + \frac{1}{Cs}\right) \tag{117}$$

whence

$$Z = R + \frac{1}{Cs} \tag{118}$$

If we let

$$s_1 = -\frac{1}{RC} \tag{119}$$

we have

$$Z = \frac{R(s - s_1)}{s}, \qquad Y = \frac{s}{R(s - s_1)} \tag{120}$$

These are respectively similar to the Y and Z of the parallel RL combina-tion of Fig. 9, as given by Eq. 116. The implication involved here will be elaborated upon later on. The graphical representation in the com-plex frequency plane is so similar to that shown in Fig. 10 that no sep-arate discussion seems necessary.

For the parallel RC circuit of Fig. 12 it is readily seen that

$$I = E\left(Cs + \frac{1}{R}\right) \tag{121}$$

whence

$$Y = Cs + \frac{1}{R} \tag{122}$$

Or if we let

$$s_1 = -\frac{1}{RC} \tag{123}$$

this result may be written

$$Y = C(s - s_1), \qquad Z = \frac{1}{C(s - s_1)} \tag{124}$$

These forms are respectively similar to Z and Y obtained for the series

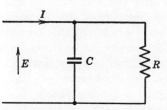

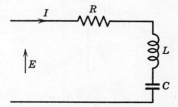

Fig. 12. Pertinent to the complex volt-ampere relation for the parallel RC circuit.

Fig. 13. Pertinent to the complex volt-ampere relation for the series RLC circuit.

RL combination as given by Eqs. 103 and 105; hence further detailed discussion may be omitted.

Next consider the series RLC circuit shown in Fig. 13. Here

$$E = I\left(R + Ls + \frac{1}{Cs}\right) \tag{125}$$

whence

$$Z = R + Ls + \frac{1}{Cs} \tag{126}$$

Using the notation

$$\alpha = R/2L, \qquad \omega_0^2 = 1/LC \tag{127}$$

as was done in the discussion of transient behavior, the impedance may be written

$$Z = \frac{L(s^2 + 2\alpha s + \omega_0{}^2)}{s} \tag{128}$$

or as

$$Z = \frac{L(s - s_1)(s - s_2)}{s} = Y^{-1} \tag{129}$$

where s_1 and s_2 are the zeros of the second-degree polynomial in Eq. 128; that is

$$s_1 = -\alpha + j\omega_d, \qquad s_2 = -\alpha - j\omega_d$$

with $\tag{130}$

$$\omega_d = \sqrt{\omega_0{}^2 - \alpha^2}$$

These are recognized as the complex natural frequencies of the RLC circuit (see Eqs. 74 and 75 of Ch. 5). As discussed earlier, the imped-ance—except for a scale factor—is a function solely of the excitation fre-quency s and the complex natural fre-quencies of the circuit in question. All of the examples bear out this contention.

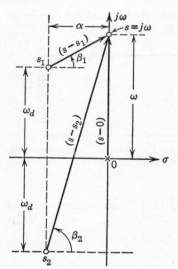

Figure 14 shows the pertinent graph-ical representation in the s plane for the impedance or admittance of Eq. 129. The so-called *frequency factors* $(s - s_1)$, $(s - s_2)$, and $(s - 0)$ are given by three vectors, all terminating upon the point $s = j\omega$ on the j axis. Except for the factor L, the impedance in magnitude equals the product of the lengths of the vectors $(s - s_1)$ and $(s - s_2)$, divided by the length of $(s - 0)$. The angle θ of the impedance Z is the angle β_1 of $(s - s_1)$ plus the angle β_2 of $(s - s_2)$ minus $\pi/2$ (the angle of $s - 0$). Again one may visually grasp how Z changes in mag-nitude and angle with changing positions of the point $s = j\omega$ for fixed s_1 and s_2,

FIG. 14. s-plane representation of the frequency factors for the impedance 129 of the series RLC circuit in Fig. 13.

or how it changes with varying locations of s_1 and s_2 for a fixed point $s = j\omega$. The circumspection gained here is tremendously helpful in all manner of problems, as will become abundantly clear in the fol-lowing discussions and in problem work assigned as exercises.

6 The Phenomenon of Resonance

In the preceding discussion of the RLC circuit it was tacitly assumed that the resistance is sufficiently small so that the natural frequencies are complex.   In other words, the natural behavior of the circuit was assumed to be oscillatory.   This tacit assumption has no influence upon the form of the impedance Z, which is correctly given for all values of R, L, and C by expression 129, in which the nature of the natural fre-

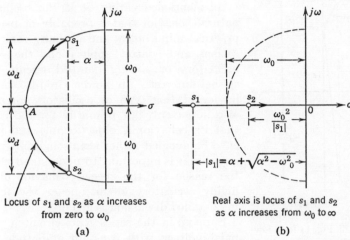

Locus of s_1 and s_2 as α increases from zero to ω_0

(a)

Real axis is locus of s_1 and s_2 as α increases from ω_0 to ∞

(b)

FIG. 15. s-plane loci of the natural frequencies of the series RLC circuit with variable damping: (a) for $0 < \alpha < \omega_0$, (b) for $\omega_0 < \alpha < \infty$.

quencies s_1 and s_2 depends upon the relative amount of damping in the circuit, as pointed out in the previous chapter.   A rather circumspect view of this situation is gained through noting, in the s plane, how the positions of the points s_1 and s_2 change for varying values of $\alpha = R/2L$ with a fixed ω_0, as shown in Fig. 15.

Part (a) of this figure is pertinent to α values within the range $0 \leq \alpha \leq \omega_0$, while part (b) pertains to the range $\omega_0 \leq \alpha \leq \infty$.   From the relations 130 which apply directly to part (a) of Fig. 15 one readily recognizes that, for a fixed ω_0 and varying α, the s plane locus must be a semicircle.   For $R = 0$ or $\alpha = 0$, s_1 and s_2 are at the points $\pm j\omega_0$ on the j axis.   As R or α increases, the complex natural frequencies move along their respective semicircular paths toward the common point A on the real axis which they reach for $\alpha = \omega_0$.   For this condition the two s values coincide, and the circuit behavior is that described earlier as critically damped; the damped radian frequency ω_d has just become zero.   The force-free circuit behavior just fails to be oscillatory, for its period of oscillation has become infinite.

Part (b) of Fig. 15 shows how the complex natural frequencies s_1 and s_2 move in the s plane as α increases beyond the value ω_0. It is observed that the two s values again become distinct but both remain real, the magnitude of one being the reciprocal of the magnitude of the other with respect to ω_0^2 (i.e. $s_1 s_2 = \omega_0^2$ for all $\alpha \gtrless \omega_0$). As $\alpha \to \infty$, $s_2 \to 0$ and $s_1 \to -\infty$.

As mentioned earlier, it is the oscillatory natural behavior that is probably of primary practical importance; and in many communications and control applications the *highly* oscillatory or *slightly* damped circuit is of special interest. In power circuits the behavior of this type of oscillatory circuit is also important, but primarily for the reason that its behavior is objectionable and hence is to be avoided rather than sought after. In any case it is important to understand clearly the reason for the special behavior of the highly oscillatory circuit; hence the following detailed discussion is given.

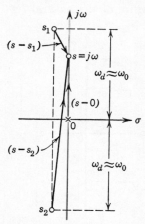

FIG. 16. The s-plane representation of the frequency factors of Fig. 14 for a low-loss circuit.

Suppose in the series RLC circuit a sinusoidal voltage with constant amplitude E is applied and the interest lies in the resulting current. The amplitude I of the latter is equal to the product of E and the admittance Y. Since E is to be regarded as constant, we may as well set it equal to unity. Then I is numerically equal to Y.

From Eq. 129 we have

$$Y = \frac{s}{L(s - s_1)(s - s_2)} \tag{131}$$

This admittance is now to be interpreted with the help of the graphical picture in Fig. 14 for a situation where α is small compared with ω_d and the latter is practically equal to ω_0. The particular appearance assumed by the diagram of Fig. 14 for this special situation is pictured in Fig. 16. We are particularly interested in noting the behavior of Y (i.e. I) with varying values of the radian frequency ω of the applied voltage source.

It is apparent by inspection of this figure that a rather critical behavior results when ω is in the neighborhood of the natural frequency $\omega_d \approx \omega_0$, for then the vector $(s - s_1)$ becomes relatively very short and the magnitude of I or Y very large. Thus, as the variable point $s = j\omega$

passes alongside of the complex natural frequency s_1, the length of $(s - s_1)$ rapidly becomes short and then longer again; correspondingly I rapidly becomes large and then relatively small again. There exists a small range of frequencies near s_1 where the current behaves rather critically with varying applied frequency $s = j\omega$, becoming exceptionally large for $\omega \approx \omega_0$. This type of behavior is called *resonance*, and the frequency range in the immediate vicinity of ω_0 is spoken of as the *resonance range*.

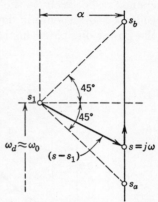

This interpretation of the resonance phenomenon is at once an exact and compact analytic representation as well as being a means for lending physical meaning to this frequently encountered property of oscillatory systems. Thus it is only natural that we should find an exceptionally large response when the driving frequency coincides or nearly coincides with the frequency of natural oscillation. If damping could be completely absent ($R = 0$), the points s_1 and s_2 would lie upon the j axis, and the length of the vector $(s - s_1)$ in Fig. 16 could then become zero—the response at resonance infinite. In any physical system there will always be present a sufficient amount of incidental loss to keep the points s_1 and s_2 just slightly to the left of the

Fig. 17. An enlarged portion of the s-plane picture in Fig. 16 for the vicinity of the critical frequency s_1; its relevance is to the discussion of resonance and to the location of the half-power frequencies.

j axis; hence the resonance response will always remain finite.

In cases where the points s_1 and s_2 are rather close to the j axis ($\alpha \ll \omega_0$) it is readily appreciated from Fig. 16 that throughout the resonance range the vectors $(s - s_2)$ and $(s - 0)$ remain essentially constant and equal respectively to the values $2j\omega_0$ and $j\omega_0$. The expression for Y, Eq. 131, is then seen to be given very nearly by the approximate form

$$ Y \approx \frac{1}{2L(s - s_1)} \tag{132} $$

Figure 17 shows an enlarged view of a portion of the s plane near the point s_1, which is helpful in visualizing the behavior of the admittance 132 as a function of $s = j\omega$. When the variable point s on the j axis is directly opposite s_1, the admittance clearly has its maximum value

$$ Y_{\max} \approx 1/2L\alpha = 1/R \tag{133} $$

The angle of the admittance here is zero, and so the current is in phase with the applied voltage at this point. A plot of $|Y| = |I|$ versus ω in the resonance vicinity evidently is symmetrical about the point $\omega_d \approx \omega_0$ as shown in Fig. 18 where the independent variable is chosen as the radian-frequency displacement from the resonance frequency ω_0 measured in units of α. Thus one such unit below and above ω_0 corresponds respectively to the points s_a and s_b in Fig. 17. Here the magnitude of the response is down to $1/\sqrt{2} = 0.707$ of its maximum value; the power dissipated in the resistance R (proportional to the square of

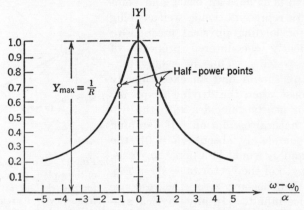

Fig. 18.   The resonance curve of the simple RLC circuit.

the current) is below the maximum value by a factor of $1/2$. Hence these points are referred to as the *half-power* points on the resonance curve of Fig. 18. At these points the angle of Y and therefore of I with respect to E is $\pm 45°$; that is, at the lower half-power point the current I leads the voltage E by $45°$, at the upper half-power point the current lags by the same amount.

The frequency range between the half-power points is usually regarded as the "width" w of the resonance curve, i.e.

$$w = 2\alpha = R/L \tag{134}$$

The ratio of the resonance frequency ω_0 to the band width w is a measure of the *selectivity* of the RLC circuit when it is used to "tune" to some desired input frequency, as in the first stages of a radio receiver. This measure of the tuning ability of the simple resonant circuit is called its Q. According to Eq. 134 one has for this factor

$$Q = \omega_0/w = L\omega_0/R \tag{135}$$

as was pointed out in Eq. 86 of Ch. 5.

When the Q of the circuit is not large, the representation of Y as given by Eq. 132 becomes rather crude. However, the exact representation in Eq. 131, together with the interpretation of its frequency factors as shown in Fig. 14, is still sufficiently clear and straightforward to enable one to see without difficulty all relevant features regarding the dependence of Y upon the parameters s, s_1, s_2. It is clear, for example, that Y_{max} does not occur when s is directly opposite s_1 but rather at a slightly larger value of ω because of the lengthening of the factors $(s - s_2)$ and $(s - 0)$ with ω. Also, the angle of Y is not exactly zero when s is opposite s_1. Usually these refinements are of little importance, but it is significant to note that the graphical interpretation in Fig. 14 places in visual evidence even these more detailed matters.

7   Rectangular versus Polar Forms of Impedance and Admittance Functions; an Alternative Interpretation of Resonance

In the discussion of impedance or admittance so far, we have been referring to these complex quantities in terms of their magnitudes and angles; that is to say, we have been considering them in their so-called "polar forms." For certain applications it is more convenient to represent them in "rectangular form" in terms of their real and imaginary parts, thus:

$$Z = R(\omega) + jX(\omega) \tag{136}$$

$$Y = G(\omega) + jB(\omega) \tag{137}$$

Here $R(\omega)$ is called the "resistive part" and $X(\omega)$ the "reactive part" of the impedance Z; while $G(\omega)$ and $B(\omega)$ are referred to respectively as the "conductive part" and the "susceptive part" of Y. These terms are often abbreviated by leaving out the word "part" and speaking simply of the "resistance" and "reactance" of an impedance, or the "conductance" and "susceptance" of an admittance. Use of these abbreviated terms in the case of the real parts of Z and Y can lead to misunderstanding since the terms "resistance" and "conductance" are already being used to connote a resistance or conductance element. While such an element is always a constant whose value depends only upon the size of that element, the quantities $R(\omega)$ and $G(\omega)$ in the representations 136 and 137 in general may be functions of a collection of resistance, inductance, and capacitance elements, besides being dependent upon the source frequency ω.

Consider, for example, the impedance of the parallel RC circuit of Fig. 12, as given by Eq. 122

$$Y^{-1} = Z = \frac{R}{1 + RCs} \tag{138}$$

For $s = j\omega$ we get

$$Z = \frac{R}{1 + j\omega RC} = \frac{R - j\omega R^2 C}{1 + R^2 C^2 \omega^2} \tag{139}$$

so that

$$R(\omega) = \frac{R}{1 + R^2 C^2 \omega^2}, \qquad X(\omega) = \frac{-R^2 C \omega}{1 + R^2 C^2 \omega^2} \tag{140}$$

Thus the resistive part of Z depends upon the values of both parameters R and C as well as upon the source frequency ω.

For the series RLC circuit of Fig. 13 we have according to Eq. 126 with $s = j\omega$

$$Z = R + j\left(L\omega - \frac{1}{C\omega}\right) \tag{141}$$

Here

$$R(\omega) = R, \qquad X(\omega) = L\omega - \frac{1}{C\omega} \tag{142}$$

In this example $R(\omega)$ becomes identified with the element R alone, but this is a special case. Observe that, if we form the corresponding admittance

$$Y = \frac{1}{R + j(L\omega - 1/C\omega)} = \frac{R - j(L\omega - 1/C\omega)}{R^2 + (L\omega - 1/C\omega)^2} \tag{143}$$

we have

$$G(\omega) = \frac{R}{R^2 + (L\omega - 1/C\omega)^2}, \qquad B(\omega) = \frac{-(L\omega - 1/C\omega)}{R^2 + (L\omega - 1/C\omega)^2} \tag{144}$$

whence it is apparent that $G(\omega)$ is *not* simply $1/R$ but depends upon L, C, and ω as well.

These examples should suffice to show that, if we refer to the real part of an impedance as a "resistance" instead of "the resistive part," we do so with a certain risk in the clarity of our assertion unless the persons with whom we are carrying on the discussion are sufficiently experienced to know what is meant. A similar situation exists with regard to calling the conductive part of an admittance simply a "conductance." In analytic work where there is any chance of being misunderstood the notation $R(\omega)$ and $G(\omega)$ should suffice to prevent confusion with resistance and conductance of a single element which would be denoted as

R and G; that is, the functional dependence upon ω as implied in the notation $R(\omega)$ and $G(\omega)$ is used as a distinguishing mark.

Fortunately neither the letters X and B nor the names "reactance" and "susceptance" are used to denote circuit elements, so that the same care need not be exercised in distinguishing these quantities as the imaginary parts of Z and Y respectively.

The rectangular form for the impedance of the RLC circuit as given by Eq. 141 is frequently convenient in discussing the resonance phenomenon. According to the interpretation of resonance as a condition for which the current for a constant applied voltage is a maximum, it is obvious that resonance occurs when the reactive part of Z is zero; that is, for

$$X = L\omega - 1/C\omega = 0, \qquad \omega = 1/\sqrt{LC} = \omega_0 \qquad (145)$$

for then Z reduces to R alone. Although this way of dealing with the resonance problem is simple and checks in the end results with the conclusions found earlier, it lacks the direct physical interpretation of resonance as a coincidence or near coincidence of applied and natural frequencies, and does not possess the simple analytic interpretation in the s plane that readily permits an approximate study valid in the resonance region. The latter method, moreover, lends itself without increased manipulative complications to the consideration of resonance in more complicated circuits which possess several resonance regions because they have more natural frequencies.

Nevertheless it is proper for the student to understand each important network characteristic from more than one standpoint if possible. In this connection the interpretation of resonance as a condition of zero reactance is alternatively interesting and useful. In order to facilitate this point of view, it is expedient to write the impedance 141 for the RLC circuit as

$$Z = R + j(X_L + X_C) \qquad (146)$$

with

$$X_L = L\omega \qquad X_C = -1/C\omega \qquad (147)$$

denoting respectively the inductive and the capacitive components of the net reactance $X = X_L + X_C$. With reference to Eq. 145, which expresses the resonance condition in the series RLC circuit, it should be observed that the resonance frequency is here given as that one for which the inductive reactance X_L cancels the capacitive reactance X_C. The fact that these two component reactances are respectively positive and negative at all positive ω values evidently makes such cancelation possible. These matters are emphasized in the plot of Fig. 19 in which the component reactances are shown dotted and the resultant reactance is given as the solid curve.

From the expression

$$|Y.| = 1/\sqrt{R^2 + X^2} \qquad (148)$$

for the magnitude of the admittance (current response per volt of excitation), it is easy to see not only that $Y_{max} = 1/R$ occurs for $X = 0$,

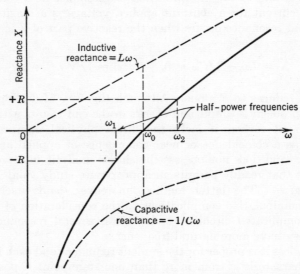

FIG. 19. The reactance X in Eq. 145 resulting from the sum of its inductive and capacitive components (Eq. 147). The half-power points occur where the value of the reactance equals the resistance; resonance occurs where the reactance is zero.

but also that $|Y| = Y_{max}/\sqrt{2}$ (defining the half-power points) occurs for $X = \pm R$. The corresponding frequencies, which are indicated in Fig. 19 as ω_1 and ω_2, are therefore the positive roots of the equation

$$L\omega - \frac{1}{C\omega} = \pm R \quad \text{or} \quad \omega^2 \mp 2\alpha\omega - \omega_0{}^2 = 0 \qquad (149)$$

which are found to be

$$\omega_{2,1} = \pm\alpha + \sqrt{\alpha^2 + \omega_0{}^2} \qquad (150)$$

with the difference

$$\omega_2 - \omega_1 = w = 2\alpha = R/L \qquad (151)$$

thus checking Eq. 134 for the "width" of the resonance curve (Fig. 18).

It is collaterally interesting to observe that the slope of the reactance curve at the resonance frequency ω_0 is found from Eqs. 142 and 145 to be

$$\left(\frac{dX}{d\omega}\right)_{\omega=\omega_0} = L + \frac{1}{C\omega_0^2} = 2L \tag{152}$$

from which an approximate expression for X valid near ω_0 (equation of the tangent to $X(\omega)$ at $\omega = \omega_0$) would be

$$X \approx 2L(\omega - \omega_0) \tag{153}$$

thus giving a corresponding approximate relation for the admittance Y that reads

$$Y \approx \frac{1}{R + j2L(\omega - \omega_0)} = \frac{1}{2L[j\omega - (-\alpha + j\omega_0)]} \tag{154}$$

and checks Eq. 132 since $s = j\omega$ and $s_1 \approx -\alpha + j\omega_0$.

8   Reciprocal and Complementary Impedances and Admittances

It has been pointed out at several times in these discussions that network properties are invariant to an interchange of quantities in the following pairs

Voltage and current.
Resistance and conductance.
Inductance and capacitance.
Series connection and parallel connection.
Open circuit and short circuit.

To this group we can now evidently add the pair of quantities

Impedance and admittance.

since one follows out of the other upon interchanging voltage and current.

To illustrate with a specific example, the impedance of the series RL circuit of Fig. 8 becomes identical with the admittance of the parallel RC circuit of Fig. 12 if the R values are reciprocal (R of one equals G of the other) and L in henrys equals C in farads. This result is clear from the fact that the $s_1 = -R/L$ of the first circuit becomes identical with $s_1 = -1/RC$ of the other, whence comparison of Eqs. 105 and 124 for the admittance or impedance functions shows that the Z of one network coincides with the Y of the other. The networks of Figs. 8 and 12, for the stated relations between element values, are *duals* of each other; the corresponding impedances are reciprocals, and the corresponding admittances are reciprocals. Thus the problem of finding a second network whose impedance is the reciprocal of that of a given network is solved through constructing the dual of that network.

Similarly, the parallel RL circuit of Fig. 9 and the series RC circuit of Fig. 11 are duals if the R values are reciprocal and L in henrys equals C in farads, for then the Z of Eq. 116 (pertaining to the RL circuit of Fig. 9) matches the Y of Eq. 120 (pertaining to the RC circuit of Fig. 11), and vice versa.

The dual of the series RLC circuit of Fig. 13 is given by the parallel $R'L'C'$ circuit of Fig. 20 with the implication that $R' = 1/R$, $L' = C$, $C' = L$ (numerically, not dimensionally). The impedance of the latter circuit is then found to be identical with the admittance (see Eq. 129) of the former, and vice versa.

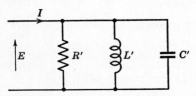

FIG. 20.   Pertinent to the complex volt-ampere relation for the parallel RLC circuit, potentially dual to the series RLC circuit of Fig. 13.

Regarding the resonance phenomenon in the circuit of Fig. 20 we should here consider the current as the source of constant amplitude and look for a maximum in the voltage response, as the frequency of the source is varied, or as the natural frequency of the circuit is varied keeping the source frequency constant. In the circuit of Fig. 20, resonance corresponds to a maximum impedance or minimum admittance, as contrasted to resonance in the circuit of Fig. 13 where the reverse is true. This difference in the detailed character of resonance in the two systems is sometimes distinguished by referring to it in the circuit of Fig. 20 as "parallel resonance" and in the circuit of Fig. 13 as "series resonance."

There was a time, not long ago, when engineers considered all sources as voltages and hence all responses as currents. Thus a maximum response (resonance) always meant a minimum impedance. In contrast, a condition of maximum impedance, as results in the circuit of Fig. 20 at resonance, was then referred to as "*anti*resonance." With the more flexible modern way of regarding sources as capable of being either voltages or currents, use of the term "antiresonance" is becoming rather infrequent, but it is sometimes employed to designate a condition of minimum response in contrast to maximum response, whatever the response may be.

The relationship of reciprocity between a pair of impedances, which we can write as

$$Z_2 = 1/Z_1 \qquad (155)$$

is an important mutual property and one that is solved in either direction through application of the principle of duality. Another important mutual relationship between a pair of impedances is that in which one is said to be the *complement* of the other. Analytically the complementary property is expressed by the relation

$$Z_1 + Z_2 = 1 \tag{156}$$

We are not yet in a position to discuss completely the problem of how the network for one of these impedances is found from that of the other, but it is nevertheless interesting and useful to point out how a

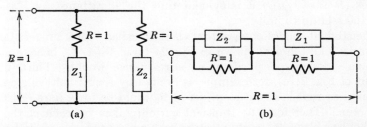

FIG. 21. A class of constant-resistance networks that involve reciprocal impedances. Circuits (a) and (b) are duals.

restricted class of such networks may be found through making use of the reciprocal relationship. Thus parts (a) and (b) of Fig. 21 show two circuit arrangements for which the resultant impedance is a pure resistance of 1 ohm if Z_1 and Z_2 are reciprocal. For the circuit of part (a) we get for the resultant admittance

$$\frac{1}{1 + Z_1} + \frac{1}{1 + Z_2} = \frac{1}{1 + Z_1} + \frac{Z_1}{1 + Z_1} = 1 \tag{157}$$

Hence this is a case where two admittances add up to unity. Similarly for the circuit of part (b)—which incidentally is the dual of the circuit of part (a)—we see that

$$\frac{1}{1 + (1/Z_2)} + \frac{1}{1 + (1/Z_1)} = \frac{1}{1 + Z_1} + \frac{Z_1}{1 + Z_1} = 1 \tag{158}$$

Here we have a situation where two impedances (those of Z_1 in parallel with R and Z_2 in parallel with R) add up to unity.

A simple example of the situation in Fig. 21(a) is given by considering the series RL circuit of Fig. 8 in parallel with the series RC circuit of Fig. 11, since Z_1 and Z_2 are then simply Ls and $1/Cs$ respectively which, for L numerically equal to C, are reciprocal. With $R = 1$, the admittance 105 for the series RL circuit is

$$Y = -s_1/(s - s_1) \tag{159}$$

while that for the series RC circuit, Eq. 120, becomes

$$Y = s/(s - s_1) \tag{160}$$

Since the s_1 values are alike because of the special choice of parameter values $(R/L = 1/RC)$ it is evident that the admittances of Eqs. 159 and 160 add up to unity.

The student should observe that these so-called "constant-resistance" networks, like the ones shown in Fig. 21 for $Z_2 = 1/Z_1$, behave at the terminals designated precisely as a resistance would. Thus, if the circuit of Fig. 21(a), for example, is excited by a unit voltage step, the terminal current is a unit step just as it would be for a pure resistance of 1 ohm. Therefore the transient current taken by each of the two parallel branches separately must be such a time function that the sum of the two becomes exactly unity for all $t > 0$. In the case of the example just cited, one of these currents is the exponential buildup in a series RL circuit; the other one in the series RC circuit is an exponential decay; the rates of buildup and decay respectively are equal, with the result that the sum of the two currents equals the constant value unity. The student may further exploit the details of this problem as well as others of this nature as exercises.

An additional point worth emphasizing in connection with the kind of thinking involved in the topic of the present article is the fact that the special mutual relationships between the impedances Z_1 and Z_2 of a pair of networks hold independently of the value of the source frequency s. Thus, if we consider two impedances related as $Z_1 = 1/Z_2$ we have in mind that, although Z_1 and Z_2 may individually vary as functions of s in any complicated manner, yet they *continuously* and for every possible s value fulfill the condition $Z_1 = 1/Z_2$. The same is true of the complementary relationship $Z_1 + Z_2 = 1$. Another important relationship which we will discuss later on, namely, that of *equality* ($Z_1 = Z_2$ for networks of different configuration), will receive the same general interpretation with regard to its nondependence upon s. These matters are important because there exists another basis upon which one might speak of the mutual relationships of being equal, reciprocal, and complementary; namely, when these conditions are assumed fulfilled for one specific s value only. In dealing with steady-state power circuits which operate at the fixed frequency of 60 cycles per second one may encounter such restricted use of the terms "equivalent networks," "reciprocal networks," etc. One should not confuse these trivially simple situations with the vastly more subtle and interesting ones considered here.

9 Magnitude and Frequency Scaling

Recalling the volt-ampere relations for the single-circuit elements, attention for the moment is to be focused upon the fact that, for a given current, the associated voltage is linearly proportional to the numerical value of a resistance R, or an inductance L, or an elastance $S = 1/C$. From this simple fact it should be evident that if, in a given network, all R, L, and S values are multiplied by the same positive real constant A, the effect for, say, an applied unit current is merely to multiply all voltages by A, or for an applied unit voltage to multiply all currents by $1/A$. Hence this operation leaves the impedance of a network unchanged except to multiply it by A. This process is referred to as "scaling" the impedance, or also as "changing the impedance level of the network by a factor A." Since it can easily be done at any stage in an analysis, the initial choice of an impedance multiplier is very often arbitrary.

Another important scaling process is that pertaining to the complex frequency s. We see in the simple examples treated above that the impedance or admittance function is completely determined (except for a constant multiplier) by its several frequency factors of the form $(s - s_n)$ where s_n are the complex natural frequencies of the network. In later work we shall see that this simple structure of impedance and admittance functions holds for all networks, the more complicated ones merely yielding more frequency factors. In speaking of the impedance or admittance functions rather than of the physical networks they represent, one refers to the various s_n values appearing in the frequency factors as *critical frequencies* rather than as natural frequencies.

The critical frequencies of an impedance function may be regarded as forming some constellation of dots when plotted in the complex s plane. Plotting such a constellation, however, implies a choice of scale in the s plane. For different choices of this so-called "frequency scale" the given constellation does not change with regard to the general distribution of dots but merely expands or contracts as it would appear to do if one viewed the s plane through a magnifying glass, or removed the glass. The effect of such "scaling" upon the impedance function is that of expanding or ,contracting the complex frequency variable s. One may visualize the process through imagining the

s plane to be a sheet of rubber, whence scaling corresponds to a uniform expansion or contraction in *both* coordinates of the plane.

The dimension of length in the s plane, incidentally, is reciprocal time. Thus the real parts of complex s values have been seen to be reciprocal time constants; imaginary parts are radian frequencies. Since the radian is a pure ratio and hence dimensionless, a quantity measured in radians per second has the dimension of reciprocal time. Length measured in *any* direction in the s plane, therefore, represents a reciprocal time. A uniform stretch of the s plane in both directions corresponds to a compression of the time scale appropriate to the problem dealt with, and vice versa.

In dealing with impedances or admittances as functions of the complex variable $s = \sigma + j\omega$, it is important to avoid confusion in one's mind between complex s values and corresponding complex Z values (or Y values). The latter can, of course, also be represented graphically in a complex plane, which is then referred to as the Z plane or as the Y plane. There is a tendency for the beginner to confuse the s plane with the Z plane or with the Y plane. Specifically, the scaling or stretching process in the s plane should be recognized as having nothing to do with values in the Z plane but only with points in the s plane at which these values occur. Thus, if we were considering plots of the magnitude and angle of Z versus the radian frequency ω (done in the usual manner through plotting $|Z|$ and θ as ordinates versus ω's as abscissae) then a change of scale in the s plane can be visualized through imagining these plots to be done on a rubber block which is subsequently stretched or compressed in the abscissa direction. Ordinate values are thereby not affected; only the abscissae at which they occur are influenced. The stretch in this plot of $|Z|$ versus ω or θ versus ω is one-dimensional; in the s plane it is two-dimensional.

In order to see how frequency scaling is brought about through appropriate changes in the element values of a given network, one need merely recall the expressions for the impedances of the separate elements, which are: R, Ls, and $1/Cs$. Thus the frequency s has no influence upon the impedance of a resistance element, whereas, in an inductance or capacitance element, invariance of the impedance with changes in s requires that L and s or C and s vary *inversely*. If in a given network the values of the R's are left unchanged but the L's and C's are divided by some number $n > 1$, then any impedance value that previously occurred at the value $s = s_a$ now occurs for $s = ns_a$: that is, at a frequency n times as great. Hence division of all L's and C's by $n > 1$ is equivalent to stretching the constellation of critical frequencies in the s plane, thus making all time constants n times smaller and the network response n times faster. Multiplication of all L's and C's by $n > 1$ has the opposite effect.*

10   Vector Diagrams

Although the Ohm's law relation linking complex voltage and current amplitudes through the impedance of the circuit is so simple that it hardly needs any further clarification to be fully understood, yet it may in some cases be found additionally helpful to give to this relation its corresponding graphical interpretation. Such representation is particularly useful when a given problem involves more voltages and cur-

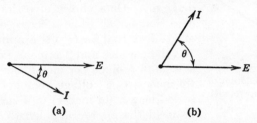

(a)   (b)

Fɪɢ. 22.   Vector diagrams illustrating relative magnitude and phase-angle relationships between complex voltage and current amplitudes. In (a) the current lags while in (b) it leads the voltage which is chosen as the reference vector.

rents (those in other branches of the network), for it lends circumspection and unity to the sum total of volt-ampere relations involved and enables one more readily to recognize significant special amplitude and phase relationships and the circuit conditions for which they arise.

Figure 22 shows such a graphical representation—called a *vector diagram*—for the simplest case in which only one voltage vector E and current vector I are involved. Part (a) of the figure represents a situation in which the angle of the impedance Z is positive (specifically $\theta = +30°$), while in part (b) of the same figure the angle of the impedance is assumed negative (specifically $\theta = -60°$). In the first case the current vector lags the voltage vector; in the second it leads.

The relative lengths of the voltage and current vectors in these diagrams are completely arbitrary, for, although they are related through the magnitude of the impedance Z, the scales determining length may be chosen independently for voltage and current. Thus, suppose the

* Although frequency scaling has no effect upon the amplitude of an impedance or admittance function since it involves only the independent variable (the frequency s), a closer study reveals that the time function characterizing the transient response of the pertinent network not only has its independent variable (the time t) affected, but its amplitude becomes multiplied by a constant also. These matters are discussed in Art. 6 of Ch. 9 and are summarized there in the statement 132.

voltage magnitude were 1 and the impedance magnitude 10, so that the current magnitude becomes 0.1. If we choose a voltage scale of 2 inches per volt and a current scale of 20 inches per ampere, the vectors E and I have equal length; whereas, if we change to a current scale of 10 inches per ampere, the I vector has half the length of the E vector. Unless the diagram contains several voltage or current vectors, relative lengths have not much meaning, but relative angles have.

Elaborating upon this theme, we may say that a choice of scales for the quantities E and I fixes a scale for the associated impedance Z

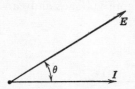

Fig. 23. The diagram of Fig. 22(a) redrawn with the current chosen as the reference vector.

(which may or may not appear on the same diagram). Or a choice of scales for I and Z fixes that for E; while a choice of scales for E and Z fixes that for I. For example, a choice of 10 volts per inch and 2 amperes per inch implies a scale of 5 ohms per inch if the scaled length (in inches) of a voltage vector divided by the scaled length (in inches) of a current vector is to yield the appropriate length in inches for the associated impedance vector. For these scales, a voltage vector 2.5 inches long represents 25 volts; a current vector 2.0 inches long represents 4 amperes; the length of the associated impedance vector is $2.5/2.0 = 1.25$ inches and represents $5 \times 1.25 = 6.25 = 25/4$ ohms.

One may tacitly assume for Z the scale of 1 ohm per inch, whence it follows that the scales for E and I become equal; that is, the number of volts per inch equals the number of amperes per inch. This tacit condition need, however, not always apply; and in fact it may in many problems be difficult to accommodate.

Observe, with regard to angles, that we specifically use the term *relative* angles. Thus the diagram of Fig. 22(a) could just as well be drawn as shown in Fig. 23, or in any one of an infinite number of additional possible angular orientations. The one significant fact which this simple diagram portrays is that the current lags the voltage by θ radians.

Since the angular orientation of the diagram as a whole is thus perfectly arbitrary, one is free to choose that orientation which seems to be appropriate to the physical conditions of the problem. For example, if the source is a voltage, then it is customary to choose the angle of E as being zero; if the source is a current, the angle of I is usually taken to be zero. In the first of these choices the vector E serves as *phase reference* for the diagram; in the second choice the vector I becomes the phase reference. Whichever vector is chosen to have zero angle is designated as the *reference vector*. Although several different voltages and currents may be involved in a given problem, it is clear that the angle of only one voltage or of one current vector may arbitrarily be set equal to zero.

When the impedance is represented in rectangular form, the volt-ampere relation may be separated into a sum of terms corresponding to the resistive and the reactive components of Z, as in

$$E = IZ = IR(\omega) + jIX(\omega) \tag{161}$$

The separate vector components of E represented by the terms $IR(\omega)$ and $IX(\omega)$—called the *resistance drop* and *reactance drop* respectively—may be indicated in the corresponding vector diagram. If this is done for the situation depicted in Fig. 22(a), the result has the appearance shown in Fig. 24. Observe that the vector $IR(\omega)$ must have the same angular orientation as the vector I, since $R(\omega)$ is merely a positive real number. We express this fact by stating that the *IR drop* is *in phase* with the vector I. The voltage component given by $jIX(\omega)$, on the other hand, clearly is

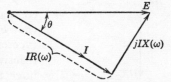

FIG. 24. The diagram of Fig. 22(a) with the resistive and reactive components of the voltage drop added according to their definition in Eq. 161.

$\pi/2$ radians in advance of I; that is, it leads the vector I by $90°$. This fact is alternatively expressed by stating that the *IX drop* is *in quadrature* with the vector I, although this terminology is a bit ambiguous since *quadrature* merely implies a right-angle relationship without regard to lead or lag.

Observe that the resistive and reactive components of E vectorially add to yield E. The lengths of these component vectors are fixed, for a given impedance angle θ, as soon as a length for the vector E is chosen. The vector I in the diagram must coincide in direction (must be *in phase*) with the IR vector; its length (as already mentioned) is arbitrary.

In dealing with certain problems it may be convenient or useful to decompose the current vector I into components that are respectively in phase with E and in quadrature with E; or it may be expedient to subdivide the components of Z into subcomponents. A common example of the latter procedure arises in dealing with the series RLC circuit for an impressed voltage E. Here

$$Z = R + j\omega L + \frac{1}{j\omega C} \tag{162}$$

which may be written

$$Z = R + jX_L + jX_C \tag{163}$$

with X_L and X_C as given in Eq. 147.

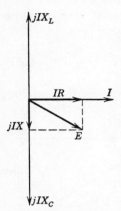

In drawing the vector diagram for this example, it is effective to choose the current as phase reference, notwithstanding the fact that the voltage may be the source function. The resulting diagram, shown in Fig. 25, is drawn for a condition in which the capacitive reactance X_C predominates so that the net voltage E lags the current I (the latter leads the voltage). Note that the net reactance drop IX is small compared with either component IX_L or IX_C, so that even the total voltage E, which includes (vectorially) the IR drop, is smaller than either reactive component drop. If $X_L + X_C = 0$, we have the resonant condition for which $E = IR$ alone. The vector diagram makes more evident the fact that, at resonance, one may have voltages across the inductance and capacitance elements separately that can be many times larger than the net applied voltage. For this reason it is important that caution be exercised when experimenting with resonance in the laboratory unless the power source used is small enough so as to preclude the possibility of dangerous shock due to accidental contact with the apparatus.

Fig. 25. Vector diagram for the series RLC circuit showing the capacitive and inductive reactance drops as well as the net reactance and the resistance drops. Note that the net reactance drop is smaller than either of its components (at resonance it is zero).

Another example that illustrates the circumspection afforded through use of a vector diagram, is the circuit schematically shown in Fig. 26, which consists of the three impedances Z_1, Z_2, Z_3 in series. Suppose we write each in its rectangular form as

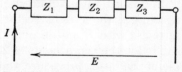

$$Z_1 = R_1 + jX_1$$
$$Z_2 = R_2 + jX_2 \tag{164}$$
$$Z_3 = R_3 + jX_3$$

Fig. 26. Schematic representation of a circuit involving three arbitrary impedances in series.

Figure 27 shows the vector diagram in which the current is chosen as phase reference and the impedances Z_1 and Z_2 are assumed to be inductively reactive ($X_1 > 0$ and $X_2 > 0$), while Z_3 is assumed to be capacitively reactive ($X_3 < 0$). The diagram shows all three *impedance drops* (that is, voltages across the separate impedances) broken down into resistive and reactive components, as well as their vector sum which equals the net voltage E. The circumspection which this diagram affords relative to magnitudes and phase relationships of all voltages with respect to the common current I cannot be had in equal measure from the purely analytic relationship involved. It is this property of the vector diagram that justifies its use.

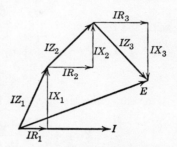

Fig. 27. The vector diagram associated with the circuit of Fig. 26 showing all resistance and reactance drops as well as the net current and voltage vectors.

Although these remarks have been made with specific reference to the impedance as parameter linking E and I, it is evident that one may equally well carry through the graphical procedure in terms of the reciprocal parameter Y. Thus, if the impedances of Fig. 26 were connected in parallel, such a "switch" to an admittance basis would be indicated. The details of this situation would then be exactly analogous to the ones given above with the roles of E and I interchanged, R's replaced by G's, and X's by B's.

11 More Elaborate Impedance Functions; Their Properties and Uses

As pointed out in Eq. 37, Art. 2 of Ch. 5, the differential equation linking current $i(t)$ in some part of a network with voltage $e(t)$ at the same point or at any other point is always of the form

$$a_n \frac{d^n i}{dt^n} + a_{n-1} \frac{d^{n-1} i}{dt^{n-1}} + \cdots + a_1 \frac{di}{dt} + a_0 i$$

$$= b_m \frac{d^m e}{dt^m} + b_{m-1} \frac{d^{m-1} e}{dt^{m-1}} + \cdots + b_1 \frac{de}{dt} + b_0 e \quad (165)$$

in which $a_n \cdots a_0$ and $b_m \cdots b_0$ are real constants. They are all positive if $e(t)$ and $i(t)$ refer to the same point in the network; otherwise either some a's or some b's may be negative according to whether $i(t)$ or $e(t)$ is the excitation function.*

* These matters are fully elaborated upon in Arts. 4 and 5 of Ch. 9.

For an excitation of the form e^{st}, the particular integral yielding the steady-state response must have the same form. Hence for the steady-state solution to the differential Eq. 165 it is appropriate to substitute

$$e(t) = Ee^{st} \quad \text{and} \quad i(t) = Ie^{st} \tag{166}$$

with the result

$$(a_n s^n + a_{n-1} s^{n-1} + \cdots + a_1 s + a_0) I e^{st} =$$
$$(b_m s^m + b_{m-1} s^{m-1} + \cdots + b_1 s + b_0) E e^{st} \tag{167}$$

After canceling the common factor e^{st}, one has

$$\frac{E}{I} = Z(s) = \frac{a_n s^n + a_{n-1} s^{n-1} + \cdots + a_1 s + a_0}{b_m s^m + b_{m-1} s^{m-1} + \cdots + b_1 s + b_0} = \frac{P(s)}{Q(s)} \tag{168}$$

If the polynomials $P(s)$ and $Q(s)$ are factored in terms of their zeros, the impedance $Z(s)$ assumes the form

$$Z(s) = \frac{H(s - s_1)(s - s_3) \cdots (s - s_{2n-1})}{(s - s_2)(s - s_4) \cdots (s - s_{2m})} \tag{169}$$

in which $H = a_n/b_m$ is a positive real constant.

If the excitation is $e(t)$, the transient (force-free) part of the solution is determined by Eq. 165 with $e = 0$. Assuming for the solution to this homogeneous differential equation the expression

$$i_0(t) = A e^{pt} \tag{170}$$

leads through direct substitution to

$$P(p) \cdot A e^{pt} = 0 \tag{171}$$

whence a nontrivial solution ($A \neq 0$) demands

$$P(p) = a_n p^n + a_{n-1} p^{n-1} + \cdots + a_1 p + a_0 = 0 \tag{172}$$

This is the characteristic equation determining the complex natural frequencies associated with the transient current. We observe that they are the critical frequencies $s_1, s_3, \cdots s_{2n-1}$ appearing in the numerator of the impedance 169. The complete response (transient plus steady state) is thus given by

$$i(t) = A_1 e^{s_1 t} + A_3 e^{s_3 t} + \cdots + A_{2n-1} e^{s_{2n-1} t} + \frac{E}{Z(s)} e^{st} \tag{173}$$

If the excitation is $i(t)$, the transient (force-free) part of the solution is determined by Eq. 165 with $i = 0$. Assuming for the solution to this homogeneous differential equation the expression

$$e_0(t) = Be^{pt} \qquad (174)$$

yields

$$Q(p) \cdot Be^{pt} = 0$$

and a nontrivial solution $(B \neq 0)$ demands

$$Q(p) = b_m p^m + b_{m-1} p^{m-1} + \cdots + b_1 p + b_0 = 0 \qquad (175)$$

This is the characteristic equation determining the complex natural frequencies associated with the transient voltage. We observe that they are the critical frequencies s_2, s_4, $\cdots$, s_{2m} appearing in the denominator of the impedance 169. The complete response (transient plus steady state) is in this case given by

$$e(t) = B_2 e^{s_2 t} + B_4 e^{s_4 t} + \cdots + B_{2m} e^{s_{2m} t} + IZ(s)e^{st} \qquad (176)$$

The transient amplitudes $A_1 \cdots A_{2n-1}$ in Eq. 173 and $B_1 \cdots B_{2m}$ in Eq. 176 are determined from the known state of the network at the time the excitation is applied and the demands made by the steady-state response function at that same instant, the discrepancies between these two factors being the quantities upon which the sizes of these amplitudes depend. The details of their determination do not interest us at the moment.* It is significant to point out however that, for a nonzero initial state, the results 173 and 176 are meaningful, even when the respective excitation functions are zero. When $e(t)$ and $i(t)$ refer to the same point in the network and the voltage excitation is zero $(E = 0)$, Eq. 173 is said to represent the *short-circuit transient* behavior of the given network, while for a zero current excitation $(I = 0)$ Eq. 176 is said to represent the *open-circuit transient* behavior.

We thus see that the *zeros* $(s_1 \cdots s_{2n-1})$ and *poles* $(s_2 \cdots s_{2m})$ of the impedance function 169 are identifiable respectively with the short-circuit and open-circuit complex natural frequencies of the pertinent network. That is to say, the impedance for any linear passive lumped network, however complicated, has the same form in terms of its frequency factors $(s - s_\nu)$ and the same physical significance regarding the critical frequencies involved in these factors as does the impedance for any of the simple two- and three-element circuits discussed in the foregoing articles. The truth of this statement and some of its useful consequences will become additionally plausible through consideration of the following examples.

---

* For such a determination, see the discussion in Art. 4 of Ch. 9.

The first of these represents the logical extension of the simple tuned circuit discussed in Art. 6, or of its dual as described in Art. 8 and illus-

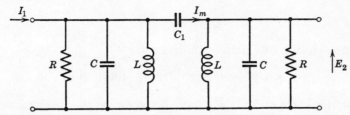

FIG. 28.   The so-called "double-tuned" circuit which is commonly used in radio receivers and similar electronic circuits.

trated in Fig. 20.   Specifically the circuit we wish to study consists of two such tuned circuits coupled by means of a small capacitance, as shown in Fig. 28. Let the problem be to consider the transfer impedance

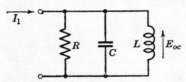

FIG. 29.   Pertinent to the analysis of the double-tuned circuit in Fig. 28.

$$Z_{12}(s) = E_2/I_1 \qquad (177)$$

Determination of the expression for this impedance is facilitated through use of Thévenin's theorem. Thus, suppose we break the circuit into two halves and compute the open-circuit voltage produced by the first half, as shown in Fig. 29.   This part of the circuit is familiar from the earlier discussions in this chapter.   Denoting by Z the impedance of this parallel RLC combination, we obtain

$$E_{oc} = I_1 Z = \frac{I_1 s}{C(s^2 + 2\alpha s + \omega_a{}^2)} \qquad (178)$$

in which we have according to the previous analysis of this simple circuit

$$\alpha = 1/2RC, \qquad \omega_a{}^2 = 1/LC \qquad (179)$$

Next we note that the current I_m (Fig. 28) is given by the quotient of E_{oc} and the total impedance encountered by this current, which is $2Z + (1/C_1 s)$. Thus

$$I_m = \frac{I_1 Z}{2Z + (1/C_1 s)} \qquad (180)$$

Finally, we see that the output voltage E_2 is related to I_m in exactly the same manner that E_{oc} is related to I_1 (Fig. 29).   Hence we have

$$\frac{E_2}{I_1} = \frac{Z^2}{2Z + (1/C_1 s)} = \frac{Z^2 C_1 s}{1 + 2Z C_1 s} \tag{181}$$

Substitution for Z from Eq. 178 yields

$$\frac{E_2}{I_1} = Z_{12} = \frac{(C_1/C)s^3}{C(s^2 + 2\alpha s + \omega_a{}^2)(s^2 + 2\alpha s + \omega_a{}^2 + (2C_1/C)s^2)} \tag{182}$$

Further detailed consideration of this result becomes interesting if the value of C_1 is chosen to be small compared with C (of the order of 1 per cent); that is, if

$$C_1/C \ll 1 \tag{183}$$

The RLC combination of Fig. 29 we will assume to be highly oscillatory so that $\alpha \ll \omega_a$.   The second quadratic factor in the denominator of Eq. 182, which may be written

$$(1 + 2C_1/C)s^2 + 2\alpha s + \omega_a{}^2 = (1 + 2C_1/C)(s^2 + 2\beta s + \omega_b{}^2) \tag{184}$$

with

$$\beta = \frac{\alpha}{1 + 2C_1/C} \approx \alpha(1 - 2C_1/C) \tag{185}$$

$$\omega_b{}^2 = \frac{\omega_a{}^2}{1 + 2C_1/C} \approx \omega_a{}^2(1 - 2C_1/C) \tag{186}$$

$$\omega_b \approx \omega_a(1 - C_1/C) \tag{187}$$

is seen to be approximately replaceable by

$$s^2 + 2\alpha s + \omega_b{}^2 \tag{188}$$

Regarding the approximations indicated in Eqs. 185, 186, and 187, the reader should recall that, if a quantity x is small compared to unity, then $1/(1 + x)$ is very nearly $1 - x$, and $\sqrt{1 + 2x}$ is very nearly $1 + x$, as is readily seen through making the appropriate series expansions and dropping the square and higher terms.   In arriving at the quadratic factor 188 from 184, we first of all regard the factor $(1 + 2C_1/C)$ as essentially equal to unity, and then note that the difference between β and α is negligible compared with the difference between ω_b and ω_a since α itself is small compared with ω_a.   For example, if C_1 is 1 per cent of C, and α is 1 per cent of ω_a, then $\omega_a - \omega_b$ is roughly 1 per cent of ω_a while $\alpha - \beta$ is only about 1/50th of 1 per cent of ω_a.   Another way of putting this result is to say that, if C_1/C is *extremely* small, then the second quadratic factor in the denominator of Eq. 182 is negligibly different from the first, but, as the value of C_1/C becomes somewhat larger, the effect of its presence is noticeable in the difference $\omega_a - \omega_b$ long before it is detectable in the difference $\alpha - \beta$ in the same units of measurement or observation.

Under these circumstances, which are described by saying that the two highly oscillatory RLC combinations in Fig. 28 are *loosely* coupled through the capacitance C_1, we find for the transfer impedance (Eq. 182)

$$\frac{E_2}{I_1} = Z_{12}(s) \approx \frac{(C_1/C^2)s^3}{(s^2 + 2\alpha s + \omega_a{}^2)(s^2 + 2\alpha s + \omega_b{}^2)} \tag{189}$$

where α, ω_a, ω_b are given by Eqs. 179 and 187.

If we write

$$(s^2 + 2\alpha s + \omega_a{}^2) = (s - s_1)(s - s_2)$$
$$s_1 = -\alpha + j\omega_a, \qquad s_2 = -\alpha - j\omega_a \tag{190}$$

and

$$(s^2 + 2\alpha s + \omega_b{}^2) = (s - s_3)(s - s_4)$$
$$s_3 = -\alpha + j\omega_b, \qquad s_4 = -\alpha - j\omega_b \tag{191}$$

then Z_{12} assumes the general form given in Eq. 169, namely,

$$Z_{12}(s) = \frac{(C_1/C^2)(s - 0)(s - 0)(s - 0)}{(s - s_1)(s - s_2)(s - s_3)(s - s_4)} \tag{192}$$

Representation in the s plane of the critical frequencies of this impedance function is shown in Fig. 30. The values s_1, s_2, s_3, s_4, which are referred to as *poles* of Z_{12} are indicated by crosses; the difference $\omega_a - \omega_b$, which is considered to be of the same order of magnitude as α, is to be regarded as small compared with either ω_a or ω_b. The three frequency factors in the numerator of Z_{12} all have the form $(s - 0)$. In general these factors indicate the complex frequencies at which the impedance is zero and for this reason are said to represent the *zeros* of this function. The present $Z_{12}(s)$ has three coincident zeros (also called a third-order zero) at $s = 0$. Zeros are indicated in the s plane by small circles. In Fig. 30 the third-order zero of Z_{12} at $s = 0$ is indicated by three small concentric circles at this point.

The frequency variable s is again regarded as a point that moves along the j axis. As this point passes alongside of the pair of poles s_1 and s_3, we expect a critical behavior similar to that obtained for the simple series or parallel RLC circuit under resonance conditions, with the difference, however, that the effect is now enhanced, owing to the presence of two poles near the resonance region instead of only one.

Figure 31 shows an enlarged view of the frequency factors $(s - s_1)$ and $(s - s_3)$ in the resonance region. Here the other factors in the

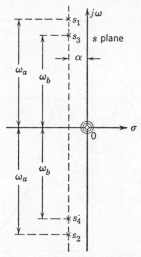

FIG. 30. Representation in the complex frequency plane of the poles (crosses) and zeros (circles) of the transfer impedance 192 pertinent to the double-tuned circuit shown in Fig. 28.

FIG. 31. An enlarged portion of the s-plane picture in Fig. 30 pertinent to the discussion of the response characteristics shown in Fig. 32.

expression 192 for Z_{12} are substantially constant (i.e., $s - s_2 \approx s - s_4 \approx j2\omega_0$, and $s \approx j\omega_0$), so that an approximate relation valid for the resonance vicinity becomes

$$Z_{12}(s) \approx \frac{j(C_1/C)\omega_0}{4C(s - s_1)(s - s_3)}$$

(193)

in which

$$\omega_0 = \tfrac{1}{2}(\omega_a + \omega_b)$$

(194)

is the so-called *midband* frequency since it refers to the center of the resonance region.

Various particular characteristics on the part of the function $Z_{12}(s)$ are possible, according to the relative values of $(\omega_a - \omega_b) = 2a$ and α. If the poles at s_1 and s_3 are relatively far apart compared with α, it is clear by inspection of Fig. 31 that the magnitude of Z_{12} as a function of ω will exhibit two maxima, one at the point $s = j\omega$ approximately opposite the pole at s_3 and another one opposite s_1. Our present circuit has two distinct resonance frequencies.

As the separation of the poles ($2a$ in Fig. 31) relative to α is decreased, the two maxima in the curve of Z_{12} vs. ω move toward each other. At some nonzero value of a the double-humped character of this curve disappears, and the resultant behavior is similar to that shown earlier for the simple resonant RLC circuit, except that the resonance curve now falls off more rapidly as one passes beyond the resonance region.

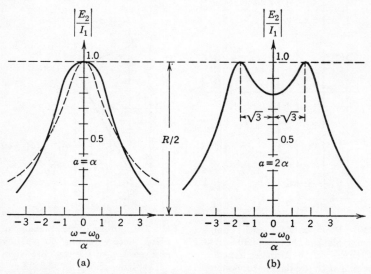

Fig. 32. Frequency response characteristics (known as double-humped resonance curves) for the double-tuned circuit of Fig. 28. The curve of (a) is for the so-called "maximally flat" adjustment corresponding to coincidence of the maxima shown in (b) with the minimum at $\omega = \omega_0$. The dashed curve in (a) is the simple resonance curve of Fig. 18 which is added for comparison purposes.

That is to say, our present doubly resonant circuit exhibits a higher degree of selectivity than the simple RLC circuit.

These results are shown in Fig. 32 where part (a) is drawn for the condition $a = \alpha$, while in part (b) $a = 2\alpha$. In the latter case the curve exhibits a double-humped character. The condition $a = \alpha$, for which part (a) of Fig. 32 is drawn, corresponds to the critical case in which the two maxima just merge with the minimum at $\omega = \omega_0$. For a smaller value of a the curve remains single-humped in character, but the maximum response at $\omega = \omega_0$ drops below the value $R/2$.

For the so-called *critically coupled* case shown in Fig. 32(a), we have according to Eq. 187 and the significance of the parameter a as shown in Fig. 31

$$a = \tfrac{1}{2}(\omega_a - \omega_b) = \tfrac{1}{2}(C_1/C)\omega_a \approx \tfrac{1}{2}(C_1/C)\omega_0 = \alpha \qquad (195)$$

or

$$C_1/C = 2\alpha/\omega_0 \qquad (196)$$

which fixes the pertinent degree of capacitive coupling. Equation 193 for $Z_{12}(s)$ may then be written

$$Z_{12}(s) \approx \frac{j\alpha}{2C(s - s_1)(s - s_3)} \qquad (197)$$

At the point $s = j\omega_0$, each of the frequency factors $(s - s_1)$ and $(s - s_3)$ has the magnitude $\alpha\sqrt{2}$ as is evident by inspection of Fig. 31, and,

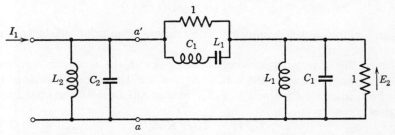

Fig. 33. An alternate circuit capable of realizing the transfer characteristics of the double-tuned circuit of Fig. 28 as well as other more general ones.

since $\alpha = 1/2RC$ (Eq. 179), we see that the midband value of Z_{12} equals $R/2$ as noted in Fig. 32. The dotted curve in part (a) of this figure shows the behavior of the simple resonant RLC circuit and is drawn here for purposes of comparison.

There are numerous other circuits that can be devised to have the same general response characteristic as this so-called *double-tuned* circuit of Fig. 28. One rather obvious way of achieving a similar result is through use of two simple resonant RLC circuits appropriately cascaded. Thus, if we begin with a single-tuned circuit like that in Fig. 29 and place the complement of this impedance in series with its input terminals, the resulting input impedance equals the resistance R and hence can be put in the place of R in another single-tuned circuit. The same process can be repeated as often as we please.

A circuit constructed on this basis is shown in Fig. 33. The parallel combination of L_1, C_1, and 1 ohm at the right-hand end forms the first tuned circuit, with the impedance

$$Z_1(s) = \frac{s}{C_1(s - s_1)(s - s_2)} \qquad (198)$$

where s_1 and s_2 are the pertinent complex natural frequencies. The series branch consisting of 1 ohm in parallel with a series LC combination is the complement of the first tuned circuit. In this complement, the inductance has C_1 henrys and the capacitance has L_1 farads, as explained in Art. 8 [see Fig. 21(b) and pertinent text, noting that the series L_1C_1 combination is the dual of the parallel L_1C_1 combination]. The net circuit to the right of the terminals $a-a'$ is thus equivalent to a resistance of 1 ohm, which takes the place of a 1-ohm resistance in the second tuned circuit involving L_2 and C_2, for which the impedance is given by

$$Z_2(s) = \frac{s}{C_2(s - s_3)(s - s_4)} \qquad (199)$$

s_3 and s_4 being the complex natural frequencies appropriate to this second circuit.

Since the impedance looking to the right at the terminal pair $a-a'$ is a resistance of 1 ohm, the voltage at $a-a'$ and the current at this point are both numerically equal to I_1Z_2, whence the over-all response function is given by

$$E_2/I_1 = Z_1(s) \times Z_2(s) \qquad (200)$$

It is thus clear that the complete circuit of Fig. 33 can be made to yield results similar to those given by the double-tuned circuit of Fig. 28.

The circuit of Fig. 33 is not quite as economical from the standpoint of total elements required, but it affords greater flexibility in the variety of particular results obtainable. Thus the poles in Fig. 30 can be moved into any relative positions (maintaining pairs of conjugates of course) with the greatest of ease when the network of Fig. 33 is used, while the pole locations obtainable with the network of Fig. 28 are not only restricted but are not so simply related to the element values. Thus one may want to have the poles in Fig. 30 coincide in pairs so as to obtain a resultant characteristic that is essentially the simple resonance curve *squared*. In the circuit of Fig. 28 this condition corresponds to $C_1 = 0$; the two tuned circuits become completely decoupled, and the response falls to zero. In the circuit of Fig. 33, however, this special condition is as easily obtainable as any other.

There are, of course, many variations to the theme suggested by the circuit of Fig. 33. Thus we can use series tuned circuits instead of parallel tuned circuits; or we can use these two types in combination, observing of course that, if we use a series tuned circuit, then its complement must be placed in parallel since our reasoning then is done in terms of admittances instead of impedances. Although it is not our object at the moment to discuss these matters in detail, the reader can appreciate from what has been said that impedance functions with any desired allocations of critical frequencies in the s plane are constructible in various ways, and that some of these require for their understanding nothing more complicated than the simple fundamental principles set forth in this chapter.

He can also appreciate the circumspection gained through representing an impedance as a quotient of frequency factors (Eq. 169) and in using the complex s plane as a means for interpreting the behavior of individual frequency factors as functions of the variable $s = j\omega$. Thus, for example, one may visualize the properties of double-tuned circuits as easily as one does the behavior of the single-tuned circuit. Not only this but the further generalization to circuits possessing any degree of multiple resonance is made evident. These matters impress themselves upon us with increasing clarity as we proceed with the consideration of more difficult topics in network theory.

PROBLEMS

1. Given the currents

$$i_1(t) = 10 \sin (2t + 30°)$$

$$i_2(t) = 5 \cos (2t - 30°)$$

$$i_3(t) = 5 \cos (2t + 30°)$$

(a) Plot $i_1(t)$ and $i_2(t)$ to the same scale.

(b) Plot $\int i_1(t)\, dt$. What are the effects of integration upon a sinusoidal wave?

(c) Plot $d[i_2(t)]/dt$. What are the effects of differentiation upon a sinusoidal wave?

(d) Plot $[i_1(t) + i_2(t)]$. Obtain the analytical expression for this wave and check it with the graphical solution.

(e) Plot $[i_1(t) + (d/dt)i_3(t)]$. Comment on the result.

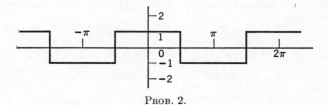

PROB. 2.

2 The Fourier series for a square wave of the form shown above is

$$f(t) = \frac{4}{\pi} \left(\cos t - \frac{1}{3} \cos 3t + \frac{1}{5} \cos 5t - \cdots \right)$$

(a) Plot the first three terms and obtain their sum graphically. (b) Supposing that the origin were to be shifted a distance of $\pi/2$ to the left, write down the new Fourier series for the wave.

3. Consider the complex numbers

$$A = a_1 + ja_2$$

$$B = b_1 + jb_2$$

(a) Show that $|A| \times |B| = |A \times B|$.

(b) Show that $\dfrac{|A|}{|B|} = \left|\dfrac{A}{B}\right|$.

(c) Assuming $|B| > |A|$, show from a geometrical construction that $|B + A| \le |B| + |A|$; $|B - A| \ge |B| - |A|$.

4. Consider the complex numbers

$$A = a_1 + ja_2$$

$$B = b_1 + jb_2$$

(a) Show that Re $[A \pm B]$ = Re $[A] \pm$ Re $[B]$ and Im $[A \pm B]$ = Im $[A] \pm$ Im $[B]$.

(b) Show that Re $[AB]$ = Re $[A]$ Re $[B]$ − Im $[A]$ Im $[B]$ and Im $[AB]$ = Re $[A]$ Im $[B]$ + Im $[A]$ Re $[B]$. *Note.* Re $[AB] \ne$ Re $[A]$ Re $[B]$.

(c) Find Re $[Ae^{j\theta}]$ where A is real. What does this result become when $A = a_1 + ja_2$?

(d) Find Re $[(3 + j4)(0.2 + j0.2)]$.

5. Given the complex impedance

$$Z = R + jX \text{ ohms}$$

(a) Find the impedance in the polar form $Z = |Z| \underline{/\theta}$. (b) Express it in the form $Z = Ae^{jb}$. (c) Find Z^n and $Z^{1/n}$.

6. Given a current $I = a + jb$ amperes in an impedance $Z = R + jX$ ohms, find the voltage drop E in the direction of the current. Express the result in (a) rectangular form, (b) polar form, (c) exponential form, (d) as an instantaneous cosine function assuming $i(t) =$ Re $[Ie^{j\omega t}]$. (e) What is the magnitude of the voltage? (f) What is its phase with respect to the current?

7. Change the following complex numbers to polar form; that is, find the values of A and θ in the equivalent form $Ae^{j\theta}$. Express θ in degrees or radians, which ever is more convenient.

$(3 + j4)$	$(1 + j0.1)$
$(3 - j4)^{-1}$	$(0.1 - j1)$
$(0.5 + j0.866)$	$(-1000 + j1000)$
$(-50 + j86.6)$	$(-100 + j1)$

The ones in the second column above can be done without slide rule or tables; try this.

8. Carry out the indicated addition in the following examples. State the answer in either polar or rectangular form. They can be done by inspection of pertinent sketches.

$$1\underline{/60°} + 1\underline{/-60°}, \qquad 1\underline{/60°} - 1\underline{/-60°}$$

$$j\underline{/-60°} + j\underline{/60°}, \qquad j\underline{/-60°} - j\underline{/60°}$$

$$70.7\underline{/45°} + 70.7\underline{/-45°}, \qquad 0.707\underline{/45°} - 0.707\underline{/-45°}$$

$$69.7\underline{/15°} + 69.7\underline{/135°} + 69.7\underline{/-105°}$$

$$69.7\underline{/15°} + 69.7\underline{/135°} - 69.7\underline{/-105°}$$

9. Put the following expressions into as compact a form as possible, using the method of vector addition. Include with your solutions the pertinent vector diagrams.

$$i(t) = \sin(\omega t + 30°) + 2\cos(\omega t + 60°)$$

$$i(t) = \frac{1}{2}\cos(\omega t - 30°) - \frac{\sqrt{3}}{2}\sin(\omega t - 30°) - \sin(\omega t + 60°)$$

$$i(t) = \cos\left(100t - \frac{\pi}{4}\right) + \frac{3}{2}\cos\left(200t + \frac{\pi}{6}\right) + 2\cos\left(300t + \frac{\pi}{12}\right)$$

$$- \sin\left(100t + \frac{\pi}{4}\right) + \frac{3}{2}\sin\left(200t - \frac{\pi}{3}\right) + \sqrt{3}\sin\left(300t - \frac{\pi}{4}\right)$$

10. Evaluate the following expressions giving the answers both in rectangular and in polar forms.

(a) $7.2\underline{/16.3°} + \dfrac{16.3\underline{/4.2°} + 9\underline{/61°}}{1\underline{/45°} + 13.2\underline{/86°}}.$

(b) $\dfrac{(18.2 + j13.4)(6.21 + j49.2)}{(3.46 - j0.728)(-6.49 + j9.07)}.$

(c) $\dfrac{(12 + j16)(42 + j84)}{(-18 + j18)}.$

11. The complex current in a steady-state a-c circuit is given by the formula

$$I = V/Z$$

where V = complex voltage, Z = complex impedance. Fill in the missing values in the following table:

V	I	Z
110		$10 + j20$
$110\underline{/45°}$		$10 + j20$
$16\underline{/13.2°}$	$1.00 - j0.748$	
	$13\underline{/76°}$	$19.1 + j0.909$
	$4\underline{/85°}$	$-11 + j18.2$
$110\underline{/90°}$	$2.38\underline{/6°}$	
$76 + j54$	$7.19 - j4.89$	

12. Using appropriate Maclaurin expansions from the list given below, evaluate numerically the following complex expressions, retaining only first-order terms. Estimate the accuracy of your answers.

$$\frac{e^{j(\pi/2)}}{\ln(100+j) - \ln(100)}, \qquad \frac{\sqrt{100+j} - 10}{0.01j}$$

$$\frac{100e^{j0.01} - j2}{10 - j0.1}, \qquad \frac{\sin(\pi/6 + 0.1j)}{\sin(\pi/6 - 0.1j)}$$

$$e^x = 1 + x + \frac{x^2}{2!} + \frac{x^3}{3!} + \cdots$$

$$\sin x = x - \frac{x^3}{3!} + \frac{x^5}{5!} - + \cdots$$

$$\cos x = 1 - \frac{x^2}{2!} + \frac{x^4}{4!} - + \cdots$$

$$\frac{1}{1-x} = 1 + x + x^2 + x^3 + x^{\cdot} + \cdots$$

$$\sqrt{1+x} = 1 + \frac{x}{2} - \frac{x^2}{8} + \cdots$$

$$\tan^{-1} x = x - \frac{x^3}{3} + \frac{x^5}{5} - \frac{x^7}{7} + - \cdots$$

$$\ln(1+x) = x - \frac{x^2}{2} + \frac{x^3}{3} - \frac{x^4}{4} + - \cdots$$

$\ln N$ = natural logarithm of $N = \log N/\log e = 2.3027 \log N$ where $\log N$ = logarithm to the base 10

13. Consider the function $u + jv = \dfrac{1}{x+jy} = Ae^{j\theta}$, and, from the relations $A = 1/\sqrt{x^2+y^2}$, $\theta = -\tan^{-1}(y/x)$, deduce that the polar amplitude A as a function of θ for constant values of x or of y is given respectively by

$$A(x, \theta) = \cos\theta/x \quad \text{and} \quad A(y, \theta) = -\sin\theta/y$$

From the familiar circular polar loci of $\sin\theta$ and $\cos\theta$, establish that the loci of $(x+jy)^{-1}$ for constant x and variable y or for variable x and constant y are those shown in the following sketches. From these results, find the corresponding loci for the function

$$u + jv = \frac{1 - (x+jy)}{1 + (x+jy)} = \frac{2}{(1+x) + jy} - 1$$

indicating all significant data as is done in the sketches below, and show that the half-plane defined by $x > 0$ lies within the unit circle about the origin in the $(u + jv)$ plane. (*Note.* The loci of this function for $x > 0$ occur frequently in electrical as well as in aerodynamic problems. For example, they form the basis for a useful type of transmission-line chart known as the "Smith chart.")

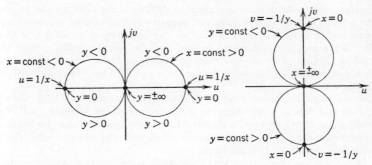

PROB. 13.

14. The circuit shown is used to produce range marker pips on the indicator scope of a radar set. When the vacuum tube is conducting, a current i_L flows through the inductor L. At time $t = 0$ a negative pulse is applied to the grid of the vacuum tube. This negative voltage on the grid cuts the tube off, and the current through the tube ceases to flow. The circuit in the figure will therefore oscillate as an ordinary LC circuit with an initial current i_L through the inductor. These oscillations are fed into a pulse-shaping (clipping) circuit where they are formed into almost

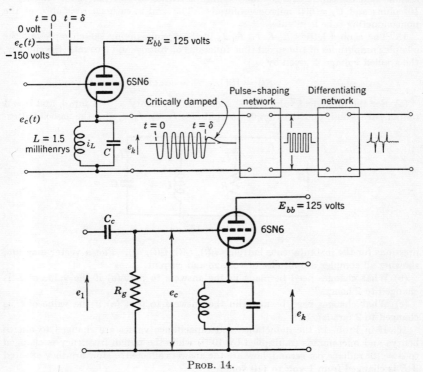

PROB. 14.

rectangular pulses. After passing through a differentiating network the pulses appear as a series of alternate positive and negative spikes, equally spaced along the time axis with a spacing depending only on the frequency of oscillation of the LC circuit. If the negative spikes are removed and the positive spikes applied to the radar scope, a series of equidistant markers appear on the screen, and the distance to any object causing an indication on the scope can thus be determined with reference to these markers.

When the negative pulse is removed from the grid at time $t = \delta$, the tube starts conducting and acts as a low damping resistance across the oscillating LC circuit. The oscillations, therefore, rapidly die out. By choosing proper values for the parameters involved we can make the oscillating circuit critically damped when the tube is conducting, as indicated on the figure.

(a) It is desired to produce markers at intervals corresponding to 2000 yards, corresponding to a period of oscillation of 12.2 microseconds. If $L = 15$ millihenrys what value must C have to produce the desired result? The initial current through L is 14.2 milliamperes. What is the amplitude of e_k?

(b) What should the equivalent tube resistance be in order to make the oscillating circuit critically damped when the tube is conducting (after $t = \delta$)?

(c) If the grid input circuit is as shown in the lower diagram, and if our input voltage, instead of being a negative pulse e_c as before, is a negative step $e_1(t) = -150u_{-1}(t)$, how long is the interval δ during which the tube will remain cut off if we assume that the tube starts conducting abruptly when $e_c = -125$ volts? Let $R_g = 10^6$ ohms and $C_c = 690$ micromicrofarads. The grid-to-cathode resistance of the nonconducting tube is infinite.

15. The capital letters E, I, I_1, I_2, I_3 in the accompanying sketch represent the complex amplitudes of sinusoidal time functions of voltage and current. Specifically, the applied voltage is given by

$$e(t) = \operatorname{Re}\,[Ee^{j\omega t}] = \cos \omega t$$

(a) For the numerical values: $R = 1$ ohm, $L = 1$ henry, $C = 1$ farad, and $\omega = 1$ radian per second, find the complex amplitudes I_1, I_2, I_3, I, and the associated ex-

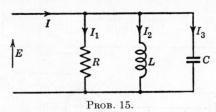

PROB. 15.

pressions for the instantaneous currents $i_1(t)$, $i_2(t)$, $i_3(t)$, $i(t)$. Plot a vector diagram, showing all complex amplitudes of voltage and current.

(b) What changes need be made in the answers to part (a) if the value of L is changed to 2 henrys?

(c) What changes need be made in the answers to part (a) if the value of C is changed to 2 farads?

16. If in Prob. 15 the inductance and capacitance values are changed to microhenrys and microfarads (multiplied by 10^{-6}) while the radian frequency is changed to $\omega = 10^6$ radians per second, how are the answers affected? How are they affected if E is changed from 1 volt to 110 volts?

17. Given $e(t) = \text{Re} [Ee^{j\omega t}] = \cos t$. Find I and $i(t) = \text{Re} [Ie^{j\omega t}]$.

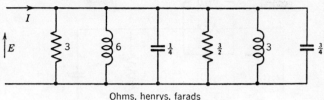

Ohms, henrys, farads

PROB. 17.

18. In Prob. 17, suppose the given quantity is $i(t) = \cos t$. (a) Find E and $e(t)$. (b) Find the current as a function of time in the 1.5-ohm resistor; in the 0.75-farad capacitor. (c) Find the answers to part (b) if the given quantity is $e(t) = \cos t$, and note the difference in the computational procedure in the two cases.

19. In the circuit of Prob. 15, show that, if we write

$$Z = |Z| e^{j\theta}, \qquad Y = Z^{-1} = |Y| e^{-j\theta}$$

we have $\tan \theta = (R/L\omega - RC\omega)$, and

$$Y = \frac{1 - j \tan \theta}{R} = \frac{e^{-j\theta}}{R \cos \theta}, \qquad Z = R \cos \theta \times e^{j\theta}$$

Plot the vectors Y and Z for $R = 1$ ohm, and the range $-\pi/2 \le \theta \le \pi/2$ at $15°$ intervals. Sketch the loci of the tips of these vectors. Show that the results apply also to a series RLC circuit with the expressions for Y and Z interchanged.

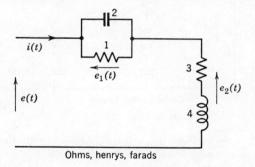

Ohms, henrys, farads

PROB. 20.

20. Given $e(t) = \text{Re} [Ee^{j\omega t}] = \cos t$. Find:

$$i(t) = \text{Re} [Ie^{j\omega t}]$$

$$e_1(t) = \text{Re} [E_1 e^{j\omega t}]$$

$$e_2(t) = \text{Re} [E_2 e^{j\omega t}]$$

Plot a vector diagram showing the complex quantities E, I, E_1, E_2.

21. If in Prob. 20 the given quantity is $i(t) = \cos t$, find $e(t)$, $e_1(t)$, $e_2(t)$, and plot a vector diagram showing all the complex quantities I, E, E_1, E_2.

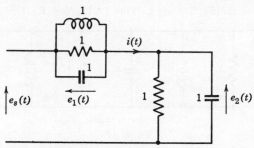

Parameter values in ohms, henrys, farads

PROB. 22.

22. Given $e_s(t) = \text{Re}\,[E_s e^{j\omega t}] = \cos t$. Find

$$i(t) = \text{Re}\,[I e^{j\omega t}]$$

$$e_1(t) = \text{Re}\,[E_1 e^{j\omega t}]$$

$$e_2(t) = \text{Re}\,[E_2 e^{j\omega t}]$$

and plot the associated vector diagram showing E_s, E_1, E_2, I.

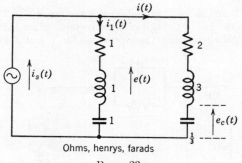

Ohms, henrys, farads

PROB. 23.

23. Given $i_s(t) = \cos t$. Find $i_1(t)$, $i(t)$, $e(t)$, $e_c(t)$, and plot the vector diagram showing the complex amplitudes of all five time functions.

24. Given $e_s(t) = 15 \cos t$. Find $i(t)$ and $e(t)$.

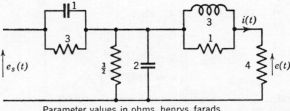

Parameter values in ohms, henrys, farads

PROB. 24.

25. Given $i_s(t) = 10 \cos t$; find $i(t)$. *Note.* In Probs. 22 through 25 Thévenin's or Norton's theorems may be used to good advantage.

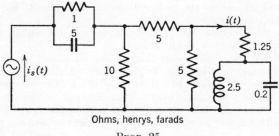

Ohms, henrys, farads

PROB. 25.

26. For a series RL circuit with $R = 1$ ohm and $L = 1$ henry, the impedance is $Z(s) = (s + 1)$ and the admittance $Y(s) = 1/(s + 1)$, the latter being numerically identical with the vector current per volt applied. For certain types of analysis it is expedient to separate $Y(j\omega)$ into its real and imaginary components and study their behavior as a function of the radian frequency ω. Compute and plot these functions neatly over the range $0 < \omega < 5$. Now show that these plots do not merely apply to the particular numerical choice $R = L = 1$ and to the frequency range $0 < \omega < 5$, but may be used to represent the real and imaginary parts of the Y of *any* series RL circuit over an appropriate frequency range.

27. Reconsider Prob. 26 but for a series RC circuit with $R = 1$ ohm and $C = 1$ farad, plotting the real and imaginary parts of $Y(j\omega)$ again over the range $0 < \omega < 5$, and demonstrating the complete generality of these plots.

28. Show that the universal curves of Prob. 26 apply (through use of the principle of duality) to the real and imaginary parts of the impedance $Z(j\omega)$ of a parallel RC circuit with $R = 1$ ohm and $C = 1$ farad; and, through a process of generalization analogous to that used in Probs. 26 and 27, show that the results apply to any parallel RC circuit.

29. Show that the universal curves of Prob. 27 apply (through use of the principle of duality) to the real and imaginary parts of the impedance $Z(j\omega)$ of a parallel RL circuit with $R = 1$ ohm and $L = 1$ henry; and, through a process of generalization analogous to that used in Prob. 27, show that the results apply to any parallel RL circuit.

30. The ideas brought out in Probs. 26 through 29 apply in essentially unaltered form to the magnitude and angle (that is, to the polar representations) of $Y(j\omega)$ and of $Z(j\omega)$. Compute and plot the two relevant sets of universal curves, and discuss their applicability to pertinent specific circuits, parameter values, and frequency ranges.

31. Consider a series RL circuit in parallel with a series RC circuit so as to form a resultant network whose $Y(j\omega)$ is, of course, given by the sum of the two admittances pertaining to the RL and RC circuits respectively. With the plots of Probs. 26 and 27 before you (or reasonably good sketches of them), consider how you would in general make $Y(j\omega) = 1/R$ mhos, independent of the frequency ω. Check your conclusions analytically.

32. The circuit of Prob. 31 is excited by a unit step voltage. If the relative parameter values are such that $Y(j\omega) = 1/R$, determine and plot the transient currents through each of the two parallel branches of this circuit, and show that their sum

is a step of the value $1/R$ amperes. Does this last result agree with what you expected in the first place? Why?

33. Consider the dual of Prob. 31, making use in this case of the universal curves of Probs. 28 and 29. Draw the pertinent circuit arrangement, and work out all relevant analytic relationships.

34. Consider the complete dual of Prob. 32, drawing the circuit, specifying the appropriate transient problem and its solution.

35. In practice it frequently occurs that a series RL circuit (excited by a direct or alternating voltage) must suddenly be interrupted. The contacts involved in the switch or relay or circuit breaker in a situation of this kind may rapidly deteriorate if subjected to frequent repetitions of circuit interruption, particularly if the excitation is direct current. Explain why this is so, and, in the light of the results of Prob. 32, describe one way in which the situation might be relieved, assuming that any questions of practical feasibility can somehow be met (this method, incidentally, is one that is used practically to relieve arcing on relay contacts in some d-c control circuits).

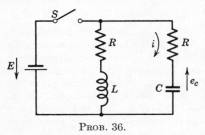

PROB. 36.

36. The accompanying sketch shows a circuit to which the discussion of the preceding problem applies when $R^2 = L/C$. Suppose the switch S is closed for a long time so that a steady condition obtains. At the instant $t = 0$ the switch is suddenly opened. Determine the current $i(t)$ in the remaining closed loop as well as the voltage $e_C(t)$ across the capacitance for $t > 0$. What is the voltage across the parallel combination of RL and RC circuits for $t > 0$? What is the value of total stored energy in the circuit at $t = 0$, and where does it reside? Describe qualitatively how the energy in the circuit flows after $t = 0$.

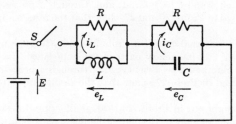

PROB. 37.

37. In the circuit shown above, $R^2 = L/C$. The switch S closes at $t = 0$. For $t > 0$ determine the voltages $e_L(t)$, $e_C(t)$, as well as the currents $i_L(t)$ and $i_C(t)$ circulating in the meshes. If, after a steady condition obtains, the switch S is suddenly opened, what are the two voltages and the two currents as functions of time relative to the instant of circuit interruption?

38. A vector voltage $E = 1$ is applied to a series RL circuit. The resulting vector current I should be 1 ampere lagging at an angle of $45°$. If the radian frequency ω is unity, what are the values of R in ohms and L in henrys? Ditto for $\omega = 2\pi \times 60$, and $\omega = 2\pi \times 1000$. Repeat all this for $E = 100$ volts. Now repeat all of the above if the current lag angle is $30°$; again for $60°$. If the applied voltage as a time func-

tion is written $e(t) = E \cos \omega t$ (with E real), what are the expressions for the current as a time function appropriate to the various cases specified above?

39. A current $i(t) = I \cos \omega t$ (with I real) is applied to a parallel RC circuit. If $I = 1$, and the resultant voltage is to be $e(t) = 62.4 \sin (\omega t + 30°)$, what are the appropriate values of R in ohms and C in farads when (a) $\omega = 377$ radians per second, (b) $\omega = 1000$ radians per second, (c) $\omega = 5000$ radians per second, (d) $\omega = 10^9$ radians per second?

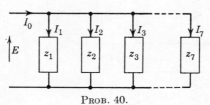

PROB. 40.

40. In the circuit shown here, $E = 1$ volt (reference phase) and the currents I_1, I_2, $\cdots$, I_7 all have unit magnitude. Their phase angles are respectively $\phi_1 = 0°$, $\phi_2 = 10°$, $\phi_3 = 20°$, $\cdots$, $\phi_7 = 60°$. You are to find appropriate contents for the boxes labeled z_1, z_2, etc., not exceeding two-element combinations in complexity. Assume $\omega = 1$ radian per second to start with, and later convert your design to the frequency $\omega = 2\pi \times 60$, and again to $\omega = 2\pi \times 1000$. If there exist other solutions of no greater complexity, state what they are. Draw a vector diagram showing E, I_1, I_2, $\cdots$, I_7 and the resultant current I_0. Obtain an exact analytic expression for the latter. If the phase angles involved are replaced by lag angles, what changes in the circuits are needed?

41. The element values in the circuits shown in the accompanying sketches are in ohms and henrys. Determine the impedance Z in each case as a function of the complex frequency s, and put it into the normal form of a quotient of frequency factors. Make a sketch of the s plane, showing the critical frequencies and some point $s = j\omega$ on the j axis. By inspection of this diagram, what are $|Z|$ and θ (the angle of Z) for $\omega = 1$ and $\omega = 2$? At what ω value is θ largest, and what is this largest value? Sketch $|Z|$ and θ versus ω. If a unit step current is applied to each circuit, find the resultant transient voltage at the input terminals. If the frequency scale is stretched so that the point

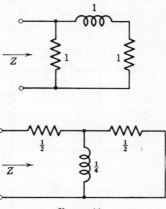

PROB. 41.

$\omega = 1$ becomes $\omega = 1000$ (and all other points are changed in the same ratio), what do the circuit element values become in ohms and henrys? What is the effect upon the critical frequencies of Z? What is the effect upon the transient response obtained above?

42. The element values in the circuits shown in the sketches are in ohms and henrys. Determine the expression for the impedance $Z(s)$ in each case, and put it into the normal form of a quotient of frequency factors. Plot the critical frequencies in the s plane appropriate to each Z. Do the results suggest anything of interest

or possible practical value? If the frequency scale is stretched so that $\omega = 1$ becomes $\omega = 10^5$, what do the element values become?

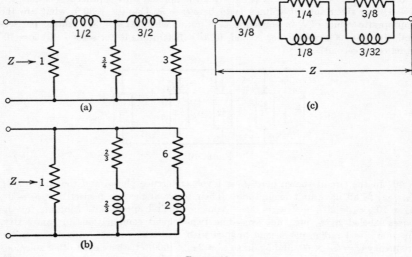

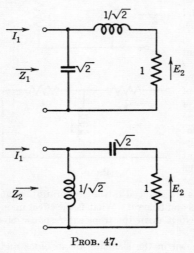

PROB. 42.

43. Find networks that are dual to those given in Prob. 41; that is, ones that will have reciprocal Z values. If a unit voltage step is applied to either one of these, what is the resultant transient current (using the results found in Prob. 41, of course)?

Find the new element values corresponding to a stretch of the frequency scale that shifts $\omega = 1$ to $\omega = 1000$.

44. Find the networks that are dual to those given in Prob. 42; that is, those that will have reciprocal Z values. Write their Z functions as a quotient of frequency factors. Find the revised element values in these networks corresponding to a stretch of the frequency scale that shifts $\omega = 1$ to $\omega = 10^5$. How do the critical frequencies change?

45. For the circuits of Prob. 41 find networks which when placed respectively in series with each given network will yield a resultant impedance equal to unity at all frequencies; that is to say, find (by the method discussed in the text) those networks having complementary impedances. May these networks be used interchangeably to form constant-resistance resultants?

46. Find networks that are complementary to those given in Prob. 42.

47. The element values in the networks shown at the left are in ohms, henrys, and

PROB. 47.

farads. Find the expressions for $Z_1(s)$ and $Z_2(s)$ as quotients of frequency factors. For each impedance, sketch the locations of its critical frequencies in the s plane. Form $Z_1 + Z_2$. How are these impedances related? Compute the real and imaginary parts of these impedances, and sketch (neatly) versus ω for the range $0 < \omega < 3$, putting both real parts on one sheet and both imaginary parts on another.

48. For the networks of Prob. 47 determine the *transfer* impedances $Z_{12} = E_2/I_1$ in the form of quotients of frequency factors, and sketch the critical frequencies in the s plane. Compute the squared magnitude of $Z_{12}(j\omega)$ in each case, and sketch versus ω on the same sheet for range $0 < \omega < 3$. Compare with the real-part plots of Prob. 47.

49. Obtain the duals of the networks given in Prob. 47, and combine these so as to yield a constant-resistance combination. Using the results of Prob. 48, what are the transfer admittances $Y_{12} = I_2/F_1$ for the dual networks, and what are their squared magnitudes as functions of ω? Does the constant-resistance combination suggest any practical application? How would you revise this resultant network corresponding to a stretch of the frequency scale that puts the point $\omega = 1$ at $\omega = 2\pi \times 1000$?

50. The admittance of a series RLC circuit has the form

$$Y(s) = \frac{s}{(s - s_1)(s - s_2)}$$

with $s_1 = -0.1 + j1$, $s_2 = -0.1 - j1$. If you drew the resonance curve for this circuit, what would be the resonance frequency and the width of the curve at its half-power points? What is the Q of the circuit? What are the values of its parameters in ohms, henrys, and farads? How do these parameter values change if the frequency scale is stretched by a factor 10,000 (so as to make the resonance frequency 10,000 times higher)? How do the critical frequencies change? How does the width of the resonance curve at the half-power points change, and what is the effect upon Q? How do the parameter values change if Y is to become 1000 times larger (at all frequencies)? Does this change have any effect upon the shape of the resonance curve or upon Q? Returning to the original situation, suppose the real parts only of the critical frequencies are changed from -0.1 to -0.01, what are (a) the resonance frequency, (b) the width of the resonance curve at the half-power points, (c) the Q of the circuit, (d) the parameter values?

51. For the circuit shown in the sketch, show that the admittance is given by the expression

$$Y(s) = \frac{C(s - s_1)(s - s_2)}{(s - s_3)}$$

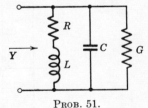

PROB. 51.

and determine the critical frequencies s_1, s_2, s_3 in terms of the parameters R, L, C, G. If $s_1 = -0.1 + j10$; $s_2 = -0.1 - j10$; $s_3 = -0.1$, what are the values of R, L, and G relative to C? If the circuit is driven by a current source and a resonance curve is taken for the voltage, what are the resonance frequency and the width at the half-power points? What is the value of Q? What is the magnitude of the impedance 5 per cent above or below resonance relative to its value at resonance? Suppose the values of R and G are changed to R' and G', keeping the quantity $(R'/L) + (G'/C) = (R/L) + (G/C)$, what is the net effect upon the impedance or admittance? If the Q of the circuit is large, is this net effect significant so far as the resonance behavior is concerned?

52. A circuit of the sort shown in Prob. 51 but with $G = 0$ is to be designed to have an impedance with a maximum absolute value of 100,000 ohms at a frequency of 1.5×10^6 cycles per second. At frequencies 10 per cent above and below resonance, the impedance magnitude should be not more than one-tenth of 1 per cent of its resonance value. What are the appropriate parameter values? What is the Q of this circuit? Suppose the data are changed by requiring that the impedance magnitude need not be smaller than 1 per cent of its resonance value at 10 per cent above or below resonance, what then are the answers to the above questions?

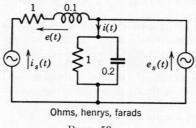

Ohms, henrys, farads

PROB. 53.

53. In the circuit shown, the current and voltage sources are

$$i_s(t) = 5 \cos 10t, \qquad e_s(t) = 10 \sin 5t$$

In the steady state, find the time functions $e(t)$ and $i(t)$.

54. The admittance of the network N at the terminals 1–1' has the form

$$Y(s) = \frac{(s - s_1)}{(s - s_2)(s - s_3)}$$

in which the critical frequencies s_1, s_2, s_3, are located in the complex frequency plane

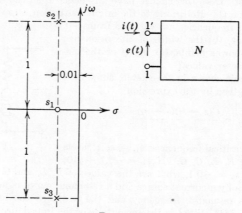

PROB. 54.

as indicated in the accompanying sketch. If the applied voltage is given by

$$e(t) = 1 + \cos \tfrac{1}{2}t + \cos t$$

find the steady state $i(t)$.

In view of the relatively small real parts of the critical frequencies, computation of the magnitudes and angles of the factors $(s - s_n)$ to an accuracy of a few per cent is sufficient. It is suggested that you formulate, by means of a sketch, a picture of what you are calculating before making the actual computations.

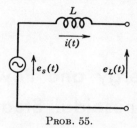

PROB. 55.

55. A circuit, the behavior of which represents the steady-state performance of a synchronous generator (the type that supplies about 95 per cent of the world's electric power), is given in the diagram. $e_s(t)$ is the internal generated voltage, $e_L(t)$ is the terminal voltage, and ωL is known as the synchronous reactance. If

$$e_L(t) = 230\sqrt{2} \cos \omega t$$

$$e_s(t) = 230\sqrt{2} \cos (\omega t + \theta)$$

and $\quad i(t) = 20\sqrt{2} \cos (\omega t + \varphi), \qquad |\varphi| < 90°$

$$L = 0.0305 \text{ henry}, \qquad \text{frequency} = f = 60 \text{ cycles per second}$$

Find θ and φ both by a vector diagram and by use of complex algebra. Is there more than one solution?

CHAPTER SEVEN

Energy and Power
in the Sinusoidal Steady State

1 Energy in the Storage Elements

The inductance L and capacitance C are frequently referred to as the *storage elements* since energy is stored in their associated magnetic and electric fields, and none of this energy is lost within these elements themselves. By assumption, they are not contaminated with resistance, which is the "lossy" element. Any energy that may, throughout a given time interval, be absorbed by an inductance or capacitance element must ultimately be wholly returned. The rate of energy absorption, integrated over a sufficiently long time interval, must be zero; therefore, the *average* power taken by such an element in the sinusoidal steady state must be zero. Let us check this situation more carefully.

The expressions for stored energy in the inductance and capacitance elements, familiar to most students from their fundamental studies in physics, are

$$\text{Magnetic stored energy} = T = \tfrac{1}{2}Li^2 \tag{1}$$

$$\text{Electric stored energy} = V = \tfrac{1}{2}Ce^2 \tag{2}$$

in which $i(t)$ and $e(t)$ are respectively the current in the inductance and the voltage across the capacitance. These may be any functions of the time t, whence T and V are correspondingly time functions that yield values of the stored energies at any instant. They are spoken of as representing the *instantaneous* stored energies.

Through use of the volt-ampere relation for the inductance or capacitance element, expressions 1 and 2 may be written in alternative forms that prove convenient in subsequent discussions. Thus, for the inductance element one has the familiar relation

$$e = L \, (di/dt) \tag{3}$$

which actually stems from the more basic one

$$e = d\psi/dt \tag{4}$$

in which ψ represents the flux linkages pertinent to the inductive element.

Since the inverse of 4 reads

$$\psi = \int e\, dt \tag{5}$$

that of 3 may evidently be written

$$i = \psi/L \tag{6}$$

and so we can alternatively write in place of 1

$$T = \psi^2/2L \tag{7}$$

If we introduce a symbol for reciprocal inductance (no name has as yet been adopted), letting

$$\Gamma = 1/L \tag{8}$$

we have for the magnetic stored energy

$$T = \tfrac{1}{2}\Gamma\psi^2 \tag{9}$$

which in general form again matches 1 or 2.

Similarly for the capacitance element one has

$$i = C\,(de/dt) \tag{10}$$

or inversely

$$e = \frac{1}{C}\int i\, dt \tag{11}$$

The time integral of the current is the charge. If we write for charge the symbol

$$q = \int i\, dt \tag{12}$$

and recall that reciprocal capacitance is elastance (denoted by the letter S), we see that the expression 2 for stored electric energy may be written

$$V = \tfrac{1}{2}Sq^2 \tag{13}$$

In summary, we have

$$T = \tfrac{1}{2}Li^2 = \tfrac{1}{2}\Gamma\psi^2 \tag{14}$$

$$V = \tfrac{1}{2}Ce^2 = \tfrac{1}{2}Sq^2 \tag{15}$$

where e and i are voltage and current; and ψ and q are flux linkage and charge (respectively the time integrals of voltage and current).

2   Energy in the Storage Elements When Voltage and Current Are Sinusoids

Suppose the current $i(t)$ in an inductance L is sinusoidal; that is,

$$i(t) = |I| \cos \omega t \tag{16}$$

Since by trigonometry

$$\cos^2 \omega t = \tfrac{1}{2}(1 + \cos 2\omega t) \tag{17}$$

one obtains for the instantaneous stored magnetic energy

$$T = \tfrac{1}{4}L|I|^2(1 + \cos 2\omega t) \tag{18}$$

This result is shown plotted in Fig. 1. We see that the stored energy varies sinusoidally between zero and a maximum value which is $\tfrac{1}{2}L|I|^2$,

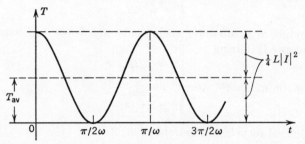

FIG. 1. The instantaneous energy stored in the magnetic field associated with an inductance when the current in it is a sinusoid of radian frequency ω.

the radian frequency being twice that of the current $i(t)$. Alternatively, one may say that T as a function of time consists of a constant component

$$T_{\text{av}} = \tfrac{1}{4}L|I|^2 \tag{19}$$

plus a double-frequency alternating component. Since the average value of the latter is zero, the constant component is the average value of T and is appropriately so designated.

The power taken by the inductive element is given by the time derivative of T. From Eq. 18 one has

$$\frac{dT}{dt} = -\frac{\omega}{2}L|I|^2 \sin 2\omega t \tag{20}$$

which is simply a double-frequency sinusoid. Its average value is obviously zero; that is,

$$(dT/dt)_{\text{av}} = 0 \tag{21}$$

as predicted in the opening paragraph of the preceding article where it is pointed out that a storage element cannot absorb energy indefinitely at a nonzero rate (since it would ultimately have to burst).

From the plot in Fig. 1 we see that the peak value of the stored magnetic energy equals just twice the average value; that is, $T_{\text{peak}} = 2T_{\text{av}}$. This simple relationship is not necessarily true for a circuit containing several inductances and also resistances and capacitances. In such more general situations * one usually finds that $T_{\text{peak}} < 2T_{\text{av}}$, or that the amplitude of the oscillatory component of T is smaller than T_{av}. It can evidently never be larger than T_{av} since in that event T would become *negative* during some portions of a cycle, a result that manifestly is impossible with passive elements.

Similar remarks apply to the capacitive element. If in Eq. 15 we let

$$e(t) = \mid E \mid \cos \omega t \tag{22}$$

there results

$$V = \tfrac{1}{4}C\mid E \mid^2 (1 + \cos 2\omega t) \tag{23}$$

from which we have

$$V_{\text{av}} = \tfrac{1}{4}C\mid E \mid^2 \tag{24}$$

and

$$\frac{dV}{dt} = -\frac{\omega}{2} C\mid E \mid^2 \sin 2\omega t \tag{25}$$

whence

$$(dV/dt)_{\text{av}} = 0 \tag{26}$$

The time plot of V has the same appearance as that of T. Again one finds in general for circuits with R's and L's as well as C's that $V_{\text{peak}} \leq 2V_{\text{av}}$, the equals sign holding only in special cases.

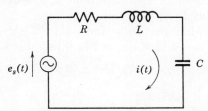

Fig. 2.   Pertinent to deriving the energy relations in a series RLC circuit.

3   Energy and Power Relations in a Complete Circuit

Let us now consider the series RLC circuit of Fig. 2 excited by the voltage source $e_s(t)$. The familiar equilibrium equation reads

$$L\frac{di}{dt} + Ri + \frac{1}{C}\int i\, dt = e_s(t) \tag{27}$$

* These are discussed in Ch. 10.

Suppose each term in this equation is multiplied by $i(t)$. We then have

$$Li\frac{di}{dt} + Ri^2 + \frac{i}{C}\int i\,dt = e_s \times i \tag{28}$$

Using Eq. 14, we note that

$$dT/dt = Li\,(di/dt) \tag{29}$$

which is the first term in Eq. 28. The third term, through use of 12, may be written

$$\frac{i}{C}\int i\,dt = Sq\frac{dq}{dt} \tag{30}$$

while from Eq. 15 we get

$$dV/dt = Sq\,(dq/dt) \tag{31}$$

The equilibrium equation 27 is thus seen to be equivalent to

$$Ri^2 + \frac{d}{dt}(T + V) = e_s \times i \tag{32}$$

which is an expression of the conservation of energy. Thus Ri^2 represents the instantaneous rate of energy dissipation by the resistive element in the circuit; $\frac{d}{dt}(T + V)$ is the instantaneous rate of energy absorption by the storage elements; and $e_s \times i$ is the instantaneous rate of energy supply from the source.

Now let us see what particular form Eq. 32 takes when $e_s(t)$ and $i(t)$ are sinusoids. As pointed out in Ch. 6 we must write here

$$e_s(t) = \tfrac{1}{2}(E_s e^{j\omega t} + \bar{E}_s e^{-j\omega t}) \tag{33}$$

$$i(t) = \tfrac{1}{2}(I e^{j\omega t} + \bar{I} e^{-j\omega t}) \tag{34}$$

instead of dropping the "real part" operator and writing just the single exponential term, because quadratic operations are involved. The vector quantities E and I are, however, the same as before and are related through the circuit impedance in the usual manner. The bar indicates a conjugate value.

For the charge $q(t)$, according to 12, we have through formally integrating 34

$$q(t) = \frac{1}{2j\omega}(I e^{j\omega t} - \bar{I} e^{-j\omega t}) \tag{35}$$

For the squared current or charge one obtains in a straightforward manner

$$i^2(t) = \tfrac{1}{4}I^2e^{j2\omega t} + \tfrac{1}{4}\bar{I}^2e^{-j2\omega t} + \tfrac{1}{2}I\bar{I} \tag{36}$$

$$q^2(t) = -\frac{1}{4\omega^2}(I^2e^{j2\omega t} + \bar{I}^2e^{-j2\omega t} - 2I\bar{I}) \tag{37}$$

which may alternatively be written

$$i^2(t) = \tfrac{1}{2}|I|^2 + \tfrac{1}{2}\mathrm{Re}[I^2e^{j2\omega t}] \tag{38}$$

$$q^2(t) = \frac{1}{2\omega^2}|I|^2 - \frac{1}{2\omega^2}\mathrm{Re}[I^2e^{j2\omega t}] \tag{39}$$

The magnetic and electric stored energy functions according to 14 and 15 thus become

$$T = \tfrac{1}{4}L|I|^2 + \tfrac{1}{4}L\,\mathrm{Re}[I^2e^{j2\omega t}] \tag{40}$$

$$V = \frac{1}{4\omega^2}S|I|^2 - \frac{1}{4\omega^2}S\,\mathrm{Re}[I^2e^{j2\omega t}] \tag{41}$$

The first terms in these expressions are respectively T_{av} (Eq. 19) and V_{av} (equivalent to the form given in Eq. 24 since the capacitance current $|I|$ equals the capacitance voltage $|E|$ multiplied by $C\omega$). In forming the time derivatives of T and V these constant terms drop out, so that one has

$$\frac{dT}{dt} = \frac{1}{2}\,\mathrm{Re}[Lj\omega I^2e^{j2\omega t}] \tag{42}$$

$$\frac{dV}{dt} = \frac{1}{2}\,\mathrm{Re}\left[\frac{1}{Cj\omega}I^2e^{j2\omega t}\right] \tag{43}$$

Substitution of these results into Eq. 32 gives

$$\frac{1}{2}R|I|^2 + \frac{1}{2}\mathrm{Re}\left[\left(R + Lj\omega + \frac{1}{Cj\omega}\right)I^2e^{j2\omega t}\right] = e_s \times i \tag{44}$$

So far as the right-hand side is concerned, Eqs. 33 and 34 yield

$$e_s \times i = \tfrac{1}{2}\,\mathrm{Re}\,[\bar{E}_sI] + \tfrac{1}{2}\,\mathrm{Re}\,[E_sIe^{j2\omega t}] \tag{45}$$

Regarding the left-hand side of Eq. 44, one should note that $(R + Lj\omega + 1/Cj\omega)$ is the circuit impedance, and this multiplied by I equals the vector voltage E_s. Hence Eq. 44 can be written

$$e_s \times i = \tfrac{1}{2}R|I|^2 + \tfrac{1}{2}\,\mathrm{Re}\,[E_sIe^{j2\omega t}] \tag{46}$$

The product $e_s \times i$ is the instantaneous power supplied to the circuit by the voltage source. Equations 45 and 46 show that this power as a function of time consists of a constant component which is

$$P_{av} = \tfrac{1}{2} \operatorname{Re} [\overline{E}_s I] = \tfrac{1}{2} R |I|^2 \text{ (watts)} \qquad (47)$$

and a superimposed double-frequency alternating component given by the term

$$\tfrac{1}{2} \operatorname{Re} [E_s I e^{j2\omega t}] \qquad (48)$$

The average value of the supplied power is evidently given by the constant term 47, which is therefore appropriately designated as P_{av}.

If E_s is chosen as the reference vector (which implies no loss in generality), E_s and $\overline{E}_s$ are the same. The angle of $\overline{E}_s I$ or the angle of $E_s I$ is then simply the negative of the impedance angle θ, so that

$$\overline{E}_s I = E_s I = |E_s| \times |I| e^{-j\theta} \qquad (49)$$

whence

$$P_{av} = \tfrac{1}{2} |E_s| \times |I| \cos \theta \qquad (50)$$

A vector interpretation of this result is shown in Fig. 3 where part (a) suggests that the product $|E_s| \times |I| \cos \theta$ be regarded as $|E_s|$

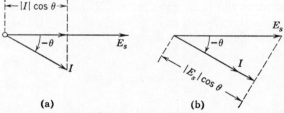

(a)   **(b)**

FIG. 3. The average power absorbed is expressible either as $(1/2)$ the product of the voltage and the in-phase component of the current (a), or as $(1/2)$ the product of the current and the in-phase component of the voltage (b).

multiplied by the component of I that is in phase with E_s, namely, $|I| \cos \theta$; in part (b) the same product is regarded as formed through multiplying $|I|$ by the component of E_s in phase with I, that is, by $|E_s| \cos \theta$.

According to the definition of the impedance angle θ it should be clear that

$$\cos \theta = R/|Z| \qquad (51)$$

whence Eq. 50 is seen to be equivalent to

$$P_{av} = \frac{1}{2} \frac{|E_s| \times |I| R}{|Z|} = \frac{1}{2} R |I|^2 \qquad (52)$$

which independently checks the alternative form for P_{av} expressed in Eq. 47.

Returning to Eq. 45 we may now write this result in the more explicit form

$$e_s \times i = \tfrac{1}{2}\big|\,E_sI\,\big|\cos\theta + \tfrac{1}{2}\big|\,E_sI\,\big|\cos(2\omega t \div \theta) \qquad (53)$$

in which E_s is again chosen as the reference vector.

A plot of this expression for the instantaneous power supplied by the source is shown in Fig. 4 for an assumed $\theta = 60°$. We see that the

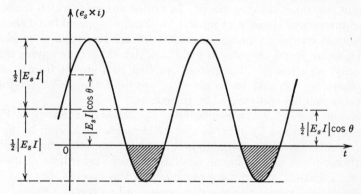

FIG. 4.   The power as a function of time is the sum of a constant and a double-frequency sinusoidal term.

instantaneous power is negative during portions of every period as is emphasized in the figure through cross-hatching. The area of each cross-hatched portion represents an amount of energy that is being returned to the source by the storage elements in the circuit.

The significant feature about the power supplied to a circuit in the sinusoidal steady state is that it is not represented by a uniform flow of energy, but rather that this flow has a pulsating character and that, in general, energy flows in *both* directions; that is to say, it flows from the circuit back into the source as well as from the source into the circuit. If the latter contains lossy elements (resistances), then on the average more energy flows into the network than is returned to the source, the net amount supplied per second by the source being P_{av} as given by Eqs. 47 or 50. The extent to which the circuit is lossy is evidently characterized through the value of $\cos\theta$, which is unity for $\theta = 0$ and zero for $\theta = \pm\pi/2$. According to Eq. 51 we note that $\cos\theta$ becomes unity only if Z equals R which, we recall, occurs at resonance (that is, for $L\omega = 1/C\omega$). On the other hand, for $R = 0$, $\cos\theta$ becomes zero. In this limiting case the curve of Fig. 4 oscillates symmetrically about the zero axis (yielding zero average power supplied), while for $Z = R$ the curve lies wholly above the zero axis so that the cross-hatched portions are just eliminated.

Since $\cos \theta$ thus characteristically indicates the extent to which the circuit absorbs power from the source, it is called the *power factor* of the circuit. The expression for P_{av} given by Eq. 50 is referred to as the *power product* of the source voltage and current. Except for the factor $1/2$, the power product of a vector voltage and a vector current is formed through the product of the lengths of these vectors and the cosine of the angle between them. In vector analysis (which deals with three-dimensional space vectors but is likewise applicable to the two-dimensional complex numbers considered here) this type of product is called a *scalar product* because it yields a scalar value (one having magnitude only) as a result. The power supplied to a circuit from a source may, therefore, be said to be given by one-half the scalar product of the vector voltage and current at the source.

Although derived above in relation to the series RLC circuit of Fig. 2, the results expressed by Eqs. 45 and 47 through 53, having to do with an interpretation of the input power $e_s \times i$ alone, obviously apply at the driving point of any linear passive network, regardless of its complexity. Identical remarks are pertinent to the Eqs. 54, 55, and 56 of the next article, relating to reactive power and to vector power.

4 Active and Reactive Power; Vector Power

Let us reflect for a moment upon the results of the previous article and contrast them with the simpler ones applying to the computation of power in d-c circuits. There the power supplied is simply equal to the product of voltage and current at the source. Apart from the factor $1/2$, about which we will have a bit more to say later on, the most significant feature about the power relation pertaining to a-c circuits is the appearance of the power factor $\cos \theta$. If the circuit contains no storage elements but only resistance, then to be sure the power factor equals unity and the only remaining difference between d-c and a-c power calculation lies in the factor $1/2$ entering in the a-c case. In general, however, storage elements are present, and they make their presence felt through absorbing and returning energy during each cycle but absorbing no net energy on the average.

One might argue that, so long as these storage elements absorb no net energy on the average, their presence or their effect upon the circuit behavior implies no net cost to the one who has to pay for the energy consumed (and only energy actually consumed means work done by some agency). The fallacy in this argument lies in the assumption that only the energy consumed has to be paid for, or that energy that is borrowed for a short while and then returned (undamaged) should cost nothing. On the contrary, companies who are in the business of supplying electric energy at a price justifiably feel that they are entitled to some fee for energy that is only temporarily used by the customer and returned in good condition, because the company has to go to the same trouble and expense to generate and distribute the energy, whether borrowed or consumed, notwithstanding the fact that only the consumed energy materially diminishes the coal pile.

Thus it is seen that somehow the energy that is swapped back and forth between the source and the circuit has to be kept track of. Although the term "power" is not well suited as a designation for this "swappage" of energy, since power means energy flow and on the average there isn't any, nevertheless the term *reactive power* or *wattless power* is used as a means of reference to the phenomenon we are discussing.

In order to define more accurately what is meant by reactive power (so that its amount may be computed with the same exactness as is possible for the actual average power), one is led rather naturally to a reasonable formulation through reference to the vector diagram, part (a) of Fig. 3. Here the average power is represented as given by one-half the product of E_s and the component of I that is in phase with E_s. It seems rather natural to choose (as an arbitrary definition) one-half the product of E_s and the *quadrature* component of I (that component at right angles to E_s) as yielding the wattless or the reactive "power" supplied to the circuit. Accordingly, the component of source current $90°$ out of phase with the source voltage is sometimes referred to as the *wattless* component of the current.

According to Eq. 47, the average power supplied by the source is given by the real part of $\frac{1}{2}(\overline{E}_s I)$. Since the reactive power, as just defined, is equal to the imaginary part of $\frac{1}{2}(\overline{E}_s I)$, it seems logical to regard the complex quantity $\frac{1}{2}(\overline{E}_s I)$ as a *vector power*. Its real part is the actual average power supplied by the source (also referred to as the *active power*), while the imaginary part (by definition) is the reactive or wattless power. The active or average power is denoted by the symbol P_{av} (as has been done above), and the reactive power by Q_{av} (not to be confused with the Q of a resonant circuit). Thus we have

$$\text{Vector power} = P_{av} + jQ_{av} = \tfrac{1}{2}[\overline{E}_s I] \tag{54}$$

Since $I = E_s/Z = E_s Y$, one may alternatively write

$$P_{av} + jQ_{av} = \tfrac{1}{2}\overline{E}_s E_s Y = \tfrac{1}{2}\left| E_s \right|^2 \times Y \tag{55}$$

It is just as useful in any actual case to compute the power per volt of excitation, inasmuch as the power for any other applied voltage is obtained simply through multiplying by the square of that voltage. The expression for vector power then becomes particularly simple, namely,

$$(P_{av} + jQ_{av})_{E_s=1} = \tfrac{1}{2}Y = \tfrac{1}{2}[G(\omega) + jB(\omega)] \tag{56}$$

Thus numerically (not dimensionally) the active power P_{av} (per volt applied) is simply one-half the conductive part of the admittance, while the reactive power Q_{av} is one-half the susceptive part. The active power in a linear passive circuit clearly is always positive; the reactive power, however, may have either sign, being positive in a capacitive circuit and negative in an inductive one. The units of Q_{av} are called "vars"—a contraction of "volt-amperes reactive."

Instead of Eq. 55 we can alternatively write

$$P_{av} + jQ_{av} = \tfrac{1}{2}\bar{I}IZ = \tfrac{1}{2}|I|^2 \times \bar{Z} \tag{57}$$

and have

$$(P_{av} + jQ_{av})_{I=1} = \tfrac{1}{2}\bar{Z} = \tfrac{1}{2}[R(\omega) - jX(\omega)] \tag{58}$$

This form for the vector power supplied to an impedance Z is appropriate if the associated current rather than the voltage is known. Thus one can say that the vector power absorbed by an impedance per peak ampere passing through it equals one-half the conjugate of that impedance.

In terms of the effective or rms values of voltage and current discussed in the following article, the results expressed by Eqs. 56 and 58 become even simpler in that the factors $1/2$ drop out. That is to say, the vector power absorbed by an admittance Y per rms volt applied to it is numerically equal to Y; and the vector power absorbed by an impedance Z per rms ampere passing through it is numerically equal to the conjugate of Z.

In a complex circuit consisting of the interconnection of many branches, the above results are simply summed over all the branches in order to obtain the total vector power. Thus, if E_k and I_k are the complex voltage drop and current in branch k having the impedance Z_k or admittance Y_k so that $E_k = I_k Z_k$ or $I_k = E_k Y_k$, then the total vector power is given by

$$P_{av} + jQ_{av} = \frac{1}{2}\sum_k \bar{E}_k I_k = \frac{1}{2}\sum_k |I_k|^2 \bar{Z}_k = \frac{1}{2}\sum_k |E_k|^2 Y_k \tag{59}$$

where the summation extends over all branches in the network.

Although the above precise definition of reactive power gives one a means of computing its value, and hence provides a numerically secure basis upon which electric power companies can bargain with regard to fees that are due them for the loan of energy to supply storage elements, we are at this stage not in a very satisfactory frame of mind regarding the physical meaning of this mysterious reactive "power" that isn't power.

In order to clarify the situation we return to the circuit of Fig. 2 and the equilibrium Eq. 27. For $e_s(t) = E_s e^{j\omega t}$ and $i(t) = I e^{j\omega t}$, we get in the usual fashion

$$RI + j\omega \left(LI - \frac{I}{C\omega^2} \right) = E_s \tag{60}$$

or its conjugate

$$\bar{E}_s = R\bar{I} + j\omega \left(\frac{\bar{I}}{C\omega^2} - L\bar{I} \right) \tag{61}$$

Multiplying by I and taking one-half, we get the vector power

$$\frac{1}{2} (\bar{E}_s I) = \frac{1}{2} R| I |^2 + j2\omega \left(\frac{| I |^2}{4C\omega^2} - \frac{1}{4} L| I |^2 \right) \tag{62}$$

Here, according to Eq. 24,

$$\frac{| I |^2}{4C\omega^2} = \frac{1}{4} C| E |^2 = V_{av} \tag{63}$$

since the capacitance voltage $| E | = | I |/C\omega$; and by Eq. 19

$$\tfrac{1}{4} L| I |^2 = T_{av} \tag{64}$$

Therefore we see that Eq. 62 yields

$$\tfrac{1}{2}[\bar{E}_s I] = P_{av} + jQ_{av} = \tfrac{1}{2} R| I |^2 + j2\omega(V_{av} - T_{av}) \tag{65}$$

We are, in particular, interested in the result

$$Q_{av} = 2\omega(V_{av} - T_{av}) \tag{66}$$

which states that the reactive power is proportional to the difference between the average energy stored in the electric field and that stored in the magnetic field. Although derived here for the simple series RLC circuit only, relation 66 holds true for all linear passive networks, however complicated.*

If the two fields associated with a given circuit store, on the average, equal amounts of energy, then they merely swap a certain amount of energy back and forth between them, and the source is *not* called upon to enter into this interplay once it has reached a steady repetitive pat-

* For a demonstration of this fact, see Art. 6, Ch. 10.

tern (that is, in the steady state). It is only when $V_{av} \neq T_{av}$ that some of the stored energy is continuously played back and forth between the source and the circuit. The reactive power Q_{av} is thus seen to be a measure of the extent to which the *source* participates in the interplay of stored energy, because it is proportional to the excess in the average value of electric as compared with the magnetic stored energy.

The fact that this excess may be numerically negative as well as positive makes it physically possible for one passive circuit to supply the reactive power called for in another. Such a process, which relieves the source from the burden of entering into the role of an energy lending agency (and relieves the customer of the burden of paying an additional fee) is referred to in electric power circles as "power-factor correction," a term that evidently is appropriate since the reactive power is zero when the power factor is unity, and vice versa. Reactive power is thus seen to be something that a passive circuit can supply, and we note again the need for appropriately interpreting the term "power" in this connection.

An additional point worth brief mention is seen through reference to Fig. 4, showing a plot of the instantaneous supplied power. We are now in a position to recognize that, whereas the active power is the average value or constant term in the expression for the instantaneous supplied power, the *magnitude of the vector power* is the amplitude of its double frequency alternating component.

5   Root-Mean-Square, or Effective Values

The measurement of a sinusoidal alternating current is accomplished by means of an instrument in which the torque actuating the indicator is instantaneously proportional to the square of the current. Owing to the inertia of the movable element, the actual deflection is steady in spite of the pulsating nature of the torque and is proportional to the average of the instantaneous squared current. According to Eq. 38, therefore, the a-c ammeter has a deflection proportional to $|I|^2$. Through an appropriately chosen scale, this instrument can provide a direct reading for the quantity $|I|^2$, or for $|I|$, or $|I|$ multiplied by any desired constant. If arranged to read $|I|^2$, the scale divisions will be uniformly spaced, whereas, if $|I|$ or $|I|$ times some constant factor is to be read, the scale divisions will need to be nonuniform like the ordinates corresponding to $y = x^2$ for equal intervals in x.

If such a nonuniform scale is provided, and the constant factor of $|I|$ chosen equal to $1/\sqrt{2}$, then one observes from Eq. 47 that the loss in a resistance carrying this current is given through the product of R

and the square of the meter reading, just as with d-c circuits.   The value $1/\sqrt{2}$ times $\mid I \mid$ is seen to be a quantity that plays the same role with regard to the computation of power loss in the sinusoidal case as does the value of a constant current in the d-c case.   Similar remarks apply with regard to voltage since, by duality, all that is said above concerning power remains intact upon interchange of voltage with current and impedance with admittance (resp. R with G and X with B). The values $1/\sqrt{2}$ times $\mid I \mid$ or times $\mid E \mid$ are, therefore, referred to as the *effective* values of sinusoidal alternating current or voltage.   They are in a sense the equivalent d-c values since their power-loss effects are the same as those obtained with equal values of constant current or voltage.

Since the average power dissipated in a resistance R by a sinusoidal current $i(t)$ is given by

$$P_{\mathrm{av}} = \frac{1}{\tau} \int_0^\tau Ri^2 \, dt, \qquad \left(\tau = \frac{2\pi}{\omega} \right) \qquad (67)$$

which may be written

$$P_{\mathrm{av}} = RI_{\mathrm{eff}}^2 \qquad (68)$$

with

$$I_{\mathrm{eff}}^2 = \frac{1}{\tau} \int_0^\tau i^2 \, dt \qquad (69)$$

we see that the effective value may be expressed as the square root of the mean value of the squared current.   Therefore the effective value is alternatively known as the *root-mean-square value* (abbreviated *rms value*).   The same comment applies to voltage.

The foregoing analysis shows that the rms value of a sinusoid equals $1/\sqrt{2}$ times its peak value, a result that may readily be verified independently since

$$\frac{1}{2\pi} \int_0^{2\pi} \cos^2 x \, dx = \frac{1}{4\pi} \int_0^{2\pi} (1 + \cos 2x) \, dx$$

$$= \frac{x}{4\pi} \bigg]_0^{2\pi} + \frac{\sin 2x}{8\pi} \bigg]_0^{2\pi} = \frac{1}{2} + 0 \quad (70)$$

When values of voltage and current are stated in connection with sinusoidal steady-state circuit work, they are usually understood to be rms or effective values, since these are the values that are read on a-c meters.   In dealing with vector voltages and currents one can have it understood that the symbols E and I represent effective complex values (the actual ones multiplied by $1/\sqrt{2}$).   Since voltages and currents are linearly proportional to each other, all interrelationships are the same whether the E's and I's represent effective complex values or actual complex values, as they do in the discussions of the previous chapter. With regard to the analysis in the present chapter, the result of having the E's and I's denote effective values is simply that the factors $1/2$ disappear from all the expressions for active, reactive, and vector power.

Most textbooks on a-c circuits use effective values throughout, and the expressions for power given in them differ from those given here by the factor $1/2$. Thus in most textbooks vector voltages and currents are understood to be effective values unless otherwise stated, while in this text the absolute values of current and voltage vectors are the peak values of the sinusoids they represent. If sinusoids of only a single frequency are involved (as in most a-c power work at 60 cycles per second), the use of effective values throughout is possible and convenient. However, this scheme becomes awkward if not impossible to adhere to in more general situations (such as are met in communications and control circuits) where sinusoids of different frequencies must simultaneously be considered. The present text is written from the point of view that it shall be the groundwork for a more complete study rather than the complete treatment of a restricted case.

6 Impedance or Admittance in Terms of Energy Functions

Equation 65, together with the usual definitions of impedance and admittance, yields

$$\tfrac{1}{2}(\overline{E}_sI) = \tfrac{1}{2}\big| E_s \big|^2Y = \tfrac{1}{2}\big| I \big|^2\overline{Z} = P_{\mathrm{av}} + j2\omega(V_{\mathrm{av}} - T_{\mathrm{av}}) \qquad (71)$$

Hence one can express the admittance as

$$Y(\omega) = \frac{2P_{\mathrm{av}} + j4\omega(V_{\mathrm{av}} - T_{\mathrm{av}})}{\big| E_s \big|^2} \qquad (72)$$

and the impedance as

$$Z(\omega) = \frac{2P_{\mathrm{av}} + j4\omega(T_{\mathrm{av}} - V_{\mathrm{av}})}{\big| I \big|^2} \qquad (73)$$

If the functions P_{av}, V_{av}, T_{av} in Eq. 72 are assumed to be evaluated for $E_s = 1$ volt, then the admittance $Y(\omega)$ is expressed explicitly in terms of these power and energy functions. A similar interpretation may be given the impedance expression 73 on the tacit assumption that P_{av}, T_{av}, V_{av} are evaluated for $I = 1$ ampere. In connection with the simple RLC circuit, these results are only of nominal interest since the conventional expressions for $Y(\omega)$ and $Z(\omega)$ in this case are even more compact than the relations 72 and 73, and so it is only the novelty of seeing these functions expressed in terms of power and energy that makes them interesting. It is significant to mention that Eqs. 72 and 73 are found to apply as well to linear passive networks of arbitrary complexity,* the expressions for P_{av}, T_{av}, and V_{av} being correspondingly more elaborate.

In terms of these results one may see again that a condition of resonance implies $T_{av} = V_{av}$. That is to say, when the average energies stored by the electric and magnetic fields are equal, the impedance or admittance at the driving point reduces to a real quantity; the system is in resonance. Conversely, whenever the driving-point impedance or admittance has a zero imaginary part, then one may conclude that the average electric and magnetic stored energies are equal; the power factor is unity, and the reactive power is zero.

Since the quantities P_{av}, T_{av}, V_{av} are implicit functions of the frequency ω, the expressions 72 and 73 are not useful in the study of $Y(\omega)$ or $Z(\omega)$ as functions of ω except in some very special circumstances. A case in point is the consideration of the behavior of $Z(\omega)$ in the vicinity of a resonance frequency. In the simple RLC circuit considered here, Eq. 64 shows that $T_{av}/|I|^2$ is a constant. In more elaborate circuits one finds that the current ratios throughout the network are almost constant over any frequency range near a resonance point, and hence that $T_{av}/|I|^2$, which depends only upon the current distribution, is in general almost constant in the vicinity of resonance.

Since V_{av} must equal T_{av} for $\omega = \omega_0$, Eq. 63 shows that we can write for this vicinity †

$$V_{av} \cong T_{av} \cdot \omega_0^2/\omega^2 \tag{74}$$

where ω_0 is the resonance frequency in question, and thus have in place of Eq. 73

$$Z(\omega) \cong \frac{2P_{av} + j4\omega T_{av}(1 - \omega_0^2/\omega^2)}{|I|^2} \tag{75}$$

For values of ω near ω_0, one may use the approximation

$$\frac{\omega^2 - \omega_0^2}{\omega} = \frac{(\omega + \omega_0)(\omega - \omega_0)}{\omega} \cong 2(\omega - \omega_0) \tag{76}$$

* See Art. 8, Ch. 10.

† For the simple RLC circuit treated here, this expression, as well as the one given by Eq. 75, is of course exact, but in more general situations these are approximate relations which are, however, very nearly correct throughout any pronounced resonance vicinity.

and thus obtain for the impedance $Z(\omega)$ the following explicit function valid near ω_0

$$Z(\omega) \cong \frac{2P_{\text{av}} + j8T_{\text{av}}(\omega - \omega_0)}{|I|^2} = R + jX \tag{77}$$

whence

$$R = \frac{2P_{\text{av}}}{|I|^2}, \qquad X \cong \frac{8T_{\text{av}}}{|I|^2}(\omega - \omega_0) \tag{78}$$

The expression for R (which is exact) checks with Eq. 52 as, of course, it should; the expression for X, through use of Eq. 64, checks with the approximate expression for the reactance of the RLC circuit given by Eq. 153 in Ch. 6. Again the significant feature about this result is that one finds it to apply generally for all low-loss networks.

As pointed out in Ch. 6 and illustrated there in Fig. 19, the half-power points on the associated resonance curve lie where $X = \pm R$ or, using Eqs. 78, where

$$(\omega - \omega_0) = \pm P_{\text{av}}/4T_{\text{av}} \tag{79}$$

Hence the radian-frequency increment w between the half-power frequencies (width of the resonance curve) becomes

$$w = P_{\text{av}}/2T_{\text{av}} \tag{80}$$

and the Q of the circuit is found to be expressible as

$$Q = \omega_0/w = 2\omega_0 T_{\text{av}}/P_{\text{av}} \tag{81}$$

The behavior of T vs. time shown in Fig. 1 (applying to the simple RLC circuit) is found to be representative of any low-loss system near resonance. Thus, $2T_{\text{av}} \cong T_{\text{peak}}$, and Eq. 81 can be written

$$Q \cong \frac{\omega_0 T_{\text{peak}}}{P_{\text{av}}} = \frac{2\pi T_{\text{peak}}}{\tau_0 P_{\text{av}}} \tag{82}$$

or

$$Q \cong \frac{2\pi T_{\text{peak}}}{\text{loss per cycle}} = \frac{2\pi V_{\text{peak}}}{\text{loss per cycle}} \tag{83}$$

since at or near resonance the stored energy merely swaps back and forth between the electric and magnetic fields and so the peak value of this energy is the same whether expressed electrically or magnetically. The loss per cycle clearly equals the average rate of loss (P_{av}) times the period $\tau_0 = 2\pi/\omega_0$.

Thus the factor Q which characterizes the critical behavior of a low-loss network near resonance may be computed entirely on an energy basis. Not only is the result 83 useful because it provides an independent approach to the computation of this important figure of merit (an approach that is found to be usable in situations where parameter calculations are difficult or not feasible) but also because it provides an excellent basis for describing what is meant by a "low-loss" or "high-Q" system. Namely, it is one in which the loss per cycle is small compared with the peak value of the total stored energy. In order to obtain a circuit with an extremely sharp resonance curve, one must strive to obtain as large an energy storage as possible relative to the associated loss per cycle.

7 Computation of the Energy Functions for More Complex Networks

When the network under consideration has several inductive and capacitive branches, the expressions for the total instantaneous stored energies T and V are obtained through simply summing the relations 40 and 41 over all pertinent branches.* Symbolically we may indicate this procedure by writing

$$T = \frac{1}{4} \sum_k L_k |I_k|^2 + \frac{1}{4} \operatorname{Re}[e^{j2\omega t} \sum_k L_k I_k^2] \tag{84}$$

and

$$V = \frac{1}{4\omega^2} \sum_k S_k |I_k|^2 - \frac{1}{4\omega^2} \operatorname{Re}[e^{j2\omega t} \sum_k S_k I_k^2] \tag{85}$$

In Eq. 84, I_k denotes the vector current in an inductive branch having the inductance L_k, and the summation extends over all inductive branches in the network. In Eq. 85, I_k denotes the vector current in a capacitive branch having elastance (reciprocal capacitance) S_k, and the summation extends over all capacitive branches in the network.

The first terms in Eqs. 84 and 85 are T_{av} and V_{av} respectively for the total network. Note that the sums yielding these quantities involve the squared *absolute* values of the branch currents, while the second terms in Eqs. 84 and 85, which are double-frequency sinusoids, involve the squared *complex* values of the branch currents. The sums in these terms, therefore, involve complex addition (not merely the addition of absolute values), and it is the angle of the resultant complex number that determines the time phase of the pertinent sinusoid. Since the sum of a set of complex values has a resultant magnitude that is always less than or at most equal to the sum of the absolute values of this set

---

* Mutual coupling between inductive branches is here assumed to be absent. A treatment not subject to this restriction is given in Art. 6 of Ch. 10.

of complex numbers, it is clear that the amplitude of the sinusoidal component of either T or V is in general less than T_{av} or V_{av} respectively, and can equal this constant component only if all squared branch currents are in phase, a condition that exists in all lossless networks (for a single sinusoidal excitation) and is nearly attained in low-loss networks operating at or near a resonance frequency.

In computing V it is sometimes more convenient to do so in terms of the branch voltages instead of the branch currents. Since such a branch voltage is related to its current by the expression

$$E_k = S_k I_k / j\omega \tag{86}$$

giving

$$S_k I_k{}^2 / \omega^2 = -C_k E_k{}^2 \tag{87}$$

we see that Eq. 85 may be written

$$V = \tfrac{1}{4} \sum_k C_k \big| E_k \big|^2 + \tfrac{1}{4} \operatorname{Re} \left[e^{j2\omega t} \sum C_k E_k{}^2 \right] \tag{88}$$

which looks like Eq. 84 except for an interchange of E with I and C with L, as we might have predicted through use of the principle of duality.

8   Some Illustrative Examples

In order to show how these results are applied to a specific circuit, consider the one in Fig. 5. If we denote by E_k the voltage drop in a

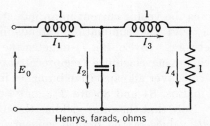

Henrys, farads, ohms

Fig. 5.   Circuit to which the computations 89 are pertinent.

branch in which the current is I_k, and assume $E_4 = 1$ volt, then the following sequence of calculations for an assumed $\omega = 1$ radian per second are self-explanatory

$$I_3 = I_4 = 1 + j0, \qquad E_3 = j1$$

$$E_2 = E_3 + E_4 = 1 + j1, \qquad I_2 = jE_2 = -1 + j1 \tag{89}$$

$$I_1 = I_2 + I_3 = j1, \qquad E_1 = jI_1 = -1, \qquad E_0 = E_1 + E_2 = j1$$

From these values we readily have

$$I_1{}^2 = -1, \qquad |I_1|^2 = 1$$
$$I_2{}^2 = -j2, \qquad |I_2|^2 = 2 \qquad (90)$$
$$I_3{}^2 = 1, \qquad |I_3|^2 = 1$$

and so Eqs. 84 and 85 yield

$$T = \tfrac{1}{2} + 0 \cos 2t, \qquad V = \tfrac{1}{2} - \tfrac{1}{2} \sin 2t \qquad (91)$$

Since $P_{av} = \tfrac{1}{2}|I_4|^2$ we then have

$$P_{av} = \tfrac{1}{2} \text{ watt}, \qquad T_{av} = V_{av} = \tfrac{1}{2} \text{ joule} \qquad (92)$$

We see that the circuit is evidently not a low-loss system, for the stored energies are not large compared with the loss. Although the circuit is in resonance, $T_{peak} = \tfrac{1}{2}$ is not equal to $V_{peak} = 1$. There is no point in computing a Q since it would have little meaning anyway.

It is interesting to find the impedance from the energy functions according to Eq. 73, thus,

$$Z = \frac{1 + j4 \times 0}{1} = 1 \qquad (93)$$

which checks with $Z = E_0/I_1$ according to the values 89.

Now suppose we change the value of the resistance in Fig. 5 to 1/10th ohm. The computations 89 then become

$$I_3 = I_4 = 10 + j0, \qquad E_3 = j10$$
$$E_2 = 1 + j10, \qquad I_2 = -10 + j1 \qquad (94)$$
$$I_1 = j1, \qquad E_1 = -1, \qquad E_0 = j10$$

and in place of the results 90 we have

$$I_1{}^2 = -1, \qquad |I_1|^2 = 1$$
$$I_2{}^2 = 99 - j20, \qquad |I_2|^2 = 101 \qquad (95)$$
$$I_3{}^2 = 100, \qquad |I_3|^2 = 100$$

The magnetic and electric stored energy functions, according to Eqs. 84 and 85, become

$$T = 25.25 + 24.75 \cos 2t, \qquad V = 25.25 - 25.25 \cos (2t - 11.5°) \qquad (96)$$

So now

$$T_{av} = V_{av} = 25.25 \text{ joules}, \qquad P_{av} = 5 \text{ watts} \qquad (97)$$

which looks a bit more like the results for a low-loss system should.

We observe from Eqs. 96 also that

$$T_{\text{peak}} = 50.0, \qquad V_{\text{peak}} = 50.5 \tag{98}$$

The loss per cycle equals $\tau_0 \times P_{\text{av}} = 2\pi \times 5 = 10\pi$ joules, and so the factor Q, computed from either Eqs. 81 or 83, yields

$$Q = \frac{50}{5} = \frac{2\pi \times 50}{10\pi} = 10 \tag{99}$$

Although the resonance is not extremely sharp, it is well defined.

The input impedance, according to Eq. 73, for this case becomes

$$Z = \frac{10 + j4(0)}{1} = 10 \tag{100}$$

while from the values 94 we get $Z = E_0/I_1 = 10$, thus substantiating again the equivalence of these relationships.

Suppose now we restore the resistance to the value of 1 ohm, but add two more reactive branches as shown in Fig. 6. This procedure should

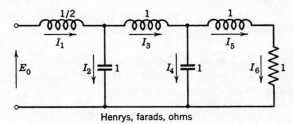

Henrys, farads, ohms

FIG. 6.   Circuit to which the computations 101 are pertinent.

increase the stored energy relative to the loss, and hence yield a sharper resonance. In order to maintain resonance at $\omega = 1$ radian per second, the first inductance now needs to be 1/2 henry as shown. This result is easily arrived at through first computing the currents in all of the other branches, following the pattern used above, and then noting the value of the first inductance needed to make $T_{\text{av}} = V_{\text{av}}$.

The sequence of calculations appropriate to this circuit, assuming $E_6 = 1$ volt, read

$$I_6 = I_5 = 1 + j0, \qquad E_5 = j1$$
$$E_4 = 1 + j1, \qquad I_4 = -1 + j1, \qquad I_3 = j1$$
$$E_3 = -1, \qquad E_2 = j1, \qquad I_2 = -1 \tag{101}$$
$$I_1 = -1 + j1, \qquad E_1 = -(\tfrac{1}{2}) - j(\tfrac{1}{2})$$
$$E_0 = -(\tfrac{1}{2}) + j(\tfrac{1}{2})$$

From these we get

$$I_5{}^2 = 1, \qquad |I_5|^2 = 1$$

$$I_4{}^2 = -j2, \qquad |I_4|^2 = 2$$

$$I_3{}^2 = -1, \qquad |I_3|^2 = 1 \qquad (102)$$

$$I_2{}^2 = 1, \qquad |I_2|^2 = 1$$

$$I_1{}^2 = -j2, \qquad |I_1|^2 = 2$$

and Eqs. 84 and 85 then give

$$T = \tfrac{3}{4} + \tfrac{1}{4} \sin 2t$$

$$V = \frac{3}{4} - \frac{\sqrt{5}}{4} \cos (2t - 63.5°) \qquad (103)$$

Since $P_{av} = 1/2$ watt, and the loss per cycle is 3.14 joules, it is clear that this situation, although somewhat better than the one in the first example above, is still not a low-loss case. Thus $T_{peak} = 1$ is only moderately equal to $V_{peak} = 1.31$. If we compute a Q at all, it is better to use Eq. 81, which gives

$$Q = \frac{2\omega_0 T_{av}}{P_{av}} = \frac{2 \times (\tfrac{3}{4})}{(\tfrac{1}{2})} = 3 \qquad (104)$$

For the input impedance we have, using Eq. 73,

$$Z = \frac{1 + j4 \times 0}{2} = \frac{1}{2} \qquad (105)$$

while from the values 101 we get

$$Z = \frac{E_0}{I_1} = \frac{\tfrac{1}{2}(-1 + j1)}{-1 + j1} = \frac{1}{2} \qquad (106)$$

These examples show that it is a straightforward matter to compute T_{av}, V_{av}, P_{av} from a given current distribution. Since the latter or its equivalent must in any event be determined in the course of an impedance computation, it turns out that it is no more tedious to find the impedance in terms of the energy functions than in the normal manner. The result in terms of energy functions contains more information. For example, if $T_{av} \neq V_{av}$ but $T_{av} - V_{av}$ is small compared with either T_{av} or V_{av}, then we can conclude that the frequency considered is near a pronounced resonance, especially if P_{av} is small compared with either T_{av} or V_{av}. Through making a single computation at a resonance frequency, we are able to perceive the entire character of the resonance curve, which is much more than the value of Z at resonance can tell us. To compute Q in the normal manner, we must compute many values of Z near resonance and plot a curve. In terms of energy considerations we get the same information from a single calculation made at the resonance frequency.

Another way of expressing these thoughts is to call attention to the fact that, when we calculate the impedance of the series RLC circuit through noting the values of the resistance R, the inductive reactance $L\omega$, the capacitive reactance $-1/C\omega$, and the net reactance $X = L\omega - (1/C\omega)$, their relative magnitudes not only enable us to see whether the frequency in question is at or near resonance but they also determine the character of the resonance curve. All this information is ours for the trouble of making a calculation at only one frequency. In more elaborate circuits such as those shown in Figs. 5 and 6, we are not in a position to get this much per unit of computing effort unless we avail ourselves of the technique of expressing impedance in terms of energy functions, for this scheme virtually reduces the impedance of any circuit to the basic form that it has for the series RLC circuit.

PROBLEMS

1. Given $e_s(t) = 100 \cos 377t$, $P_{av} = 200$ watts, $Q_{av} = -150$ vars (angle of Z is positive). (a) Find the power factor of Z. (b) Find the current $i(t)$.

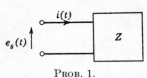

A capacitor is now added in parallel with Z which makes the over-all power factor equal to 0.9 lagging, $e_s(t)$ remaining the same. (c) Find P_{av} and Q_{av}. (d) Find the new $i(t)$.

PROB. 1.

2. (a) Calculate the smaller of two possible values of C which will give a voltage across the load of 100 volts magnitude.

(b) Draw the corresponding vector diagram to show (i) load voltage in reference phase, (ii) voltage drops in source resistance and line impedance, (iii) source voltage E_s.

(c) Calculate the power delivered by the voltage E_s when C is not present and when it has the value found in part (a). Calculate the percentage of the power lost in the source and in the line for both cases.

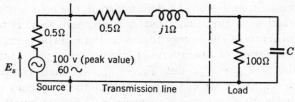

PROB. 2.

3. When a series RLC circuit is excited by a sinusoidal voltage source $e_{s1} = 100 \cos 1000t$, the current is found to be 5 amperes (peak) and the power factor is 0.8 lagging. When the circuit is excited by a sinusoidal voltage source $e_{s2} = 80 \cos 500t$, the average active power dissipated is 200 watts and the average reactive power is zero. Find R, L, and C.

4. A load impedance, consisting of a 10-ohm resistance and a 20-ohm inductive reactance in series, receives power from a 60-cycle-per-second sinusoidal voltage source. A voltmeter across the load reads 100 volts.

(a) What are the average active power and reactive power absorbed by the load?

(b) A condenser is to be connected in parallel with the load impedance to improve the power factor. What reactive power should be drawn by the condenser so that the over-all power factor will be unity?

(c) What is the required capacitance for this condition?

(d) Repeat (b) and (c) to obtain a lagging power factor (current lags voltage) of 0.9.

5. (a) What is the rms value of the periodic current wave sketched in the figure? (This should correspond to the reading of a dynamometer instrument.) (b) What is the average value of the current? (This should correspond to the reading of a D'Arsonval instrument.) (c) If the current is in a 10-ohm resistor, at what average rate is energy dissipated in the resistor?

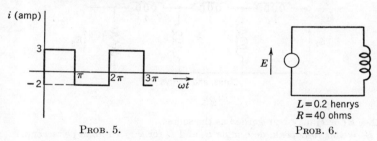

PROB. 5.

$L = 0.2$ henrys
$R = 40$ ohms

PROB. 6.

6. A 60-cycle source of sinusoidal alternating voltage E having an effective value of 110 volts supplies power to an inductance coil with constants as shown in the figure. What are the values of the following: (a) the maximum instantaneous current, (b) the maximum instantaneous rate of energy dissipation (i.e., energy transformed to heat), (c) the maximum instantaneous rate of energy storage in the magnetic field of the coil, (d) the instantaneous current when the rate of energy storage and the rate of energy dissipation are equal?

7. For the network shown in the accompanying sketch, assume 1 volt across the 1-ohm resistance, and compute the currents in the remaining branches as well as the input impedance for a frequency of 10 radians per second. Compute the quan-

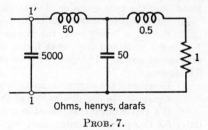

Ohms, henrys, darafs

PROB. 7.

tities T, V, T_{av}, V_{av}, P_{av} and thus establish that 10 radians per second is very nearly a resonance frequency. Compute Q by Eq. 81, and check the input impedance calculated above through use of Eq. 73.

8. The circuit shown represents an a-c system consisting of a 60-cycle-per-second generator whose internal impedance is taken as zero for this problem, a transmission

line having resistance $R = 2$ ohms and $L = 0.00172$ henry, and a load impedance whose magnitude is known to be 20 ohms at 60 cycles per second. The power output at the generator is $P_g = 7200$ watts, and the generated voltage is $E_g = 440$ volts (rms). The power consumed at the load is $P_{\text{load}} = 6400$ watts.

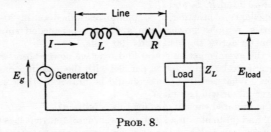

PROB. 8.

(a) Determine the simplest sequence for computing the following and obtain their values: Power factor at the load $= PF_L$, PF_g, $I_{(\text{rms})}$, $E_{\text{load(rms)}}$. (b) What are the resistive and reactive parts of the load impedance?

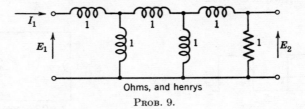

Ohms, and henrys

PROB. 9.

9. Either E_1 or I_1 may be regarded as the source.

(a) If $E_2 = 100$ volts peak, determine E_1 and I_1 for $\omega = 1$ radian per second.

(b) For the same value of ω, what do E_1 and I_1 become if all element values are multiplied by 10?

(c) For $\omega = 10$ radians per second, what are E_1 and I_1 if only the inductances are multiplied by 1/10th?

(d) For the condition under (a), find the average active and reactive power at the input, and the average value of the stored energy.

(e) What do the answers under (d) become if $|E_2|$ is changed to 10 volts?

10. For $E_s = 1$ volt peak, the average power entering the circuit at the terminals 1–1' is 0.1 watt and the power factor is unity. Each impedance absorbs an equal amount of power. The power factor of the impedance Z_2 at its terminals 2–2' is 0.5 lagging.

(a) Determine the current amplitude I.

(b) Compute the complex values of the impedances Z_1 and Z_2.

(c) If a capacitance C is placed in parallel with Z_2 so as to make the power factor unity for this parallel combination, what will be the average power delivered by E_s at the terminals 1–1', and what is the average power delivered at terminals 2–2'?

(d) What do the answers to part (c) become if E_s is changed to 100 volts peak?

11. In the sketch shown, E_1 and E_2 are ideal voltage sources and Z is a linear passive impedance. Given $E_1 = 100\underline{/30°}$, $E_2 = 100\underline{/-30°}$ (peak values), determine (a) the direction of average energy flow (i.e., from left to right or from right to left),

and (b) the power delivered by each voltage source assuming (i) $Z = 10$ ohms, (ii) $Z = j10$ ohms, (iii) $Z = -j10$ ohms.

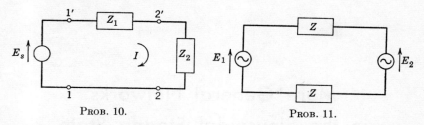

PROB. 10.   PROB. 11.

12. The circuit shown in the accompanying sketch takes 50 watts at 0.8 lagging power factor. If the radian frequency is unity, what are (a) the peak value of the applied voltage, (b) the value of C, (c) the reactive power? If the input is a current with a 10-ampere peak value, what is the vector power?

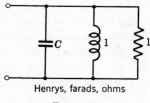

Henrys, farads, ohms

PROB. 12.

13. When the circuit shown is excited at terminals 1–1′ (with terminals 2–2′ open) by a current $I_1 = 10$ amperes rms, the active power taken is 50 watts at a 0.555 lagging power factor. When terminals 1–1′ are free and a current $I_2 = 20$ amperes rms is applied to the terminals 2–2′, the power is 300 watts at 0.316 lagging power factor. The radian frequency is $\omega = 10$.

(a) Determine R_1, L_1, R_2, L_2.

(b) With I_1 and I_2 impressed simultaneously, find (i) the total active and reactive power, (ii) expressions for the instantaneous stored energies T and V, (iii) the value of Q_{av} computed from Eq. 66 and check with the reactive power found in part (i).

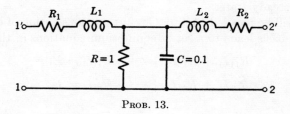

PROB. 13.

More General Networks in the Sinusoidal Steady State

1 The Steady-State Equilibrium Equations

We have seen that the impedance concept enables one to deal with sinusoidal steady-state problems in a manner that is identical in form with the methods used in the analysis of purely resistive circuits (which are less accurately but rather commonly referred to as *d-c circuits* * since for constant voltages and currents only the resistance parameter is relevant). Since Ohm's law, in terms of complex current, voltage, and impedance, applies to the determination of steady-state a-c circuit * behavior just as it does in terms of real quantities to the formulation of d-c circuit response, one may apply to such a-c circuit studies the same formal process of generalization that has (in Chapters 1, 2, and 3) already been seen to apply to the simpler d-c problem. More specifically, what has been said about network geometry, about loop and node methods of writing equilibrium equations, about their formal algebraic or numerical solution through use of determinants and other methods, about the reciprocity theorem which one recognizes by inspection from the determinantal form of solution—all these things are recognized at once as applying without alteration in form to the a-c case in the steady state.

Thus it will be recalled (Art. 6, Ch. 2) that the solution of d-c circuits on the loop basis leads to a set of equilibrium equations of the form

$$R_{11}I_1 + R_{12}I_2 + \cdots + R_{1l}I_l = E_1$$
$$R_{21}I_1 + R_{22}I_2 + \cdots + R_{2l}I_l = E_2$$
$$\cdot \; \cdot \; \cdot \; \cdot \; \cdot \; \cdot \; \cdot \; \cdot \; \cdot \; \cdot \; \cdot \; \cdot \; \cdot \; \cdot \; \cdot \tag{1}$$
$$R_{l1}I_1 + R_{l2}I_2 + \cdots + R_{ll}I_l = E_l$$

---

* The terms "d-c" and "a-c" are abbreviations for "direct current" and "alternating current," the first being a common designation for constant current or voltage, and the second for sinusoidally varying quantities.

in which R_{11}, R_{22}, $\cdots$, R_{ll} are respectively the total resistance found on the closed contours designated as loop 1, loop 2, $\cdots$, loop l; R_{12} or R_{23}, etc. are resistances in the branches common to loops 1 and 2 or 2 and 3, etc. (considered numerically positive or negative according to whether the respective loop reference arrows are confluent or contra-fluent in the common branch *); $I_1 \cdots I_l$ are the "Maxwell loop currents" in the chosen set of closed contours; and $E_1 \cdots E_l$ are net applied source voltages in these loops.

The only change that appears in the sinusoidal steady-state analysis of circuits is that the resistance parameters R_{sk} are replaced by complex impedance parameters ζ_{sk}, and the E's and I's are complex numbers. The physical significance of a particular ζ_{sk} is the same as that of the R_{sk} which it replaces. Thus ζ_{11}, ζ_{22}, etc. are the total impedances that one finds on the contours of loops 1, 2, etc., computed from the resistance, inductance, and capacitance elements on these contours just as one would if each contour were presented as a separate problem. Similarly, ζ_{12} or ζ_{23}, etc. are the impedances of branches common to the loops to which their subscripts refer, with the same rule regarding algebraic sign that applies to the R_{sk}'s in the d-c case.

Entirely analogous is the parallelism between the a-c and the d-c methods of analysis on the node basis. For the d-c case one has the equations

$$G_{11}E_1 + G_{12}E_2 + \cdots + G_{1n}E_n = I_1$$

$$G_{21}E_1 + G_{22}E_2 + \cdots + G_{2n}E_n = I_2$$

$$\cdot \quad \cdot \quad \cdot \quad \cdot \quad \cdot \quad \cdot \quad \cdot \quad \cdot \quad \cdot \quad \cdot \quad \cdot \quad \cdot \quad \cdot \quad \cdot$$ (2)

$$G_{n1}E_1 + G_{n2}E_2 + \cdots + G_{nn}E_n = I_n$$

in which G_{11}, G_{22}, $\cdots$, G_{nn} are respectively the total conductance converging toward nodes 1, 2, $\cdots$, n, while G_{12} or G_{23}, etc. are conductances in the branches joining nodes 1 and 2 or 2 and 3, etc. (all considered numerically negative since reference arrows for the nodes relative to a common datum are consistent in that they all point from the datum to the node); $E_1 \cdots E_n$ are the potentials (with respect to datum) or the voltages of the respectively numbered nodes; † and $I_1 \cdots I_n$ are current sources feeding these nodes and returning through the common datum.

---

* If the network is mappable on a plane, the meshes (as in a fish net) are chosen as loops, and reference arrows are consistently clockwise, then all signs are negative.

† One may alternatively introduce voltage variables that are potential differences between any independent set of node pairs as is shown for pure resistance networks in Ch. 2.

In making the transition to the a-c steady state, the only essential change is that the G_{sk} are replaced by a set of complex admittances η_{sk}, their physical significance remaining the same. Thus η_{11}, η_{22}, etc. are the total admittances of the various branches that converge toward nodes 1, 2, etc., computed from the conductance, capacitance, and inductance elements in these branches just as one would the resultant admittance of the parallel combination of these branches. Similarly η_{12} or η_{23}, etc. are the admittances of branches joining nodes 1 and 2 or 2 and 3, with the same rule regarding algebraic sign that applies to the G_{sk}'s in the d-c case.

It will also be recalled from the discussion of the analogous d-c problem that, if b denotes the total number of branches in the network and n_t the total number of nodes, then the number of independent node pairs (number of independent Kirchhoff current-law equations) is

$$n = n_t - 1 \tag{3}$$

and the number of independent loops or meshes (number of independent Kirchhoff voltage-law equations) is

$$l = b - n = b - n_t + 1 \tag{4}$$

The number of independent variables on the loop basis is l, and on the node basis n. Choice between the two methods of analysis in a given problem depends upon which of the two numbers l or n is less, and also upon other factors that can best be recognized through experience with both methods.

It is also significant to point out that a branch may be defined in various ways. While the basic definition of a branch is to consider it as a separate element $(R, L,$ or $C)$, it is possible to regard any aggregate (series, parallel, or series-parallel combination) of elements as a branch. Each individual problem will usually indicate a choice in this regard.

On the loop basis, then, we have the sinusoidal steady-state equilibrium equations:

$$\zeta_{11}I_1 + \zeta_{12}I_2 + \cdots + \zeta_{1l}I_l = E_1$$

$$\zeta_{21}I_1 + \zeta_{22}I_2 + \cdots + \zeta_{2l}I_l = E_2 \tag{5}$$

$$\cdot \ \cdot \ \cdot \ \cdot \ \cdot \ \cdot \ \cdot \ \cdot \ \cdot \ \cdot \ \cdot \ \cdot \ \cdot \ \cdot$$

$$\zeta_{l1}I_1 + \zeta_{l2}I_2 + \cdots + \zeta_{ll}I_l = E_l$$

If we denote the determinant of this set of equations by Z and its cofactors by Z_{sk}, then according to "Cramer's rule" (see Art. 2, Ch. 3) we get

$$I_k = \frac{1}{Z} (Z_{1k}E_1 + Z_{2k}E_2 + \cdots + Z_{lk}E_l) \tag{6}$$

As a further means of abbreviation we may introduce the admittances

$$y_{ks} = Z_{sk}/Z \tag{7}$$

and write the solution expressed by 6 as

$$I_k = y_{k1}E_1 + y_{k2}E_2 + \cdots + y_{kk}E_k + \cdots + y_{kl}E_l \tag{8}$$

Here the first term represents the current that would result in the kth loop if a voltage E_1 alone were applied in loop 1; the second term is that current that would result in the kth loop if E_2 alone were applied in loop 2, and so forth. The quantity y_{k1} is the *transfer admittance* from loop 1 to loop k; y_{k2} is the transfer admittance from loop 2 to loop k; etc. The quantity y_{kk}, which is the ratio of current in loop k to applied voltage in loop k (assuming no other voltages are applied), is regarded as the *driving-point* admittance of the kth loop. Equation 7 defines the complete set of driving-point and transfer admittances for the network with respect to the chosen set of loops or meshes.

Since the determinant of the Eqs. 5 is symmetrical about its principal diagonal (because of the way in which the elements ζ_{sk} are defined, namely, such that $\zeta_{sk} = \zeta_{ks}$), one finds according to determinant theory that $Z_{sk} = Z_{ks}$ and hence that $y_{sk} = y_{ks}$. Thus the ratio of current in loop s to voltage in loop k is the same as the ratio of current in loop k to voltage in loop s, a result that is known as the *reciprocity theorem*.* One way of expressing it verbally is to say that the ratio of response to excitation is invariant to an interchange in the points of excitation and observation.

Analogously on the node basis one has the system of n equilibrium equations

$$\eta_{11}E_1 + \eta_{12}E_2 + \cdots + \eta_{1n}E_n = I_1$$
$$\eta_{21}E_1 + \eta_{22}E_2 + \cdots + \eta_{2n}E_n = I_2$$
$$\cdots \cdots \cdots \cdots \cdots \cdots \cdots \cdots \tag{9}$$
$$\eta_{n1}E_1 + \eta_{n2}E_2 + \cdots + \eta_{nn}E_n = I_n$$

for which the determinant may be denoted by Y and its cofactors by Y_{sk}. Cramer's rule then yields the solution in the form

$$E_k = \frac{1}{Y} (Y_{1k}I_1 + Y_{2k}I_2 + \cdots + Y_{nk}I_n) \tag{10}$$

---

* Its discussion in Art. 6 of Ch. 3 with respect to resistance networks is directly applicable here through use of the impedance or admittance concept (specifically, through replacing the g_{sk} of Eqs. 76, Ch. 3, by the η_{sk}, Eq. 17, defined here).

which may be written

$$E_k = z_{k1}I_1 + z_{k2}I_2 + \cdots + z_{kk}I_k + \cdots + z_{kn}I_n \tag{11}$$

with

$$z_{ks} = Y_{sk}/Y \tag{12}$$

defined as a set of driving-point and transfer impedances, since the terms in Eq. 11 have the same physical interpretation as those in Eq. 8, with reference to current and voltage interchanged.

The symmetry among the coefficients of 9 expressed by $\eta_{sk} = \eta_{ks}$ again results in reciprocity since it yields $z_{sk} = z_{ks}$. That is, the ratio of voltage at node k to source current entering node s is the same as the ratio of voltage at node s to current fed into node k. Or the ratio of response to excitation is invariant to an interchange of the points of excitation and observation.

It should be emphasized in connection with the reciprocity theorem that it applies only to an impedance or to an admittance—not to a dimensionless transfer ratio. Thus of the two quantities—excitation and response—one must be a current and the other a voltage. On the loop basis the excitation is a voltage and the response a current; on the node basis the reverse is true. On the loop basis the source is impedanceless, and its insertion into any branch of the network has no effect "impedancewise." Hence, if we consider the current in loop s due to a voltage in loop k, or alternatively think of the voltage source switched to loop s while we observe the current in loop k, it is clear that the network impedance coefficients ζ_{sk} remain unchanged. If we considered the source in this connection to be a current, then its insertion into a given loop would open-circuit that loop because of the open-circuit character of the current source. Switching a current source from one loop to another does change the physical character of the network, and we have no reason to suppose that the current response in the alternative loop is independent of the source location.

Similarly on the node basis, where sources are currents and, therefore, are open circuits, the shifting of a source from one node pair to another leaves the network unchanged "impedancewise," and the ratio of response (which is a voltage between nodes) to excitation is unaffected by an interchange of the two node pairs in question. If the excitation in this case were considered to be a voltage, or if the response were regarded as a current, one would again find that an interchange in the points of observation and excitation (which implies the removal of a source from one part of the network and its insertion somewhere else) would imply a change in certain of the characterizing admittances η_{sk}, and there would be no assurance that the ratio of response to excitation is left unchanged.

Reciprocity applies to the y_{sk} of Eq. 7 or to the z_{sk} of Eq. 12. It may still apply to the ratio of two voltages or to two currents in some very special arrangements, but generally speaking the reciprocity theorem applies to a transfer impedance or to a transfer admittance, not to a dimensionless transfer function.

2 Use of Parameter Matrices

The coefficients ζ_{sk} in Eqs. 5 have the detailed structure indicated in

$$\zeta_{sk} = R_{sk} + L_{sk}s + S_{sk}/s \qquad (13)$$

in which R_{sk}, L_{sk}, and S_{sk} are the so-called resistance, inductance, and elastance parameters on the loop basis. In writing these parameters down for a specific network it is expedient to assemble their values in

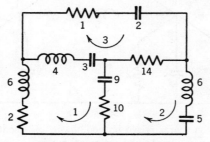

FIG. 1.   Network to be characterized on loop basis.   Element values are in ohms, henrys, and darafs.

matrix form since the row and column positions may then be used for their individual identification, with an obvious conservation of space and writing effort, as the example in Fig. 1 will serve to illustrate. Here we have:

$$\text{Loop resistance matrix} = [R] = \begin{bmatrix} 12 & -10 & 0 \\ -10 & 24 & -14 \\ 0 & -14 & 15 \end{bmatrix} \qquad (14)$$

$$\text{Loop inductance matrix} = [L] = \begin{bmatrix} 10 & 0 & -4 \\ 0 & 6 & 0 \\ -4 & 0 & 4 \end{bmatrix} \qquad (15)$$

$$\text{Loop elastance matrix} = [S] = \begin{bmatrix} 12 & -9 & -3 \\ -9 & 14 & 0 \\ -3 & 0 & 5 \end{bmatrix} \qquad (16)$$

The row-and-column position of a matrix element identifies the parameter it represents. Thus in $[R]$ the element in the second row and third column is $R_{23} = -14$, etc. The process of writing down these matrices by inspection of the network with its chosen loops, reference arrows, and element values is clearly indicated.

Analogously on the node basis the structure of the coefficients η_{sk} in Eqs. 9 is given by

$$\eta_{sk} = G_{sk} + C_{sk}s + \Gamma_{sk}/s \qquad (17)$$

in which G_{sk}, C_{sk}, and Γ_{sk} are respectively the conductance, capacitance, and reciprocal inductance parameters on the node basis. In a specific

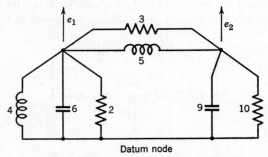

FIG. 2. Network to be characterized on node basis. Element values are in mhos, farads, and reciprocal henrys.

case, these too are written down in matrix form by inspection of the network, as the one in Fig. 2 will illustrate. Here we find:

$$\text{Node conductance matrix} = [G] = \begin{bmatrix} 5 & -3 \\ -3 & 13 \end{bmatrix} \qquad (18)$$

$$\text{Node capacitance matrix} = [C] = \begin{bmatrix} 6 & 0 \\ 0 & 9 \end{bmatrix} \qquad (19)$$

$$\text{Node (inductance)}^{-1} \text{ matrix} = [\Gamma] = \begin{bmatrix} 9 & -5 \\ -5 & 5 \end{bmatrix} \qquad (20)$$

Multiplication of a matrix by a factor is equivalent to multiplying each of its elements by that factor, and addition of matrices is carried out through adding elements having corresponding row-column positions. Hence

$$[Z] = [L]s + [R] + [S]s^{-1} \qquad (21)$$

is a matrix with the elements (Eq. 13)

$$\zeta_{sk} = L_{sk}s + R_{sk} + S_{sk}s^{-1} \tag{22}$$

From its determinant Z and cofactors Z_{sk} the driving-point and transfer admittances y_{sk} are computed according to Eq. 7.

Similarly

$$[Y] = [C]s + [G] + [\Gamma]s^{-1} \tag{23}$$

is a matrix with the elements (Eq. 17)

$$\eta_{sk} = C_{sk}s + G_{sk} + \Gamma_{sk}s^{-1} \tag{24}$$

From its determinant Y and cofactors Y_{sk} the driving-point and transfer impedances z_{sk} are computed according to Eq. 12.

3 Duality Again

For easily recognizable reasons, the loop and node bases are regarded as dual procedures. In terms of the preceding compact formulation of network impedances and admittances one may state in rather general terms the conditions under which two networks A and B are regarded as duals of each other. Namely, they are so regarded if the set of impedances z_{sk} of one is identical with the set of admittances y_{sk} of the other. This situation will come about if the loop impedance matrix $[Z]$, Eq. 21, of one is identical with the node admittance matrix $[Y]$, Eq. 23, of the other, which in turn requires that the parameter matrices $[C]$, $[G]$, $[\Gamma]$ of one network be identical respectively with $[L]$, $[R]$, $[S]$ of the other. A necessary condition for the latter situation is obviously that the number of independent nodes n for one network be equal to the number of independent loops l of the other.

The further details are best illustrated through an example. Suppose, therefore, that one wishes to find that network which is dual to the one shown in Fig. 2. Since this one has the node-parameter matrices 18, 19, 20, its dual must have the loop-parameter matrices

$$[R] = \begin{bmatrix} 5 & -3 \\ -3 & 13 \end{bmatrix} \tag{25}$$

$$[L] = \begin{bmatrix} 6 & 0 \\ 0 & 9 \end{bmatrix} \tag{26}$$

$$[S] = \begin{bmatrix} 9 & -5 \\ -5 & 5 \end{bmatrix} \tag{27}$$

These are readily recognized as being the loop-parameter matrices of the network shown in Fig. 3.

It follows that the driving-point and transfer impedances z_{11}, z_{22}, z_{12} of the network of Fig. 2 are equal respectively to the driving-point and transfer admittances y_{11}, y_{22}, y_{12} of the network of Fig. 3. For example, the impedance between node 1 and datum in Fig. 2 (z_{11}) equals the admittance at a terminal pair obtained through cutting a branch of the network of Fig. 3 at the point P (this is the admittance y_{11}). Similarly, the impedance between node 2 and datum in the network of Fig. 2 (z_{22})

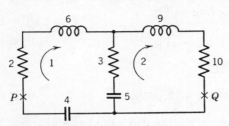

Fig. 3. Network dual to that in Fig. 2. Element values are in ohms, henrys, and darafs.

equals the admittance (y_{22}) found for the network of Fig. 3 through cutting it at the point Q. The ratio of complex current in loop 2 to voltage inserted at P (Fig. 3), which is y_{12}, is equal to the ratio of complex voltage at node 2 to current fed into node 1 (this is z_{12}) for the network of Fig. 2.

4 Mutual Inductance and How to Deal with It

Figure 4 shows a number of inductances in random orientation whose magnetic fields are supposed somehow to be linked so that a time-varying current in any one inductance induces voltage not only in that inductance itself but in all the others as well. The amount and direction of the induced voltage relative to the value of the time-varying current is in each inductance uniquely characterized by an appropriate inductance coefficient; and wherever the induced voltage appears in an inductance other than the one carrying the inducing current, the coefficient is spoken of as a *mutual* inductance.

To be more specific, suppose that the inducing current is carried by inductance number 1. Let us call this current i_1 and assume that at some moment (instant of time) its rate of change di_1/dt is $+1$. By

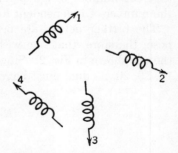

Fig. 4. Random set of mutually coupled inductances.

this we mean that the current i_1 in the inductance 1 is *increasing* in the indicated arrow direction at the rate of 1 ampere per second (it could physically be produced through the application of an appropriate voltage source which need not interest us at the moment and is not shown in Fig. 4). This time-varying current induces, first of all, a voltage in the inductance 1 itself which clearly must be a voltage drop in the direction of the current i_1 since this induced voltage according to Lenz's law tends to oppose the current increase that is producing it. Thus we have in the inductance 1 an increasing current in the reference arrow direction and an induced voltage drop which is also in the reference-arrow direction. If we denote this voltage drop by v_1 we have

$$v_1 = l_{11} \, (di_1/dt) = l_{11} \tag{28}$$

The numerical coefficient l_{11}, which is positive, is called the self-inductance (or simply the inductance) of coil number 1.

Because the magnetic field set up by the current i_1 links the other inductances also, this time-varying current induces voltages there. These voltages may have directions that are *a priori* in no way related to the reference arrows placed upon the inductances in which they appear. For example, the voltage induced in coil 2 by the $di_1/dt = +1$ in coil 1 may be such as to make either the tip end or the tail end of coil 2 momentarily positive with respect to the opposite end. Experimentally one can readily determine which end is the positive one. If it is the tail end, then the induced voltage is such as to be a voltage drop in the arrow direction. In this case, the mutual-inductance coefficient between coils 1 and 2 is said to be *positive* because the voltage induced in coil 2 is the same in direction as it would be if it were induced by a positive di_2/dt. Note well that this same mutual-inductance coefficient would be considered numerically negative if we changed the reference arrow on coil 2, which we can certainly do if we wish since reference arrows are chosen at will. However, once the reference arrows on coils 1 and 2 are fixed, the algebraic sign of the mutual inductance between them becomes fixed. It is positive if a positive di/dt in one coil induces a positive voltage drop in the other (according to the arrows which determine reference directions both for currents and voltage drops); otherwise the mutual is negative.

The same rule regarding the algebraic sign of a mutual inductance holds between all coils taken in pairs. Thus, with coils 2, 3, and 4 open-circuited and a nonzero di_1/dt produced in coil 1, we have in addition to the self-induced voltage given by 28

$$v_2 = l_{21} \frac{di_1}{dt}, \qquad v_3 = l_{31} \frac{di_1}{dt}, \qquad v_4 = l_{41} \frac{di_1}{dt} \tag{29}$$

all of which are regarded as voltage drops according to the reference arrows on their respective coils. The mutual-inductance coefficients l_{21}, l_{31}, l_{41}, for $di_1/dt = +1$, are numerically equal to and have the same algebraic signs as do the voltage drops v_2, v_3, v_4 respectively.

It is important to observe that, although we may be dealing with a group of many coils, the determination of any one mutual-inductance coefficient such as l_{31}, say, involves only the two coils 1 and 3 and is the same whether the other coils are present or not (except as the removal of the other coils may physically alter the medium in which the magnetic field associated with coils 1 and 3 resides). That is to say, if one were to determine the coefficients l_{21}, l_{31}, l_{41}, etc., experimentally, each determination is concerned with one pair of coils only and can wholly ignore the presence of the others (except to see to it that they remain open-circuited during the experiment so that there will be no other nonzero (di/dt)'s except the one specifically intended to be nonzero). For this reason the determination of the mutual-inductance coefficients for a large group of coils is every bit as simple and straightforward as it is for just two coils, because one considers only two coils at a time and the others are meanwhile ignored.

For a chosen set of reference arrows on the coils, as shown in Fig. 4, the set of self- and mutual-inductance coefficients is completely fixed as to both sign and magnitude. Specifically, if i_1, i_2, i_3, i_4 are the coil currents and v_1, v_2, v_3, v_4 are the voltage drops, both with regard to the same set of reference arrows, then we can relate these currents and voltages through the equations

$$v_1 = l_{11}\frac{di_1}{dt} + l_{12}\frac{di_2}{dt} + l_{13}\frac{di_3}{dt} + l_{14}\frac{di_4}{dt}$$

$$v_2 = l_{21}\frac{di_1}{dt} + l_{22}\frac{di_2}{dt} + l_{23}\frac{di_3}{dt} + l_{24}\frac{di_4}{dt}$$

$$v_3 = l_{31}\frac{di_1}{dt} + l_{32}\frac{di_2}{dt} + l_{33}\frac{di_3}{dt} + l_{34}\frac{di_4}{dt}$$

$$v_4 = l_{41}\frac{di_1}{dt} + l_{42}\frac{di_2}{dt} + l_{43}\frac{di_3}{dt} + l_{44}\frac{di_4}{dt}$$

(30)

Here l_{11}, l_{22}, l_{33}, l_{44} are respectively the self-inductances of coils 1, 2, 3, 4, while the remaining $l_{sk} = l_{ks}$ are the mutual inductances between pairs of coils to which the subscripts refer.

Equations 30 may formally be integrated with respect to time, yielding

$$\int v_1 \, dt = l_{11}i_1 + l_{12}i_2 + l_{13}i_3 + l_{14}i_4$$

$$\int v_2 \, dt = l_{21}i_1 + l_{22}i_2 + l_{23}i_3 + l_{24}i_4$$

$$\int v_3 \, dt = l_{31}i_1 + l_{32}i_2 + l_{33}i_3 + l_{34}i_4 \qquad (31)$$

$$\int v_4 \, dt = l_{41}i_1 + l_{42}i_2 + l_{43}i_3 + l_{44}i_4$$

The quantities involved here are flux linkages (since their time derivatives are voltages). These equations may be solved for the coil currents in terms of the flux linkages by any algebraic process applying to the solution of simultaneous linear equations (such as the determinant method), yielding

$$i_1 = \gamma_{11}\psi_1 + \gamma_{12}\psi_2 + \gamma_{13}\psi_3 + \gamma_{14}\psi_4$$

$$i_2 = \gamma_{21}\psi_1 + \gamma_{22}\psi_2 + \gamma_{23}\psi_3 + \gamma_{24}\psi_4$$

$$i_3 = \gamma_{31}\psi_1 + \gamma_{32}\psi_2 + \gamma_{33}\psi_3 + \gamma_{34}\psi_4 \qquad (32)$$

$$i_4 = \gamma_{41}\psi_1 + \gamma_{42}\psi_2 + \gamma_{43}\psi_3 + \gamma_{44}\psi_4$$

in which the flux linkages are denoted by

$$\psi_k = \int v_k \, dt \qquad (33)$$

and the γ_{sk} denote the numerical coefficients found in the process of solving Eqs. 31 for the i_k's. For example, if the determinant of the coefficients in 31 is denoted by

$$\Delta = \begin{vmatrix} l_{11} & \cdots & l_{14} \\ \cdot & \cdots & \cdot \\ l_{41} & \cdots & l_{44} \end{vmatrix} \qquad (34)$$

and its cofactors by Δ_{sk}, then by Cramer's rule

$$\gamma_{sk} = \Delta_{ks}/\Delta \qquad (35)$$

Whether the student completely understands the details of solving simultaneous equations is at the moment of little importance. The point in writing these things down here is rather to be able to call attention to the fact that one can (through well-defined algebraic methods) express the currents in the set of mutually coupled coils (Fig. 4) in terms of their voltage drops (specifically in terms of the voltage integrals) as straightforwardly as one can express the voltage drops in these coils in terms of their currents (specifically in terms of the current derivatives). The latter is done in Eqs. 30, the former in Eqs. 32. In Eqs. 30 the coefficients are the self- and mutual inductances for the given group of coils; in Eqs. 32 the coefficients are the self- and mutual reciprocal inductances for the same group of coils. The latter coefficients are related to the former in a manner expressed by Eqs. 34 and

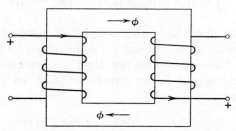

Fig. 5.   Relevant to the determination of the algebraic sign of a mutual inductance.

35, namely, as are the coefficients in inverse sets of simultaneous linear equations. Thus, while the reciprocal inductance coefficients γ_{sk} are *not* simply the respective reciprocals of the inductance coefficients l_{sk}, they are nevertheless related in a one-to-one rational algebraic manner, which, once understood, is simple and straightforward in its application (although tedious if the number of coefficients is large).

Before continuing with the discussion of how the present relations are used in the process of setting up equilibrium equations when a group of mutually coupled coils such as those in Fig. 4 is imbedded in a given network, a number of additional remarks may be in order with regard to the determination of algebraic signs for mutual inductances in situations where the relative directions of coil windings and mutual magnetic fields are indicated schematically. A situation of this sort is shown in Fig. 5. Here the preferred path taken by the magnetic field is indicated as a closed rectangular core structure (which may be the iron core of a transformer), and the windings of the coils are drawn in such a manner that one recognizes the directions in which they encircle the core.

If a battery is applied to the left-hand winding so as to make the indicated terminal positive, current in this winding increases in the arrow direction, and, according to the right-hand screw rule, the flux ϕ

in the core increases in the direction shown by its arrow. By the rule for induced voltages (which is a left-hand screw rule because of Lenz's law), we see that the increasing core flux ϕ induces a voltage in the right-hand winding so as to make the bottom terminal plus with respect to the top. If we place a reference arrow on the right-hand winding as indicated, we note that the induced voltage there is a voltage rise or a negative drop. Hence, for the reference arrows shown, the mutual inductance is seen to be numerically negative; it becomes positive, however, if the reference arrow on either winding (not both) is reversed.

We may say in this example that the plus-marked ends of the two windings are *corresponding ends* in the sense that they will always become plus together or minus together when a voltage is induced in one winding by a changing current in the other, regardless of which winding is doing the inducing. Since the marked ends may become negative as well as positive, the plus sign might be regarded as inappropriate. For this reason many writers (and apparatus manufacturers) prefer to mark corresponding winding ends simply with dots instead of plus signs, and this is a widely accepted practice.

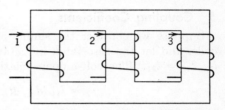

FIG. 6. Relevant to the sign determination of a set of three mutual inductances.

Note, however, that this scheme of relative polarity marking cannot always be used without modification when more than two windings are associated with the same magnetic structure, as the following discussion of the example in Fig. 6 will show. If we assume the top terminal in winding 1 to be positive with respect to the bottom one, current enters this coil and increases in the arrow direction, thus producing a flux that increases upward in the core of winding 1 and downward in the cores of windings 2 and 3. From their winding directions relative to their cores, one deduces that it is the bottom ends of coils 2 and 3 that become positive. Hence we would place a dot at the top of coil 1, and corresponding dots at the bottoms of coils 2 and 3. If we now move the source from coil 1 to coil 2 and make the bottom terminal (the dot-marked one) positive, we see that flux increases downward in the core of coil 2 and hence upward in the cores of coils 1 and 3. Thus the top terminals of both of these coils become positive. For coil 1 this terminal is the dot-marked one, but for coil 3 it isn't. Therefore, it becomes clear that dot-marked terminals can in general indicate relative polarities correctly only for a specific pair of coils. One would have to use a different set of dots for the pair of coils 2 and 3 from those that are already placed upon these coils in pairing them separately with coil 1.

While the method of marking relative polarities of mutually coupled coils by means of dots is thus seen to become prohibitively confusing where many coupled coils are involved, the determination of a set of self- and mutual-inductance coefficients consistent with assumed reference arrows remains simple and unambiguous, as already explained. In the example of Fig. 6 we clearly find all three mutual-inductance coefficients l_{12}, l_{13}, l_{23} numerically negative. Once these are known, the volt-ampere relations for the group of coils is unambiguously written down as is done in Eqs. 30 or 32.

5 Coupling Coefficients

Suppose we consider the simple case of just two mutually coupled coils, and let the associated inductance coefficients be denoted by l_{11}, l_{22}, $l_{12} = l_{21}$. The volt-ampere relations read

$$v_1 = l_{11}\,(di_1/dt) + l_{12}\,(di_2/dt)$$
$$v_2 = l_{21}\,(di_1/dt) + l_{22}\,(di_2/dt) \tag{36}$$

If we multiply these equations respectively by i_1 and i_2 and add, we have

$$v_1 i_1 + v_2 i_2 = l_{11} i_1 \frac{di_1}{dt} + l_{12} i_1 \frac{di_2}{dt} + l_{21} i_2 \frac{di_1}{dt} + l_{22} i_2 \frac{di_2}{dt} \tag{37}$$

which we may alternatively write as

$$v_1 i_1 + v_2 i_2 = dT/dt \tag{38}$$

with

$$2T = l_{11} i_1{}^2 + l_{12} i_1 i_2 + l_{21} i_2 i_1 + l_{22} i_2{}^2$$

or

$$T = \tfrac{1}{2}(l_{11} i_1{}^2 + 2l_{12} i_1 i_2 + l_{22} i_2{}^2) \tag{39}$$

Equation 38 states a simply understandable physical fact, namely, that the instantaneous power absorbed by the pair of coils $(v_1 i_1 + v_2 i_2)$ is equal to the time rate of change of the energy T stored in the associated magnetic fields, the latter being given by expression 39. Algebraically this expression is homogeneous and quadratic in the current variables i_1 and i_2 (known as a *quadratic form*). Physically it is clear that T must be positive no matter what values (positive or negative) the currents i_1 and i_2 may have. Mathematicians have found that this requirement on T imposes conditions on the coefficients l_{sk}. Specifically one can show that, if 39 is to be a positive definite quadratic form, it is necessary and sufficient that $l_{11} > 0$, $l_{22} > 0$, and in addition

$$l_{11}l_{22} - l_{12}^2 > 0 \tag{40}$$

which can be written

$$l_{12}^2/l_{11}l_{22} < 1 \tag{41}$$

Since the quantity

$$k = |l_{12}|/\sqrt{l_{11}l_{22}} \tag{42}$$

is defined as the *coupling coefficient* for the pair of coils in question, the requirement that the associated stored energy be positive for all values of the coil currents leads to the condition

$$|k| < 1 \tag{43}$$

The limiting condition expressed by $|k| = 1$, which is approachable but never attainable in a pair of physical coils, is spoken of as a condition of *perfect* coupling or *close coupling*. Physically it represents a situation in which all the flux links all of the windings of both coils. If the coupling coefficient k (Eq. 42) is derived from the standpoint of flux linkages, condition 43 is arrived at on the basis that the state of perfect coupling is manifestly an upper limit. A difficulty with this method of deriving condition 43 is that it does not lend itself to generalization while the method based upon stored energy is readily extended to any number of coupled coils.

A logical extension of the reasoning leading from Eq. 36 to Eq. 39 shows that the stored energy is in general expressible as *

$$
\begin{aligned}
2T = l_{11}i_1{}^2 &+ l_{12}i_1i_2 + \cdots + l_{1n}i_1i_n \\
+ l_{21}i_2i_1 &+ l_{22}i_2{}^2 + \cdots + l_{2n}i_2i_n \\
&\cdot \cdot \cdot \cdot \cdot \cdot \cdot \cdot \cdot \cdot \cdot \cdot \cdot \\
+ l_{n1}i_ni_1 &+ l_{n2}i_ni_2 + \cdots + l_{nn}i_n{}^2
\end{aligned}
\tag{44}
$$

Since the self-inductances l_{11}, l_{22}, etc. are positive in any case, the conditions assuring T positive are expressed by stating that the determinant

$$
\begin{vmatrix}
l_{11} & l_{12} & \cdots & l_{1n} \\
l_{21} & l_{22} & \cdots & l_{2n} \\
\cdot & \cdot & \cdots & \cdot \\
l_{n1} & l_{n2} & \cdots & l_{nn}
\end{vmatrix}
\tag{45}
$$

* See Art. 6, Ch. 10.

and all minors formed through cancelation of the first row and column, the first two rows and columns, the first three rows and columns, etc. (called the principal minors) are positive. Although it is not the purpose of the present discussion to go deeply into matters of this sort, it is nevertheless useful to point out (wherever this can easily be done) what methods are available for extending our considerations to more elaborate situations.

6   Forming the Equilibrium Equations When Mutual Inductances Are Present

The procedure is most easily presented in terms of a specific example. For this purpose consider the network of Fig. 7, for which the equi-

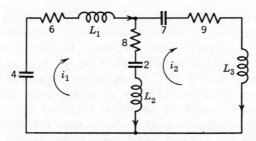

FIG. 7.   A circuit for which the equilibrium equations are to be found on the loop basis.   Numerical element values are in ohms and darafs.   The coupled coils are characterized by the self- and mutual-inductance values in matrix 46.

librium is to be formulated on the loop basis. So far as the resistance and elastance parameter matrices are concerned, there is no new problem presented here. Hence we need concern ourselves only with the formation of the inductance parameter matrix.

In this regard we are given the three mutually coupled coils L_1, L_2, L_3, which, for the reference arrows indicated, shall be characterized by the self- and mutual-inductance matrix.

$$[l_{sk}] = \begin{bmatrix} 2 & -1 & 2 \\ -1 & 3 & -2 \\ 2 & -2 & 5 \end{bmatrix} \tag{46}$$

That is to say, the self-inductance of L_1 is 2 henrys, the mutual between it and L_2 is -1 henry, and so forth. If the voltage drops in these coils are denoted by v_1, v_2, v_3, then, since the corresponding currents are respectively i_1, $(i_1 - i_2)$, and i_2, we have

$$v_1 = 2\frac{di_1}{dt} - 1\frac{d}{dt}(i_1 - i_2) + 2\frac{di_2}{dt} = \frac{di_1}{dt} + 3\frac{di_2}{dt}$$

$$v_2 = -1\frac{di_1}{dt} + 3\frac{d}{dt}(i_1 - i_2) - 2\frac{di_2}{dt} = 2\frac{di_1}{dt} - 5\frac{di_2}{dt} \qquad (47)$$

$$v_3 = 2\frac{di_1}{dt} - 2\frac{d}{dt}(i_1 - i_2) + 5\frac{di_2}{dt} = 0\frac{di_1}{dt} + 7\frac{di_2}{dt}$$

The total inductive voltage drop around loop 1 is $v_1 + v_2$, and that around loop 2 is $-v_2 + v_3$. From Eq. 47 this gives

$$v_1 + v_2 = 3\frac{di_1}{dt} - 2\frac{di_2}{dt}, \qquad -v_2 + v_3 = -2\frac{di_1}{dt} + 12\frac{di_2}{dt} \quad (48)$$

whence the loop inductance matrix is seen to be

$$[L] = \begin{bmatrix} 3 & -2 \\ -2 & 12 \end{bmatrix} \qquad (49)$$

The fact that L_{12} must be equal to L_{21} serves as a partial check on the numerical work.

Now let us consider a simple example on the node basis. Let the network be that shown in Fig. 8. Here only the method of finding the

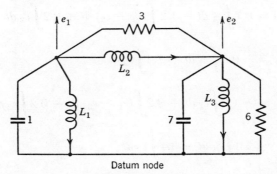

FIG. 8. A circuit for which the equilibrium equations are to be found on the node basis. Numerical element values are in mhos and farads. The coupled coils are characterized by the self- and mutual-inductance values in matrix 50.

reciprocal inductance matrix for the node basis need be discussed since the rest of the problem presents no new features. The three coils L_1, L_2, L_3 are again supposed to be mutually coupled, the matrix giving the pertinent self- and mutual inductances being

$$[l_{sk}] = \begin{bmatrix} 6 & 2 & -4 \\ 2 & 1 & -1 \\ -4 & -1 & 8 \end{bmatrix} \tag{50}$$

in which the algebraic signs of mutual inductances are fixed relative to the reference arrows on the coils.

The first step here is to find the matrix with the reciprocal inductance coefficients γ_{sk} as given by Eq. 35. Denoting the determinant of Eq. 50 by Δ and its cofactors by Δ_{sk}, we find $\Delta = 10$, and

$$\Delta_{11} = 7, \qquad \Delta_{12} = -12, \qquad \Delta_{13} = 2$$
$$\Delta_{22} = 32, \qquad \Delta_{23} = -2, \qquad \Delta_{33} = 2 \tag{51}$$

Hence

$$[\gamma_{sk}] = \begin{bmatrix} 0.7 & -1.2 & 0.2 \\ -1.2 & 3.2 & -0.2 \\ 0.2 & -0.2 & 0.2 \end{bmatrix} \tag{52}$$

If the currents in the coils are denoted by i_{l1}, i_{l2}, i_{l3}, then, since the corresponding flux linkages are respectively the time integrals of e_1, $(e_1 - e_2)$, and e_2, we have according to Eqs. 32

$$i_{l1} = 0.7 \int e_1 \, dt - 1.2 \int (e_1 - e_2) \, dt + 0.2 \int e_2 \, dt$$

$$= -0.5 \int e_1 \, dt + 1.4 \int e_2 \, dt$$

$$i_{l2} = -1.2 \int e_1 \, dt + 3.2 \int (e_1 - e_2) \, dt - 0.2 \int e_2 \, dt$$

$$= 2.0 \int e_1 \, dt - 3.4 \int e_2 \, dt \tag{53}$$

$$i_{l3} = 0.2 \int e_1 \, dt - 0.2 \int (e_1 - e_2) \, dt + 0.2 \int e_2 \, dt$$

$$= 0.0 \int e_1 \, dt + 0.4 \int e_2 \, dt$$

The total inductive current diverging from node 1 is $i_{l1} + i_{l2}$, and that diverging from node 2 is $-i_{l2} + i_{l3}$. From 53 this gives

$$i_{l1} + i_{l2} = 1.5 \int e_1 \, dt - 2.0 \int e_2 \, dt$$
$$-i_{l2} + i_{l3} = -2.0 \int e_1 \, dt + 3.8 \int e_2 \, dt$$

(54)

whence the reciprocal inductance matrix on the node basis is seen to be

$$[\Gamma] = \begin{bmatrix} 1.5 & -2.0 \\ -2.0 & 3.8 \end{bmatrix}$$

(55)

The fact that Γ_{12} must equal Γ_{21} serves as a partial check.

7 Computation of Driving-Point and Transfer Impedances for Ladder Networks

As pointed out in connection with pure resistance networks in Art. 3 of Ch. 3, a structural form of network that occurs frequently in practice is the so-called *unbalanced ladder network* shown in Fig. 9. The boxes labeled y_1, z_2, $\cdots$ are any two-terminal lumped networks, the

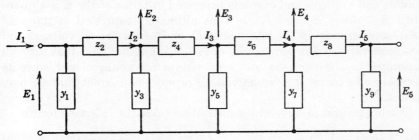

FIG. 9. An unbalanced ladder network to which the relations 56–72 are relevant.

y's representing their pertinent admittances and the z's their impedances. The boxes labeled with z's are referred to as the series branches of the ladder, and those labeled with y's as the shunt branches.

In a practical problem one is interested in the distribution of current and voltage throughout the various branches of this network in the sinusoidal steady state. Although the general method of analysis discussed in the preceding article is, of course, applicable in a straightforward manner, one finds that a more direct procedure (following the pattern used with resistive ladder networks) can here be used with considerable economy in computational effort, as already illustrated by the examples in Art. 8 of the previous chapter and further emphasized in the following paragraphs.

Let the quantities I_1, I_2, $\cdots$, E_1, E_2, $\cdots$, as indicated in the figure, be the complex amplitudes of voltage and current as usually defined. Then the following sequence of relations is evident:

$$I_5 = y_9E_5 \tag{56}$$

$$E_4 = z_8I_5 + E_5 \tag{57}$$

$$I_4 = y_7E_4 + I_5 \tag{58}$$

$$E_3 = z_6I_4 + E_4 \tag{59}$$

$$I_3 = y_5E_3 + I_4 \tag{60}$$

$$E_2 = z_4I_3 + E_3 \tag{61}$$

$$I_2 = y_3E_2 + I_3 \tag{62}$$

$$E_1 = z_2I_2 + E_2 \tag{63}$$

$$I_1 = y_1E_1 + I_2 \tag{64}$$

Through substituting 56 into 57, then the resulting relation together with 56 into 58, and continuing in an obvious manner, one successively obtains all voltages and currents expressed in terms of the single quantity E_5. Since E_1 and I_1 are thus ultimately expressed in terms of E_5—or alternatively, E_5 in terms of E_1 or I_1—one has all voltages and currents expressed in terms of E_1 or I_1. It is likewise clear that through appropriate substitutions one may obtain all voltages and currents expressed in terms of any one voltage or any one current that we may select.

Such a process of successive substitution takes the following form:

$$E_4 = (z_8y_9 + 1)E_5 \tag{65}$$

$$I_4 = (y_7z_8y_9 + y_7 + y_9)E_5 \tag{66}$$

$$E_3 = (z_6y_7z_8y_9 + z_6y_7 + z_6y_9 + z_8y_9 + 1)E_5 = AE_5 \tag{67}$$

$$I_3 = (y_5z_6y_7z_8y_9 + y_5z_6y_7 + y_5z_6y_9 + y_5z_8y_9 + y_7z_8y_9$$
$$+ y_5 + y_7 + y_9)E_5 = BE_5 \tag{68}$$

$$E_2 = (A + z_4B)E_5 \tag{69}$$

$$I_2 = [y_3A + (y_3z_4 + 1)B]E_5 \tag{70}$$

$$E_1 = [(z_2y_3 + 1)A + (z_2y_3z_4 + z_2 + z_4)B]E_5 \tag{71}$$

$$I_1 = [(y_1z_2y_3 + y_1 + y_3)A + (y_1z_2y_3z_4 + y_1z_2 + y_1z_4 + y_3z_4 + 1)B]E_5$$
$$\tag{72}$$

From these expressions any transfer ratio, such as E_5/E_1 or E_5/I_1, as well as the input impedance E_1/I_1, may readily be computed in terms of the component y's and z's.   Incidentally, it is worth noting that, if the z's are inductances and the y's capacitances, then all of the bracketed expressions become simple polynomials in the complex frequency vari-

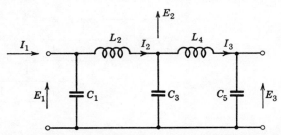

FIG. 10.   A lossless unbalanced ladder having the transfer relation given by Eq. 77.

able s.   As an example, consider the network of Fig. 10.   Here we have

$$I_3 = E_3 C_5 s \tag{73}$$

$$E_2 = (L_4 C_5 s^2 + 1)E_3 \tag{74}$$

$$I_2 = [L_4 C_5 C_3 s^3 + (C_3 + C_5)s]E_3 \tag{75}$$

$$E_1 = [L_2 L_4 C_5 C_3 s^4 + (L_2 C_3 + L_2 C_5 + L_4 C_5)s^2 + 1]E_3 \tag{76}$$

$$I_1 = \{L_2 L_4 C_5 C_3 C_1 s^5 + [L_2(C_3 + C_5)C_1 + (L_4 C_1 + L_4 C_3)C_5]s^3$$
$$+ (C_1 + C_3 + C_5)s\}E_3 \tag{77}$$

When parameter values are given numerically, these expressions become far more compact, and the procedure loses the still somewhat formidable appearance that, in the above relationships, may leave the reader with a not too favorable impression regarding its brevity.   He will find in any case, however, that the computational method suggested here is vastly more direct than the formal one in terms of mesh equations and determinants.

Regarding the input impedance E_1/I_1, an alternative method of formation is additionally helpful in some practical situations.   This procedure follows the simple rule regarding the computation of impedance when branches are connected in series or in parallel.   With reference to Fig. 9, one begins at the right-hand end of the ladder, combining the components alternately in series and in parallel as indicated in expression 78 which is constructed by starting at the lower right and proceeding toward the upper left-hand end in a readily understood fashion. Algebraically this form for the driving-point impedance

$$(E_1/I_1) = \cfrac{1}{y_1 + \cfrac{1}{z_2 + \cfrac{1}{y_3 + \cfrac{1}{z_4 + \cfrac{1}{y_5 + \cfrac{1}{z_6 + \cfrac{1}{y_7 + \cfrac{1}{z_8 + \cfrac{1}{y_9}}}}}}}}} \tag{78}$$

is called its *continued-fraction* development. It is especially useful as an analytic representation in problems where the network is to be found (rather than the network given and the impedance to be found) since the respective branch impedances and admittances are placed in evidence once such a development is obtained. In analysis problems it sets the pattern for a straightforward computational procedure.

8 Networks Embodying Symmetry in Structure and Source Distribution—Polyphase Circuits

In electric-power generation, transmission, and distribution systems and in various other practical situations one encounters circuits that inherently exhibit symmetry with regard to both their geometrical structure and element values as well as their mode of excitation. Such networks are commonly referred to as *polyphase* systems, the term "phase" here being used not as the usual designation of time phase but rather as a reference to one of the structurally identical parts of the network into which the symmetrical whole may be decomposed. A typical three-phase network, according to these ideas, is illustrated in Fig. 11, and one "phase" of it is shown in Fig. 12. The three sinusoidal voltage sources, whose internal impedances are denoted by Z_s, are identical except for a uniform time-phase displacement between them; that is

$$E_1 = E_3\underline{/\pm 120°}, \qquad E_2 = E_1\underline{/\pm 120°}, \qquad E_3 = E_2\underline{/\pm 120°} \tag{79}$$

the algebraic signs of the phase displacements being either consistently positive or consistently negative (if negative, the convention is to say that the voltages form a *positive* sequence; if positive, a negative one).

The sum of such a set of symmetrically oriented voltages (Fig. 14) or currents is evidently zero.

In an n-phase system, consisting of n identical and symmetrically associated parts, the sources have equal magnitudes and phase displacements equal to $2\pi/n$ radians or $360/n$ degrees.

From the inherent symmetry in the circuit of Fig. 11 it follows that the currents I_1, I_2, I_3 likewise are identical except for a uniform phase

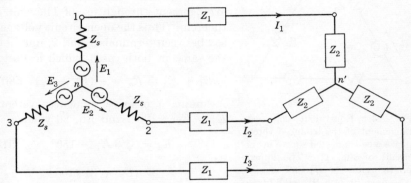

FIG. 11.   A balanced wye-connected three-phase circuit.

displacement of 120°; and, incidentally, the points n and n' are at the same potential, as may be seen from the fact that a connection of n and n' is trivial, since by Kirchhoff's current law the current in it equals the sum $I_1 + I_2 + I_3$ which is zero.   In practice the "neutral" points n and n' are usually connected, since the effect of an accidental unbalance in the circuit arrangement then causes less corresponding unbalance in the circuit behavior.   Since the "neutral connection," as the link n–n' is called, carries no current, its presence or absence in a balanced system is seen to be immaterial. Under balanced conditions one can compute the currents through considering a single phase of the system by itself; that is, through solving only the circuit of Fig. 12 for its cur-

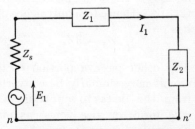

FIG. 12.   "Per-phase" representation of the circuit in Fig. 11.

rent I_1 and then writing down the expressions for I_2 and I_3 as I_1 displaced in phase by 120° and 240° respectively (in either a lagging or leading sequence according to that applying to the source voltages).

It may occur that the source arrangement, instead of having the so-called wye form in Fig. 11, is in the delta configuration shown in Fig. 13. In combination with the rest of the circuit of Fig. 11, the delta

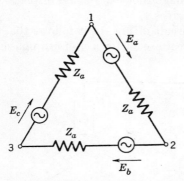

source arrangement lends itself less readily to analysis on the "per-phase" basis indicated in Fig. 12. One can, however, easily convert the wye arrangement into an equivalent delta arrangement through use of Thévenin's theorem. Thus the open-circuit voltage, say between terminals 1 and 2, must be the same in both cases, which leads to

$$-E_1 + E_2 = E_a = -(E_b + E_c) \quad (80)$$

Assuming a positive sequence system, $E_2 = E_1 \underline{/-120°}$, and Eq. 80 yields

$$E_a = \sqrt{3}\,E_1 \underline{/-150°} \quad (81)$$

or

$$E_1 = (E_a/\sqrt{3})\,\underline{/150°}$$

FIG. 13. Equivalent delta arrangement of the balanced three-phase wye-connected source in the circuit of Fig. 11. The appropriate values of E_a and Z_a are given by Eqs. 81 and 82.

as is readily seen from the geometry in Fig. 14. The remaining voltages in either sequence are related in an identical manner.

So far as the passive part of the two source arrangements is concerned, one observes that, if the sources are dead, the impedance between terminals 1 and 2 of Fig. 11 (with the rest of the system disconnected) is $2Z_s$ while in Fig. 13 it is $(2/3)Z_a$. Hence for equivalence one has

$$Z_a = 3Z_s \quad (82)$$

Any other passive portion of the circuit may similarly be converted from the delta to an equivalent wye form, or vice versa, as may be required in an analysis.*

Thus polyphase circuits (when they are completely balanced) readily lend themselves to analysis

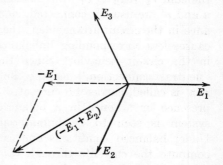

FIG. 14. Vector diagram illustrating the quantities involved in Eqs. 80 and 81 pertinent to the source equivalence to which Fig. 13 is relevant.

---

* The wye-delta and delta-wye transformation relations discussed in Art. 4 of Ch. 3 for resistance networks are formally applicable to impedances and admittances.

on a per-phase basis. Although the discussion of more detailed aspects of such systems logically falls outside the present studies, it is appropriate to point out a few significant features of polyphase systems having to do with power and energy relationships.

In this regard it is, for example, interesting to note that it is more efficient to transmit electric power over a three-phase transmission line than over a single-phase line. Let us suppose that a total amount of power P is to be transmitted at a voltage V (conductor to conductor in the single-phase line, or conductor to neutral in the polyphase line). For a 100 per cent power-factor condition, the current in the single-phase line is $I = P/V$ and the total line losses are $2I^2R = 2P^2R/V^2$ where R is the resistance per line conductor. In a three-phase line the current per conductor is $I = P/3V$ because the total power transmitted is three times the power per phase, or, for a given total power, each phase transmits one-third. For the same resistance per conductor as in the single-phase line, the total line losses are $3I^2R = P^2R/3V^2$, an amount that is only one-sixth as large as that for the single-phase line.

This comparison is not quite fair since the three-phase line requires three conductors compared with only two conductors for the single-phase line, so that the three-phase line requires one and one-half times as much copper for its construction. A fair comparison, therefore, should allow the same total amount of copper for both lines. On this basis the resistance per conductor of the three-phase line is three-halves that of the single-phase line, and the total losses of the three-phase line become three-halves times the value computed above. Thus the three-phase line losses become one-fourth instead of one-sixth as large as those for the single-phase line, which is still a respectable improvement.

This result is by no means the only factor that suggests the practical use of a three-phase system, since there are other schemes whereby the efficiency of power transmission can be improved. One of the further advantages of a three-phase system becomes evident from a consideration of the total instantaneous power existing in such a circuit. Thus in the circuit of Fig. 11 let the instantaneous source voltage and current in phase 1 be

$$e_1(t) = |E_1| \cos \omega t, \qquad i_1(t) = |I_1| \cos (\omega t + \phi) \qquad (83)$$

The instantaneous power delivered by this source is

$$p_1 = e_1 i_1 = |E_1 I_1| \cos \omega t \cos (\omega t + \phi)$$

$$= \frac{|E_1 I_1|}{2} [\cos \phi + \cos (2\omega t + \phi)] \qquad (84)$$

In the other two phases the voltages and currents are given by the expressions 83 advanced (or retarded) by 120° and 240° respectively; or we can say that the quantity (ωt) in 83 is replaced by $(\omega t \pm 120°)$ and $(\omega t \pm 240°)$ respectively. The corresponding expressions for instantaneous power in these phases are, therefore, the same as p_1 in Eq. 84, except that (ωt) is replaced by $(\omega t \pm 120°)$ and $(\omega t \pm 240°)$. Thus the total instantaneous power becomes

$$p_1 + p_2 + p_3 = e_1 i_1 + e_2 i_2 + e_3 i_3$$

$$= \frac{|E_1 I_1|}{2} [3 \cos \phi + \cos (2\omega t + \phi) + \cos (2\omega t + \phi \pm 240°) \tag{85}$$

$$+ \cos (2\omega t + \phi \pm 480°)]$$

Since the last three terms in this expression cancel, we have simply

$$p_1 + p_2 + p_3 = \frac{3|E_1 I_1|}{2} \cos \phi \tag{86}$$

The important part about this result is that the pulsating components in the several phases neutralize each other, so that the net instantaneous power is composed of the steady component alone. It is simply three times the average active power per phase.

In three-phase rotating machinery this feature results in a steady torque rather than one containing a pulsating component. The practical advantage thus gained is significant.

PROBLEMS

1. Two inductances are characterized by the matrix

$$[l] = \begin{bmatrix} 4 & -3 \\ -3 & 6 \end{bmatrix}$$

Find the value of the net inductance when they are connected in the ways shown in the diagrams (a) through (d).

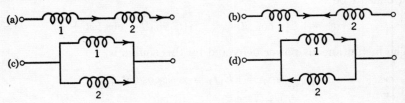

PROB. 1.

2. For the given branch inductance matrix, find the net inductance of the indicated series and parallel combinations.

$$[l] = \begin{bmatrix} 1 & \frac{1}{2} & \frac{1}{4} & \frac{1}{8} \\ \frac{1}{2} & 1 & \frac{1}{2} & \frac{1}{4} \\ \frac{1}{4} & \frac{1}{2} & 1 & \frac{1}{2} \\ \frac{1}{8} & \frac{1}{4} & \frac{1}{2} & 1 \end{bmatrix}$$

If the common constant current in the series connection is one ampere, compute the flux linkages in the separate inductances (in weber-turns) and the total flux linkage. Compute the total energy (in joules) stored in the associated magnetic field.

If the common constant flux linkage in the parallel connection is 1 weber-turn, compute the currents in the separate inductances and the total current. Compute the total energy stored.

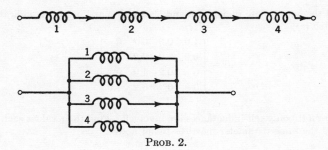

PROB. 2.

3. Given the physical arrangement of inductance windings on a common core as indicated in the drawing and their various possible interconnections as shown in sketches (a) through (f). Each self-inductance = 2; each mutual inductance in absolute value = 1. Compute the net inductance in each case.

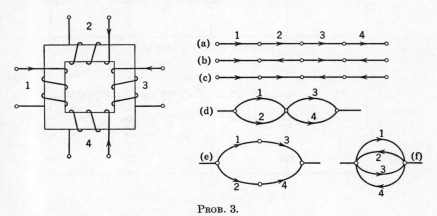

PROB. 3.

4. For the inductances specified in the preceding problem, find the reciprocal inductance parameter matrix for the node-to-datum set of node pairs indicated in sketch (a), and from this matrix construct an equivalent circuit having only self-inductances. Do the same for the graph shown in sketch (b).

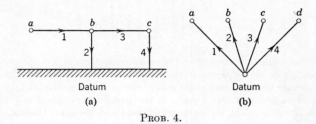

Datum (a)

Datum (b)

PROB. 4.

5. Find the appropriate inductance and elastance matrices on the indicated mesh basis [sketch (a)].

$$[l] = \begin{bmatrix} 1.0 & 0.2 & 0 & 0 \\ 0.2 & 1.0 & 0.2 & 0 \\ 0 & 0.2 & 1.0 & 0.2 \\ 0 & 0 & 0.2 & 1.0 \end{bmatrix}$$

In diagram (b) only self-inductances are involved. Find their values such that the circuit has the same parameter matrices found above.

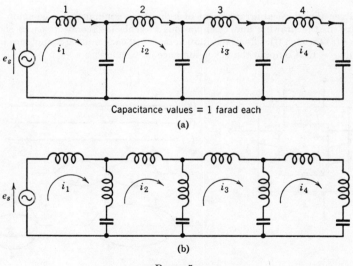

Capacitance values = 1 farad each

(a)

(b)

PROB. 5.

6. Find the capacitance and reciprocal inductance matrices on a node-to-datum basis as indicated. The values of the capacitances shown in the sketch are 1 farad each; the branch inductance matrix is that given in Prob. 5.

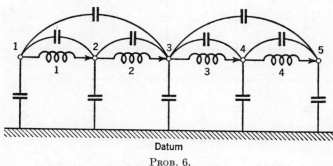

Datum

PROB. 6.

7. Draw a circuit with capacitances and only self-inductances that has the same matrices on a node-to-datum basis as the one in Prob. 6. Assign all element values in henrys and farads.

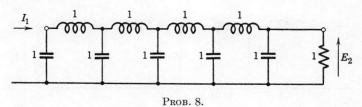

PROB. 8.

8. In the above sketch, the element values are in henrys, farads, and ohms. Show that for this form of network, regardless of the number of meshes involved, the transfer impedance always has the form

$$Z_{12}(s) = \frac{E_2}{I_1} = \frac{\text{constant}}{\text{polynomial of degree } n}$$

where n = total number of reactive elements (capacitances and self-inductances) Find $Z_{12}(s)$ for the specific network given.

9. Assume all element values to be unity. Show in each case that the transfer impedance has the form

$$Z_{12}(s) = \frac{\text{constant} \times s}{\text{polynomial of 7th degree}}$$

Substantiate this result on a heuristic basis through use of the results of Prob. 8 and an appropriate circuit which is asymptotically valid for $s \to 0$ and another for

$s \to \infty$ in each case. Check through evaluation of each transfer impedance. Show how the asymptotic circuits can be used to evaluate the constant multiplier.

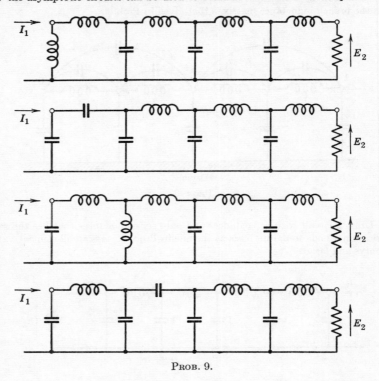

PROB. 9.

10. Element values in ohms, henrys, and farads are all unity, and no mutual inductances are involved. Using the principles learned in Probs. 8 and 9, predict in this case that

$$Z_{12} = \frac{(\text{constant}) \times s^3}{\text{polynomial of 7th degree}}$$

Then check through numerical evaluation.

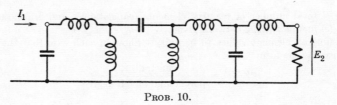

PROB. 10.

11. In the graph all branches are 1-ohm resistances. For the choice of meshes indicated, write down the loop resistance parameter matrix $[R]$. Now revise the

loops to be the following mesh combinations: $(1 + 2)$, $(2 + 3)$, $(3 + 4)$, $(4 + 5)$, $(5 + 1)$. Find the new matrix $[R]$. Are the corresponding equilibrium equations independent?

If loops are chosen to be the mesh combinations: 1, $(1 + 2)$, $(1 + 2 + 3)$, $(1 + 2 + 3 + 4)$, $(1 + 2 + 3 + 4 + 5)$, find $[R]$ and state whether the associated equations are independent.

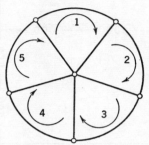

PROB. 11.

12. Element values in the sketch below are in ohms, henrys, and darafs. For the indicated choice of meshes, write down the loop-parameter matrices $[R]$, $[L]$, $[S]$. Now assume that there exists a second network whose node-parameter matrices on a node-to-datum basis are

$$[G] = [R], \qquad [C] = [L], \qquad [\Gamma] = [S]$$

Construct this dual network, and indicate all of its element values. How many variables would be needed to characterize the given network on a node basis or its dual on a loop basis?

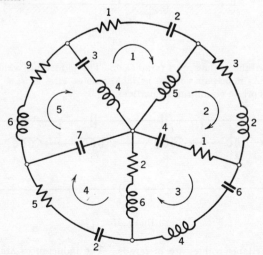

PROB. 12.

13. The inductances in the sketch have values as specified in Prob. 2. The capacitance values are in farads. For the indicated choice of meshes, find the appropriate parameter matrices, and write the equilibrium equations.

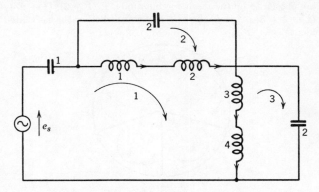

PROB. 13.

14. The capacitances are 1 farad each. The inductances are as specified in Prob. 2. Write the equilibrium equations on the indicated node-to-datum basis.

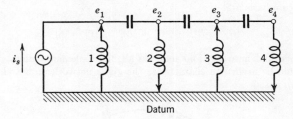

PROB. 14.

15. The capacitance values are 1 farad each. The inductance values are specified as in Prob. 3. As node-pair voltage variables choose $e_1 = v_1$, $e_2 = v_2$, $e_3 = v_3$, and derive the appropriate equilibrium equations.

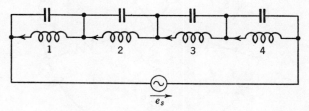

PROB. 15.

16. The capacitance values are in farads. The inductances are as specified in Prob. 3. Derive the differential equation which determines e_2 in terms of e_1.

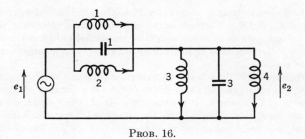

PROB. 16.

17. The circuit is that of a balanced, positive-sequence, three-phase system. The resistance values indicated are in ohms. If $|E_1| = 100$ volts, what must $|E_a|$ be? What is the phase position of E_a relative to E_1; of E_b relative to E_2; of E_c relative to E_3? What are the line currents I_1, I_2, I_3 in magnitude and phase relative to the phase of E_1? What are the currents in the delta?

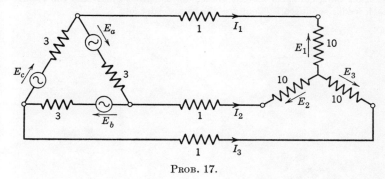

PROB. 17.

18. The arrangement of current sources and resistances in sketch (b) is to be equivalent (with respect to the terminals 1, 2, 3) to the balanced three-phase delta

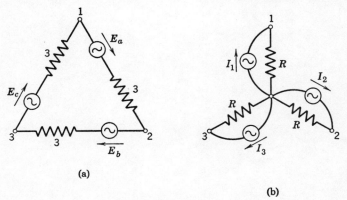

(a)

(b)

PROB. 18.

involving the 3-ohm resistances shown in sketch (a). Find the values of R and I_1, I_2, I_3 in terms of E_a, E_b, E_c. Through converting the current sources in the wye into equivalent voltage sources in series with their respective resistances, obtain voltage sources in a wye arrangement equivalent to the given delta arrangement and check Eq. 81 in the text.

19. One thousand (1000) kilowatts of power are transmitted single phase at a line voltage of 33,000 volts rms and unity power factor for a distance of 25 miles with a total line loss of 11.7 kilowatts. If the same amount of power were transmitted three phase with the same line-to-line voltage, the same total transmission line copper, the same distance, and unity power factor, what would be the line losses? What would they be at 0.8 power factor lagging? What would they be if the total transmitted power were 2000 kilowatts, all other quantities remaining the same as in the first question?

20. A balanced three-phase motor takes 12 kilowatts at 0.8 lagging power factor and 250 volts rms line to line. Compute the line current. If this motor is fed from a transformer through a three-phase feeder line, and each line conductor has a resistance of 0.1 ohm, compute the line voltage at the transformer, and the voltage drop in each feeder conductor. Compute the total feeder loss.

CHAPTER NINE

Additional Topics Dealing with Steady-State and Transient Behavior of Lumped Linear Circuits

1 Transient Response with Alternating Excitation

The discussion in Ch. 5 dealing with step function and impulse response of simple circuits yields the behavior following the sudden insertion (through an appropriate switching operation) of a voltage or current having some constant value. The circuit behavior under such circumstances is sometimes referred to as a "d-c" transient, the letters "d-c" (an abbreviation for "direct current") being descriptive of the constant character of the excitation after its insertion into the circuit. Now that we have given some thought to the steady-state response of these same circuits for a sinusoidal excitation, it is logical to consider also their behavior following the sudden insertion of a sinusoid; that is to say, it seems appropriate at this point to

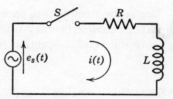

FIG. 1. Relative to the determination of an a-c switching transient.

inquire into the determination of so-called "a-c" transients (the letters "a-c" being an abbreviation for the words "alternating current").

As we shall see, there is nothing essentially different about the determination of these a-c transients as contrasted with the d-c transients considered in Ch. 5. The same methods of analysis apply, but some of the detailed results are sufficiently different and interesting to justify spending additional time on the discussion of this topic. An important by-product is a better understanding of the impedance concept and of the notion of complex frequency.

Let us consider again the simple RL circuit shown in Fig. 1, but this time with the voltage excitation $e_s(t)$ assumed to be a sinusoid. The switch S closes abruptly at $t = 0$, thus inserting the source and permitting a current $i(t)$ to exist. It is this current for $t > 0$ that we wish to determine.

The differential equation for $t > 0$ reads

$$L\frac{di}{dt} + Ri = \text{Re}[Ee^{s_p t}] \tag{1}$$

where s_p is the complex frequency of the voltage excitation. A particular integral, according to the discussion in Art. 2 of Ch. 5, is given by

$$i_p(t) = \text{Re}[Ie^{s_p t}] \tag{2}$$

Dropping the Re sign for the moment (as justified by the discussion in Art. 2 of Ch. 6), direct substitution gives, after cancelation of the factor $e^{s_p t}$,

$$(Ls_p + R)I = L(s_p - s_1)I = E \tag{3}$$

with

$$s_1 = -R/L \tag{4}$$

whence

$$i_p(t) = \text{Re}\left[\frac{E}{L(s_p - s_1)}e^{s_p t}\right] \tag{5}$$

This is the steady-state part of the complete solution. For the transient part, or complementary function, we consider the force-free or homogeneous differential equation (as discussed in Art. 2 of Ch. 5), namely:

$$L\,(di/dt) + Ri = 0 \tag{6}$$

Since this equation does not depend upon the excitation, it is the same for an a-c transient as for a d-c transient, and, hence, the complementary function or transient part of the solution is the same in form as discussed previously for a step function or impulse response, that is,

$$i_0(t) = Ae^{s_1 t} \tag{7}$$

where s_1 is the characteristic value (complex natural frequency) given by Eq. 4.

The complete solution is obtained through addition of the steady-state part, Eq. 5, and the transient part, Eq. 7, thus:

$$i(t) = \text{Re}\left[\frac{Ee^{s_p t}}{L(s_p - s_1)}\right] + Ae^{s_1 t} \tag{8}$$

As in the procedure for finding step-function response, the integration constant A is determined from the condition to be satisfied at the initial instant. Since in the present example, the net current must be zero at $t = 0$, we find

$$A = -\text{Re}\left[\frac{E}{L(s_p - s_1)}\right] \tag{9}$$

so that Eq. 8 becomes

$$i(t) = \text{Re}\left[\frac{Ee^{s_pt}}{L(s_p - s_1)}\right] - \text{Re}\left[\frac{E}{L(s_p - s_1)}\right]e^{s_1t} \tag{10}$$

The reader should observe that the transient amplitude A as given by Eq. 9 is the negative of the instantaneous current demanded by the steady state at $t = 0$. Its value is the discrepancy between the steady-state demand and the circuit's resources at this moment, since the circuit is initially without any current. As pointed out in Art. 2 of Ch. 5, the transient assumes the role of a shock absorber in that it affords a smooth transition from the initial state of the circuit to the demand made by the driving function. It should also be noted in this regard that the functional form of this transition (i.e. the transient function) is characterized by the circuit (not by the nature of the driving function) and hence is the same, regardless of the form of the driving function (whether d-c or a-c). Only the *amplitude* of the transient function depends upon the driving function, and merely upon the demand it makes at the initial instant. In other words, the only difference between an a-c transient and a d-c transient is in the expression for its amplitude. Its functional form is the same, and the method for its determination is the same.

Interpretation of the result, as given by Eq. 10, is however somewhat different, largely because there is involved an additional parameter, as contrasted with the d-c case, namely, the time phase of the sinusoidal excitation; that is, the angle of the complex voltage amplitude E. For a fixed absolute value for this amplitude, one may encounter a variety of transients according to the assumed phase of the excitation. There is nothing unexpected about this result, since the steady-state current function, being sinusoidal, passes through a variety of values in the course of each period, and the transient amplitude A is the negative of whatever value this sinusoidal current function (particular integral) has at the initial instant, which is any moment we wish to designate. If at this instant the steady-state current function (Eq. 5) has a peak value, then the transient amplitude has the largest possible value; if, on the other hand, the initial instant is chosen to fall at a moment when this steady-state current function passes through zero, then the transient amplitude is zero, and there is no transient.

By reference to Eq. 9 or 10, one can readily investigate these conditions more precisely. Thus the value of the transient amplitude is expressed as the real part of the complex quantity enclosed in the square brackets of Eq. 9. Evidently this real part is zero if the angle of the complex quantity is $\pm\pi/2$ radians, and it is a maximum when this angle is zero. This angle equals the angle of E, minus the angle of $(s_p - s_1)$. The angle of E is the phase of the voltage excitation, which may be varied according to the choice made for $t = 0$, the instant of switch closure (Fig. 1). Except for the factor L, the quantity $(s_p - s_1)$ is the impedance $Z(s_p)$ of our circuit. The sketch in Fig. 2 aids visualization of the impedance angle θ in its dependence upon the parameter

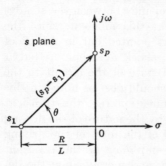

FIG. 2. s-plane sketch pertinent to the impedance of the circuit in Fig. 1 when the applied voltage is a steady sinusoid.

$s_1 = -R/L$ and the complex applied frequency s_p which is a point on the j axis if the voltage source is a sinusoid with steady amplitude.

If the phase angle of the voltage (angle of E) is 90° larger or smaller than the impedance angle θ, the value of A in Eq. 9 and hence the second term in Eq. 10 is zero. Under these circumstances there is no transient for the reason that the steady-state current function (the first term in Eq. 10) is zero for $t = 0$ so that the driving function makes no demand upon the circuit at the initial instant.

However, if the angle of E is equal to the impedance angle θ, then the steady-state current function has its maximum absolute value at $t = 0$, and the associated transient term likewise becomes a maximum.

In many practical circuits it turns out that $Ls_p = j\omega L$ (the inductive reactance) is large compared with the resistance R in the circuit, a condition that may alternately be expressed by writing: $|s_1| \ll |s_p|$. Under these circumstances the impedance angle θ, according to Fig. 2, is very nearly 90°. Essentially no transient then occurs if the angle of E is zero, that is, if the voltage excitation is

$$e_s(t) = \operatorname{Re}[Ee^{j\omega t}] = |E|\cos\omega t \tag{11}$$

while the most severe transient results if the angle of E is $\pm\pi/2$; that is, for a voltage excitation

$$e_s(t) = \operatorname{Re}[|E|e^{j(\omega t \pm \pi/2)}] = \mp|E|\sin\omega t \tag{12}$$

At first sight these results are exactly opposite to what one might expect, since the sudden insertion of the voltage function 11 at $t = 0$ introduces a maximum initial voltage jump (from zero to $|E|$), while the insertion of the function 12 at $t = 0$ introduces no initial voltage jump (the sine function is zero for $t = 0$). Since the voltage function 11 thus subjects the circuit to an initial shock, while the function 12 does not, one may easily be led to conclude that the excitation 11 will cause a severe transient and that the excitation 12 will cause none. The actual state of affairs is exactly the reverse, however, since it is the initial discrepancy between the steady-state *current* demand made by the excitation and that which the circuit can provide that determines the severity of the transient. Under the present assumption that

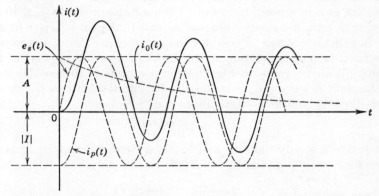

Fig. 3.   Depicting the current in the circuit of Fig. 1 following switch closure.

$\theta \approx \pi/2$, the steady-state current lags the applied voltage by essentially 90°, so that it is a sine function when $e_s(t)$ is a cosine, and vice versa. When the steady-state current is a sine function, so that it is zero for $t = 0$, there is no initial current discrepancy and hence no transient. This condition requires that $e_s(t)$ be a *cosine* function, not a sine.

Figure 3 shows the response in a highly reactive RL circuit under conditions yielding a maximum transient. Shown dotted are the suddenly applied voltage $e_s(t)$ which is a sine function, the steady-state current function $i_p(t)$ lagging 90° behind $e_s(t)$ and hence having its negative maximum value at $t = 0$, and the transient component of current $i_0(t)$ which is a simple exponentially decaying function with initial amplitude A equal in magnitude but opposite in sign to the initial amplitude of $i_p(t)$. The sum of $i_p(t)$ and $i_0(t)$ is the net current depicted by the solid curve. It starts from the value zero, rises in its initial upward surge to almost double its normal amplitude, and in successive half-cycles gradually comes closer to the steady-state function (particular integral) $i_p(t)$.

One may visualize the net current $i(t)$ as though it were the function $i_p(t)$ oscillating about the dotted curve $i_0(t)$ as an axis. Since $i_0(t)$ gradually comes closer to the time axis, $i(t)$ smoothly merges with $i_p(t)$. In the absence of any damping $(R = 0)$, $i_0(t)$ maintains the constant value A, and $i(t)$ becomes the cosine function $i_p(t)$ elevated so as to lie just above the time axis; the net current then oscillates continuously between zero and double its normal steady amplitude. Though such a condition cannot occur in a passive physical system, the response in a very slightly damped circuit during a short interval following switch closure can closely resemble this limiting behavior.

We are now in a position to exploit the solution given by Eq. 10 for other than pure imaginary values of s_p and thus gain a better understanding of the concept of complex frequency as well as of the impedance function and its relation to the natural frequency $(s = s_1)$ of the circuit. With reference to Fig. 2, what we propose to consider is to let the point s_p leave the j axis and wander into the left half-plane. As we do this, the voltage excitation function

$$e_s(t) = \text{Re } [Ee^{s_p t}] \tag{13}$$

ceases to be a steady sinusoid, and becomes instead a damped sinusoid. Thus, for $s_p = \sigma + j\omega$, and $E = |E|e^{j\psi}$, Eq. 13 yields

$$e_s(t) = |E|e^{\sigma t} \cos (\omega t + \psi) \tag{14}$$

For a numerically negative value of σ (a point s_p in the left half-plane) Eq. 14 represents an exponentially decaying sinusoid with initial amplitude $|E|$.

An important fact to recognize is that the current response as given by Eq. 10 applies to an assumed excitation voltage of the form 13 with any complex value for s_p as well as it does for an s_p value on the j axis. Hence Eq. 10 yields as well the behavior of the series RL circuit for a suddenly applied voltage $e_s(t)$ equal to the sinusoidal function with *exponentially modulated amplitude* as given by Eq. 14. We can, incidentally, consider σ to be numerically positive as well as negative, except that a numerically positive σ value represents a physically unstable condition since the "steady-state" portion of the response then grows without limit.

Of greater interest at the moment is the response 10 for an s_p value with negative real part, for then we can consider what happens when the point s_p in Fig. 2 falls upon s_1. Physically this condition is one of "perfect resonance" since the complex frequency of the driving force then coincides exactly with the natural frequency of the circuit. In Ch. 6 we refer to a resonance condition in the simple RLC circuit as one for which the frequency $s_p = j\omega$ of the sinusoidal source has substantially the same value as the imaginary part of the complex natural frequency of this circuit. The impedance for this condition becomes a minimum (assuming a relatively small amount of damping so that the complex natural frequencies lie near the j axis) and the current response becomes a maximum (see Figs. 16 and 18 of Ch. 6).

So long as we limit the complex frequency of the source to the j axis, the point s_p cannot become coincident with a complex natural frequency of the circuit, although it may come close to it. That is to say, so long as we consider only a sinusoidal driving force with constant amplitude, we can approach quite closely to a condition of perfect resonance, but we cannot attain it. When we consider a damped sinusoidal driving function, however, it is possible to achieve coincidence between the frequency of the source and that of the circuit and thus evaluate a state of true resonance.

In our present RL circuit we are, of course, dealing with a degenerate case inasmuch as the natural frequency s_1 has no imaginary part, and the circuit exhibits no tendency to oscillate. Nevertheless one should regard the coincidence of s_p with s_1 as a resonance condition, and it is interesting, therefore, to evaluate Eq. 10 for this situation as a stepping stone to the consideration of an analogous condition involving the RLC circuit.

When $s_p = s_1$, the impedance $Z(s_p) = L(s_p - s_1)$ becomes zero, and both terms in Eq. 10 have infinite amplitudes. The relation for the current $i(t)$ assumes the indeterminate form $\infty - \infty$. This meaningless result may be avoided if we do not rush headlong, so to speak, into the condition $s_p = s_1$, but first let $s_p - s_1 = \delta$ and regard δ as a small quantity which we will ultimately allow to become zero. We thus find that Eq. 10 yields

$$i(t) = \frac{Ee^{s_1 t}}{L} \operatorname{Re} \left[\frac{e^{\delta t} - 1}{\delta} \right] \tag{15}$$

which is valid for any δ. Since we wish to evaluate the quantity within the square brackets for small values of δ, it is appropriate to write its Maclaurin expansion, thus:

$$\frac{e^{\delta t} - 1}{\delta} = t + \frac{\delta t^2}{2!} + \frac{\delta^2 t^3}{3!} + \cdots \tag{16}$$

The result for $\delta \to 0$ is now obvious, and Eq. 15 is seen to yield

$$i(t) = Ete^{s_1 t}/L \tag{17}$$

which can alternately be written

$$i(t) = \frac{E}{R} \cdot \frac{Rt}{L} \cdot e^{-Rt/L} \tag{18}$$

In parts (a) and (b) of Fig. 4 are shown respectively the excitation voltage 13 for $s_p = s_1$ and the current response corresponding to Eq. 18.

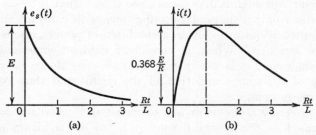

FIG. 4.   The current (b) in the circuit of Fig. 1 when the applied voltage is the damped exponential shown in (a).

Both are aperiodic functions as may be expected from the fact that the circuit under consideration is nonoscillatory.   One observes that the response is quite finite in spite of the impedance $Z(s_p)$ being zero, since the excitation decays and is unable to sustain even a finite response, let alone an infinite one.

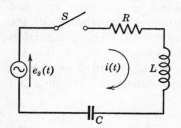

FIG. 5.   Relative to an a-c switching transient in the series RLC circuit.

We now turn our attention to the analogous problem involving the RLC circuit shown in Fig. 5.   The voltage excitation will again be assumed to have the form given by Eq. 13, and we make no commitment as yet as to the specific value of s_p to be considered, whether pure imaginary or complex.   The differential equation expressing equilibrium after closure of the switch S reads

$$L\frac{di}{dt} + Ri + \frac{1}{C}\int i\,dt = Ee^{s_p t} \tag{19}$$

where we have dropped the Re sign on the voltage excitation, since we can solve the equation as it stands and take the real part of the solution afterward.   For the particular integral we can write

$$i_p(t) = Ie^{s_p t} \tag{20}$$

whence substitution into Eq. 19 and cancelation of the factor $e^{s_p t}$ yields

$$(Ls_p + R + 1/Cs_p)I = E \tag{21}$$

According to the discussion in Art. 5 of Ch. 6, we can thus write

$$I = \frac{s_p E}{L(s_p - s_1)(s_p - s_2)} \tag{22}$$

with

$$s_1 = -\alpha + j\omega_d, \qquad s_2 = -\alpha - j\omega_d$$

where

$$\alpha = R/2L, \qquad \omega_0{}^2 = \alpha^2 + \omega_d{}^2 = 1/LC \tag{23}$$

The complementary function (transient part of the solution) is an integral of the homogeneous equation corresponding to 19, namely,

$$L\frac{di}{dt} + Ri + \frac{1}{C}\int i\,dt = 0 \tag{24}$$

and hence has the same general form as for step function or impulse response calculations, that is:

$$i_0(t) = Ae^{st} \tag{25}$$

Verification through substitution into Eq. 24 gives

$$(Ls + R + 1/Cs)A = 0 \tag{26}$$

leading, for a nonzero A, to the complex natural frequencies $s = s_1$ and $s = s_2$ given by the relations 23.   Hence the complete transient part of the solution is

$$i_0(t) = A_1 e^{s_1 t} + A_2 e^{s_2 t} \tag{27}$$

and the net solution reads

$$i(t) = i_p(t) + i_0(t) = Ie^{s_p t} + A_1 e^{s_1 t} + A_2 e^{s_2 t} \tag{28}$$

with the complex steady-state current amplitude I given by Eq. 22.

Integrating Eq. 28, we get the capacitance charge

$$q(t) = \frac{I}{s_p} e^{s_p t} + \frac{A_1}{s_1} e^{s_1 t} + \frac{A_2}{s_2} e^{s_2 t} \tag{29}$$

For initial rest conditions $[i(0) = q(0) = 0]$, Eqs. 28 and 29 yield

$$A_1 + A_2 = -I, \qquad \frac{A_1}{s_1} + \frac{A_2}{s_2} = -\frac{I}{s_p} \qquad (30)$$

With the use of Eq. 22 for I, these give

$$A_1 = \frac{s_1 E}{L(s_1 - s_p)(s_1 - s_2)}, \qquad A_2 = \frac{s_2 E}{L(s_2 - s_p)(s_2 - s_1)} \qquad (31)$$

Substituting into Eq. 28 and taking the real part, we have

$$i(t) = \mathrm{Re}\left[\frac{E}{L}\left\{\frac{s_p e^{s_p t}}{(s_p - s_1)(s_p - s_2)} + \frac{s_1 e^{s_1 t}}{(s_1 - s_2)(s_1 - s_p)}\right.\right.$$

$$\left.\left. + \frac{s_2 e^{s_2 t}}{(s_2 - s_p)(s_2 - s_1)}\right\}\right] \qquad (32)$$

A number of interesting special forms of this result may be considered for a sinusoidal voltage excitation with steady amplitude ($s_p = j\omega$). These are distinguished according to whether the given circuit is assumed to be highly damped or highly oscillatory, whether the frequency ω of the source is small or large compared with the natural frequency ω_d, or is equal or nearly equal to it. Further, these various conditions may be considered for several characteristically different phase angles of the source at the moment of switch closure. All of these results, many of them widely different in their appearance and significance, are contained in the solution as given by Eq. 32.

We do not wish at this time to enter upon an elaboration of such extent, but shall content ourselves with the consideration of the condition of perfect resonance for which $s_p = s_1$. Being mindful of the analogous situation involving the RL circuit, we let $s_p = s_1 + \delta$ wherever it appears that setting $s_p = s_1$ leads to difficulty, and tentatively consider δ to be a small quantity. Assuming also that the circuit is *highly* oscillatory so that $\alpha \ll \omega_d$ and $\omega_d \approx \omega_0$, we have

$$s_p - s_2 \approx s_1 - s_2 \approx j2\omega_0 \qquad (33)$$

and Eq. 32 is found to yield

$$i(t) = \mathrm{Re}\left[\frac{E}{2L}\left(\frac{e^{\delta t} - 1}{\delta} + \frac{1}{j2\omega_0} - \frac{e^{-j2\omega_0 t}}{j2\omega_0}\right)e^{s_1 t}\right] \qquad (34)$$

Use of the Maclaurin series 16 and consideration of the limit $\delta \to 0$ converts Eq. 34 into

$$i(t) = \text{Re}\left[\frac{Ee^{-\alpha t}}{2L}\left(te^{j\omega_0 t} + \frac{e^{j\omega_0 t}}{j\omega_0} - \frac{e^{-j\omega_0 t}}{j2\omega_0}\right)\right] \qquad (35)$$

Extracting the real part, assuming a zero phase angle so that E is real, gives

$$i(t) = \frac{Ee^{-\alpha t}}{2L}\left(t \cos \omega_0 t + \frac{3 \sin \omega_0 t}{2\omega_0}\right) \qquad (36)$$

Because of the factor $1/2\omega_0$, the second term in this expression is negligible compared with the first so far as the general character of the result

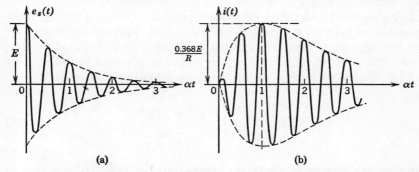

(a)   **(b)**

Fig. 6. The current (b) in the circuit of Fig. 5 when the applied voltage is the damped sinusoid shown in (a). Note that the envelope functions are the same as the total functions in Fig. 4.

is concerned. Consistency with the other approximations made suggests that we drop it, and the first term may be written

$$i(t) = \frac{E}{R} \cdot \alpha t \cdot e^{-\alpha t} \cdot \cos \omega_0 t \qquad (37)$$

This result is the same in form as that for the RL circuit (Eq. 18) except for the factor $\cos \omega_0 t$ which gives the present response its oscillatory character. Plots of the voltage excitation and of the current response are shown respectively in parts (a) and (b) of Fig. 6. Again it is significant to observe that although the impedance $Z(s_p)$ becomes zero for $s_p = s_1$ and the "steady-state" amplitude I (Eq. 22) is infinite, the net result is finite and meaningful, as is also the concept of complex frequency, which in this example plays its role without reservations of any kind.

It should be clear that without the concept of complex frequency the solution to the present problem would not have the above straight-forward character, nor could a discussion of the phenomenon of resonance include the attainment of this condition in its fullest sense both theoretically and physically. It is with the further elaboration of these ideas that the topic of the next article is concerned.

2   Further Exploitation of the Concepts of Complex Frequency and Impedance

In the preceding article we made use, among other things, of the fact that the complex frequency s_p of the source may assume values in the plane as well as on the j axis. It was pointed out that such complex s_p values correspond to sources that are exponentially growing or decaying sinusoids, and that the formal procedure relating to the determination of network response yields results that apply unaltered whether pure imaginary or complex s_p values are ultimately substituted.

In this light let us reconsider briefly the response of the RL circuit of Fig. 1 as given by Eq. 10 which we rewrite below in the form

$$i(t) = \operatorname{Re}\left[\frac{E(e^{s_p t} - e^{s_1 t})}{L(s_p - s_1)}\right] \tag{38}$$

and for the interpretation of the impedance $Z(s_p) = L(s_p - s_1)$ let us consider a redrawn version of Fig. 2, permitting s_p the freedom of the s plane, as indicated in Fig. 7. With s_p thus unrestricted, it is plain to see that the impedance of the RL circuit can take on any complex value at all. If s_p lies on the real axis to the left of s_1, for example, the impedance $Z(s_p)$ becomes a negative resistance. The particular integral, Eq. 5, then is a damped exponential like $e_s(t)$, but opposite in algebraic sign. The net result as given by Eq. 38, however, remains alike in sign to $e_s(t)$, and in fact has an appearance not unlike in character to that shown in Fig. 4 for the condition $s_p = s_1$.

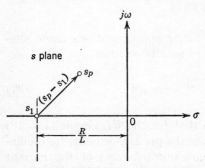

Fig. 7. s-plane sketch pertinent to the impedance of the circuit in Fig. 1 when the applied voltage is a damped sinusoid. (Compare with Fig. 2.)

Nevertheless our attitude toward and our reasoning in terms of the impedance concept becomes more flexible as a result of regarding the source frequency s_p to be unrestricted.

Thus we notice, for instance, that the expression 38 is completely symmetrical with regard to the two values s_p and s_1; interchanging them leaves the function unchanged. Hence we could just as well regard s_1 as the source frequency and s_p as the natural frequency of the circuit. It follows that the result is the same whether the source is more highly damped than the circuit or the circuit more highly damped than the source.

If we put s_p back on the j axis and then regard s_1 as defining the source and s_p as defining a circuit, we no longer have the same circuit. If we evaluate the real part in Eq. 38 by adding to the expression within the bracket, its conjugate, we see that s_p and its conjugate are involved and that we now have a circuit with a pair of conjugate imaginary values for its natural frequencies. This arrangement of natural frequencies we recall from the discussion in Art. 5, Ch. 5, characterizes the LC circuit and we see, therefore, that Eq. 38 can represent the response of an LC circuit excited by a damped exponential voltage as well as representing the response of an RL circuit to an applied sinusoidal voltage, whether damped or undamped.

The thoughts unleashed in one's mind by this sort of reasoning are rather prodigious, since the idea of trading circuits with sources, so to speak, promises to lead, in more elaborate situations, to a host of interesting possibilities. Even in examples as simple as the RL circuit, the introduction of such interpretative thinking allows us to recognize that seemingly widely different physical situations like the LC circuit excited by a damped exponential and the RL circuit excited by a steady sinusoid are in fact "brothers under the skin" since one simple expression (like Eq. 38) describes the behavior of both. The economy and circumspection which this result and its more general exploitation portend are in themselves significant.

A similar situation may be seen to exist with regard to Eq. 32 representing the response of an RLC circuit to the sudden application of a voltage with the complex frequency s_p. Here the expression within the curved brackets is recognized as being completely symmetrical with respect to the three quantities s_p, s_1, s_2. With s_p real, the first term in this bracket expression is real and the last two are conjugate complex. The entire expression within the square brackets is then real, and the Re sign has no significance. If we now regard s_p as defining a simple aperiodic system like the RL circuit, and the conjugates s_1 and s_2 as defining a damped sinusoidal source, we obtain a valid physical interpretation for the relationship expressed by Eq. 32 that is other than the one assumed in its derivation, and again the trading of a source with a circuit is involved. These matters are now expressed more precisely through the additional detailed discussion which follows.

3 Frequency and Time Domains

The interpretations given in this article are those normally associated with the Fourier and Laplace transform methods to be discussed later on. Their presentation at this point has a twofold objective, namely, to show that the same circumspect and flexible viewpoint may just as logically and easily be obtained through the classical approach involving a conventional solution to the differential equations, and thus, in the light of that background, to make possible the ultimate achievement of a clearer and more facile understanding of transform methods.

To begin with, let us rewrite the response of the RL circuit to an applied voltage with complex frequency s_p (as given by Eq. 10) in the following form

$$i(t) = \mathrm{Re}\,[A_p e^{s_p t} + A_1 e^{s_1 t}] \tag{39}$$

where the constants A_p and A_1 are expressible as

$$A_k = \left[\frac{(s - s_k)E}{L(s - s_p)(s - s_1)} \right]_{s=s_k} \quad \text{for} \quad k = p, 1 \tag{40}$$

Thus, setting $k = p$ and then letting $s = s_p$, we get

$$A_p = E/L(s_p - s_1) \tag{41}$$

while, for $k = 1$ and $s = s_1$, formula 40 gives

$$A_1 = E/L(s_1 - s_p) \tag{42}$$

It is readily seen that substitution of 41 and 42 into 39 yields the result expressed by Eq. 10.

Since the admittance $Y(s)$ of the RL circuit to an applied voltage with complex frequency s is

$$Y(s) = 1/L(s - s_1) \tag{43}$$

we can write formula 40 for A_k in the form

$$A_k = \left[(s - s_k) \cdot Y(s) \cdot \frac{E}{(s - s_p)} \right]_{s=s_k} \tag{44}$$

Apart from the factor $(s - s_k)$, which is in this formula merely to cancel either of the factors $(s - s_p)$ or $(s - s_1)$ according to whether $k = p$ or $k = 1$, this expression consists of the product of two things, namely:

$$Y(s) = 1/L(s - s_1) \quad \text{and} \quad E(s) = E/(s - s_p) \tag{45}$$

The first of these, Eq. 43, as mentioned above, is the admittance of the circuit to an applied voltage

$$e_s(t) = Ee^{st} \tag{46}$$

Since $Y(s)$ is a function of the complex variable s, this admittance is regarded as representing the circuit in the so-called s *domain* or *frequency* domain.

The second of the two quantities 45 is analogously spoken of as a representation of the *source* in the frequency domain, since it is the source that determines E and s_p. As a function of time, this source is represented by expression 46 for $s = s_p$, which is referred to as a representation of the source in the *time domain*. The source is thus regarded as having two representations, namely, one in the time domain (this is, the familiar $e_s(t)$ function) and one in the frequency domain, which is the function $E(s)$ in 45. One can formulate by inspection a simple process that converts the frequency function $E(s)$ into the time function $e_s(t)$, namely:

$$[(s - s_p) \cdot E(s) \cdot e^{st}]_{s=s_p} = Ee^{s_p t} = e_s(t) \tag{47}$$

Application of the same process to $Y(s)$ yields

$$[(s - s_1) Y(s) e^{st}]_{s=s_1} = \frac{1}{L} e^{-Rt/L} \tag{48}$$

which is recognized as being the unit voltage impulse response of the RL circuit expressing, as we recall, its natural behavior. That is to say, it is a time function that represents how, following an initial shock, the circuit behaves when left alone and is, therefore, a function that characterizes the circuit itself in the time domain.

Returning our attention to Eqs. 44 and 45, we now can say that the product of $E(s)$ and $Y(s)$ represents, in the frequency domain, the response of the circuit to the applied voltage $e_s(t)$, since Eq. 44 together with Eq. 39 yields the transformation of this response from the frequency to the time domain according to a logical extension of the patterns set by Eqs. 47 and 48.

Taking the real part of the resulting bracket expression in Eq. 39 is necessitated by the fact that the desired $i(t)$ is not the response to the complex constituent voltage $e_s(t)$ in 47, but rather it is the response to an excitation equal to the real part of 47. As explained earlier (Art. 2, Ch. 6), the process of taking the real part can be postponed until the end of the calculations.

We have thus established the useful concept that all three quantities that we are concerned with in circuit theory, namely, the circuit, the excitation, and the response, have representations both as functions of s (that is, in the frequency domain) and as functions of t (that is, in the time domain). Further, we have established the fact that the response in the frequency domain is found simply through multiplying together the representations for the source and the circuit in that domain; and finally we have recognized a pattern for converting a frequency-domain function into a time-domain function. Although the usefulness of these ideas does not become strongly apparent until one begins dealing with more elaborate network problems, it is well to make their acquaintance in a preliminary way while still discussing the simplest of representative examples.

In further discussions and applications of these ideas, it is preferable not to be annoyed by having to consider taking the real part of the result as in Eq. 39. A simple cure for this difficulty is had through adding to the expression contained within the square brackets in Eq. 39, the corresponding one for an applied voltage that is the conjugate of the constituent 47; that is, a voltage

$$e_s(t) = \bar{E} e^{s_q t} \tag{49}$$

where $s_q = \bar{s}_p$ and the bar is a designation for the conjugate complex quantity. One-half of this sum (the bracket expression in Eq. 39 plus the corresponding one for the conjugate excitation) is equal to the desired real part.

If we indicate the end result of these manipulations in the form

$$i(t) = A_1 e^{s_1 t} + A_p e^{s_p t} + A_q e^{s_q t} \tag{50}$$

we find from Eq. 44 (through use of the superposition principle) that the appropriate constants A_k are now given by

$$A_k = \frac{1}{2} \left[(s - s_k) \cdot Y(s) \cdot \left(\frac{E}{s - s_p} + \frac{\bar{E}}{s - s_q} \right) \right]_{s = s_k} \tag{51}$$

which may be rewritten as

$$A_k = \frac{1}{2} \left[(s - s_k) \cdot Y(s) \cdot \frac{(s - s_0)(E + \bar{E})}{(s - s_p)(s - s_q)} \right]_{s = s_k} \tag{52}$$

with

$$s_0 = \frac{E s_q + \bar{E} s_p}{E + \bar{E}} \tag{53}$$

Since the assumed voltage excitation is

$$e_s(t) = \tfrac{1}{2}(E e^{s_p t} + \bar{E} e^{s_q t}), \qquad s_q = \bar{s}_p \qquad (54)$$

its representation in the frequency domain must be that part inside the bracket of Eq. 52 other than $(s - s_k)Y(s)$, prefixed by the factor $1/2$; thus:

$$E(s) = \frac{1}{2} \cdot \frac{(s - s_0)(E + \bar{E})}{(s - s_p)(s - s_q)} \qquad (55)$$

If E is real $(E = |E|)$ and $s_p = j\omega_p$ so that $s_q = -j\omega_p$, then Eq. 54 becomes

$$e_s(t) = |E| \cos \omega_p t \qquad (56)$$

Equation 53 then yields $s_0 = 0$, and the frequency function 55 is

$$E(s) = |E| s/(s^2 + \omega_p{}^2) \qquad (57)$$

On the other hand, if E is negative imaginary $(E = -j|E|)$ and $s_p = j\omega_p$, then Eq. 54 reads

$$e_s(t) = |E| \sin \omega_p t \qquad (58)$$

and Eqs. 53 and 55 yield (in spite of $s_0 \to \infty$)

$$E(s) = |E| \omega_p/(s^2 + \omega_p{}^2) \qquad (59)$$

These are two common forms that expression 54 for the applied voltage may take, while more generally (with E and s_p complex) it is capable of representing a damped sinusoid with any frequency, damping constant, and phase (the angle of E). Equations 50 and 51 or 52 give the net response of the RL circuit to such an applied voltage.

In any case, one can write, instead of Eq. 51 or 52,

$$A_k = [(s - s_k) \cdot Y(s) \cdot E(s)]_{s=s_k} \qquad (60)$$

where $E(s)$ is defined by Eqs. 53 and 55, and $Y(s)$ is the admittance function of the circuit, Eq. 43. What was said earlier about trading circuits and sources can now be restated more specifically through pointing out that one may, in expression 60, confuse the functions $Y(s)$ and $E(s)$ in whole or in part. So long as their product does not change, nothing in the result 50 changes.

As things stand, the first term in Eq. 50 represents the transient part of the solution (complementary function), while the other two terms together are the particular integral or "steady state." If we interchange the identities of $Y(s)$ and $E(s)$, that is to say, let $E(s)$, Eq. 55, be the admittance of a circuit and regard $Y(s)$, Eq. 43, as the frequency-domain representation of a voltage excitation (its time-domain representation is given by Eq. 48), then Eq. 50 correctly yields the net response, but now the first term is a particular integral and the last two terms are the complementary function or transient part of the response.

The exact physical structure of the implied circuit is not immediately evident unless we happen to know of a circuit that has an admittance $Y(s)$ at some pair of terminals that matches the form of expression 55. We will find later that there are many circuits that can have an admittance like the function 55. With $s_0 = 0$ we see from Eq. 129 of Ch. 6 that it can be the admittance of the series RLC circuit. For a pure imaginary s_p value, it becomes the admittance of an LC circuit. Equation 50 is seen, therefore, to be capable of representing the net response of an RLC circuit or of an LC circuit to an applied voltage that is a decaying exponential like the one in Eq. 48.

It is important always to be aware of the fact that the time functions involved in these discussions are pertinent only to the interval following switch closure (the moment the excitation is applied) which is tacitly assumed to occur at $t = 0$. Thus, the time functions involved are to be considered as applying only for $t > 0$. For $t < 0$ the circuit is assumed to be dead, and all time functions are identically zero throughout this interval. Thus, when we say, for example, that $E(s) = E/(s - s_p)$ is the frequency-domain representation (called the *transform*) of $e_s(t) = Ee^{s_p t}$, we expect it to be tacitly understood that $e_s(t)$ is dead before $t = 0$ and equal to the stated exponential function only for $t \geqq 0$.

Now, if $s_p = 0$, the statement just made is still true, because it is true for any complex s_p value, and hence it must be true for a zero value. For $s_p = 0$, the $e_s(t)$ function is one that is zero for $t < 0$, and equal to the constant E for $t > 0$. This is the description of a step function of value E; and so we see that its transform is E/s. That is to say, we have the result that E/s is the frequency-domain representation of $Eu_{-1}(t)$.

From an examination of Eq. 47, describing the process of transformation from the frequency to the time domain, we now observe that this relationship remains valid if we differentiate it with respect to the time. Since $E(s)$ inside the square bracket thus becomes multiplied by s, we recognize the simple rule that *differentiation in the time domain corresponds to multiplication by s in the frequency domain;* and, since integration is the reverse process in the time domain, it must correspond in the frequency domain to division by s, as may be verified through integration on both sides of Eq. 47.

Recalling that the unit impulse $u_0(t)$ is the derivative of the unit step $u_{-1}(t)$, we now see that the transform of $u_0(t)$ must be the constant *unity* since the transform of $u_{-1}(t)$ has just been shown to be $1/s$. The transforms of other singularity functions in the family $u_n(t)$ are thus evident.

Returning to the expressions 50 and 60, we can now inject even greater flexibility into their interpretation. Thus we may, for example, regard the product $Y(s) \cdot E(s)$ in Eq. 60 as a new admittance $Y'(s)$ and associate it with a function $E'(s) = 1$ so that $Y(s) \cdot E(s) = Y'(s) \cdot E'(s)$. Since the corresponding time function, referred to as the *inverse transform* of $E'(s)$, is a unit impulse, Eq. 50 now is interpreted as the impulse response of a circuit having the admittance function (Eqs. 43 and 55)

$$Y'(s) = \frac{H(s - s_0)}{(s - s_1)(s - s_p)(s - s_q)} \quad \text{with} \quad H = \frac{E + \bar{E}}{2L} \quad (61)$$

We cannot at this time discuss the problem of how a circuit having this admittance may be found but, whatever physical structure it may have, we know that its natural behavior is described by Eq. 50. That is to say, for the pertinent equilibrium equation of this network, Eq. 50 represents only the complementary function; all three quantities s_1, s_p, s_q are complex *natural* frequencies.

These interesting and useful ways of interpreting a given expression representing network response are seen to suggest themselves quite naturally once we have established the idea of the frequency- and time-domain aspects of the quantities we have to deal with, together with the result contained in Eq. 60 to the effect that the response in the frequency domain is the product of the frequency-domain functions characterizing the circuit and the excitation. As mentioned above, these functions $[Y(s)$ and $E(s)]$ are spoken of as the *transforms* of the respective time functions, and the latter as the *inverse transforms* of the frequency functions. The product of $Y(s)$ and $E(s)$ is the transform of the desired response, and the corresponding inverse transform, or time function, is found through the simple process made evident by Eqs. 50 and 60. In the following article these matters are generalized to apply to any finite lumped-parameter circuits.

4 The Complete Solution for Any Finite Lumped-Constant Network

In this article we wish to generalize the preceding discussion to show that the same simple procedure applies no matter what the network complexity may be. Although in these discussions we shall assume the voltage $e(t)$ to be an excitation and the current $i(t)$ a response, the procedure remains essentially unaltered if the roles of $e(t)$ and $i(t)$ are interchanged. The derivation of the differential equation expressing the network's equilibrium must, of course, take into account which of the functions, $e(t)$ or $i(t)$, is the excitation and which is the desired response; and the same equation in general does not apply to both situations. The details involved in these matters are supplied in the subsequent article; at the moment we are concerned only with the question of solving the differential equation.

In general such an equation has the form

$$\left(a_n \frac{d^n}{dt^n} + a_{n-1} \frac{d^{n-1}}{dt^{n-1}} + \cdots + a_1 \frac{d}{dt} + a_0 \right) i(t)$$

$$= \left(b_m \frac{d^m}{dt^m} + b_{m-1} \frac{d^{m-1}}{dt^{m-1}} + \cdots + b_1 \frac{d}{dt} + b_0 \right) e(t) \quad (62)$$

We shall consider, to begin with, the following simpler form which this equation may under appropriate circumstances take, and later show what modifications in the procedure are needed to accommodate the general case

$$\left(\frac{d^n}{dt^n} + a_{n-1} \frac{d^{n-1}}{dt^{n-1}} + \cdots + a_1 \frac{d}{dt} + a_0 \right) i(t) = e(t) \quad (63)$$

Essentially, this simplified version of Eq. 62 involves no derivative terms for the excitation $e(t)$. Choosing the coefficient $a_n = 1$ evidently implies no restriction.

The solution of Eq. 63 is sought for the specifications

$$e(t) = 0 \qquad \text{for} \quad t < 0$$

and

$$e(t) = Ee^{s_p t} \quad \text{for} \quad t \geq 0$$

$\quad (64)$

For the particular integral one assumes

$$i_p(t) = B_p e^{s_p t} \quad \text{for} \quad t > 0 \quad (65)$$

whence direct substitution into Eq. 63 leads, in a now familiar manner, to

$$B_p = \frac{E}{s_p{}^n + a_{n-1}s_p{}^{n-1} + \cdots + a_1 s_p + a_0} \quad (66)$$

If the zeros of the polynomial

$$P(s) = s^n + a_{n-1}s^{n-1} + \cdots + a_1 s + a_0 \quad (67)$$

are denoted by $s_1, s_2, \cdots s_n$, result 66 may be expressed in the form

$$B_p = \frac{E}{(s_p - s_1)(s_p - s_2) \cdots (s_p - s_n)} \tag{68}$$

Next we turn our attention to the corresponding homogeneous form of Eq. 63 (the force-free equilibrium equation)

$$\left(\frac{d^n}{dt^n} + a_{n-1}\frac{d^{n-1}}{dt^{n-1}} + \cdots + a_1\frac{d}{dt} + a_0\right) i(t) = 0 \tag{69}$$

and assume for its solution

$$i_0(t) = Be^{st} \tag{70}$$

whereupon substitution and cancelation of the factor e^{st} yields

$$(s^n + a_{n-1}s^{n-1} + \cdots + a_1s + a_0)B = P(s)\cdot B = 0 \tag{71}$$

Demanding a nontrivial solution ($B \neq 0$) leads to the characteristic equation

$$P(s) = 0 \tag{72}$$

and hence to the characteristic values $s_1, s_2, \cdots, s_n$, which are also known as the complex natural frequencies of the circuit. Since an exponential function of the form given in Eq. 70 satisfies Eq. 69 for s equal to each of the n roots of Eq. 72, the most general complementary function reads

$$i_0(t) = B_1e^{s_1t} + B_2e^{s_2t} + \cdots + B_ne^{s_nt} \tag{73}$$

The complete solution to the differential Eq. 63 is thus given by

$$i(t) = i_0(t) + i_p(t) = B_1e^{s_1t} + B_2e^{s_2t} + \cdots + B_ne^{s_nt} + B_pe^{s_pt} \tag{74}$$

Here B_p is determined from Eq. 66. The $B_1 \cdots B_n$ are integration constants that must be determined from a knowledge of the state of the network at $t = 0$. This determination is readily accomplished in the following manner.

From the specification of the excitation function made in Eq. 64 we observe that $e(t)$ is discontinuous at $t = 0$. That is to say, at the initial instant, $e(t)$ jumps from zero to the value E. Hence the value of the left-hand side of Eq. 63 must at this instant likewise jump from zero to E. It is not hard to see that this jump is restricted to the term d^ni/dt^n, for, if any lower derivative were discontinuous at $t = 0$, then all higher derivatives would have infinite values, and the required finite discontinuity could not result. Since $i(t) = 0$ for $t < 0$ (the circuit is assumed to be dead before $t = 0$), the continuity requirement just stated yields

$$i(t) = \frac{di}{dt} = \frac{d^2i}{dt^2} = \cdots = \frac{d^{n-1}i}{dt^{n-1}} = 0 \quad \text{at} \quad t = 0 \tag{75}$$

where by $t = 0$ is meant the instant immediately *after* switch closure.

These n so-called initial conditions suffice to determine the n integration constants in the formal solution 74, for they yield the equations

$$
\begin{aligned}
B_1 + \quad & B_2 + \cdots + \quad & B_n = \quad & -B_p \\
s_1 B_1 + \quad & s_2 B_2 + \cdots + \quad & s_n B_n = \quad & -s_p B_p \\
s_1{}^2 B_1 + \quad & s_2{}^2 B_2 + \cdots + \quad & s_n{}^2 B_n = \quad & -s_p{}^2 B_p \\
& \cdots \cdots \cdots \cdots \cdots \cdots \cdots \cdots \cdots \\
s_1{}^{n-1} B_1 + \quad & s_2{}^{n-1} B_2 + \cdots + \quad & s_n{}^{n-1} B_n = \quad & -s_p{}^{n-1} B_p
\end{aligned}
\tag{76}
$$

which are obtained through considering Eq. 74 and its $n - 1$ successive derivatives for $t = 0$.

The determinant of this system of equations has numerous interesting properties (according to studies due principally to Vandermonde and Cauchy) which enable one to write the desired solutions for the $B_1 \cdots B_n$ by inspection. This determinant reads

$$
D = \begin{vmatrix}
1 & 1 & 1 & \cdots & 1 \\
s_1 & s_2 & s_3 & \cdots & s_n \\
s_1{}^2 & s_2{}^2 & s_3{}^2 & \cdots & s_n{}^2 \\
s_1{}^3 & s_2{}^3 & s_3{}^3 & \cdots & s_n{}^3 \\
\cdot & \cdot & \cdot & \cdots & \cdot \\
s_1{}^{n-1} & s_2{}^{n-1} & s_3{}^{n-1} & \cdots & s_n{}^{n-1}
\end{vmatrix}
\tag{77}
$$

According to determinant theory, its value is unchanged if the elements in the second column are replaced by the differences between their given values and those of the respective elements of the first column. This modified version of D has the form 78 from which all of the ele-

$$
D = \begin{vmatrix}
1 & (s_2{}^0 - s_1{}^0) & 1 & \cdots & 1 \\
s_1 & (s_2{}^1 - s_1{}^1) & s_3 & \cdots & s_n \\
s_1{}^2 & (s_2{}^2 - s_1{}^2) & s_3{}^2 & \cdots & s_n{}^2 \\
s_1{}^3 & (s_2{}^3 - s_1{}^3) & s_3{}^3 & \cdots & s_n{}^3 \\
\cdot & \cdot & \cdot & \cdots & \cdot \\
s_1{}^{n-1} & (s_2{}^{n-1} - s_1{}^{n-1}) & s_3{}^{n-1} & \cdots & s_n{}^{n-1}
\end{vmatrix}
\tag{78}
$$

ments of the new second column are seen to contain the factor $(s_2 - s_1)$, and hence D must contain this factor.

From an alternative modified version of D formed through replacing the elements of the third column in 77 by the differences between their given values and those of the respective elements of the first column, one similarly finds that D must also contain the factor $(s_3 - s_1)$. In like manner one is led to conclude that D must contain the factors $(s_4 - s_1)$, $(s_5 - s_1)$, $\cdots$, $(s_n - s_1)$; and, through forming new 3d, 4th, etc. columns by subtracting the respective elements of the second, one recognizes that $(s_3 - s_2)$, $(s_4 - s_2)$, $\cdots$, $(s_n - s_2)$ must be factors of D.

Continuation and final summary of these thoughts leads to the result that all factors of the form $(s_i - s_j)$ for all $i > j = 1, 2, \cdots, n - 1$ must be contained in D. Since the total number of these factors is $(n - 1) + (n - 2) + \cdots + 1 = n(n - 1)/2$, and, since the terms in any conventional computation of D (obtained, for example, through the usual expansion procedure) are by inspection seen to be homogeneous and of the degree $1 + 2 + 3 + \cdots + (n - 1) = n(n - 1)/2$ in s, we recognize that the value of D can differ from the product of all of these factors by at most a constant multiplier. That is to say, the determinant 77 must be expressible as

$$D = k(s_2 - s_1)(s_3 - s_1)(s_4 - s_1)(s_5 - s_1) \cdots (s_n - s_1)$$

$$(s_3 - s_2)(s_4 - s_2)(s_5 - s_2) \cdots (s_n - s_2)$$

$$(s_4 - s_3)(s_5 - s_3) \cdots (s_n - s_3)$$

$$(s_5 - s_4) \cdots (s_n - s_4) \tag{79}$$

$$\cdots \cdots \cdots \cdots$$

$$(s_n - s_{n-1})$$

in which k is a constant and all the rows of factors are to be multiplied together. From the form of expression 79 it is evident that one of the terms obtained in the process of its evaluation reads $ks_2 s_3^2 s_4^3 \cdots s_n^{n-1}$. Inspection of form 77 shows, on the other hand, that the product of elements on the principal diagonal, which is a term in the expansion of D, is $1 \cdot s_2 s_3^2 s_4^3 \cdots s_n^{n-1}$. It follows that $k = 1$, and so one has the simple result

$$D = \text{II}(s_i - s_j) \quad \text{for all} \quad i > j = 1, 2, \cdots, n - 1 \tag{80}$$

By Cramer's rule the solution for any unknown B_k in the Eq. set 76 reads

$$B_k = -\frac{B_p}{D} \begin{vmatrix} 1 & 1 & 1 \\ s_1 & s_p & s_n \\ s_1^2 & s_p^2 & s_n^2 \\ \cdot & \cdot & \cdot \\ \cdot & \cdot & \cdot \\ \cdot & \cdot & \cdot \\ s_1^{n-1} & s_p^{n-1} & s_n^{n-1} \end{vmatrix} \tag{81}$$

in which the array is the same as in 77 except that the elements 1, s_p, s_p^2, $\cdots$, s_p^{n-1} occupy the kth column. The determinant involved here evidently differs from D only in that the quantity s_p takes the place of s_k. Hence in the resulting expression for B_k all factors $(s_i - s_j)$ cancel except those in the numerator for which $i = p$ or $j = p$, and those in the denominator for which $i = k$ or $j = k$. Hence (as may best be seen through reference to 79) Eq. 81 yields

$$B_k = \frac{-B_p(s_p - s_1)(s_p - s_2) \cdots (s_p - s_{k-1})(s_{k+1} - s_p) \cdots (s_n - s_p)}{(s_k - s_1)(s_k - s_2) \cdots (s_k - s_{k-1})(s_{k+1} - s_k) \cdots (s_n - s_k)} \tag{82}$$

After writing those factors $(s_i - s_j)$ starting with $i = k + 1$ as $(s_j - s_i)$, which can be done because the number of such factors is the same in numerator and denominator, reference to Eq. 68 for B_p shows that its substitution into Eq. 82 will cause cancelation of all the numerator factors in 82 with all denominator factors in 68 except $(s_p - s_k)$. Writing this factor as $-(s_k - s_p)$ and canceling the minus sign with that in Eq. 82 gives

$$B_k = \frac{E}{(s_k - s_1)(s_k - s_2) \cdots (s_k - s_{k-1})(s_k - s_{k+1}) \cdots (s_k - s_n)(s_k - s_p)} \tag{83}$$

With the use of $P(s)$ of Eq. 67 written in the factored form

$$P(s) = (s - s_1)(s - s_2) \cdots (s - s_n) \tag{84}$$

one can express the result given by Eq. 83 in the more compact form

$$B_k = \left[\frac{(s - s_k)E}{(s - s_p)P(s)} \right]_{s=s_k}, \qquad (k = 1, 2, \cdots, n, p) \tag{85}$$

which is seen for $k = p$ to contain also the result shown in Eq. 68. Thus all the constants in the complete solution given by Eq. 74 are evaluated. The ones for $k = 1, 2, \cdots, n$ are those associated with the complementary function $i_0(t)$ and that for $k = p$ yields the amplitude for the particular integral.

Returning now to the general differential equation as given by Eq. 62 we can regard the right-hand side as the sum of the excitation voltages

$$b_0 e(t), \ b_1 \frac{de}{dt}, \cdots, b_m \frac{d^m e}{dt^m} \tag{86}$$

The corresponding net solution is given by adding together

b_0 multiplied by Eq. 74

b_1 multiplied by the first derivative of Eq. 74

b_2 multiplied by the second derivative of Eq. 74

. . . .

b_m multiplied by the mth derivative of Eq. 74

Therefore, if we write the resulting solution to Eq. 62 as

$$i(t) = A_1 e^{s_1 t} + A_2 e^{s_2 t} + \cdots A_n e^{s_n t} + A_p e^{s_p t} \tag{87}$$

then it follows that

$$A_k = B_k Q(s_k) \tag{88}$$

with

$$Q(s) = b_m s^m + b_{m-1} s^{m-1} + \cdots + b_1 s + b_0 \tag{89}$$

If we define

$$Y(s) = Q(s)/P(s) \tag{90}$$

then Eqs. 85 and 88 give

$$A_k = \left[(s - s_k) \cdot Y(s) \cdot \frac{E}{s - s_p} \right]_{s = s_k}, \qquad (k = 1, 2, \cdots, n, p) \tag{91}$$

which is seen to be identical in form with Eq. 44 pertaining to the RL circuit. The only difference in the present general case is that the admittance function $Y(s)$, given by Eq. 90 instead of by Eq. 43, has an appropriately generalized form.

Since all of these derivations are pertinent to the complex constituent excitation voltage $Ee^{s_p t}$ as given by Eq. 64, the actual solution (as in the simpler RL case) is given by the real part of the complex form 87. We can obviate the necessity for indicating this step, just as we did in the discussion of the previous article pertaining to the RL circuit, through adding to Eq. 87 the corresponding result obtained for the conjugate complex voltage excitation. This process leads to the final solution

$$i(t) = A_1 e^{s_1 t} + A_2 e^{s_2 t} + \cdots + A_n e^{s_n t} + A_p e^{s_p t} + A_q e^{s_q t} \qquad (92)$$

which in form looks like Eq. 87 except that a term with $s_q = \bar{s}_p$ is added, but in which the constants A_k are no longer given by Eq. 91. Instead, these new constants are expressible as indicated in Eq. 51 pertinent to the discussion of the RL circuit. The end result is summarized by Eq. 92 together with the following formula (like Eq. 60) for the constants

$$A_k = [(s - s_k) \cdot Y(s) \cdot E(s)]_{s=s_k}, \qquad k = 1, 2, \cdots, n, p, q \qquad (93)$$

and the reminder that the excitation voltage in the time domain

$$e(t) = \tfrac{1}{2}(E e^{s_p t} + \bar{E} e^{s_q t}), \qquad (s_q = \bar{s}_p) \qquad (94)$$

has the transform

$$E(s) = \frac{1}{2} \cdot \frac{(s - s_0)(E + \bar{E})}{(s - s_p)(s - s_q)} \qquad (95)$$

with

$$s_0 = \frac{E s_q + \bar{E} s_p}{E + \bar{E}} \qquad (96)$$

The last steps are identical with the analogous ones discussed for the RL circuit and need not be further elaborated.

All that is said in the previous article about time-domain and frequency-domain representations of both the source and the network, as well as of an interchange, in whole or in part, of the functions $Y(s)$ and $E(s)$ and an appropriate interpretation of the results is thus seen to apply in unaltered form to the most general lumped linear network.

5   The Derivation of Equilibrium Equations for Driving-Point and Transfer Situations; Reciprocity Again

In terms of the relationship between the admittance function $Y(s)$ and the pertinent differential equation, as made evident by inspection of Eqs. 62, 67, 89, and 90, it is seen that one may derive this differential equation through constructing the appropriate admittance or impedance. Since the procedure for doing this follows the same pattern as is used in computing the input or transfer relation for a purely resistive network, one recognizes that the desired differential equation can in most cases be found without recourse to mesh or node equations and the use of tedious elimination procedures. An illustrative example will best serve to show what is meant by these remarks.

In the network of Fig. 8, E_1 is the complex amplitude of a voltage source; I_1 and I_2 are the complex amplitudes of input and output current responses. The given numerical element values are in ohms, henrys, and farads. The problem is to write differential equilibrium equations linking an excitation $e_1(t) = E_1 e^{st}$ with response currents $i_1(t) = I_1 e^{st}$ and $i_2(t) = I_2 e^{st}$.

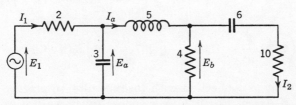

FIG. 8.   Circuit to which the differential Eqs. 104 and 105 are pertinent.

By inspection of Fig. 8, using the impedance concept, we may write the following equations, assuming for the moment that $I_2 = 1$,

$$E_b = 10 + \frac{1}{6s} = \frac{60s + 1}{6s} \tag{97}$$

$$I_a = 1 + \frac{E_b}{4} = \frac{84s + 1}{24s} \tag{98}$$

$$E_a = E_b + 5sI_a = \frac{420s^2 + 245s + 4}{24s} \tag{99}$$

$$I_1 = I_a + 3sE_a = \frac{1260s^3 + 735s^2 + 96s + 1}{24s} \tag{100}$$

and

$$E_1 = E_a + 2I_1 = \frac{2520s^3 + 1890s^2 + 437s + 6}{24s} \tag{101}$$

Because of the linearity of the network, the corresponding voltages and currents for any other value of I_2 are given by the above expressions multiplied by I_2. Hence one has

$$\frac{I_1}{E_1} = Y_{11}(s) = \frac{1}{Z_{11}(s)} = \frac{1260s^3 + 735s^2 + 96s + 1}{2520s^3 + 1890s^2 + 437s + 6} \tag{102}$$

and

$$\frac{I_2}{E_1} = Y_{12}(s) = \frac{24s}{2520s^3 + 1890s^2 + 437s + 6} \tag{103}$$

The appropriate differential equations are now recognized to be

$$\left(2520\,\frac{d^3}{dt^3} + 1890\,\frac{d^2}{dt^2} + 437\,\frac{d}{dt} + 6\right) i_1(t)$$

$$= \left(1260\,\frac{d^3}{dt^3} + 735\,\frac{d^2}{dt^2} + 96\,\frac{d}{dt} + 1\right) e_1(t) \quad (104)$$

and

$$\left(2520\,\frac{d^3}{dt^3} + 1890\,\frac{d^2}{dt^2} + 437\,\frac{d}{dt} + 6\right) i_2(t) = 24\,\frac{de_1}{dt} \quad (105)$$

It is important, in connection with these results, to observe that both $Y_{11}(s)$ and $Z_{11}(s)$ in Eq. 102 are response functions (ratios of output

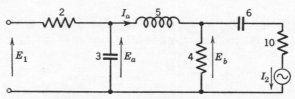

FIG. 9. The circuit of Fig. 8 in which the roles of excitation and response are interchanged, showing that the differential Eq. 110 rather than 105 now applies.

to input), but that the reciprocal of the *transfer* admittance $Y_{12}(s)$ in Eq. 103 is not. That is to say, the so-called *driving-point* function $Y_{11}(s)$ or $Z_{11}(s)$ links E_1 and I_1, regardless of which is the source and which is the response (in Fig. 8 we can equally well regard the source as injecting the current I_1, and interpret E_1 as the resulting terminal voltage), while the transfer function $Y_{12}(s)$ represents the relationship between E_1 and I_2 only if E_1 is the excitation and I_2 the response, as is inherent in the derivation of this function. Correspondingly, we may use the differential Eq. 104 to describe the equilibrium conditions at the input end of the network with either $e_1(t)$ or $i_1(t)$ as the source, while Eq. 105 describes the indicated transfer relationship only with $e_1(t)$ as the source.

Thus, if we wish to regard $i_2(t)$ as an excitation and $e_1(t)$ as a response, it is necessary to consider the redrawn version of Fig. 8 as shown in Fig. 9, which differs in two important respects. First in order to permit E_1 to be a response, the input terminals must be open-circuited, and hence I_1 is zero. Second, since I_2 is a source, E_b is no longer simply the passive voltage drop through the 6-farad capacitance in series with the 10-ohm resistance, but is the algebraic sum of this passive voltage and the terminal voltage of the source (Eq. 97 is no longer applicable). Inasmuch as this terminal voltage is not known, we cannot proceed in the same manner as before.

We can, however, begin at the other end of the network and assume E_1 to be 1 volt. Since $E_1 = E_a$, we then have

$$I_a = -3sE_a = -3s \tag{106}$$

$$E_b = E_a - 5sI_a = 1 + 15s^2 \tag{107}$$

and

$$I_2 = I_a - \frac{E_b}{4} = \frac{15s^2 + 12s + 1}{-4} \tag{108}$$

For any E_1, these values are E_1 times as great. Hence

$$\frac{E_1}{I_2} = Z_{12}(s) = \frac{-4}{15s^2 + 12s + 1} \tag{109}$$

This result is not even similar to the reciprocal of $Y_{12}(s)$ in Eq. 103, thus substantiating the statement that the reciprocal of a transfer function is not also a transfer function. The transfer impedance 109 is pertinent only when I_2 is the excitation, while the transfer admittance 103 applies only when E_1 is the excitation.

The differential equation appropriate to the situation depicted in Fig. 9 is seen from Eq. 109 to be

$$\left(15 \frac{d^2}{dt^2} + 12 \frac{d}{dt} + 1 \right) e_1(t) = -4i_2(t) \tag{110}$$

A response function is always regarded as the ratio of response to excitation, or output to input. Thus, multiplication of a response function by the given excitation yields the associated response. When both of these (excitation and response) pertain to the same point in the network, we refer to their ratio as a driving-point function [like $Y_{11}(s)$ or $Z_{11}(s)$ in Eq. 102]; when the response and excitation are at different points, a transfer function [like $Y_{12}(s)$ in Eq. 103 or Z_{12} in Eq. 109] is involved. As has previously been pointed out, the latter is invariant to an interchange of the points of excitation and observation, a statement known as the *reciprocity theorem*. Its proof in terms of the impedance concept follows the same pattern as that given in Art. 6, Ch. 3, for resistance networks.

As a result of these thoughts we may say that the ratio of I_1 to E_2 in the circuit of Fig. 10 is identical with the ratio of I_2 to E_1 (Eq. 103) in Fig. 8; and, similarly, the ratio of E_2 to I_1 in the circuit of Fig. 11 is identical with the ratio of E_1 to I_2 (Eq. 109) in Fig. 9. In comparing the arrangements of Figs. 8 and 10, it is worth noting that one could

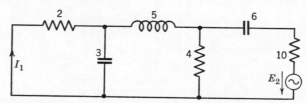

Fig. 10.   The circuit of Fig. 8 with the points of excitation and observation interchanged (application of reciprocity theorem), showing that the differential Eq. 105 (with letters e and i interchanged) does apply to this situation.

combine these by drawing both voltage sources in the same circuit. Because of the short-circuit character of a voltage source, the situation in Fig. 8 then results for $E_2 = 0$, and that in Fig. 10 for $E_1 = 0$. In a similar manner we may combine Figs. 9 and 11, being mindful of the open-circuit character of a current source.

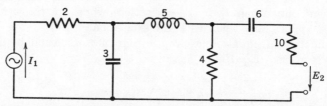

Fig. 11.   The circuit of Fig. 10 with the roles of excitation and response interchanged, or that of Fig. 9 with the points of excitation and observation interchanged. By the reciprocity theorem, the differential Eq. 110 (with letters e and i interchanged) does apply to this situation.

Thus, for a transfer *impedance* function, the points of excitation and observation are both *open-circuited*, while for a transfer *admittance* function they are both *short-circuited*. In either case, the pertinent source has the same open- or short-circuit character, so that its transfer from one of these points to the other leaves the circuit undisturbed. It is this circumstance that is essential in any specific application of the theorem.

It is relevant in this connection also to point out that, if, for a given network, we consider any (open-circuit) driving-point or transfer impedance (the ratio of voltage response across any node pair to current excitation applied at the same or at any other node pair), then all such impedance functions *must have the same poles* because these are the natural frequencies of the given network. That is to say, they are the frequencies of natural oscillation resulting from a disturbancè such as pushing a slug of charge into the network through the application of a current source across a node pair, or the tossing of charges at the capacitances from an electron gun. No matter where the excitation is applied or where we observe a voltage response, the frequencies and decrements involved are obviously the same because they characterize the natural behavior of the total network under force-free conditions.

If the excitation of this same network is a voltage source in series with a branch and the response is a current in the same branch or in any other branch, then the ratio of response to excitation is a (short-circuit) driving-point or transfer admittance; and all such functions have the same poles, which are moreover the same as the poles of the impedances referred to above since they are again the natural frequencies of the same network under the same conditions. Partial evidence of these matters may be seen in the functions given by Eqs. 102 and 103. Awareness of these facts greatly simplifies the solution to many practical problems (see, for example, Prob. 4 at the end of this chapter). Further discussion of these ideas is given in Art. 8.

6 Properties of the General Solution

Let us return now to the complete solution derived in Art. 4, and point out some of its properties that are found to be useful in dealing with many practical problems. In this discussion it is assumed that the excitation is a voltage and the response a current. The response function, therefore, is the driving-point or transfer admittance $Y(s)$, Eq. 90, and the excitation function in the frequency domain is the voltage $E(s)$ defined by Eqs. 95 and 96. If, instead, the excitation is a current and the response a voltage, then the pertinent response function becomes an impedance $Z(s)$, and the excitation in the frequency domain is a current function $I(s)$. Except for this almost trivial change in notation, the form of the solution and the pertinent equations yielding the constants involved in it are precisely the same.

Formally the solution may be written in a way that is free from any tacit assumption as to the nature of either the excitation or the response, and at the same time is perfectly flexible with regard to the proportion in which the excitation and the network share in determining the response. Thus, since the function $Y(s) \cdot E(s)$ or $Z(s) \cdot I(s)$ is in any case a quotient of polynominals in the frequency variable s, we denote this *product* as the single frequency function

$$F(s) = N(s)/D(s) \tag{111}$$

in which $N(s)$ and $D(s)$ are respectively the products of the numerator and denominator polynominals in $Y(s)$ and $E(s)$ or whatever pair of functions is pertinent.

The so-called *poles* of this function are the zeros of the denominator polynomial in $F(s)$. These are contributed in part by the pertinent response function $Y(s)$ or $Z(s)$, and additionally by the excitation function $E(s)$ or $I(s)$. They are placed in evidence through writing

$$D(s) = (s - s_1)(s - s_2)(s - s_3) \cdots (s - s_n) \tag{112}$$

where n is the degree of this polynomial and is larger than the degree n of the polynomial $P(s)$ in Art. 4 by the number of poles associated with the excitation function. That is to say, we are now lumping all the poles into one group, denoting their total number by n, and are not specifically indicating which of these belong to the circuit and which are contributed by the source.

The solution in the time domain, in contrast to Eq. 92, is now written (for $t \geq 0$) more simply as

$$f(t) = A_1 e^{s_1 t} + A_2 e^{s_2 t} + \cdots + A_n e^{s_n t} \tag{113}$$

where the terms in Eq. 92 involving A_p and A_q are no longer set apart as being analytically different from any of the rest, and the symbol $f(t)$ is noncommittal with regard to its identity as either a voltage or a current. Those terms in solution 113 that are associated with the particular poles in the group $s_1 \cdots s_n$ contributed by the source are physically identified with the steady-state portion of the response while the rest collectively represent the transient portion. However, analytically there is no need to make this distinction, since, following the pattern given in Eq. 93, the constants A_k are obtained from the single formula

$$A_k = [(s - s_k)F(s)]_{s=s_k}, \qquad k = 1, 2, \cdots, n \tag{114}$$

$F(s)$ and $f(t)$ are respectively the frequency-domain and the time-domain representations of the network response, and Eq. 114 describes the process by which one obtains the constants in the time-domain representation from a given frequency function $F(s)$. The latter is obtained simply through multiplying together the pertinent response function of the network [$Y(s)$ or $Z(s)$ as the case may be] and the frequency-domain representation of the source. If the latter is the singularity function $u_n(t)$, then (as pointed out in Art. 3) its frequency-domain representation is simply s^n. For the unit impulse $u_0(t)$, this is the constant unity; for the unit step $u_{-1}(t)$ it is $1/s$. For the time function

$$e(t) = \begin{array}{ll} 0 & \text{for} \quad t < 0 \\ Ee^{s_pt} & \text{for} \quad t \geq 0 \end{array} \tag{115}$$

which may more simply be written

$$e(t) = u_{-1}(t) \cdot Ee^{s_pt} \tag{116}$$

the frequency function (as determined in Art. 3) is

$$E(s) = E/(s - s_p) \tag{117}$$

and for

$$e(t) = \tfrac{1}{2}(Ee^{s_pt} + \overline{E}e^{\bar{s}_pt}) \tag{118}$$

it becomes

$$E(s) = \frac{E}{s - s_p} + \frac{\overline{E}}{s - \bar{s}_p} \tag{119}$$

which may alternately be written as in Eqs. 95 and 96.

Thus the formulation of $F(s)$ pertinent to any specific example is a straightforward matter, and its conversion to the time function 113 through use of formula 114 is equally simple in form although in some cases a bit tedious computationally. Application of these compact results to several interesting examples is made in the next article. Before considering these problems, however, it is very helpful to be aware of several properties of our solution which we are now in a position to recognize by inspection.

First in this regard we wish again to call attention to the fact (mentioned in Art. 3) that differentiation in the time domain corresponds to multiplication by s in the frequency domain, and time integration corresponds to division by s. More specifically,

If $f(t)$ is replaced by df/dt

$$\tag{120}$$

Then $F(s)$ becomes replaced by $sF(s)$

and

If $f(t)$ is replaced by $\int f(t)\, dt$

$$\tag{121}$$

Then $F(s)$ becomes replaced by $\dfrac{1}{s} F(s)$

The truth of these statements is obvious from Eqs. 113 and 114. Thus, if we replace $F(s)$ in Eq. 114 by $sF(s)$, it follows that A_k becomes replaced by s_kA_k, and in Eq. 113 this change results from differentiation with respect to t. On the other hand, if $F(s)$ in Eq. 114 is replaced by $\frac{1}{s} F(s)$, then this formula yields $\frac{A_k}{s_k}$, which result is obtained in the time-domain representation 113 through indefinite integration with respect to t.

A frequently useful modification of the time function is that accompanying the replacement of the independent variable t by $t - t_0$ where t_0 is a constant, for this change amounts to a revision of the time origin, or to a displacement of the time function as a whole. Thus, for a positive t_0, the time function is delayed by t_0 seconds. If this change is introduced in Eq. 113, we note that each constant A_k becomes replaced by $A_k e^{-s_k t_0}$, which results in formula 114 if $F(s)$ is there replaced by $e^{-s t_0} F(s)$. Hence we observe that multiplication in the frequency domain by $e^{-s t_0}$ is equivalent to a delay of the time function by t_0 seconds. Specifically,

$$If \ f(t) \ is \ replaced \ by \ f(t - t_0)$$
$$Then \ F(s) \ becomes \ replaced \ by \ e^{-s t_0} F(s)$$

(122)

The manipulation complementary to this one is that of replacing the frequency variable s by $s - s_0$, which corresponds to a displacement of the function $F(s)$ in the s plane. The meaning of such a displacement in the s plane is readily understood if we consider the effect of the change $s \rightarrow (s - s_0)$ upon a typical frequency factor $(s - s_k)$, which may be regarded not only as representing a pole of $F(s)$ through being a factor of the denominator polynomial $D(s)$ as in Eq. 112, but also as being a possible factor of the numerator polynomial $N(s)$ and hence representing any zero of $F(s)$. Since such a frequency factor is converted into $[s - (s_k + s_0)]$, it is clear that displacement of the function $F(s)$ in the s plane should be interpreted as a displacement of all the critical frequencies (zeros and poles) of $F(s)$ by the same amount s_0. We say that the entire pole-zero *constellation* characterizing $F(s)$ is translated as a unit by the amount s_0.

Note carefully the switch in algebraic sign in the statement that if $s \rightarrow (s - s_0)$, then $s_k \rightarrow (s_k + s_0)$; the reason is obvious from the above discussion. Note also that s_0 can have any *complex* value. Specifically, if s_0 is real, the displacement of the pole-zero constellation in the s plane is in the horizontal direction (parallel to the real axis); if s_0 is imaginary, the displacement is in the vertical direction (parallel to the imaginary axis).

The effect upon the time function is immediately evident from Eq. 113, for, if we replace each s_k by $s_k + s_0$, the entire function becomes multiplied by $e^{s_0 t}$. Hence we have the statement:

$$\textit{If } F(s) \textit{ is replaced by } F(s - s_0)$$

$$\textit{Then } f(t) \textit{ becomes replaced by } e^{s_0 t} \cdot f(t) \tag{123}$$

A specific elaboration of this result is indicated by the following:

$$\textit{If } F(s) \to \tfrac{1}{2}[F(s - j\omega_0) + F(s + j\omega_0)]$$

$$\textit{Then } f(t) \to f(t) \cos \omega_0 t \tag{124}$$

The pole-zero constellation of $F(s - j\omega_0)$ is that of $F(s)$ displaced in the positive j axis direction by an amount ω_0, while the constellation of $F(s + j\omega_0)$ is that of $F(s)$ displaced negatively in the j axis direction by ω_0. The frequency-domain function within the brackets has the poles but not the zeros of these displaced constellations (as is obvious from the fact that the sum of two functions is infinite where either one is infinite but not necessarily zero where either one is zero). Usually the locations of the zeros are not of interest since the evaluation of the constants A_k by formula 114 requires only a knowledge of the poles. Since the resultant time function in 124 is a general expression for an amplitude-modulated carrier wave, this particular statement has many useful applications.

In terms of the result formalized by statement 123 it is a simple matter to determine one complementary to the property expressed in statements 120 and 121. That is to say, we may readily determine the effect upon the time function of differentiating or integrating the frequency function $F(s)$. Thus, if we denote a small increment in s by Δs, it follows according to the statement 123 that

$$\textit{If } F(s) \to F(s + \Delta s)$$

$$\textit{Then } f(t) \to e^{-\Delta s t} f(t) \approx (1 - \Delta s t) f(t) \tag{125}$$

If we define

$$F^*(s) = \frac{F(s + \Delta s) - F(s)}{\Delta s} \tag{126}$$

then it follows from 125 that

$$\textit{If } F(s) \to F^*(s)$$

$$\textit{Then } f(t) \to -t f(t) \tag{127}$$

The approximation contained in 125 becomes exact as Δs is allowed to become smaller and smaller, while $F^*(s)$ as given by Eq. 126 approaches the derivative of $F(s)$ with respect to s. Since this process can obviously be repeated any finite number of times in a forward or reverse direction, we have the result that

If $F(s)$ is replaced by $d^n F/ds^n$

Then $f(t)$ is replaced by $(-t)^n f(t)$ $\qquad$ (128)

where negative-integer values for n imply repeated indefinite integration (which, according to elementary principles, cancels a like number of repeated differentiations).

In Art. 9 of Ch. 6 we discussed the process of frequency scaling. It is appropriate that we consider this topic again in the light of our present more general relations. Thus, if in the function $F(s)$ we introduce the change of variable indicated by letting $s = a\lambda$ with a equal to a real constant, then the frequency function $F(s)$ becomes replaced by $\hat{F}(\lambda)$. The critical frequencies are subject to the same transformation, and hence $s_k = a\lambda_k$, where λ_k are the critical frequencies of $\hat{F}(\lambda)$. The formula 114 is replaced by

$$\hat{A}_k = [(\lambda - \lambda_k)\hat{F}(\lambda)]_{\lambda = \lambda_k} \qquad (129)$$

and, since the functions $F(s)$ and $\hat{F}(\lambda)$ have identical values for $s = a\lambda$ while $(s - s_k) = a(\lambda - \lambda_k)$, a comparison of Eqs. 114 and 129 shows that

$$\hat{A}_k = A_k/a \qquad (130)$$

Hence the time function $\hat{f}(\tau)$, related to $\hat{F}(\lambda)$ in the same manner that $f(t)$ is related to $F(s)$, is given by

$$\hat{f}(\tau) = \sum_{k=1}^{n} \hat{A}_k e^{\lambda_k \tau} = \frac{1}{a} \sum_{k=1}^{n} A_k e^{s_k \tau/a} = \frac{1}{a} f\left(\frac{\tau}{a}\right) = \frac{1}{a} f(t) \qquad (131)$$

We may summarize these results in the statement:

If in the function $F(s)$ we make the change of variable $s = a\lambda$ so as to obtain the new frequency function $\hat{F}(\lambda)$, then the time function $f(t)$ becomes replaced by $\hat{f}(\tau) = (1/a)f(t)$ with $\tau = at$. $\qquad$ (132)

For $a < 1$ the transformation $s = a\lambda$ corresponds to a magnification of the pole-zero constellation of the frequency function. That is to say, the function $\hat{F}(\lambda)$ has the same values as $F(s)$ except that they occur at frequencies $(1/a)$ times larger. The frequency-domain function is stretched by a factor $(1/a)$. Since the corresponding transformation of the independent variable in the time domain reads $t = \tau/a$, we see that the time function is compressed in the abscissa direction. Corresponding values of the time function occur $(1/a)$ times sooner. We may say that the frequency scale is contracted and the time scale expanded by the same factor $(1/a)$. Meanwhile the ordinates of the time function are amplified in the same ratio, so that the net effect upon this function is to make it taller and shorter. Scaling the frequency variable s thus has an effect upon both the independent and the dependent variables in the time domain, and these effects are mutually inverse.

A closely related result having comparable practical value is obtained from the following reasoning. When the excitation function applied to a given network is the unit impulse, then $F(s)$ is identical with the response function, for example, with the transfer impedance $Z_{12}(s)$ of that network (for the reason that the transform of the unit impulse is unity). If we consider a unit step excitation applied to this same network, the steady-state response is clearly equal to the value of $Z_{12}(0)$ because the unit step ultimately acts like a direct current and the zero-frequency value of the transfer function determines the d-c response. However, since the unit step response is the integral of the unit impulse response, the ultimate value of the unit step response equals the total area under the unit impulse response curve. Hence we see that

$$\int_0^\infty f(t) \, dt = F(0) \tag{133}$$

Since the relationship between $f(t)$ and $F(s)$ is independent of how $F(s) = I(s) \cdot Z(s)$ or $F(s) = E(s) \cdot Y(s)$ is apportioned between the transform $I(s)$ or $E(s)$ of the excitation and the network response function $Z(s)$ or $Y(s)$, the result expressed by Eq. 133 is generally true, regardless of whether $f(t)$ is actually an impulse response or instead is the response to a more arbitrary excitation. The total area enclosed by the time function equals the zero-frequency value of its transform. In cases where this area is not finite, the value of $F(0)$ will likewise not be finite, and the result becomes meaningless. Since the value of $F(0)$ is unaffected by the change of variable $s = a\lambda$ (with a finite), it is clear that this change cannot affect the net area enclosed by $f(t)$, whence a horizontal contraction of this function must be accompanied by a proportionate vertical expansion or vice versa. The result found through considering a change in the frequency scale is thus seen to be in agreement with that expressed by Eq. 133.

Through use of the property contained in statement 128, we can generalize Eq. 133 to read

$$\int_0^\infty (-t)^n f(t) \, dt = \left(\frac{d^n F}{ds^n}\right)_{s=0} \tag{134}$$

which is, of course, meaningful only if the nth derivative of $F(s)$ for $s = 0$ has a finite value.

The result expressed by Eq. 133 has an interesting implication if $F(0) = 0$, for then the character of $f(t)$ must be such that the net area under a plot of this function is zero. If $f(t)$ has a damped oscillatory character (it must in any case change sign at least once), then the areas enclosed by its positive and negative humps must cancel.* More generally, if $F(s)$ has a zero of order k at $s = 0$ (that is, if it contains the factor s^k), then

$$F(0) = \left(\frac{dF}{ds}\right)_{s=0} = \left(\frac{d^2F}{ds^2}\right)_{s=0} = \cdots \left(\frac{d^{k-1}F}{ds^{k-1}}\right)_{s=0} = 0 \qquad (135)$$

and it follows from the more general relation 134 that

$$\int_0^\infty t^n f(t)\, dt = 0 \quad \text{for} \quad n = 0, 1, 2, \cdots, k - 1 \qquad (136)$$

This result enables one in some cases to draw useful conclusions regarding the asymptotic character of $f(t)$, which is thus seen to be related to the behavior of $F(s)$ for $s = 0$.

The complementary relationship, namely, that linking the asymptotic behavior of $F(s)$ with the character of $f(t)$ for $t = 0$, may also be seen from the general solution given above. If we write Eq. 111 for $F(s)$ in the more explicit form

$$F(s) = \frac{b_m s^m + b_{m-1} s^{m-1} + \cdots + b_1 s + b_0}{a_n s^n + a_{n-1} s^{n-1} + \cdots + a_1 s + a_0} \qquad (137)$$

then the discussion in Arts. 4 and 5 shows that we may regard $f(t)$ as the solution to the differential equation

$$\left(a_n \frac{d^n}{dt^n} + \cdots + a_1 \frac{d}{dt} + a_0\right) f(t) = \left(b_m \frac{d^m}{dt^m} + \cdots + b_1 \frac{d}{dt} + b_0\right) u_0(t) \qquad (138)$$

where the excitation function $u_0(t)$ is the familiar unit impulse. If we consider also the differential equation

$$\left(a_n \frac{d^n}{dt^n} + \cdots + a_1 \frac{d}{dt} + a_0\right) f_0(t) = u_{-1}(t) \qquad (139)$$

---

* Degenerate cases for which this result does not necessarily follow occur if $F(s)$ has j-axis poles so that $f(t)$, according to Eq. 113, has terms that do not decay exponentially. A case in point is $f(t) = \cos \omega t$ for which Eq. 57 shows that $F(s) = s/(s^2 + \omega^2)$. Although $F(0) = 0$, the net area under $f(t)$ is not definable.

in which the excitation function is the unit step, then it is clear that

$$f(t) = b_0 f_0^{(1)}(t) + b_1 f_0^{(2)}(t) + \cdots + b_m f_0^{(m+1)}(t) \qquad (140)$$

where $f_0^{(k)}(t)$ denotes the kth derivative of $f_0(t)$.

As pointed out in Art. 4, the discontinuity in the right-hand member of Eq. 139 at $t = 0$ is met by the highest derivative term on the left, and all lower derivative terms remain continuous at this instant, wherefore

$$f_0^{(n-1)}(0) = f_0^{(n-2)}(0) = \cdots = f_0(0) = 0 \qquad (141)$$

Since Eq. 140 yields

$$f^{(k)}(0) = b_0 f_0^{(k+1)}(0) + b_1 f_0^{(k+2)}(0) + \cdots + b_m f_0^{(k+m+1)}(0) \quad (142)$$

we may conclude that

$$f^{(k)}(0) = 0 \quad \text{for} \quad k + m + 1 \leq n - 1 \qquad (143)$$

or that

$$f^{(k)}(0) = 0 \quad \text{for} \quad k = 0, 1, 2, \cdots, \nu = n - m - 2 \qquad (144)$$

while the asymptotic behavior of $F(s)$ according to Eq. 137 is described by

$$F(s) \rightarrow \frac{b_m/a_n}{s^{\nu+2}} \quad \text{for} \quad s \rightarrow \infty \qquad (145)$$

Thus, if $F(s)$ for large s disappears as $1/s^{\nu+2}$, then we can immediately predict that the associated time function $f(t)$ and its successive derivatives through the order ν are zero for $t = 0$; the first nonzero initial derivative has the order $\nu + 1$. For the singularity functions, $f(t) = u_n(t)$ and $F(s) = s^n$, so that $\nu = -(n + 2)$. The unit linear ramp having the order $n = -2$ thus yields $\nu = 0$; the unit parabolic ramp for which $n = -3$ yields $\nu = 1$, and so forth. These results are obviously in agreement with statement 144.

If $f(t)$ and a number of its successive derivatives are zero for $t = 0$, then it is clear that the time function is rather slow in getting under way. In a practical problem this fact means that the transient response is slow in building up. The property stated by relations 144 and 145 makes this character of the response obvious from an inspection of the frequency function $F(s)$.

7 Illustrative Examples

The first example that we shall consider is illustrated by the sequence of networks shown in Fig. 12 for which the transfer function is the impedance

$$Z_{12}^{(n)}(s) = E_2/I_1 = 1/(s+1)^n \tag{146}$$

for $n = 1, 2, 3, 4, 5$ respectively.* These networks are readily found

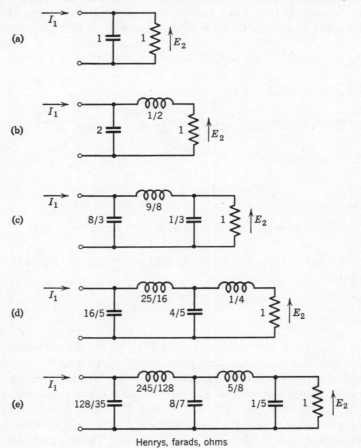

Henrys, farads, ohms

FIG. 12. A sequence of networks having the transfer impedance 146 for integer values of n from 1 through 5.

from the stated transfer impedance $Z_{12}(s)$ by a method of synthesis to be discussed later on. The reader may check the result 146 in each case as an exercise.

* The superscript (n) is here used merely as a designation for the impedance associated with a pole of like order.

The function 146 is said to have an nth-order pole at the point $s = -1$ on the negative real axis of the complex frequency plane. Let our problem be that of finding the unit impulse response of this series of networks. That is to say, assuming the input current to be $i_1 = u_0(t)$, we wish to compute the output voltage $e_2(t)$ for $t \geq 0$.

Since the transform of the excitation in this case is unity, we have $F(s) = Z_{12}(s)$. Beginning with the simplest network for which $n = 1$, we have from past experience (or by the method of this chapter) the time function

$$e_2^{(1)}(t) = f_1(t) = e^{-t} \quad \text{for} \quad t \geq 0 \tag{147}$$

Next we observe that

$$Z_{12}^{(2)}(s) = 1/(s+1)^2 = -dZ_{12}^{(1)}/ds \tag{148}$$

and hence the property 128 immediately tells us that the time function corresponding to $n = 2$ reads

$$e_2^{(2)}(t) = f_2(t) = tf_1(t) = te^{-t} \quad \text{for} \quad t \geq 0 \tag{149}$$

Noting that

$$\frac{d}{ds}\left[\frac{1}{(s+1)^2}\right] = \frac{-2}{(s+1)^3} \tag{150}$$

we obtain in like manner the time function corresponding to $n = 3$, namely:

$$e_2^{(3)}(t) = f_3(t) = \frac{t}{2}f_2(t) = \frac{t^2}{2}e^{-t} \quad \text{for} \quad t \geq 0 \tag{151}$$

At this stage it is fairly evident that the impulse response of nth order is given by

$$f_n(t) = \frac{1}{(n-1)!}t^{n-1}e^{-t} \quad \text{for} \quad t \geq 0 \tag{152}$$

which for $n = 1, 2, 3$ checks the results given by Eqs. 147, 149, and 151, and for a larger integer value of n yields at once the impulse response for the network of corresponding order.

If for these same networks we wish to know the unit step response, we have but to integrate the time functions just found. Through integration by parts, beginning with $f_2(t)$ and proceeding in sequence, it is not hard to find that the unit step response of order n is given by

$$h_n(t) = \int_0^t f_n(t)\, dt = 1 - [f_1(t) + f_2(t) + \cdots + f_n(t)] \tag{153}$$

or more explicitly

$$h_n(t) = 1 - \left[1 + t + \frac{t^2}{2!} + \frac{t^3}{3!} + \cdots + \frac{t^{n-1}}{(n-1)!}\right] e^{-t} \quad \text{for} \quad t \geq 0 \tag{154}$$

It is interesting to observe that the bracket expression equals the first n terms of the Maclaurin expansion of e^t. Throughout the time interval $0 \leq t < t_1$ for which these terms represent a reasonable approximation to e^t, the bracket times e^{-t} is approximately equal to unity, and $h_n(t)$ is nearly zero. Beyond this interval the bracket times e^{-t} tends toward zero, and $h_n(t)$ tends toward unity which is its ultimate value. The unit step input is thus seen to be delayed and stretched into a gradual rise by this type of network with the response function 146.

The interval $0 \leq t < t_1$ is referred to as the "precursor" interval during which the response is substantially zero, and the one immediately following, during which the response gradually rises, is the so-called interval of "signal formation." Thereafter the response is equal essentially to its permanent state.

Returning to expression 152 for the impulse response, we observe that it has the character of a single hump with a maximum equal to

$$(f_n)_{\max} = \frac{(n-1)^{n-1} e^{-(n-1)}}{(n-1)!} \tag{155}$$

occurring at

$$t_{\max} = (n-1) \text{ seconds} \tag{156}$$

Since the impulse response is the derivative of the step response, we note that the value 155 represents the maximum slope of the step response, and Eq. 156 yields the time of its occurrence, which is roughly at the center of the interval of signal formation. This most important part of the transient response is thus seen to be delayed in time proportional to the order of the pole in the response function 146.

We can easily shorten this delay time as much as we wish through making a transformation of the frequency scale according to statement 132. Thus if, for example, we let

$$\lambda = (n-1)s \tag{157}$$

then the time variable becomes

$$\tau = t/(n-1) \tag{158}$$

and the impulse response is given by

$$\hat{f}_n(\tau) = \frac{(n-1)^{n-1}}{(n-2)!} (\tau e^{-\tau})^{n-1} \tag{159}$$

which has the maxima

$$(\hat{f}_n)_{\max} = \frac{(n-1)^{n-1}e^{-(n-1)}}{(n-2)!} \tag{160}$$

occurring at

$$\tau_{\max} = 1 \text{ second} \tag{161}$$

We may say that the particular frequency scaling given by Eq. 157 has resulted in a normalization of our time scale, since the time of signal formation now occurs at 1 second, independent of the order n. Since the frequency transformation 157 becomes degenerate for $n = 1$, these results are relevant to the orders $n = 2, 3, \cdots$.

The corresponding transfer impedance is changed from the value given by Eq. 146 to

$$Z_{12}^{(n)}(\lambda) = \frac{(n-1)^n}{[\lambda + (n-1)]^n} \tag{162}$$

and the pertinent networks for n values up to 5 are those given in Fig. 12 with all inductance and capacitance values divided by $(n-1)$, due regard being paid to the n value appropriate to each order. In this new sequence the second network (which is the same as before) is characterized by a transfer function having a double pole at $\lambda = -1$; for the third network the transfer function has a third-order pole at $\lambda = -2$; for the fourth, the transfer function has a fourth-order pole at $\lambda = -3$, and so forth.

Plots of the unit impulse response for this sequence of networks are shown in Fig. 13 for the orders $n = 2, 3, 4, 5$, while Fig. 14 shows the

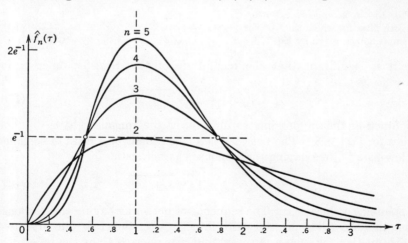

FIG. 13. The unit impulse response (Eq. 159) of the networks in Fig. 12 modified by having their L and C values divided by $(n-1)$.

appearance of the step response for $n = 5$ only. Even for this order it is a rather slowly rising function. Networks of this type are characterized by a sluggish response which stems from the fact that the natural

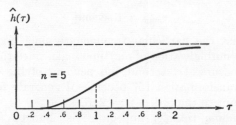

FIG. 14. The unit step response of the network in Fig. 12(e) with its L and C values divided by 4.

frequencies are nonoscillatory. We shall now consider some cases where this restriction no longer applies.

The network shown in Fig. 15 has the transfer impedance

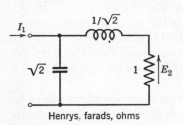

Henrys, farads, ohms

FIG. 15. A second-order Butterworth filter for which the transfer impedance is given by Eq. 163.

$$Z_{12}(s) = \frac{E_2}{I_1} = \frac{1}{s^2 + s\sqrt{2} + 1} \qquad (163)$$

which may be written

$$Z_{12}(s) = \frac{1}{(s - s_1)(s - s_2)} \qquad (164)$$

with

$$s_1 = \frac{-1 + j}{\sqrt{2}}, \qquad s_2 = \frac{-1 - j}{\sqrt{2}} \qquad (165)$$

It is significant that the magnitude of this transfer function for $s = j\omega$ is

$$|Z_{12}(j\omega)| = 1/\sqrt{1 + \omega^4} \qquad (166)$$

a function that approximates unity over the range $-1 < \omega < 1$ and zero for $|\omega| > 1$. The network is a constituent of a class of so-called "low-pass" filters having the response characteristic

$$|Z_{12}(j\omega)| = 1/\sqrt{1 + \omega^{2n}} \qquad (167)$$

for integer values of n. The sequence of networks having this response function are called "Butterworth filters" (after the chap who first used this function for such a purpose) and n is referred to as the order of a particular network of this type. Thus the circuit of Fig. 15 is referred to as a second-order Butterworth filter, the one of first order being identical with the first in the sequence defined by Eq. 146 and hence is network (a) in Fig. 12.

In Fig. 16 are shown the first three functions of this type. They all pass through the point $1/\sqrt{2}$ (the half-power point) at $\omega = 1$, and

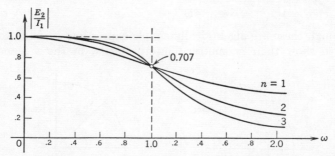

Fig. 16. Steady-state a-c response characteristics (Eq. 167) for Butterworth filters of orders 1, 2, and 3.

with a further increase in n yield a better approximation to the rectangle shown dotted, this being the ideal low-pass filter characteristic.

If we wish to find the unit impulse response of this network, then $Z_{12}(s)$ of Eq. 164 is identified with the frequency function $F(s)$ in Eq. 114 from which we see that

$$A_1 = 1/(s_1 - s_2), \qquad A_2 = 1/(s_2 - s_1) \tag{168}$$

Using the values of the critical frequencies as given in Eq. 165 we have

$$A_1 = -j/\sqrt{2}, \qquad A_2 = j\sqrt{2} \tag{169}$$

and Eq. 113 yields the time function

$$f(t) = \frac{-j}{\sqrt{2}} (e^{jt/\sqrt{2}} - e^{-jt/\sqrt{2}})e^{-t/\sqrt{2}} = \sqrt{2}\,e^{-t/\sqrt{2}} \sin{(t/\sqrt{2})} \tag{170}$$

If we are interested in the unit step response, we may integrate the impulse response just found or consider the appropriately modified function $F(s)$. Thus, since the transform of the excitation now is $I_1(s) = 1/s$, we may write

$$F(s) = I_1(s) \cdot Z_{12}(s) = \frac{1}{(s - s_0)(s - s_1)(s - s_2)} \tag{171}$$

and consider that we now have the critical frequency $s_0 = 0$ in addition to those given by Eq. 165. Use of Eq. 114 then yields

$$A_0 = \frac{1}{(s_0 - s_1)(s_0 - s_2)}, \qquad A_1 = \frac{1}{(s_1 - s_0)(s_1 - s_2)}$$

$$A_2 = \frac{1}{(s_2 - s_0)(s_2 - s_1)} \tag{172}$$

Although these are algebraically simple expressions, it is nevertheless useful to show their geometrical interpretation in the s plane, since

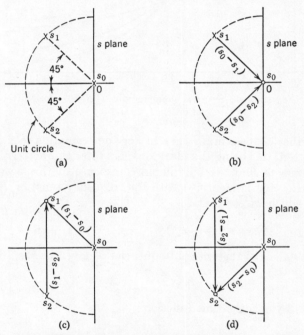

Fig. 17. s-plane sketches of (a) the poles of the function 171; and (b), (c), and (d), the frequency factors in the expressions 172 for the coefficients A_0, A_1, A_2 respectively (relative to computation of the step response of the second-order Butterworth filter shown in Fig. 15).

such interpretation becomes extremely helpful in more elaborate situations. With reference to the sketches in Fig. 17, part (a) is a portion of the s plane with crosses marking the positions of the poles s_0, s_1, s_2 of the function $F(s)$ of Eq. 171. In parts (b), (c), (d) are shown respectively the vector interpretations for the frequency factors $(s_i - s_j)$ entering into the expressions 172 for A_0, A_1, A_2. From the sketch of part (b) we see by inspection that the angles of the two vectors cancel, and since the length of each is unity we have at once that $A_0 = 1$, a result that is much more easily seen from the graphical portrayal of the frequency factors than it is obtainable through their numerical substitution into the pertinent algebraic expression. In fact, one can set down the values for the A's almost at a glance. Thus from the sketch in part (c) we see that the net angle equals 90° plus 135°, and that the product of the magnitudes of the two factors is $\sqrt{2}$; so $A_1 = -e^{-j\pi/4}/\sqrt{2} \cdot A_2$ according to the sketch of part (d) obviously has the conjugate value.

Observe that the vectors representing the frequency factors for A_0 have their tips at s_0; those for A_1 have their tips at s_1, and those for A_2 have their tips at s_2. In each case the factors collectively form a bunch of vectors emanating from the various other critical frequencies, and all converge upon the particular critical frequency pertinent to the A_k in question; that is to say, they all converge upon s_0 for the determination of A_0, upon s_1 for the determination of A_1, and so forth. The A_k in question is then given by the reciprocal product of the pertinent vectors. We will see that this simple geometrical picture applies in all cases, although in more general situations the expressions for the A's will involve numerator as well as denominator factors.

In our present example (the unit step response of the network of Fig. 15) we thus have

$$A_0 = 1, \qquad A_1 = -e^{-j\pi/4}/\sqrt{2}, \qquad A_2 = -e^{j\pi/4}/\sqrt{2} \qquad (173)$$

and hence the associated time function according to Eq. 113 becomes

$$h(t) = 1 - (1/\sqrt{2})\left(e^{j\left(\frac{t}{\sqrt{2}}-\frac{\pi}{4}\right)} + e^{-j\left(\frac{t}{\sqrt{2}}-\frac{\pi}{4}\right)}\right)e^{-t/\sqrt{2}}$$

$$= 1 - \sqrt{2}\, e^{-t/\sqrt{2}} \cos\left[(t/\sqrt{2}) - (\pi/4)\right] \qquad (174)$$

The reader may check this result through integration of Eq. 170. He may, incidentally, check Eq. 170 through noting that the present problem is identical with the series RLC circuit in Fig. 21 of Ch. 5, and, since $R = 1$, the current in the circuit equals the voltage across R. Hence Eq. 77 of Ch. 5 should in essence agree with Eq. 170 above. Noting that in our present problem we have $C = \sqrt{2}$, $\omega_d = \alpha = 1/\sqrt{2}$, $\omega_0 = 1$, the agreement is verified if we recall that the excitation in the problem of Ch. 5 is a current impulse of value C.

A plot of the unit step response according to Eq. 174 is shown in Fig. 18. We observe that the interval of signal formation sets in almost immediately, and, in contrast with the response shown in Fig. 14, the

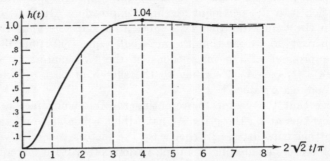

FIG. 18.   Unit step response of the second-order Butterworth filter shown in Fig. 15.

present one overshoots the ultimate value unity and approaches it in an oscillatory manner, a maximum overshoot of about 4 per cent occurring at $t = \pi\sqrt{2}$ seconds.

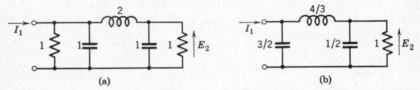

FIG. 19.   Networks whose common transfer impedance (apart from a factor 1/2) is the third-order Butterworth function given in Eqs. 175 and 176 respectively for the double-loaded circuit (a) and the single-loaded circuit (b).   Element values are in henrys, farads, and ohms.

Suppose we next consider the circuits of Fig. 19 which are third-order Butterworth filters. For the first of these [part (a)] the transfer impedance is

$$Z_{12}(s) = \frac{E_2}{I_1} = \frac{1/2}{s^3 + 2s^2 + 2s + 1} \tag{175}$$

and for the second [part (b)] we have

$$Z_{12}(s) = \frac{E_2}{I_1} = \frac{1}{s^3 + 2s^2 + 2s + 1} \tag{176}$$

In the first of these networks the current source in parallel with the input resistance can be converted into an equivalent voltage E_1 (numerically equal to I_1) in series with this resistance. The ratio E_2/E_1 is then identical with E_2/I_1. Thus the first of these two networks is actually appropriate to a resistive voltage source drive, while the second is appropriate to a lossless current source drive. Both have the same

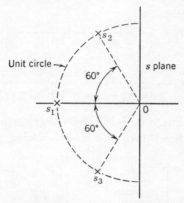

FIG. 20. Pole pattern for the third-order Butterworth function 177.

transfer function except for a factor $1/2$. Suppose we consider only the function 176. In factored form this one reads

$$Z_{12}(s) = \frac{1}{(s - s_1)(s - s_2)(s - s_3)} \qquad (177)$$

with

$$s_1 = -1, \qquad s_2 = -1/2 + j\sqrt{3}/2, \qquad s_3 = -1/2 - j\sqrt{3}/2 \qquad (178)$$

Figure 20 shows the pole pattern of this transfer function in the s plane. As for the second-order Butterworth filter, the poles are symmetrically spaced on the left half of the unit circle.

Suppose we evaluate the unit step response. Then we again have for the transform of the excitation $I_1(s) = 1/s$ and

$$F(s) = I_1(s) \cdot Z_{12}(s) = \frac{1}{(s - s_0)(s - s_1)(s - s_2)(s - s_3)} \qquad (179)$$

where the pole at $s_0 = 0$ is contributed by the source function. Equation 114 gives

$$A_0 = \frac{1}{(s_0 - s_1)(s_0 - s_2)(s_0 - s_3)}$$

$$A_1 = \frac{1}{(s_1 - s_0)(s_1 - s_2)(s_1 - s_3)}$$

$$A_2 = \frac{1}{(s_2 - s_0)(s_2 - s_1)(s_2 - s_3)}$$

$$A_3 = \frac{1}{(s_3 - s_0)(s_3 - s_1)(s_3 - s_2)}$$

(180)

The factors appropriate to these coefficients are geometrically portrayed by the s-plane sketches shown in Fig. 21. Being mindful of the sym-

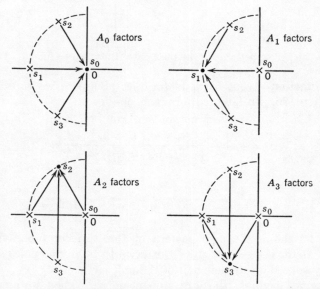

FIG. 21. s-plane sketches showing the frequency factors in the coefficients given by Eqs. 180.

metrical distribution of the poles on the unit circle, one may write by inspection of these sketches

$$A_0 = 1, \qquad A_1 = -1, \qquad A_2 = j/\sqrt{3}, \qquad A_3 = -j/\sqrt{3} \quad (181)$$

Substitution into Eq. 113 then yields the desired time function

$$f(t) = 1 - e^{-t} + \frac{j}{\sqrt{3}} (e^{j\sqrt{3}\,t/2} - e^{-j\sqrt{3}\,t/2})e^{-t/2}$$

$$= 1 - e^{-t} - (2/\sqrt{3}\,)e^{-t/2} \sin \sqrt{3}\,t/2 \tag{182}$$

A plot of this response is shown in Fig. 22. From a comparison with that in Fig. 18 we note that the step response of the third-order Butterworth filter is only slightly slower than that pertinent to the filter of

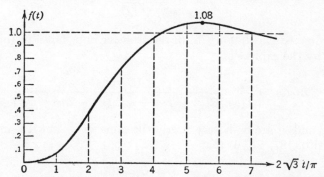

Fig. 22. Unit step response of the third-order Butterworth filters shown in Fig. 19.

second-order (the first maximum falls at about $t = 5$ seconds as compared with $t = 4.4$ seconds), but the amount of overswing and oscillation about the final value is markedly larger, the first maximum being 7.5 per cent in excess of unity while the second-order filter exhibits a 4.3 per cent excess. One might have predicted this greater tendency on the part of the third-order filter to exhibit an oscillatory response

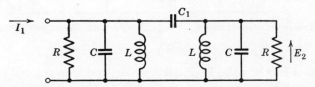

Fig. 23. The double-tuned circuit for which the sinusoidal steady-state response is discussed in Art. 11, Ch. 6.

because its pair of conjugate poles is relatively closer to the j axis. Thus in Fig. 20 we note that this pair of poles lies on radial lines that are 30° from the j axis whereas in Fig. 17 pertinent to the second-order filter they lie on 45° radial lines. The second-order network is more highly damped than the third-order one.

Let us now compute the transient response of the pair of loosely coupled RLC circuits whose sinusoidal steady-state response is evaluated in Art. 11, Ch. 6. A sketch of this circuit (Fig. 28 of Ch. 6) is redrawn here in Fig. 23. On the assumption that $(C_1/C) \ll 1$, the two parallel RLC circuits are loosely coupled, and the magnitude of the ratio E_2/I_1 exhibits a bandpass characteristic (as shown in Fig. 32 of Ch. 6) that is relatively narrow compared with the center frequency of the band which is essentially equal to the resonant frequency of either parallel LC, that is

$$\omega_0 = 1/\sqrt{LC} \tag{183}$$

According to Eq. 189 of Ch. 6, the transfer impedance of this circuit is given by the expression

$$Z_{12}(s) = \frac{E_2}{I_1} = \frac{(C_1/C)s^3}{C(s^2 + 2\alpha s + \omega_a{}^2)(s^2 + 2\alpha s + \omega_b{}^2)} \tag{184}$$

where ω_a and ω_b are both very nearly the same as ω_0, but it is important to note (Eq. 187, Ch. 6) that

$$\omega_a - \omega_b = C_1\omega_0/C \tag{185}$$

In Fig. 31 of Ch. 6, which shows a portion of the s plane near the positive resonant frequencies, the difference 185 between the imaginary

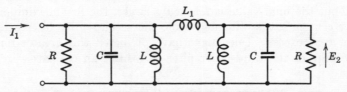

Fig. 24. The double-tuned circuit of Fig. 23 with inductive rather than capacitive coupling.

parts of this pair of poles is denoted by $2a$; and it is pointed out in the accompanying discussion that the value of the parameter a relative to the damping constant $\alpha = 1/2RC$ of the parallel RLC circuits is critical in that it controls the character of the resultant bandpass characteristic [compare parts (a) and (b) of Fig. 32, Ch. 6].

A so-called "maximally flat" characteristic results if we choose $a = \alpha$ [Fig. 32(a), Ch. 6]. With this condition implied, comparison of Fig. 31 of Ch. 6 with any one of the sketches in Fig. 17 above for the second-order Butterworth filter of Fig. 15 (ignoring the source pole at

$s_0 = 0$) reveals that, for the vicinity of their passbands, these filters have the same geometrical pole patterns. We may say that the maximally flat bandpass filter of Fig. 23 has a second-order Butterworth characteristic, albeit its passband is centered at $\omega = \omega_0$ instead of being centered at $\omega = 0$. It is incidentally of practical interest to note that one can obtain essentially the same response characteristic using inductive rather than capacitive coupling, as is shown in the circuit of Fig. 24. Here the coupling is loose if $(L/L_1) \ll 1$. The reader may show as a simple exercise that for this circuit we get

$$Z_{12}(s) = \frac{E_2}{I_1} = \frac{(L/L_1)s\omega_0{}^2}{C(s^2 + 2\alpha s + \omega_a{}^2)(s^2 + 2\alpha s + \omega_b{}^2)} \tag{186}$$

and very nearly

$$\omega_a -. \omega_b = L\omega_0/L_1 \tag{187}$$

in place of the Eqs. 184 and 185 (the identities of ω_a and ω_b are interchanged, but this is an insignificant difference).

In practical circuits the inductive coupling is commonly accomplished through allowing the magnetic fields of the two self-inductances

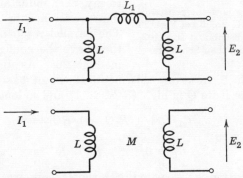

Fig. 25. Showing how the inductive coupling in Fig. 24 may be replaced by an equivalent mutual inductance.

to have mutual linkages. The inductive part of the circuit is then redrawn as shown in Fig. 25 where the top sketch shows the inductances as they appear in the circuit of Fig. 24 and the bottom one is its equivalent involving the mutual inductance M. Since by assumption the coupling is loose, it is a simple matter to establish the relationship among L, L_1, and M. Thus in the top circuit practically none of I_1 passes through L_1 because the very much smaller L is in parallel with it. The voltage drop in this parallel L, therefore, is $I_1 Ls$, and E_2 equals the fraction $L/(L + L_1)$ of this value. That is,

$$(E_2/I_1) = L^2 s/(L + L_1) \approx L^2 s/L_1 \qquad (188)$$

For the pair of mutually coupled inductances one has

$$(E_2/I_1) = Ms \qquad (189)$$

Hence we see that

$$(L/L_1) = (M/L) \qquad (190)$$

is the equivalence relation sought. Thus, if in Fig. 24 we replace the inductances by their equivalent mutually coupled pair as shown in Fig. 25, the transfer impedance 186 is changed only in that the factor (L/L_1) in the numerator is replaced by (M/L), and Eq. 187 becomes

$$\omega_a - \omega_b = M\omega_0/L \qquad (191)$$

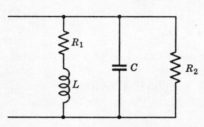

FIG. 26. Showing how the resistance in the parallel RLC circuits of Figs. 23 and 24 may be redistributed (Eq. 192) without affecting their behavior.

Regarding practical matters it should also be mentioned that some loss will be associated with the inductances in this circuit. That is to say, each inductance L will have some resistance in series with it. The parallel resonant RLC circuits then have the configuration shown in Fig. 26. As brought out in Prob. 51 of Ch. 6, however, this modified circuit has essentially the same impedance if its Q is high $(RC\omega_0 \gg 1)$ and so long as

$$R_1/L + 1/R_2 C = 1/RC \qquad (192)$$

In the extreme case

$$R_1 = 0, \qquad R_2 = R \qquad (193)$$

all of the dissipation is associated with the capacitances, as in Figs. 23 or 24. In the opposite extreme case

$$R_2 = \infty, \qquad R_1 = L/RC \qquad (194)$$

all of the dissipation is associated with the inductances. The response characteristic 184 or 186 is not affected (except for second-order effects) by such redistribution of the associated losses so long as the energy lost per cycle is small compared with the peak value of the stored energy (condition for a high-Q or low-loss circuit; see Art. 6 of Ch. 7).

Now let us choose the condition $a = \alpha$ leading to the maximally flat characteristic and proceed with a computation of the transient response of this so-called "double-tuned" circuit. Since $\alpha = 1/2RC$ and, by Eqs. 185, 187, and 190, $2a = C_1\omega_0/C = L\omega_0/L_1 = M\omega_0/L$ according to whether we choose capacitively or inductively coupled circuits, the maximally flat condition is met through setting

$$1/RC = C_1\omega_0/C = M\omega_0/L \tag{195}$$

and the transfer impedances for these circuits are given respectively by

$$Z_{12}(s) = \frac{s^3 2a\sqrt{L/C}}{(s - s_1)(s - s_2)(s - s_3)(s - s_4)}, \quad (C\text{-coupled}) \tag{196}$$

$$Z_{12}(s) = \frac{s\omega_0{}^2 2a\sqrt{L/C}}{(s - s_1)(s - s_2)(s - s_3)(s - s_4)}, \quad (L\text{-coupled}) \tag{197}$$

where

$$\begin{aligned}
s_1 &= -a + j(\omega_0 + a), & s_2 &= -a - j(\omega_0 + a) \\
s_3 &= -a + j(\omega_0 - a), & s_4 &= -a - j(\omega_0 - a)
\end{aligned} \tag{198}$$

Suppose we first assume an input current $i_1(t)$ equal to a unit impulse. Then $F(s)$ becomes identical with $Z_{12}(s)$, and, if we take the function 196, the evaluation of Eq. 114 gives

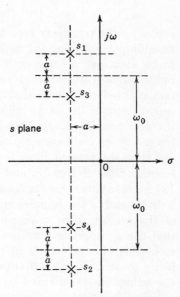

$$A_1 = \frac{s_1{}^3 2a\sqrt{L/C}}{(s_1 - s_2)(s_1 - s_3)(s_1 - s_4)}$$

$$A_2 = \frac{s_2{}^3 2a\sqrt{L/C}}{(s_2 - s_1)(s_2 - s_3)(s_2 - s_4)}$$

$$\tag{199}$$

$$A_3 = \frac{s_3{}^3 2a\sqrt{L/C}}{(s_3 - s_1)(s_3 - s_2)(s_3 - s_4)}$$

$$A_4 = \frac{s_4{}^3 2a\sqrt{L/C}}{(s_4 - s_1)(s_4 - s_2)(s_4 - s_3)}$$

Fig. 27. Pole pattern of the transfer impedance 196 or 197 relevant to the double-tuned circuits of Figs. 23 and 24.

Reference to the qualitative sketch of the pertinent pole pattern shown in Fig. 27 and awareness of the fact that $\omega_0 \gg a$ allow us to evaluate the expressions 199 by inspection. Thus we see that $s_1 \approx j\omega_0$, $(s_1 - s_2) \approx j2\omega_0$,

$(s_1 - s_3) = j2a$, $(s_1 - s_4) \approx j2\omega_0$. Hence we get

$$A_1 = A_2 = \frac{\omega_0\sqrt{L/C}}{4}, \qquad A_3 = A_4 = \frac{-\omega_0\sqrt{L/C}}{4} \qquad (200)$$

and substitution into Eq. 113 yields the time function

$$f(t) = \frac{\omega_0\sqrt{L/C}}{4}[e^{j(\omega_0+a)t} + e^{-j(\omega_0+a)t} - e^{j(\omega_0-a)t} - e^{-j(\omega_0-a)t}]e^{-at}$$

which reduces to

$$f(t) = -\omega_0\sqrt{L/C}\,e^{-at}\sin at \sin \omega_0 t \qquad (201)$$

Except for the minus sign, one obtains the same result using the transfer impedance 197, as the reader may easily verify.

Since $a \ll \omega_0$, we observe that the function 201 may be regarded as a slowly varying envelope

$$f_e(t) = \omega_0\sqrt{L/C}\,e^{-at}\sin at \qquad (202)$$

enclosing the relatively rapidly varying oscillation $\sin \omega_0 t$. Apart from an unimportant constant multiplier, this envelope function is observed to be identical in form with the impulse response 170 of the second-order Butterworth filter given in Fig. 15, a result that stems from the fact pointed out above that (for $a = 1/\sqrt{2}$) the pole pattern of our present circuit in the vicinity of its resonance region is identical with the pole pattern of the filter in Fig. 15 for the vicinity of its midband frequency or resonance region which is centered at $s = 0$. We may say that the present filter is in a sense the bandpass analogue of the lowpass filter of Fig. 15, and the property expressed by the statement 124 substantiates this conclusion.

If instead of the impulse response we evaluate the unit step response of this circuit then, since we have $I_1(s) = 1/s$, the only difference is that the appropriate function $F(s)$ is divided by s. As may readily be seen, this change results in the corresponding coefficients A_1 and A_3 being those in Eq. 200 divided by $j\omega_0$ while A_2 and A_4 turn out to be the values in 200 divided by $-j\omega_0$. These changes result in yielding the time function

$$h(t) = \sqrt{L/C}\,e^{-at}\sin at \cos \omega_0 t \qquad (203)$$

This function has the same character as the unit impulse response 201, differing only in that the envelope is ω_0 times smaller and the enclosed oscillation has its phase shifted by 90°.

In the lowpass filter the preceding examples show that there is a very decided difference in character between the impulse response and the step response. In the bandpass network the two are essentially alike except for a significant difference in amplitude. We may partially appreciate the reason for this circumstance through observing that, for the lowpass circuit, zero frequency is its midband frequency and hence the sudden application of a constant (zero frequency) amounts to suddenly applying an excitation having the midband frequency. Therefore, if we consider in the bandpass circuit the sudden application of an excitation having its midband frequency ω_0, we should obtain a response that is analogous to the step response of the lowpass circuit.

We thus consider next an excitation

$$i_1(t) = u_{-1}(t) \sin \omega_0 t \qquad (204)$$

for which the transform, according to Eq. 59, is

$$I_1(s) = \omega_0/(s^2 + \omega_0{}^2) \qquad (205)$$

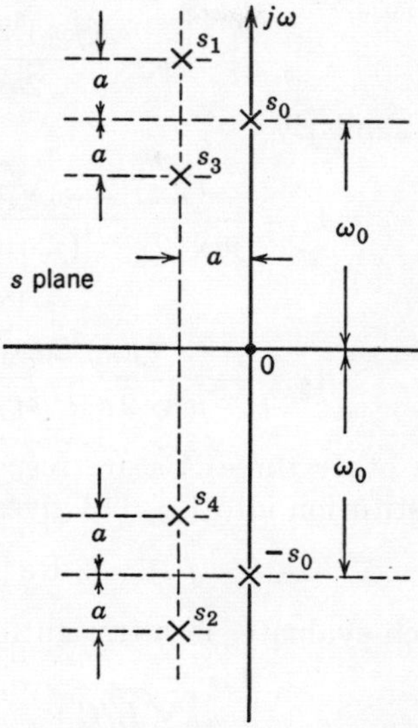

FIG. 28. Pole pattern of the function 206 pertinent to the response of the double-tuned circuit of Fig. 23 to the sinusoidal excitation 204.

and with the transfer impedance 196 we then have

$$F(s) = I_1(s) \cdot Z_{12}(s)$$

$$= \frac{s^3 2a\omega_0 \sqrt{L/C}}{(s - s_1)(s - s_2)(s - s_3)(s - s_4)(s - j\omega_0)(s + j\omega_0)} \qquad (206)$$

The s-plane sketch analogous to that in Fig. 27 is shown in Fig. 28. The present pole pattern differs only in that the poles at $\pm s_0 = \pm j\omega_0$ are added, thus yielding a pattern in the vicinity of s_0 that is like the pattern in Fig. 17(a) pertinent to the step response of the circuit of Fig. 15. We have now to evaluate six coefficients A_k using formula 114. These have the form

$$A_k = \frac{s_k{}^3 2a\omega_0 \sqrt{L/C}}{(s_k - s_1)(s_k - s_2) \cdots (s_k + j\omega_0)} \qquad (207)$$

with the factor $(s_k - s_k)$ left out. Visualizing the frequency factors as vectors in the s-plane sketch of Fig. 28, we note for the computation of A_0 that $(s_0 - s_1) = a\sqrt{2}\,e^{-j\pi/4}$, $(s_0 - s_3) = a\sqrt{2}\,e^{j\pi/4}$, $(s_0 - s_4) \approx (s_0 - s_2) \approx (s_0 + s_0) = j2\omega_0$. Hence Eq. 207 gives

$$A_0 = \frac{(j\omega_0)^3 2a\omega_0\sqrt{L/C}}{2a^2(j2\omega_0)^3} = \frac{\omega_0\sqrt{L/C}}{8a} \tag{208}$$

and similarly

$$A_1 = \frac{(j\omega_0)^3 2a\omega_0\sqrt{L/C}}{ja\sqrt{2}\,e^{j\pi/4}(j2a)(j2\omega_0)^3} = -\frac{\omega_0\sqrt{L/C}}{8a\sqrt{2}}\,e^{-j\pi/4} \tag{209}$$

and

$$A_3 = \frac{(j\omega_0)^3 2a\omega_0\sqrt{L/C}}{-ja\sqrt{2}\,e^{-j\pi/4}(-j2a)(j2\omega_0)^3} = -\frac{\omega_0\sqrt{L/C}}{8a\sqrt{2}}\,e^{j\pi/4} \tag{210}$$

The other three A's are respectively the conjugates of these. Hence substitution into Eq. 113 gives for the time function

$$f(t) = 2\,\mathrm{Re}\,[A_0 e^{s_0 t} + A_1 e^{s_1 t} + A_3 e^{s_3 t}] \tag{211}$$

which evaluates in a straightforward manner to

$$f(t) = \frac{\omega_0\sqrt{L/C}}{4a}\left[1 - \sqrt{2}\,e^{-at}\cos\left(at - \frac{\pi}{4}\right)\right]\cos\omega_0 t \tag{212}$$

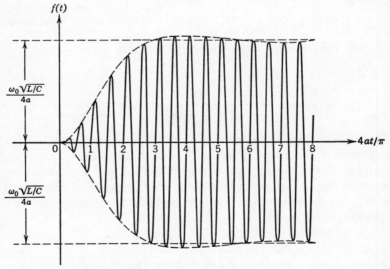

FIG. 29.   Response of the double-tuned circuit of either Fig. 23 or 24 for a suddenly applied sinusoid of midband frequency.

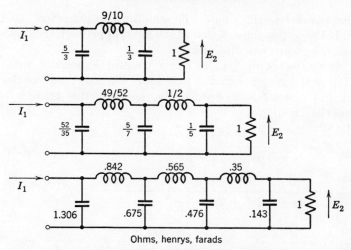

Ohms, henrys, farads

Fig. 30. A sequence of circuits having the transfer functions given by Eqs. 213, 214, 215.

For $a = 1/\sqrt{2}$, the bracket expression coincides with Eq. 174 for the step response of the lowpass second-order Butterworth filter. Therefore the plot of Fig. 18 becomes the envelope of function 212 which has the appearance shown in Fig. 29. The response of a bandpass filter to the sudden application of a sinusoid having its midband frequency is thus seen to have an envelope that is the step-function response of the lowpass analogue of that filter. If one is interested only in the manner in which the oscillatory response builds up, the computations may be markedly simplified through computing only the step response of the lowpass analogue. The latter, as we have seen, is that network whose pole pattern in the vicinity of $\omega = 0$ is geometrically a replica of the pole pattern of the bandpass network in the vicinity of $\omega = \omega_0$.

Another interesting sequence of networks, shown in Fig. 30, has a transfer impedance with the pole pattern illustrated in the s-plane sketch of Fig. 31. The poles are uniformly spaced

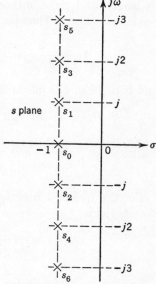

Fig. 31. Pole pattern of the transfer impedance 215.

on a line parallel to the j axis. To simplify the numerical work, the spacing between the poles as well as the interval between their locus and the j axis are chosen equal to unity.

The first network in Fig. 30 has a transfer impedance with three poles, the next has one with five poles, and the impedance of the third network has seven poles. Specifically the respective transfer impedance functions read

$$Z_{12}(s) = \frac{2}{(s+1)(s^2+2s+2)} \tag{213}$$

$$Z_{12}(s) = \frac{10}{(s+1)(s^2+2s+2)(s^2+2s+5)} \tag{214}$$

and

$$Z_{12}(s) = \frac{100}{(s+1)(s^2+2s+2)(s^2+2s+5)(s^2+2s+10)} \tag{215}$$

Considering the impulse response, the coefficients A_k are particularly easy to evaluate for this type of function since all the frequency factors $(s_i - s_j)$ are vectors in the s plane that are an integer number of units in length and point either straight up or straight down (i.e., in the j-axis direction). Thus for the three-pole function 213 we have

$$A_1 = \frac{2}{j \cdot j2} = -1 = A_2, \qquad A_0 = \frac{2}{-j \cdot j} = 2 \tag{216}$$

and hence Eq. 113 yields the impulse response

$$f(t) = (-e^{jt} + 2 - e^{-jt})e^{-t} = -(e^{jt/2} - e^{-jt/2})^2 e^{-t} \tag{217}$$

which is recognized to be

$$f(t) = 4e^{-t}\sin^2 t/2 \tag{218}$$

For the five-pole function 214, inspection of the appropriate s-plane sketch yields

$$A_3 = \frac{10}{j \cdot j2 \cdot j3 \cdot j4} = \frac{10}{4!} = A_4 \tag{219}$$

$$A_1 = \frac{10}{-j \cdot j \cdot j2 \cdot j3} = -4 \cdot \frac{10}{4!} = A_2 \tag{220}$$

$$A_0 = \frac{10}{-j \cdot (-j2) \cdot j \cdot j2} = 6 \cdot \frac{10}{4!} \tag{221}$$

and hence the impulse response becomes

$$f(t) = \frac{10}{4!} (e^{j2t} - 4e^{jt} + 6 - 4e^{-jt} + e^{-j2t})e^{-t} = \frac{10}{4!} (e^{jt/2} - e^{-jt/2})^4 e^{-t}$$

(222)

or

$$f(t) = \frac{20}{3} e^{-t} \sin^4 \frac{t}{2}$$

(223)

Similarly, for the seven-pole function 215, inspection of the s-plane sketch of Fig. 31 leads directly to

$$A_5 = \frac{100}{-6!} = A_6$$

(224)

$$A_3 = \frac{100}{5!} = 6 \cdot \frac{100}{6!} = A_4$$

(225)

$$A_1 = \frac{100}{-2 \cdot 4!} = -15 \cdot \frac{100}{6!} = A_2$$

(226)

$$A_0 = \frac{100}{3! \cdot 3!} = 20 \cdot \frac{100}{6!}$$

(227)

and to the time function

$$f(t) = -\frac{100}{6!} (e^{j3t} - 6e^{j2t} + 15e^{jt} - 20 + 15e^{-jt} - 6e^{-j2t} + e^{-j3t})e^{-t}$$

(228)

which is seen to be the equivalent of

$$f(t) = \frac{80}{9} e^{-t} \sin^6 \frac{t}{2}$$

(229)

Additional transfer functions in this sequence follow the same pattern, and the impulse response that results from this type of pole distribution is thus clear.

With the tools developed in this chapter, the transient response of networks having known pole and zero distributions are thus seen to be readily evaluated, especially if the pole-zero constellations in the s plane form some pattern with geometric symmetry or uniformity. When networks are to be found with prescribed transient behavior, it is well to be familiar with the characteristic types of response that result from certain simple pole configurations. It is partly for this reason that the above examples are presented.

8   Driving-Point and Transfer Functions

For any given network one may define numerous driving-point and transfer functions according to a variety of possible choices that can be made regarding the locations of the excitation and the response and to whether each of these two functions is a voltage or a current. A simple example will best serve further to emphasize the characteristics that such a family of transfer functions have in common, and simul-

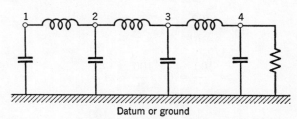

Datum or ground

Fig. 32.   Network to which the relations given by Eqs. 230 are relevant.

taneously to illustrate an effective method for their derivation applicable to ladder networks.

Consider the network shown in Fig. 32 in which all element values are assumed to equal unity. The voltages of the respective nodes relative to the datum are denoted by E_1, E_2, E_3, E_4. Currents in the series branches in the left-to-right reference direction are I_{12}, I_{23}, I_{34}. A source, connected between the datum and node 1, feeds current I_1 into this node. Beginning at the right-hand end, we have in the usual fashion

$$I_{34} = E_4(1 + s)$$

$$E_3 = E_4 + I_{34}s = E_4(1 + s + s^2)$$

$$I_{23} = I_{34} + E_3s = E_4(1 + 2s + s^2 + s^3)$$

$$E_2 = E_3 + I_{23}s = E_4(1 + 2s + 3s^2 + s^3 + s^4) \qquad (230)$$

$$I_{12} = I_{23} + E_2s = E_4(1 + 3s + 3s^2 + 4s^3 + s^4 + s^5)$$

$$E_1 = E_2 + I_{12}s = E_4(1 + 3s + 6s^2 + 4s^3 + 5s^4 + s^5 + s^6)$$

$$I_1 = I_{12} + E_1s = E_4(1 + 4s + 6s^2 + 10s^3 + 5s^4 + 6s^5 + s^6 + s^7)$$

From these equations we can readily form a considerable number of response functions (output over input). To begin with, we have the family of impedances

$$\frac{E_4}{I_1} = \frac{1}{1 + 4s + 6s^2 + 10s^3 + 5s^4 + 6s^5 + s^6 + s^7}$$

$$\frac{E_3}{I_1} = \frac{1 + s + s^2}{1 + 4s + 6s^2 + 10s^3 + 5s^4 + 6s^5 + s^6 + s^7}$$

$$\frac{E_2}{I_1} = \frac{1 + 2s + 3s^2 + s^3 + s^4}{1 + 4s + 6s^2 + 10s^3 + 5s^4 + 6s^5 + s^6 + s^7} \qquad (231)$$

$$\frac{E_1}{I_1} = \frac{1 + 3s + 6s^2 + 4s^3 + 5s^4 + s^5 + s^6}{1 + 4s + 6s^2 + 10s^3 + 5s^4 + 6s^5 + s^6 + s^7}$$

which all have the same poles, because these are the natural frequencies of the circuit under open-circuit conditions.

From the same Eqs. 230 we may also form the dimensionless response functions

$$E_4/E_1, \quad E_4/E_2, \quad E_4/E_3, \quad E_3/E_1, \quad E_3/E_2, \quad E_2/E_1 \qquad (232)$$

which the reader can readily write down for himself, and observe incidentally that only these ratios, and not perchance their reciprocals, are response functions (output over input). Of these, the first, fourth, and sixth have identical poles, they being the natural frequencies of the circuit of Fig. 32 with node 1 grounded, or the zeros of the input impedance E_1/I_1 in the group 231. The second and fifth functions have poles which are the natural frequencies of the circuit with node 2 grounded, and the poles of the third function are the natural frequencies with node 3 grounded.

The following six additional transfer impedances are also obtained from the Eqs. 230

$$E_4/I_{12}, \quad E_3/I_{12}, \quad E_2/I_{12}, \quad E_4/I_{23}, \quad E_3/I_{23}, \quad E_4/I_{34} \qquad (233)$$

These correspond to abridgments of the network of Fig. 32 rather than to the whole of it. Thus the first three functions pertain to that portion of the network remaining after deletion of the branches confluent at node 1; for the next two functions the branches confluent at node 2 are likewise discarded, and the last one finally involves only the parallel capacitance and resistance at node 4.

Now we will derive for this same network an analogous set of response functions, assuming that a source connected between the datum and node 4 injects a current I_4. Currents in the series branches in the right-to-left reference direction are now denoted by I_{43}, I_{32}, I_{21}. Beginning at the left-hand end, we then have

$$I_{21} = E_1 s, \qquad E_2 = E_1 + I_{21}s = E_1(1 + s^2)$$

$$I_{32} = I_{21} + E_2 s = E_1(2s + s^3)$$

$$E_3 = E_2 + I_{32}s = E_1(1 + 3s^2 + s^4)$$

$$I_{43} = I_{32} + E_3 s = E_1(3s + 4s^3 + s^5) \tag{234}$$

$$E_4 = E_3 + I_{43}s = E_1(1 + 6s^2 + 5s^4 + s^6)$$

$$I_4 = I_{43} + E_4(1 + s) = E_1(1 + 4s + 6s^2 + 10s^3 + 5s^4 + 6s^5 + s^6 + s^7)$$

From these relations we immediately have the transfer impedances:

$$\frac{E_1}{I_4} = \frac{1}{1 + 4s + 6s^2 + 10s^3 + 5s^4 + 6s^5 + s^6 + s^7}$$

$$\frac{E_2}{I_4} = \frac{1 + s^2}{1 + 4s + 6s^2 + 10s^3 + 5s^4 + 6s^5 + s^6 + s^7}$$

$$\frac{E_3}{I_4} = \frac{1 + 3s^2 + s^4}{1 + 4s + 6s^2 + 10s^3 + 5s^4 + 6s^5 + s^6 + s^7} \tag{235}$$

$$\frac{E_4}{I_4} = \frac{1 + 6s^2 + 5s^4 + s^6}{1 + 4s + 6s^2 + 10s^3 + 5s^4 + 6s^5 + s^6 + s^7}$$

Again we note that the same poles are involved in all of these functions, and that they are the same as the poles of the impedances 231. The reason, of course, is that they are the same open-circuit natural frequencies.

The sequence of relations 234 also yields expressions for the dimensionless transfer functions

$$E_1/E_4, \quad E_1/E_3, \quad E_1/E_2, \quad E_2/E_4, \quad E_2/E_3, \quad E_3/E_4 \tag{236}$$

and again it is important to recognize that the reciprocals of these ratios are not transfer functions.

Additional transfer impedances analogous to the group 233, obtainable from relations 234, are

$$E_1/I_{43}, \quad E_2/I_{43}, \quad E_3/I_{43}, \quad E_1/I_{32}, \quad E_2/I_{32}, \quad E_1/I_{21} \tag{237}$$

The appropriate abridgments of the network of Fig. 32 to which these correspond are obvious.

Transfer functions pertinent to current fed into node 2 or into node 3 may now easily be formed. Since I_{12} is the current entering node 2 *from* the left, and I_{21} is that divergent *toward* the left, it is clear that the sum $I_{12} + I_{21}$ for the same node potential E_2 must equal the net current I_2 fed into node 2 by a source which is connected between this node and the datum. That is to say,

$$\frac{I_2}{E_2} = \frac{I_{12}}{E_2} + \frac{I_{21}}{E_2} \tag{238}$$

From the relations 230 and 234 we have

$$\frac{I_{12}}{E_2} = \frac{1 + 3s + 3s^2 + 4s^3 + s^4 + s^5}{1 + 2s + 3s^2 + s^3 + s^4}, \qquad \frac{I_{21}}{E_2} = \frac{s}{1 + s^2} \tag{239}$$

whence

$$\frac{I_2}{E_2} = \frac{1 + 4s + 6s^2 + 10s^3 + 5s^4 + 6s^5 + s^6 + s^7}{1 + 2s + 4s^2 + 3s^3 + 4s^4 + s^5 + s^6} \tag{240}$$

Thus we obtain the transfer functions analogous to the ones given by Eqs. 231 and 235:

$$
\begin{aligned}
\frac{E_2}{I_2} &= \frac{1 + 2s + 4s^2 + 3s^3 + 4s^4 + s^5 + s^6}{1 + 4s + 6s^2 + 10s^3 + 5s^4 + 6s^5 + s^6 + s^7} \\[2mm]
\frac{E_3}{I_2} &= \frac{E_2}{I_2} \times \frac{E_3}{E_2} = \frac{(1 + s + s^2)(1 + s^2)}{1 + 4s + 6s^2 + 10s^3 + 5s^4 + 6s^5 + s^6 + s^7} \\[2mm]
\frac{E_4}{I_2} &= \frac{E_2}{I_2} \times \frac{E_4}{E_2} = \frac{(1 + s^2)}{1 + 4s + 6s^2 + 10s^3 + 5s^4 + 6s^5 + s^6 + s^7} \\[2mm]
\frac{E_1}{I_2} &= \frac{E_2}{I_2} \times \frac{E_1}{E_2} = \frac{1 + 2s + 3s^2 + s^3 + s^4}{1 + 4s + 6s^2 + 10s^3 + 5s^4 + 6s^5 + s^6 + s^7}
\end{aligned} \tag{241}
$$

It is important to note that the ratios E_3/E_2 and E_4/E_2 needed in the formation of the second and third of these impedances must be taken from Eqs. 230 whereas the ratio E_1/E_2 used in the fourth one is that pertinent to the relations 234, as may be seen from the fact that all ratios must be transfer functions.

Analogously we may obtain transfer impedances pertinent to a source current I_3 fed into node 3. Again, using relations 230 and 234, we have

$$\frac{I_{23}}{E_3} = \frac{1 + 2s + s^2 + s^3}{1 + s + s^2}, \qquad \frac{I_{32}}{E_3} = \frac{2s + s^3}{1 + 3s^2 + s^4} \tag{242}$$

from which we get

$$\frac{I_3}{E_3} = \frac{I_{23} + I_{32}}{E_3} = \frac{1 + 4s + 6s^2 + 10s^3 + 5s^4 + 6s^5 + s^6 + s^7}{(1 + s + s^2)(1 + 3s^2 + s^4)} \qquad (243)$$

and thus obtain the set of transfer impedances:

$$\frac{E_3}{I_3} = \frac{(1 + s + s^2)(1 + 3s^2 + s^4)}{1 + 4s + 6s^2 + 10s^3 + 5s^4 + 6s^5 + s^6 + s^7}$$

$$\frac{E_1}{I_3} = \frac{E_3}{I_3} \times \frac{E_1}{E_3} = \frac{(1 + s + s^2)}{1 + 4s + 6s^2 + 10s^3 + 5s^4 + 6s^5 + s^6 + s^7}$$

$$\frac{E_2}{I_3} = \frac{E_3}{I_3} \times \frac{E_2}{E_3} = \frac{(1 + s + s^2)(1 + s^2)}{1 + 4s + 6s^2 + 10s^3 + 5s^4 + 6s^5 + s^6 + s^7} \qquad (244)$$

$$\frac{E_4}{I_3} = \frac{E_3}{I_3} \times \frac{E_4}{E_3} = \frac{1 + 3s^2 + s^4}{1 + 4s + 6s^2 + 10s^3 + 5s^4 + 6s^5 + s^6 + s^7}$$

Again one should observe that all ratios must be transfer functions. The poles of the impedance functions 241 and 244 are, of course, the same open-circuit natural frequencies as before.

Now let us assume that a current source is bridged across nodes 2 and 3. That is to say, we create a driving point through soldering leads onto this pair of nodes. If we denote the current of this source by $I_2{}^3$ and assume that the reference arrow points toward node 3, then in terms of the previous node-to-datum sources we have

$$I_2{}^3 = I_3 = -I_2 \qquad (245)$$

and by superposition, the voltage at node 4, for example, becomes

$$E_4 = \left(\frac{E_4}{I_3} - \frac{E_4}{I_2}\right) I_2{}^3 \qquad (246)$$

Substitution from Eqs. 241 and 244 yields

$$\frac{E_4}{I_2{}^3} = \frac{(1 + 3s^2 + s^4) - (1 + s^2)}{1 + 4s + 6s^2 + 10s^3 + 5s^4 + 6s^5 + s^6 + s^7}$$

$$= \frac{2s^2 + s^4}{1 + 4s + 6s^2 + 10s^3 + 5s^4 + 6s^5 + s^6 + s^7} \qquad (247)$$

Similarly we obtain

$$\frac{E_3}{I_2{}^3} = \left(\frac{E_3}{I_3} - \frac{E_3}{I_2}\right) = \frac{(1 + s + s^2)(2s^2 + s^4)}{1 + 4s + 6s^2 + 10s^3 + 5s^4 + 6s^5 + s^6 + s^7}$$

$$\frac{E_2}{I_2{}^3} = \left(\frac{E_2}{I_3} - \frac{E_2}{I_2}\right) = \frac{-(s + 2s^2 + 2s^3 + 3s^4 + s^5 + s^6)}{1 + 4s + 6s^2 + 10s^3 + 5s^4 + 6s^5 + s^6 + s^7}$$

(248)

$$\frac{E_1}{I_2{}^3} = \left(\frac{E_1}{I_3} - \frac{E_1}{I_2}\right) = \frac{-(s + 2s^2 + s^3 + s^4)}{1 + 4s + 6s^2 + 10s^3 + 5s^4 + 6s^5 + s^6 + s^7}$$

If the source is a current $I_2{}^4$ between nodes 2 and 4, and the desired response is the voltage of node 3, we find the pertinent transfer impedance

$$\frac{E_3}{I_2{}^4} = \left(\frac{E_3}{I_4} - \frac{E_3}{I_2}\right) = \frac{-s + s^2 - s^3}{1 + 4s + 6s^2 + 10s^3 + 5s^4 + 6s^5 + s^6 + s^7}$$

(249)

Suppose the source is a voltage E_{23} in series with the branch connecting nodes 2 and 3. To any of the expressions 247 or 248 we can then apply a source transformation converting the current source $I_2{}^3$ in parallel with the branch in question into an equivalent voltage source in series with this branch. Since in the present example this conversion yields $I_2{}^3 = E_{23}/s$, we have from 247 for instance

$$\frac{E_4}{E_{23}} = \frac{2s + s^3}{1 + 4s + 6s^2 + 10s^3 + 5s^4 + 6s^5 + s^6 + s^7} \qquad (250)$$

Inasmuch as the current through the 1-ohm resistance at the right-hand end of the network is numerically equal to E_4, we may alternately regard this expression as a short-circuit transfer admittance for this same network, and observe (as pointed out in the closing paragraph of Art. 5 above) that its poles are the same as those of any of the open-circuit driving-point or transfer impedance functions.

Again, we might want the driving-point impedance between nodes 2 and 4. Analogous to the expression 249 we may derive the ratios $E_4/I_2{}^4$ and $E_2/I_2{}^4$, whereupon the desired result is found to be

$$\frac{E_{24}}{I_2{}^4} = \frac{E_4}{I_2{}^4} - \frac{E_2}{I_2{}^4} = \frac{2s + 8s^2 + 3s^3 + 9s^4 + s^5 + 2s^6}{1 + 4s + 6s^2 + 10s^3 + 5s^4 + 6s^5 + s^6 + s^7} \qquad (251)$$

Since this is a driving-point impedance, we can turn it upside down and multiply by the ratio 249 to form a response function E_3/E_{24} from which one can determine the potential of node 3 in terms of a *voltage* source connected across nodes 2 and 4.

It should now be clear how any desired response function may readily be formed for this or any other ladder network. It is also abundantly clear that *all* the driving-point and transfer impedances for a given network, in general, have the same poles and that these are the open-circuit natural frequencies of that network.

It is, of course, possible to create special situations for which this fact may not strictly be true, but these are degenerate forms to which the above conclusions do not necessarily apply. In any situation one can always create degenerate cases that do not fit the conclusions pertinent to the random one.

The zeros of driving-point impedances are the natural frequencies of the network with the pertinent input short-circuited. Regarding the impedance 251, for example, we may say at once, that the characteristic equation yielding the natural frequencies of the network of Fig. 32 with nodes 2 and 4 joined reads

$$2s + 8s^2 + 3s^3 + 9s^4 + s^5 + 2s^6 = 0 \qquad (252)$$

The zeros of transfer functions do not have any similar physical significance. They are those particular values of complex frequency for which the input and output points in the network are virtually isolated from each other, but these frequencies have no direct influence upon the transient behavior comparable to that which the zeros and poles of driving-point functions exert.

9   Arbitrary Initial Conditions

At the close of Ch. 5 we pointed out that a discussion of transient-network response based upon the tacit assumption of initial rest conditions is nevertheless capable of meeting any situation involving arbitrary initial conditions. This circumstance follows from the fact that the solution for any arbitrary situation is obtained simply through adding together the response for initial rest conditions and the various responses due to the initial values of currents in inductances and charges in capacitances. Since the latter may be regarded as created by appropriately chosen voltage or current sources acting at $t = 0$, the solution for the case with arbitrary initial conditions is expressible as a sum of solutions, each involving initial rest conditions.

For example, suppose we wish to compute the voltage $e_4(t)$ at node 4 of the circuit of Fig. 32 for a unit current impulse applied at node 1 when it is additionally specified that at $t = 0$ there is a charge of 1/2 coulomb in the capacitance at node 2 and a current of 3 amperes in the inductance joining nodes 2 and 3. The initial charge of 1/2 coulomb we can assume to have gotten into the capacitance at node 2 through a current impulse with the value 1/2 being applied at this node; and the initial current of 3 amperes we can imagine to be the result of applying a current step of value 3 across the node pair 2–3 or a voltage impulse of value 3 in series with the inductance linking this node pair. (In general, if this inductance has the value L_{23}, then the voltage impulse has the value $3L_{23}$.)

The desired solution is obtained through adding together a unit impulse response involving the transfer function E_4/I_1, the 1/2-multiplied unit impulse response involving the transfer function E_4/I_2, and the 3-multiplied unit step response for the transfer function $E_4/I_2{}^3$ (or the 3-multiplied unit impulse response for the transfer function E_4/E_{23}). Since all three transfer functions involve the same poles, the three additive parts of this solution involve the same damped sinusoids, albeit with different amplitudes and time phases. As might have been expected on physical grounds, the effect of the arbitrary initial conditions is thus seen merely to alter the amplitudes and phases of the damped sinusoidal terms in the expression for the network response; their frequencies and decrements are the same as they would be for initial rest conditions.

When arbitrary initial conditions are to be considered in the determination of network response, we thus see that it is necessary to determine additional appropriately chosen transfer functions. The discussion in the previous article shows that all the pertinent transfer functions may in any case be derived from the same set of basic relations in a manner that lends economy and circumspection to the total computations.* Apart from this aspect of things, a solution to the problem involving arbitrary initial conditions is found in the same way as is the response for initial rest conditions.

PROBLEMS

1. Given: $e_1(t) = 10 \sin (10/\sqrt{3})t + 10 \cos 10\sqrt{3}\, t$.

(a) Compute the impedance $Z(s)$ at the input terminals, and express it in the form of a quotient of frequency factors. Make an s-plane sketch indicating the pole locations by crosses and the zeros by circles. Through regarding the frequency factors

---

* When the network geometry is more general than that of an unbalanced ladder, it may be necessary to use the methods discussed in the following chapter to determine the necessary driving-point or transfer functions.

as vectors and evaluating them by inspection, compute the value of the impedance for $s = j10/\sqrt{3}$ and $s = j10\sqrt{3}$, the radian frequencies involved in $e_1(t)$.

(b) Determine the current $i(t)$ in the steady state.

(c) Determine the transfer ratio E_2/E_1 as a function of s. Represent its zeros and poles in an s-plane sketch as in part (a), and compute the complex values of this transfer ratio for $s = j10/\sqrt{3}$ and $s = j10\sqrt{3}$. Thus obtain the expression for $e_2(t)$.

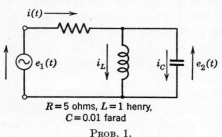

$R = 5$ ohms, $L = 1$ henry, $C = 0.01$ farad

PROB. 1.

(d) Find the currents $i_L(t)$ and $i_C(t)$ in the inductance and capacitance elements separately, and show that their sum equals $i(t)$ as found in part (b).

(e) Find the expression for the instantaneous power taken by the circuit and the value of the average power.

(f) Compute the average power taken by the circuit if: (i) the second term in $e_1(t)$ is zero, (ii) the first term in $e_1(t)$ is zero. Compare the sum of these values with the net power found in part (e).

(g) Compute the peak and the average values of the electric and magnetic stored energies under the conditions of part (f).

2. In the circuit of the preceding problem, suppose $e_1(t) = 10 \sin 10t$. Compute $i(t)$, $e_2(t)$, $i_L(t)$, $i_C(t)$. Compute the peak and the average values of the electric and magnetic stored energies. What is the power factor and the average power absorbed?

3. The impedance $Z(s)$ of the circuit drawn below has the zero s_1 and poles s_2, s_3 shown in the accompanying s-plane sketch. If $Z(0) = 1$, what are the parameter

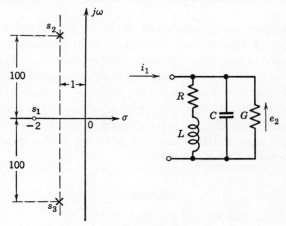

PROB. 3.

values? If $i_1(t) = 1 + \cos 100t$, what is $e_2(t)$? What is the width w of the resonance curve between its half-power points? What is the value of Q? Check this value through computing it from the stored and loss energy functions.

4. The top circuit consists of a parallel LC shunt branch loaded by the purely resistive input of a second tuned circuit and its complement. The lower network represents a pair of loosely coupled identically tuned and equally loaded resonant

tank **circuits.** The transfer impedance E_2/I_1 in each case **is to have** the pole pattern indicated in the adjacent s-plane sketch such that critical coupling yielding a maximally flat response characteristic results.

Design each circuit to meet the data: (a) Midband frequency $= \omega_0 = 2\pi 10^6$, (b) bandwidth between half-power points $= w = 2\pi 10^4$, (c) impedance level $= R = 10,000$ ohms.

In obtaining the poles of the transfer impedance for the capacitively coupled tank circuits, note that one conjugate pair is that determined by either of the two identical parallel resonant circuits considered separately, while the other pair must be

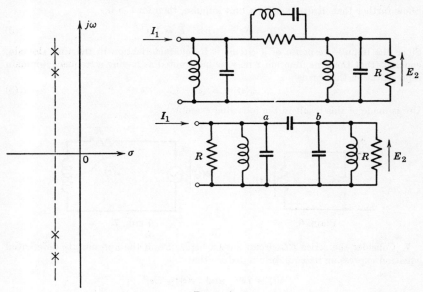

PROB. 4.

the same as that determined by the driving-point impedance for the node pair a–b, which is formed by twice the tank circuit impedance paralleled by the coupling capacitance. Since the latter is thus seen simply to lower the natural frequency of the tank circuit slightly, the second pair of natural frequencies (poles) is also obvious by inspection.

5. Given: $i_1(t) = u_0(t)$, find $e_2(t)$. If $i_1(t)$ is a unit step, how can you get the corresponding $e_2(t)$ from the solution just found?

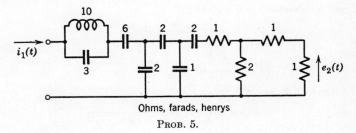

Ohms, farads, henrys

PROB. 5.

6. Consider the parallel RC circuit shown here. From the differential equation expressing the equilibrium of this network deduce that

$$i(t) = Ie^{st} \quad \text{and} \quad e(t) = Ee^{st}$$

are compatible time functions if $E = IZ(s)$ where $Z(s)$, the impedance or frequency-domain representation of this circuit, is given by

$$Z(s) = \frac{1/C}{(s - s_2)} \quad \text{with} \quad s_2 = -1/RC \tag{1}$$

Show further that, if $i(t) = u_0(t)$, a unit impulse, then for $t > 0$

$$e(t) = Ee^{s_2 t} \quad \text{with} \quad E = 1/C \tag{2}$$

Since the impulse response of a circuit is its characterization in the time domain, conclude that the time function 2 may be interpreted as having a frequency-domain representation that reads

$$E(s) = E/(s - s_2) \tag{3}$$

Use is made of this result in the following examples.

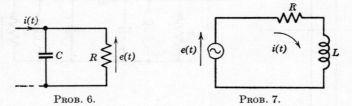

PROB. 6.   PROB. 7.

7. Consider the series RL circuit shown here. From the appropriate differential equation expressing its equilibrium deduce that

$$i(t) = Ie^{st} \quad \text{and} \quad e(t) = Ee^{st}$$

are compatible time functions if $I = EY(s)$ where $Y(s)$, the admittance or frequency-domain representation of this circuit, is given by

$$Y(s) = \frac{1/L}{(s - s_1)} \quad \text{with} \quad s_1 = -\frac{R}{L}$$

Now show that, if

$$e(t) = 0 \quad \text{for} \quad t < 0$$

$$e(t) = Ee^{s_2 t} \quad \text{for} \quad t > 0$$

the current response for $t > 0$ is given by

$$i(t) = A_1 e^{s_1 t} + A_2 e^{s_2 t}$$

with

$$A_1 = \frac{E/L}{(s_1 - s_2)}, \qquad A_2 = \frac{E/L}{(s_2 - s_1)}$$

Show further that, if we write

$$I(s) = E(s)Y(s) = \frac{E/L}{(s - s_1)(s - s_2)}$$

then these results may be written

$$A_k = [(s - s_k)I(s)]_{s=s_k}, \qquad k = 1, 2$$

8. Through setting $s_2 = 0$, show that the results in the previous problem apply to the step-function response of the series RL circuit, and conclude that the frequency domain representation (transform) of a step of value E reads

$$E(s) = E/s$$

Demonstrate the correctness of your conclusions.

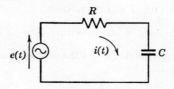

PROB. 9.

9. Consider the above series RC circuit with the admittance function

$$Y(s) = s/R(s - s_2) \quad \text{with} \quad s_2 = -1/RC$$

Assume the voltage excitation to be a unit step with the transform $E(s) = 1/s$. Show that we can again write

$$I(s) = E(s) \cdot Y(s)$$

and have

$$i(t) = A_2 e^{s_2 t} \quad \text{with} \quad A_k = [(s - s_k)I(s)]_{s=s_k}$$

10. With reference to the previous problem show that the time function $i(t)/C$ with the transform $I(s)/C$ encloses unit area and hence approaches a unit impulse as R becomes smaller and smaller. Thus show that the transform of the unit impulse $u_0(t)$ equals unity.

11. Combining the results of Probs. 7 and 10, obtain the response of the circuit of Prob. 7 for $e(t) = u_0(t)$ through use of the relations

$$I(s) = E(s) \cdot Y(s)$$

$$i(t) = A_1 e^{s_1 t} \quad \text{with} \quad A_k = [(s - s_k)I(s)]_{s=s_k}$$

and check with the conventional way of solving this problem.

12. Consider the analytic solution in Prob. 7 for the specific values $s_1 = -1$, $s_2 = -2$. If $L = 1$ henry, what is the value of the resistance R? Plot carefully the functions $e(t)$ and $i(t)$ for $-3 < t < 3$. Now repeat for the values $s_1 = -2$, $s_1 = -1$. What important conclusion can you draw from these results?

13. Consider the solution in Prob. 7 for the specific values $s_1 = -1$, $s_2 = j$, with the implication that

$$e(t) = \text{Re}\,[E e^{s_2 t}] = E \cos t \quad \text{(for } E \text{ real)}$$

and correspondingly

$$i(t) = \text{Re}\,[A_1 e^{s_1 t} + A_2 e^{s_2 t}]$$

Evaluate the solution under these assumptions and check with the conventional manner of obtaining the so-called a-c response of this simple circuit.

14. With reference to the previous problem, obviate the necessity of taking the real parts of complex expressions through use of the familiar relation

$$E \cos \omega t = \frac{E}{2} (e^{s_2 t} + e^{s_3 t}); \qquad s_2 = j\omega, \quad s_3 = -j\omega$$

leading to the transform

$$E(s) = \frac{E}{2} \left(\frac{1}{s - j\omega} + \frac{1}{s + j\omega} \right) = \frac{sE}{s^2 + \omega^2}$$

Together with the $Y(s)$ of Prob. 7 and the relation

$$i(t) = A_1 e^{s_1 t} + A_2 e^{s_2 t} + A_3 e^{s_3 t} \quad \text{with} \quad A_k = [(s - s_k)I(s)]_{s = s_k}$$

where the Re sign is no longer needed, check the solution found in Prob. 13 for $\omega = 1$.

15. Using the trigonometric identity

$$E \sin \omega t = \frac{E}{2j} (e^{s_2 t} - e^{s_3 t}); \qquad s_2 = j\omega, \quad s_3 = -j\omega$$

show that the transform (frequency-domain representation) of this time function is

$$E(s) = \omega E / (s^2 + \omega^2)$$

Obtain the response of the series RL circuit of Prob. 7 for this excitation and $\omega = 1$, using the method of Prob. 14.

16. In terms of the relation

$$f(t) = \sum_{k = 1, 2 \cdots} A_k e^{s_k t} \quad \text{with} \quad A_k = [(s - s_k)F(s)]_{s = s_k}$$

where $F(s)$ is the transform of $f(t)$, show that differentiation (resp. integration) in the time domain corresponds to multiplication of $F(s)$ by s (resp. $1/s$). Check with the transforms of $\sin \omega t$, $\cos \omega t$, and $u_0(t)$, $u_{-1}(t)$ as found above (Probs. 14, 15, and 8, 10).

17. With reference to the following series LC circuit having the admittance

$$Y(s) = \frac{(1/L)s}{(s - s_2)(s - s_3)}$$

with $s_2 = j\omega_0$, $s_3 = -j\omega_0$, $\omega_0^2 = 1/LC$, consider $e(t) = E e^{s_1 t}$ for $t > 0$, so that $E(s)$

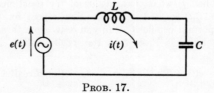

Prob. 17.

$= E/(s - s_1)$. For $s_1 = -1$ and $\omega_0 = 1$, obtain the response of this system, and compare with the results of Probs. 13 and 14. What important conclusion can you draw? Compare with that relevant to Prob. 12.

18. In the circuit of Prob. 17 consider $s_1 = 0$, and check with the step-function response of this simple circuit as found by conventional means.

19. The series RLC circuit has an admittance $Y(s)$ with the pole (crosses) and zero (circle) configuration shown in the accompanying s-plane sketch. Assume $\alpha/\omega_d =$

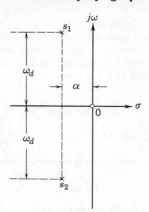

PROB. 19.

1 per cent and a unit step voltage excitation. In evaluating the resulting current according to

$$i(t) = A_1 e^{s_1 t} + A_2 e^{s_2 t}$$

with

$$A_k = [(s - s_k)I(s)]_{s = s_k}$$

interpret the relevant factors $(s_i - s_j)$ as vectors in the s plane, and obtain their values by inspection. Check your result with that found by conventional means.

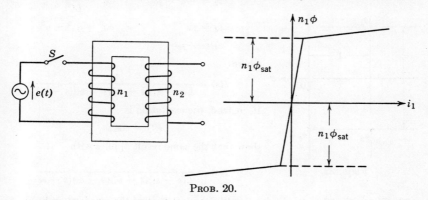

PROB. 20.

20. The sketch on the left represents an iron-core transformer excited by the sinusoidal voltage

$$e(t) = 300 \sin \omega t$$

through the switch S. The nonlinear relation between primary flux linkages and exciting current is idealized as shown in the sketch on the right. Thus, below saturation, the incremental inductance of the primary winding is $L = 15/6\pi$ henry, while above saturation it is 1/100th of this value. The saturation point is characterized by the flux linkage

$$n_1\phi_{\mathrm{sat}} = 300/\omega \text{ weber-turns}$$

and the radian frequency is $\omega = 2\pi \times 60$.

(a) Compute the maximum value of the normal exciting current in the primary. (b) Assuming a negligible primary winding resistance, compute the maximum value of the transient exciting current following switch closure at $t = 0$. (c) What is the answer to part (b) if the switch closes at $t = \pi/\omega$?

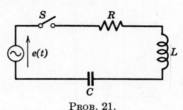

PROB. 21.

21. The voltage excitation in the above circuit is

$$e(t) = \sin \omega t$$

The switch closes at $t = 0$. Show that the resulting current is given by the expression

$$i(t) = \sum_{k=1,\, 2,\, \cdots}^{4} A_k e^{s_k t} \quad \text{with} \quad A_k = [(s - s_k)I(s)]_{s=s_k}$$

$$s_1 = -\alpha + j\omega_d \qquad \alpha = \frac{R}{2L}$$

$$s_2 = -\alpha - j\omega_d \qquad \omega_0{}^2 = \frac{1}{LC}$$

$$s_3 = j\omega \qquad \omega_d{}^2 = \omega_0{}^2 - \alpha^2$$

$$s_4 = -j\omega$$

where

$$I(s) = \frac{s\omega}{L(s - s_1)(s - s_2)(s - s_3)(s - s_4)}$$

If, instead, the excitation is

$$e(t) = \cos \omega t$$

show that the same result applies with

$$I(s) = \frac{s^2}{L(s - s_1)(s - s_2)(s - s_3)(s - s_4)}$$

PROB. 22.

22. The critical frequencies involved in the last part of the previous problem are indicated by crosses and circles in the s-plane sketch shown on the left.

If $L = 1$ henry, find the values of the parameters R and C, and determine $i(t)$ after closure of the switch S at $t = 0$ with

$$e(t) = \cos t$$

Evaluate the pertinent factors $(s_i - s_j)$ by inspection of appropriate s-plane sketches, and thus compute the coefficients A_k with a minimum of wasteful effort.

23. If in the previous problem the excitation is changed to

$$e(t) = e^{-at} (\cos t - a \sin t)$$

show how the s-plane sketch given there changes. Specifically, evaluate $i(t)$ for $a = \alpha/2 = 1/2$. Suppose we next assume that $a = 1$ and $\alpha = 1/2$. Does the same solution still apply? What changes in the circuit parameter values are appropriate?

Now consider the condition of perfect resonance resulting for $a = \alpha$, and evaluate the corresponding current response with $\alpha = 1$.

24. Given the following two situations:

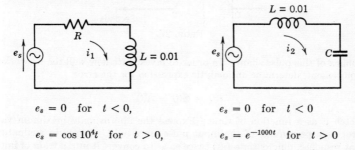

$e_s = 0$ for $t < 0$,

$e_s = \cos 10^4 t$ for $t > 0$,

$e_s = 0$ for $t < 0$

$e_s = e^{-1000t}$ for $t > 0$

Show that for $t > 0$ it is possible to have $i_1(t) \equiv i_2(t)$, and determine the appropriate values of R and C. Evaluate either i_1 or i_2.

25. When a given network is excited by a unit current impulse at its driving point, the resulting voltage at this same point is given by the expression

$$e(t) = e^{-t} + 2e^{-2t} + 3e^{-3t} \quad \text{for} \quad t > 0$$

Find the impedance function $Z(s)$, and sketch a network, giving element values, having this impedance.

26. For the circuit shown in the following sketch find

$$Z_{12}(s) = E_2/I_1$$

as a quotient of polynomials in s, and sketch the corresponding pole-zero configuration in the s plane. Determine the analytic expression for the instantaneous output voltage $e_2(t)$ if the input current $i_1(t)$ is a unit step.

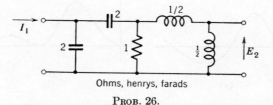

Ohms, henrys, farads

PROB. 26.

27. A given network has the transfer impedance

$$Z_{12}(s) = 10/(s + 10)$$

When the input current $i_1(t)$ is a triangular pulse as shown in the accompanying sketch, the network is supposed to yield an output voltage $e_2(t)$ that is a reasonably

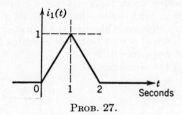

PROB. 27.

close replica of this pulse shape. In order to investigate how well the network meets this requirement, determine an analytic expression for the error

$$\epsilon(t) = e_2(t) - i_1(t)$$

and sketch it as a function of time. Express the approximate maximum value of this error as a percentage of the input pulse amplitude. *Hint.* In evaluating the transient response, differentiate $i_1(t)$ twice so as to convert it into a train of impulses, and cancel this differentiation either through subsequent integration or through division of Z_{12} by s^2.

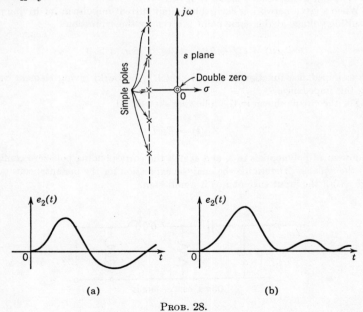

PROB. 28.

28. The transfer impedance $Z_{12}(s)$ of a certain network has the pole-zero configuration shown in the accompanying s-plane sketch. If the input current is a unit impulse, pick out which of the two $e_2(t)$ sketches represents a possible output, and prove the correctness of your choice. State how many successive initial derivatives of $e_2(t)$ are zero.

29. When a unit step voltage is applied to the terminals of a linear passive network, the current response is

$$i(t) = \sin 2t + \sin 3t \quad \text{for} \quad t > 0$$

(a) What is the driving-point admittance at the terminals of the network? (b) Synthesize a network having this admittance.

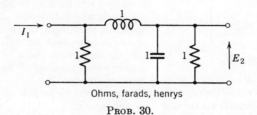

Ohms, farads, henrys

PROB. 30.

30. For the network in the figure, determine the transfer impedance

$$Z_{12}(s) = E_2/I_1$$

If the input current is $i_1(t) = u_{-1}(t) \cos t$, find the transform $E_2(s)$ of the output voltage $e_2(t)$, and make an s-plane sketch of its pole-zero pattern. Through interpretation of the frequency factors as vectors in this plane, evaluate the constants A_k in the solution for $e_2(t)$ by inspection, and formulate this solution. Now, interchanging the pole-zero patterns of the source and the circuit, determine a circuit (giving structure and element values) and a source (defining it in the time domain) for which the response is identical with $e_2(t)$.

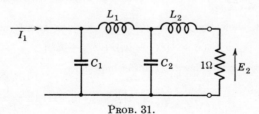

PROB. 31.

31. For the network given here show that

$$\frac{E_2}{I_1} = \frac{1}{1 + a_1 s + a_2 s^2 + a_3 s^3 + a_4 s^4} = Z_{12}(s)$$

Express the coefficients $a_1 \cdots a_4$ in terms of the circuit inductances and capacitances. Conversely, express the latter in terms of the coefficients $a_1 \cdots a_4$.

32. The poles of $Z_{12}(s)$ for the circuit of Prob. 31 are distributed as shown in the s-plane sketch on the left. (a) Compute the appropriate circuit parameter values. (b) Determine and sketch the function $|Z_{12}(j\omega)|$ vs. ω over the range $0 < \omega < 3$.

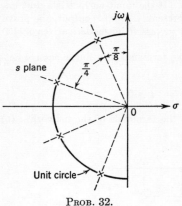

PROB. 32.

33. For the circuit of Prob. 31 with the parameter values found in Prob. 32, determine and sketch $e_2(t)$ if $i_1(t)$ is (a) a unit impulse, (b) a unit step.

34. If in the network of Probs. 31 and 32 the form of the steady-state and transient response is to remain unchanged but the desired load resistor is to be 10,000 ohms, what are the appropriate values of L_1, L_2, C_1, C_2? If in this resulting network the transient response is to proceed 10^6 times faster but retain the same wave shape, what do the parameter values become? What accompanying change takes place in the steady-state response function $Z_{12}(j\omega)$?

35. Determine the network of Prob. 31 appropriate to the pole distribution shown in the figure. Compute (a) the unit impulse response, (b) the unit step response.

36. Using the relations

$$f(t) = \sum_{k=1, 2, \cdots}^{n} A_k e^{s_k t}, \qquad A_k = [(s - s_k)F(s)]_{s=s_k}$$

show that, if

$$F^*(s) = F(s + a)$$

then

$$s^*_k = s_k - a \quad \text{and} \quad A^*_k = [(s - s^*_k)F^*(s)]_{s=s^*_k} = A_k$$

so that

$$f^*(t) = \sum_{k=1, 2, \cdots}^{n} A^*_k e^{s^*_k t} = e^{-at}f(t)$$

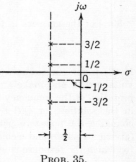

PROB. 35.

From this result, show that $f^*(t) = f(t) \cos \omega_0 t$ has the transform

$$F^*(s) = \tfrac{1}{2}[F(s - j\omega_0) + F(s + j\omega_0)]$$

37. A given lowpass filter has the transfer impedance

$$Z_{12}(s) = \frac{1}{s^2 + s\sqrt{2} + 1} \quad \text{for which} \quad |Z_{12}(j\omega)| = \frac{1}{\sqrt{1 + \omega^4}}$$

If a unit step current, having the transform $I(s) = 1/s$, is applied at the input, make an s-plane sketch (to scale), showing the poles of the output voltage transform

$$E(s) = I(s)Z_{12}(s)$$

and compute the corresponding time function $e(t)$. The corresponding bandpass filter has a transfer impedance

$$Z^*_{12}(s) = \tfrac{1}{2}[Z_{12}(s - j\omega_0) + Z_{12}(s + j\omega_0)]$$

If it is excited by the function

$$i*(t) = u_{-1}(t) \cos \omega_0 t$$

with the transform $I*(s)$ make an s-plane sketch of the output voltage transform $E*(s) = I*(s)Z*_{12}(s)$, showing its pole distribution.

If the midband frequency of the bandpass filter is large, that is, if $\omega_0 \gg 1$, show that

$$E*(s) \approx \frac{s(s^2 - \omega_0{}^2)}{(s - s_1) \cdots (s - s_6)}$$

while

$$\frac{1}{2} [E(s - j\omega_0) + E(s + j\omega_0)] \approx \frac{s(s^2 - 3\omega_0{}^2)}{(s - s_1) \cdots (s - s_6)}$$

Thus, for the vicinity of $s = j\omega_0$, observe that

$$E*(s) \approx \tfrac{1}{4}[E(s - j\omega_0) + E(s + j\omega_0)]$$

and hence that the voltage output $e*(t)$ of the bandpass filter resulting from the excitation $i*(t)$ may be written down, using the result of Prob. 36 (or the property 124) and the known step function response of the lowpass filter. Check this result independently through evaluation of the time function corresponding to $E*(s)$, taking advantage of any simplifications permitted by the assumption $\omega_0 \gg 1$.

38. Considering the bandpass filter of the preceding problem for a condition $\omega_0 \gg 1$, evaluate (a) the unit impulse response, (b) the unit step response, and note that these are essentially the same, the principal difference being the constant multiplier ω_0. Show why this is so.

39. Use the result of the first part of Prob. 36 with $a = \Delta s$ to show that

$$\frac{dF}{ds} = \left[\frac{F(s + \Delta s) - F(s)}{\Delta s} \right]_{\Delta s \to 0} = F*(s)$$

has the inverse transform $f*(t) = -tf(t)$. That is to say, differentiation in the s domain corresponds in the time domain to multiplication by $-t$. Through repeated application of this result to the function $1/(s + 1)$, find the impulse response of a network like that given in Prob. 31 with the transfer impedance

$$Z_{12}(s) = 1/(s + 1)^4$$

Evaluate the network parameters for this response function.

40. Through use of the reciprocity theorem or the principle of duality (whichever is appropriate) to the circuit involved in Probs. 31, 32, 33, show that the following networks have a transfer voltage ratio E_2/E_1 which is the same function as $Z_{12}(s)$, and compute the pertinent parameter values.

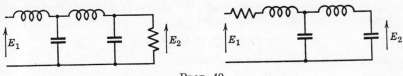

PROB. 40.

41. It is clear from the preceding exercises that, if $F(s)$ has only left half-plane poles at finite nonzero s values, then $f(t) \to 0$ as $t \to \infty$. On the other hand, if

$F(s)$ has a pole at $s = 0$ such that

$$A_0 = [sF(s)]_{s=0} \neq 0$$

then

$$f(t) = A_0 + \text{terms that vanish} \quad \text{for} \quad t \to \infty$$

For example, the step-function response usually has such an $F(s)$, and the constant term A_0 is the steady-state part of the response. The function $F(s) - (A_0/s)$ evidently is the transform of $f(t) - A_0$, and, since this time function vanishes for large t, we conclude that $F(s) - (A_0/s)$ has no pole at $s = 0$. Moreover, if A_0 turns out to have the value of the applied step, then we may say that the response shows no steady-state error. Through a straightforward extension of these thoughts, show that the property of the transform which assures a zero steady-state error when the excitation function is $u_{-n}(t)$ for $n = 1, 2, 3, \cdots$ is expressed by stating that

$$\frac{s^n F(s) - 1}{s^n} \quad \text{shall have no pole at } s = 0$$

For $n = 2$ the input is a unit ramp; for $n = 3$ it is a unit parabola, etc.

In servomechanism theory where the response is a mechanical displacement, the case $n = 1$ characterizes a servo having a zero position error; $n = 2$ yields one with a zero velocity error; $n = 3$, one with a zero acceleration error; etc. The response function of the network or system which is $s^n F(s)$, when it satisfies the above condition, is said (in the language of complex function theory) to have a *saddle point* at $s = 0$ of the order $n - 1$.

42. If the transfer impedance of a network is written in the polynomial form

$$Z_{12}(s) = \frac{a_0 + a_1 s + a_2 s^2 + \cdots + a_r s^r}{b_0 + b_1 s + b_2 s^2 + \cdots + b_k s^k}$$

show, according to the results of the preceding problem, that the steady-state error for an excitation function $u_{-n}(t)$ will be zero if

$$a_0 = b_0 \quad \text{when} \quad n = 1$$

if also

$$a_1 = b_1 \quad \text{when} \quad n = 2$$

if also

$$a_2 = b_2 \quad \text{when} \quad n = 3, \quad \text{etc.}$$

(These are the conditions that $Z_{12}(s)$ have a saddle point of order $n - 1$ at $s = 0$.)

As an illustrative numerical example consider the impedance

$$Z_{12}(s) = (1 + s)/(1 + s + s^2)$$

and assume a current excitation equal to the unit ramp function $i_1(t) = u_{-2}(t)$. Compute and plot the output voltage $e_2(t)$, and observe that its asymptote actually is the ramp function. In contrast consider

$$Z_{12}(s) = 1/(1 + s + s^2)$$

and note that a constant nonzero error remains.

Generalization of
Circuit Equations
and Energy Relations

1 Use of Matrix Algebra

Matrix algebra is a kind of shorthand that enables one to write the algebraic relations involving systems of simultaneous equations in a very compact form. Its principal value lies in the circumspection that results from this compactness, and in the facility with which one is thus enabled to carry out and visualize the significance of more elaborate sequences of related algebraic operations. In numerical problems its usefulness lies solely in the systematization that it injects into the computations; it provides no short cuts. It, therefore, is primarily a tool for facilitating analytical manipulations, but as such its usefulness easily justifies the small amount of time and attention required on the part of the uninitiated reader to understand the basic principles and rules involved.

As has previously been pointed out, the so-called *matrix* corresponding to the set of linear equations

$$a_{11}x_1 + a_{12}x_2 + \cdots + a_{1n}x_n = y_1$$
$$a_{21}x_1 + a_{22}x_2 + \cdots + a_{2n}x_n = y_2$$
$$\cdot \quad \cdot \quad \cdot \quad \cdot \quad \cdot \quad \cdot \quad \cdot \quad \cdot \quad \cdot \quad \cdot \quad \cdot \quad \cdot \quad \cdot$$
$$a_{n1}x_1 + a_{n2}x_2 + \cdots + a_{nn}x_n = y_n$$

(1)

is written

$$[A] = \begin{bmatrix} a_{11} & a_{12} & \cdots & a_{1n} \\ a_{21} & a_{22} & \cdots & a_{2n} \\ \cdot & \cdot & \cdots & \cdot \\ a_{n1} & a_{n2} & \cdots & a_{nn} \end{bmatrix}$$

(2)

and represents merely the array of coefficients a_{sk} in the same order regarding their row and column positions as they appear in the related set of systematically written equations. Unlike the determinant

$$A = \begin{vmatrix} a_{11} & a_{12} & \cdots & a_{1n} \\ a_{21} & a_{22} & \cdots & a_{2n} \\ \cdot & \cdot & \cdot & \cdot \\ a_{n1} & a_{n2} & \cdots & a_{nn} \end{vmatrix} \tag{3}$$

which is a rational function of its elements a_{sk} and has definite numerical values for given values of these elements, the matrix $[A]$ has no "value" other than the pictorial value that is provided by its outward appearance and structure in relation to the associated equations to which it belongs.

Usually the number of equations equals the number of unknowns (the quantities x_1, x_2, $\cdots$, x_n), in which case the matrix has as many rows as it has columns. That is to say, the associated matrix is composed of a *square* array, and the number of its rows or columns is referred to as the *order* of the matrix. This circumstance is not necessarily always encountered. For example, in Ch. 1 where we discuss the relations between branch currents and loop currents or between branch voltages and node-pair voltages, we encounter sets of equations with nonsquare matrices. In this respect a matrix again differs from a determinant, since the latter must always involve a square array of coefficients.

An extreme example of a nonsquare matrix is one with only a single row or a single column. Thus we may write the sets of quantities $x_1 \cdots x_n$ and $y_1 \cdots y_n$, appearing in Eqs. 1, as matrices

$$x] = \begin{bmatrix} x_1 \\ x_2 \\ \cdot \\ \cdot \\ \cdot \\ x_n \end{bmatrix} \qquad y] = \begin{bmatrix} y_1 \\ y_2 \\ \cdot \\ \cdot \\ \cdot \\ y_n \end{bmatrix} \tag{4}$$

These are referred to as *column* matrices.

In terms of matrices 2 and 4, the shorthand known as matrix algebra enables one to write the set of Eqs. 1 in the abbreviated form

$$[A] \cdot x] = y] \tag{5}$$

In order to show how this expression may be regarded as the equivalent of 1, we must provide an appropriate interpretation for each of two things or questions: (a) What is meant by the *equality* of matrices? (b) How must one define the *product* of two matrices, like $[A] \cdot x]$?

Regarding the first of these questions, it follows from what has been said about a matrix that two can be equal only if *all* of their corresponding elements are equal. A necessary (though not a sufficient) condition for equality, therefore, is that both matrices have the same number of rows and the same number of columns. Since in 5 the right-hand matrix has only one column, it must turn out that the product $[A] \cdot x]$ be a matrix with a single column. More specifically, if 1 and 5 are to be equivalent, then it becomes clear that we must have

$$
\begin{bmatrix} a_{11} & a_{12} & \cdots & a_{1n} \\ a_{21} & a_{22} & \cdots & a_{2n} \\ \cdot & \cdot & \cdots & \cdot \\ a_{n1} & a_{n2} & \cdots & a_{nn} \end{bmatrix} \times \begin{bmatrix} x_1 \\ x_2 \\ \cdot \\ x_n \end{bmatrix} = \begin{bmatrix} (a_{11}x_1 + a_{12}x_2 + \cdots + a_{1n}x_n) \\ (a_{21}x_1 + a_{22}x_2 + \cdots + a_{2n}x_n) \\ \cdots \\ (a_{n1}x_1 + a_{n2}x_2 + \cdots + a_{nn}x_n) \end{bmatrix} = \begin{bmatrix} y_1 \\ y_2 \\ \cdot \\ y_n \end{bmatrix} \quad (6)
$$

in which the sums of terms in parentheses in the intermediate matrix are single elements, so that this is a column matrix like $x]$ or $y]$ in 4 (although its appearance at first glance does not suggest this fact). Equating elements in this matrix with corresponding ones in $y]$ evidently yields Eqs. 1.

The rule for matrix multiplication made evident in Eq. 6 may be described by saying that one multiplies the elements in the rows of $[A]$ by the respective ones in the column of $x]$ and adds the results; and that the first, second, etc. elements in the resultant (column) matrix involve the first, second, etc. rows of $[A]$.

Stated in more general terms, one may say that, in forming the product of two matrices $[A]$ and $[B]$, resulting in the matrix $[C]$, one multiplies the rows of $[A]$ by the columns of $[B]$ in a manner that is most easily understood from the following example,

$$
\begin{bmatrix} a_{11} & a_{12} & a_{13} & a_{14} \\ a_{21} & a_{22} & a_{23} & a_{24} \end{bmatrix} \times \begin{bmatrix} b_{11} & b_{12} & b_{13} \\ b_{21} & b_{22} & b_{23} \\ b_{31} & b_{32} & b_{33} \\ b_{41} & b_{42} & b_{43} \end{bmatrix} = \begin{bmatrix} c_{11} & c_{12} & c_{13} \\ c_{21} & c_{22} & c_{23} \end{bmatrix} \quad (7)
$$

in which one obtains for the elements of the product matrix

$$
\begin{aligned}
c_{11} &= a_{11}b_{11} + a_{12}b_{21} + a_{13}b_{31} + a_{14}b_{41} \\
c_{12} &= a_{11}b_{12} + a_{12}b_{22} + a_{13}b_{32} + a_{14}b_{42} \\
c_{13} &= a_{11}b_{13} + a_{12}b_{23} + a_{13}b_{33} + a_{14}b_{43}
\end{aligned} \quad (8)
$$

$$
\begin{aligned}
c_{21} &= a_{21}b_{11} + a_{22}b_{21} + a_{23}b_{31} + a_{24}b_{41} \\
c_{22} &= a_{21}b_{12} + a_{22}b_{22} + a_{23}b_{32} + a_{24}b_{42} \\
c_{23} &= a_{21}b_{13} + a_{22}b_{23} + a_{23}b_{33} + a_{24}b_{43}
\end{aligned} \quad (9)
$$

Thus the so-called (s, k) element in the product matrix (the element c_{sk}) is formed through the addition of products of the respective elements in the sth row of $[A]$ and the kth column of $[B]$, a general formula for this element being

$$c_{sk} = \sum_{r=1}^{n} a_{sr} b_{rk} \tag{10}$$

in which r is regarded as the summation index. The equivalence of 5 and 6, according to this rule of formation, is readily recognized, whereupon the acceptance of the matrix Eq. 5 as being a compact way of writing the set of Eqs. 1, follows without difficulty.

In determinant multiplication, by the way, one does not have to stick to the rule that only rows of the first may be multiplied by columns of the second determinant in the product $A \cdot B$. One may equally well form elements in the product determinant through multiplying the columns of A by the rows of B, or rows by rows, or columns by columns. Any one of four different schemes may thus be used in determinant multiplication (albeit one must be consistent throughout the evaluation of a given problem). This freedom results from the fact that it is only the *value* of the product determinant that matters, and this value turns out to be the same with each one of the four schemes although the specific values for the elements in the product determinant are not the same. In matrix multiplication where the result is a matrix, only one rule of formation can apply, since the elements of this matrix are the quantities of interest.

Another point illustrated by the example of Eq. 7 is the fact that, in any product $[A] \times [B]$, the number of columns in $[A]$ must equal the number of rows in $[B]$ in order that the number of elements in any row of $[A]$ will equal the number of elements in any column of $[B]$, a necessary condition that is obvious from the way in which the row-by-column product is formed. If the given matrices in a product fulfill this condition, then that product is said to be *conformable*.

It is likewise clear from the example in Eq. 7 that the number of rows in $[A]$ and the number of columns in $[B]$ may be anything; but that the number of rows in the product matrix $[C]$ equals the number of rows in $[A]$, and the number of columns in $[C]$ equals the number of columns in $[B]$. If we use for the designation of a matrix $[A]$ with p rows and q columns the notation $[a_{pq}]$, and a similar notation for the matrices $[B]$ and $[C]$, then these remarks are summarized in the equation

$$[a_{pq}] \times [b_{qr}] = [c_{pr}] \tag{11}$$

Conformability of this product is placed in evidence through the so-called *adjacent index* q being the same in the two matrices forming the product, while the remaining indexes p and r correlate the rows of $[a_{pq}]$ with the rows of $[c_{pr}]$ and the columns of $[b_{qr}]$ with the columns of $[c_{pr}]$.

Using this notation, a conformable multiple product is, for example, indicated by

$$[a_{pq}] \times [b_{qr}] \times [c_{rs}] \times [d_{st}] = [g_{pt}] \tag{12}$$

Conformability is recognized at once from the fact that all adjacent indexes are alike, and the number of rows and columns in the resultant matrix is made evident from the number of rows in the first matrix and the number of columns in the last.

From the restricted nature of the rule for forming a matrix product, it is clear that the commutative law does not apply; that is:

$$[A] \times [B] \neq [B] \times [A] \tag{13}$$

However, the associative law does hold, which means that, in the multiple product 12, we may group the terms in any way we wish so long as we preserve their relative order. Thus we may begin the multiplication at the right with $[c_{rs}] \times [d_{st}]$ and work toward the left in successive steps, or we may begin at the left and work toward the right. Again, we may first carry out separately the products $[a_{pq}] \times [b_{qr}]$ and $[c_{rs}] \times [d_{st}]$, and then multiply the result of the first of these by the result of the second. Although the final product matrix is the same in all cases, the computational labor involved is not (herein lies one of the finer points of this subject that we shall not pursue further at this time).

A matrix is said to be *symmetrical* if its elements fulfill the condition $a_{ik} = a_{ki}$, which results in any element and its mirror image about the *principal diagonal* (upper left to lower right) being identical.

The so-called *inverse* of a matrix $[A]$ is written $[A]^{-1}$ and is defined by the relation

$$[A] \times [A]^{-1} = [A]^{-1} \times [A] = \begin{bmatrix} 1 & 0 & 0 & \cdots & 0 \\ 0 & 1 & 0 & \cdots & 0 \\ & & \cdot & \cdots & \cdot \\ 0 & 0 & 0 & \cdots & 1 \end{bmatrix} = [U] \tag{14}$$

in which $[U]$, called the *unit matrix*, has the indicated structure in which the elements on the principal diagonal are unity and all others are zero. Equations like set 1 having a unit matrix evidently read $x_1 = y_1$, $x_2 = y_2$, $\cdots$, $x_n = y_n$. Multiplication of any given matrix by the unit matrix leaves the given matrix unchanged. Hence, if we multiply on both sides of Eq. 5 by $[A]^{-1}$, we have

$$[A]^{-1} \times [A] \times x] = [U] \times x] = x] = [A]^{-1} \times y] \tag{15}$$

The set of equations corresponding to this result in the manner that 1 and 5 correspond has the form

$$b_{11}y_1 + b_{12}y_2 + \cdots + b_{1n}y_n = x_1$$
$$b_{21}y_1 + b_{22}y_2 + \cdots + b_{2n}y_n = x_2$$
$$\cdots \cdots \cdots \cdots \cdots \cdots \cdots$$
$$b_{n1}y_1 + b_{n2}y_2 + \cdots + b_{nn}y_n = x_n$$

$$(16)$$

with the matrix

$$[B] = [A]^{-1} = \begin{bmatrix} b_{11} & b_{12} & \cdots & b_{1n} \\ b_{21} & b_{22} & \cdots & b_{2n} \\ \cdots & \cdots & \cdots & \cdots \\ b_{n1} & b_{n2} & \cdots & b_{nn} \end{bmatrix} \qquad (17)$$

The inverse matrix is thus recognized to be the matrix of the inverse set of equations; that is, the equations that represent the solution to the given set. The property of being inverse is evidently a mutual one. Thus we may equally well regard set 1 as being the inverse of 16, and hence it follows that $[A]$ is the inverse of $[B]$; that is:

$$[A] = [B]^{-1}, \qquad [A] \times [B] = [B] \times [A] = [U] \qquad (18)$$

The problem of finding the inverse of a given matrix is the problem of solving a set of simultaneous equations like 1 or 16. Using determinants and Cramer's rule, one can compactly express the elements of the inverse matrix in terms of those of a given matrix. For example, if the determinant of $[A]$ is denoted by A, as in Eq. 3, and its cofactors are written A_{sk}, it follows (see Art. 2, Ch. 3) that the elements of the inverse matrix $[B]$, Eq. 17, are given by

$$b_{sk} = A_{ks}/A \qquad (19)$$

Conversely, if the determinant of $[B]$ is B, with cofactors B_{sk}, then

$$a_{sk} = B_{ks}/B \qquad (20)$$

Because of 18, formula 10 for the elements of the product matrix yields in this case

$$\sum_{r=1}^{n} a_{sr} \cdot b_{rk} = \begin{matrix} 1 & \text{for} & s = k \\ 0 & \text{for} & s \neq k \end{matrix} \qquad (21)$$

since the product matrix is the unit matrix 14.

From relations 19 and 20 it is clear that the inverse of a matrix exists only if the corresponding determinant is nonzero. Incidentally, there must be a corresponding determinant in the first place, which implies that the given matrix be a square array. A nonsquare matrix possesses no inverse. A matrix that does possess an inverse is said to be *nonsingular;* one that does not is called a *singular* matrix.

When a given matrix has the so-called *diagonal* form

$$[D] = \begin{bmatrix} d_{11} & 0 & 0 & \cdots & 0 \\ 0 & d_{22} & 0 & \cdots & 0 \\ & & \cdots & & \\ 0 & 0 & 0 & \cdots & d_{nn} \end{bmatrix} \tag{22}$$

which is like the unit matrix except that the diagonal elements are not equal to unity, then the associated equations read $d_{11}x_1 = y_1$, $d_{22}x_2 = y_2$, $\cdots$, $d_{nn}x_n = y_n$, which can be inverted by inspection. One recognizes that the inverse of $[D]$ is simply

$$[D]^{-1} = \begin{bmatrix} d_{11}^{-1} & 0 & 0 & \cdots & 0 \\ 0 & d_{22}^{-1} & 0 & \cdots & 0 \\ & & \cdots & & \\ 0 & 0 & 0 & \cdots & d_{nn}^{-1} \end{bmatrix} \tag{23}$$

That is to say, the inverse of a diagonal matrix is again a diagonal matrix with elements on its diagonal that are respectively the reciprocals of the diagonal elements in the given matrix.

Alteration of a matrix through writing its rows as columns, or vice versa, is called *transposition,* and the result is referred to as the *transposed matrix.* Thus the transposition of the matrix $[A]$, Eq. 2, yields

$$[A]_t = \begin{bmatrix} a_{11} & a_{21} & a_{31} & \cdots & a_{n1} \\ a_{12} & a_{22} & a_{32} & \cdots & a_{n2} \\ & & \cdots & & \\ a_{1n} & a_{2n} & a_{3n} & \cdots & a_{nn} \end{bmatrix} \tag{24}$$

Transposition of column matrices 4 yields row matrices

$$x]_t = \underline{x} = [x_1 \quad x_2 \quad \cdots \quad x_n]$$
$$y]_t = \underline{y} = [y_1 \quad y_2 \quad \cdots \quad y_n] \tag{25}$$

Note that the transposed matrix is indicated by the subscript t, and that column and row matrices are distinguished through writing $x]$ and $\underline{x}$ respectively.

When matrices have a large number of rows and columns, it may be effective to *partition* them into smaller sections, called *submatrices*. Such a partitioned matrix may be written

$$[A] = [a_{mn}] = \begin{bmatrix} [a_{pr}] & [a_{ps}] \\ [a_{qr}] & [a_{qs}] \end{bmatrix} \tag{26}$$

Thus the m rows and n columns of the matrix $[A]$ are partitioned into groups of p and q rows and r and s columns. That portion of $[A]$ consisting of the elements in the first p rows and first r columns (the upper left portion) is the submatrix $[a_{pr}]$, that portion involving elements in the first p rows and the last s columns (the upper right portion) is the submatrix $[a_{ps}]$, and so forth.

If a second matrix $[B]$ is likewise partitioned as shown by

$$[B] = [b_{nk}] = \begin{bmatrix} [b_{rt}] & [b_{ri}] \\ [b_{st}] & [b_{si}] \end{bmatrix} \tag{27}$$

Then the product $[A] \times [B]$ may be evaluated as though the submatrices were ordinary elements. That is to say, Eqs. 26 and 27 yield the product

$$[A] \times [B] = \begin{bmatrix} [a_{pr}] \times [b_{rt}] + [a_{ps}] \times [b_{st}] & [a_{pr}] \times [b_{ri}] + [a_{ps}] \times [b_{si}] \\ [a_{qr}] \times [b_{rt}] + [a_{qs}] \times [b_{st}] & [a_{qr}] \times [b_{ri}] + [a_{qs}] \times [b_{si}] \end{bmatrix} \tag{28}$$

which in turn may be written

$$[A] \times [B] = [C] = \begin{bmatrix} [c_{pt}] & [c_{pi}] \\ [c_{qt}] & [c_{qi}] \end{bmatrix} \tag{29}$$

Note that the partitioning of the columns of $[A]$ and of the rows of $[B]$ (both into groups of r and s) must correspond in order that the products of submatrices appearing in 28 all be conformable. The partitioning of the rows of $[A]$ and of the columns in $[B]$ is arbitrary. From the indexes appearing on the submatrices in $[A]$ and in $[B]$ one can tell the number of rows and columns in the submatrices of the product matrix 29. Partitioning thus lends circumspection where detailed manipulations with elaborate matrices must be carried out.

It may happen that a large number of elements in a rather extensive given matrix are zero so that, after partitioning, one encounters submatrices consisting entirely of zeros. A matrix whose elements are all zeros is called a *null* matrix. A partitioned matrix having such null submatrices may have the form

$$[A] = \begin{bmatrix} [a_{rr}] & 0 & 0 \\ 0 & [a_{ss}] & 0 \\ 0 & 0 & [a_{tt}] \end{bmatrix} \tag{30}$$

where we have written the null matrices as though they were simple zeros. Actually the two zeros in the top row of matrix 30 are null matrices involving r rows and respectively s and t columns. Similar comment applies to the other zeros appearing in this matrix. The matrix $[A]$ in this example is chosen to be a square array consisting of $r + s + t$ rows and a like number of columns.

Regarding the submatrices in 30 for the moment as one would ordinary elements, we would recognize this matrix $[A]$ to be in the diagonal form. It turns out (as may readily be seen) that its inverse, like that of diagonal matrix 22, is simply given by

$$[A]^{-1} = \begin{bmatrix} [a_{rr}]^{-1} & 0 & 0 \\ 0 & [a_{ss}]^{-1} & 0 \\ 0 & 0 & [a_{tt}]^{-1} \end{bmatrix} \tag{31}$$

which has the form of $[D]^{-1}$ in Eq. 23, although the diagonal members must be found by the method of matrix inversion because they are submatrices and not ordinary elements. However, it is useful in analytic work to be aware of this method of indicating the inverse of matrix 30.

2 Branch-Parameter Matrices and Volt-Ampere Relations

We wish now to reconsider the problem of setting up the differential equations expressing the equilibrium of a linear passive network, removing restrictions of any sort so that we will arrive at a formulation that is perfectly general. For certain theoretical considerations to be taken up later on, such an unrestricted point of view is essential, as may also be true in some practical situations.*

Although the basis for a general procedure is given in Ch. 2, it is there discussed specifically with reference to resistance networks. In order to remove this restriction, it is necessary that we show in detail how the volt-ampere relations pertaining to the branches (expressed formally by Eqs. 43 of Art. 7, Ch. 2) may be evaluated for inductances and capacitances as well as for resistances. For the sake of convenience, these equations are repeated below

$$(v_k + e_{sk}) = z(j_k + i_{sk}) \tag{32}$$

$$(j_k + i_{sk}) = y(v_k + e_{sk}) \tag{33}$$

* Although the discussion in Art. 6 of Ch. 8 does provide the means for dealing with an arbitrary situation, there is lacking as yet a compact form expressing the total systematic procedure involved in obtaining equilibrium equations for the general case.

and Fig. 9 of Ch. 2 to which they refer is reproduced here as Fig. 1. It depicts the most general form that a passive branch with associated voltage and current sources may take. Since j_k and v_k are the net current and voltage drop, the quantities $(j_k + i_{sk})$ and $(v_k + e_{sk})$ are seen to pertain to the passive element (resistance, inductance, or capacitance) alone.

It is the relation between the currents and voltages in the passive elements that is expressed by Eqs. 32 and 33. The first of these symbolically expresses the voltage drop in the passive element of the kth branch as a function of the passive branch currents; the second equation in this pair does the reverse. We shall now put these relations into a more explicit form.

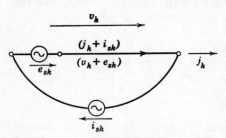

FIG. 1. Passive branch with associated voltage and current sources.

The passive branches (single elements) in the network are assumed to be numbered consecutively from 1 to b. Of this total number of b branches let us say that λ are inductive, ρ are resistive, and σ are elastive, $\lambda + \rho + \sigma$ being equal to b. The numbering of the branches, moreover, is carried out in such a fashion that numbers 1 to λ refer to inductances, numbers $\lambda + 1$ to $\lambda + \rho$ refer to resistances, and numbers $\lambda + \rho + 1$ to $\lambda + \rho + \sigma = b$ refer to elastances.

Since each inductive branch may be mutually coupled with every other branch in this group, the matrix of self- and mutual-inductance coefficients, according to the discussion in Art. 4 of Ch. 8, called the *branch-inductance matrix*, has the form

$$[l] = \begin{bmatrix} l_{11} & l_{12} & \cdots & l_{1\lambda} \\ l_{21} & l_{22} & \cdots & l_{2\lambda} \\ \cdot & \cdot & \cdots & \cdot \\ l_{\lambda 1} & l_{\lambda 2} & \cdots & l_{\lambda \lambda} \end{bmatrix} \tag{34}$$

The resistance and elastance branches, on the other hand, cannot be mutually coupled; their parameter matrices must have the diagonal form. Hence the *branch-resistance matrix* is given by

$$[r] = \begin{bmatrix} r_{\lambda+1} & 0 & 0 & \cdots & 0 \\ 0 & r_{\lambda+2} & 0 & \cdots & 0 \\ \cdot & \cdot & \cdot & \cdots & \cdot \\ 0 & 0 & 0 & \cdots & r_{\lambda+\rho} \end{bmatrix} \tag{35}$$

and the *branch-elastance matrix* is written

$$[s] = \begin{bmatrix} s_{\lambda+\rho+1} & 0 & 0 & \cdots & 0 \\ 0 & s_{\lambda+\rho+2} & 0 & \cdots & 0 \\ \multicolumn{5}{c}{\cdots\cdots\cdots\cdots\cdots\cdots} \\ 0 & 0 & 0 & \cdots & s_b \end{bmatrix} \qquad (36)$$

In these last two matrices, an element r_i or s_i is simply the resistance in ohms or the elastance in darafs of the single element (passive branch) to which the pertinent subscript refers.

The voltage drops in the passive elements in terms of the currents in these elements are expressed for the inductances by

$$(v_i + e_{si}) = \sum_{k=1}^{\lambda} l_{ik} p(j_k + i_{sk}), \qquad i = 1, 2, \cdots, \lambda \qquad (37)$$

for the resistances by

$$(v_i + e_{si}) = r_i(j_i + i_{si}), \qquad i = \lambda + 1, \cdots, \lambda + \rho \qquad (38)$$

and for the elastances by the equations

$$(v_i + e_{si}) = s_i p^{-1}(j_i + i_{si}), \qquad i = \lambda + \rho + 1, \cdots, b \qquad (39)$$

in which the abbreviations

$$p = \frac{d}{dt} \quad \text{and} \quad p^{-1} = \int dt \qquad (40)$$

are used to denote the operations of differentiation and integration respectively.

Because of the possibility of mutual coupling between inductive branches, each passive voltage drop $(v_i + e_{si})$ in one of these (i.e., for $i = 1, 2, \cdots, \lambda$) depends in general upon all of the passive currents $(j_i + i_{si})$ in these branches. That is why Eqs. 37 involve a summation extending over the inductive branches (reference to Eqs. 30 in Art. 4, Ch. 8, may also be helpful in the interpretation of 37). Each of Eqs. 38 and 39, in contrast, involves only a single term on the right-hand side because the voltage drop in a resistance or elastance depends upon the current in that branch alone.

The relations 37, 38, and 39 may be combined into a single matrix equation through defining the column matrices

$$[v + e_s] = \begin{bmatrix} v_1 + e_{s1} \\ v_2 + e_{s2} \\ \cdot \\ \cdot \\ \cdot \\ v_b + e_{sb} \end{bmatrix} \quad \text{and} \quad [j + i_s] = \begin{bmatrix} j_1 + i_{s1} \\ j_2 + i_{s2} \\ \cdot \\ \cdot \\ \cdot \\ j_b + i_{sb} \end{bmatrix} \tag{41}$$

and the branch operator matrix

$$[D] = \begin{bmatrix} [l]p & 0 & 0 \\ 0 & [r] & 0 \\ 0 & 0 & [s]p^{-1} \end{bmatrix} \tag{42}$$

in which the branch-parameter matrices 34, 35, and 36 are embedded as submatrices (the matrix $[D]$ is written in partitioned form). The scalar operators p and p^{-1} become associated with each element in the matrices $[l]$ and $[s]$, since multiplication of a matrix by a scalar multiplies each element in the matrix by that scalar (as may be seen from the fact that the matrix must vanish if the scalar is zero, and a matrix vanishes only when all elements are zero).

The desired relations expressing the voltage drops in the passive elements in terms of the currents in these elements (equivalent to Eqs. 37, 38, and 39 combined) are given by the single matrix equation

$$[v + e_s] = [D] \times [j + i_s] \tag{43}$$

Through carrying out the indicated matrix operations one thus obtains an explicit evaluation of the symbolic Eq. 32. (The uninitiated reader should write out the matrix $[D]$ completely and carry through the indicated multiplication in order to understand this result and appreciate its simplicity.)

The inverse relations 33 may similarly be evaluated. To this end the branch-parameter matrices are considered in their inverse forms as the *reciprocal inductance matrix*

$$[\gamma] = \begin{bmatrix} \gamma_{11} & \gamma_{12} & \cdots & \gamma_{1\lambda} \\ \gamma_{21} & \gamma_{22} & \cdots & \gamma_{2\lambda} \\ \cdot & \cdot & \cdots & \cdot \\ \gamma_{\lambda 1} & \gamma_{\lambda 2} & \cdots & \gamma_{\lambda\lambda} \end{bmatrix} = [l]^{-1} \tag{44}$$

the *conductance matrix*

$$[g] = \begin{bmatrix} g_{\lambda+1} & 0 & 0 & \cdots & 0 \\ 0 & g_{\lambda+2} & 0 & \cdots & 0 \\ \cdot & \cdot & \cdot & \cdot & \cdot \\ 0 & 0 & 0 & \cdots & g_{\lambda+\rho} \end{bmatrix} = [r]^{-1} \tag{45}$$

and the *capacitance matrix*

$$[c] = \begin{bmatrix} c_{\lambda+\rho+1} & 0 & 0 & \cdots & 0 \\ 0 & c_{\lambda+\rho+2} & 0 & \cdots & 0 \\ \cdot & \cdot & \cdot & \cdot & \cdot \\ 0 & 0 & 0 & \cdots & c_b \end{bmatrix} = [s]^{-1} \tag{46}$$

Since the last two are diagonal matrices, their diagonal elements are simply the reciprocals of the diagonal elements in $[r]$ and $[s]$. As shown in the preceding article, the elements in $[\gamma]$ are not so simply related to those in $[l]$. However, if the determinant of $[l]$ be Δ, with cofactors Δ_{sk}, then

$$\gamma_{sk} = \Delta_{ks}/\Delta \tag{47}$$

where the indexes s and k on either γ or Δ may be interchanged since the matrices in question are symmetrical.

In algebraic form, the desired inverse relations are expressed by

$$(j_i + i_{si}) = \sum_{k=1}^{\lambda} \gamma_{ik} p^{-1}(v_k + e_{sk}), \qquad i = 1, 2, \cdots, \lambda \tag{48}$$

$$(j_i + i_{si}) = g_i(v_i + e_{si}), \qquad i = \lambda + 1, \cdots, \lambda + \rho \tag{49}$$

and

$$(j_i + i_{si}) = c_i p(v_i + e_{si}), \qquad i = \lambda + \rho + 1, \cdots, b \tag{50}$$

In matrix form they may be combined in a single equation through defining the operator matrix (inverse to $[D]$)

$$[D]^{-1} = \begin{bmatrix} [\gamma]p^{-1} & 0 & 0 \\ 0 & [g] & 0 \\ 0 & 0 & [c]p \end{bmatrix} \tag{51}$$

whereupon the expressions for the currents in the passive elements in terms of the voltage drops in these elements are given by the matrix equation

$$[j + i_s] = [D]^{-1} \times [v + e_s] \tag{52}$$

which is the inverse of 43, and represents the explicit evaluation of the symbolic Eq. 33.

In order to obtain the equilibrium equations we can now follow precisely the same pattern set in Art. 8 of Ch. 2 for resistance networks as summarized there by Eqs. 44, 45, 46 for the loop basis and by Eqs. 48, 49, 50 for the node basis. The central equation in each of these groups of three expresses the volt-ampere relations for the branches, which we have just finished putting into matrix forms 43 and 52. The first and last equation in each group expresses respectively the pertinent Kirchhoff law and the branch variables (current or voltage) in terms of the loop or node variables. These relations involve the tie-set and cut-set schedules. We shall show next how these may conveniently be written as matrix equations and combined through straightforward substitution with Eqs. 43 or 52 to obtain the desired results.

3   Equilibrium Equations on the Node Basis

The first step is to write the pertinent cut-set schedule in the form of a matrix, thus

$$[\alpha] = \begin{bmatrix} \alpha_{11} & \alpha_{12} & \cdots & \alpha_{1b} \\ \alpha_{21} & \alpha_{22} & \cdots & \alpha_{2b} \\ \cdot & \cdot & \cdot \cdot \cdot \cdot & \cdot \\ \alpha_{n1} & \alpha_{n2} & \cdots & \alpha_{nb} \end{bmatrix} \tag{53}$$

The elements in any row of this matrix are the coefficients in a Kirchhoff current-law equation since they pertain to the selection of a cut set. Their values, therefore, will normally be either ± 1 or zero, depending on whether a pertinent branch does or does not belong to the cut set defined by a given row. Each row has b elements; but there are only n rows since this is the number of independent cut sets or node pairs. It should be recalled from the discussion in Ch. 1 that $n = n_t - 1$ where n_t equals the total number of nodes.

It is also shown in Ch. 1 that the elements in any column of the matrix $[\alpha]$ are coefficients in an equation expressing the pertinent branch-voltage drop in terms of the node-pair voltages that are consistent with cut sets defined by the rows. Therefore, if we write column matrices

$$[j] = \begin{bmatrix} j_1 \\ j_2 \\ \cdot \\ \cdot \\ \cdot \\ j_b \end{bmatrix} \quad \text{and} \quad [v] = \begin{bmatrix} v_1 \\ v_2 \\ \cdot \\ \cdot \\ \cdot \\ v_b \end{bmatrix} \tag{54}$$

for the net branch currents and voltage drops, and express similarly the associated current and voltage sources as

$$[i_s] = \begin{bmatrix} i_{s1} \\ i_{s2} \\ \cdot \\ \cdot \\ \cdot \\ i_{sb} \end{bmatrix} \quad \text{and} \quad [e_s] = \begin{bmatrix} e_{s1} \\ e_{s2} \\ \cdot \\ \cdot \\ \cdot \\ e_{sb} \end{bmatrix} \tag{55}$$

so that the column matrices 41 can be separated as indicated by

$$[j + i_s] = [j] + [i_s], \qquad [v + e_s] = [v] + [e_s] \tag{56}$$

and, if we write the node-pair voltage variables in the form of a column matrix

$$[e] = \begin{bmatrix} e_1 \\ e_2 \\ \cdot \\ \cdot \\ \cdot \\ e_n \end{bmatrix} \tag{57}$$

then the Kirchhoff-law equations are expressed in matrix form by

$$[\alpha] \times [j] = 0 \tag{58}$$

the volt-ampere relations 52 for the branches can be written

$$[j] + [i_s] = [D]^{-1} \times [v] + [D]^{-1} \times [e_s] \tag{59}$$

and the branch voltages in terms of the node-pair voltages are given by

$$[v] = [\alpha]_t \times [e] \tag{60}$$

The desired equilibrium equations are the Kirchhoff-law Eqs. 58 expressed in terms of the node-pair voltages as variables. One obtains this result through substituting the expression for $[v]$ from Eq. 60 into Eq. 59, and the ensuing relation for $[j]$ into Eq. 58. After a slight rearrangement of the terms, one finds

$$[\alpha] \times [D]^{-1} \times [\alpha]_t \times [e] = [\alpha] \times ([i_s] - [D]^{-1} \times [e_s]) = [i_n] \tag{61}$$

in which the right-hand side, representing the net equivalent current sources feeding the node pairs, is abbreviated as a column matrix

$$[i_n] = \begin{bmatrix} i_{n1} \\ i_{n2} \\ \cdot \\ \cdot \\ \cdot \\ i_{nn} \end{bmatrix} \tag{62}$$

It is interesting to note the structure of this matrix as expressed by Eq. 61. Thus the term $[i_s]$ within the parenthesis represents current sources associated with the branches, while the term involving $[D]^{-1} \times [e_s]$ represents the transformation of voltage sources associated with the branches (see Fig. 1) into equivalent current sources, the minus sign arising from the opposite reference arrows associated with e_{sk} and i_{sk}. The parenthesis expression, therefore, represents net current sources for the branches, and is to be thought of as combining these into a single column matrix. Multiplication of the matrix $[\alpha]$ into this column matrix yields again a column matrix whose elements are algebraic sums of the branch sources according to the groups of branches forming cut sets (these are the branches associated with the pertinent node pairs). The elements in this resultant column matrix $[i_n]$ are thus seen to be equivalent node-pair current sources.

Interpretation of the left-hand side of Eq. 61 is facilitated through an appropriate evaluation of the triple matrix product $[\alpha] \times [D]^{-1} \times [\alpha]_t$. A preliminary step toward achieving this end is the partitioning of the columns in the matrix $[\alpha]$ into groups of λ, ρ, σ, thus:

$$[\alpha] = [\alpha_{n\lambda} \mid \alpha_{n\rho} \mid \alpha_{n\sigma}] \tag{63}$$

The submatrix $[\alpha_{n\lambda}]$ consists of the first λ columns in $[\alpha]$; $[\alpha_{n\rho}]$ represents the succeeding group of ρ columns, and $[\alpha_{n\sigma}]$ contains the last σ columns. Using the form for $[D]^{-1}$ given in Eq. 51, one then finds

$$[\alpha] \times [D]^{-1} \times [\alpha]_t = [\alpha_{n\lambda} \mid \alpha_{n\rho} \mid \alpha_{n\sigma}] \times \begin{bmatrix} [\gamma]p^{-1} & 0 & 0 \\ 0 & [g] & 0 \\ 0 & 0 & [c]p \end{bmatrix} \times \begin{bmatrix} (\alpha_{n\lambda})_t \\ (\alpha_{n\rho})_t \\ (\alpha_{n\sigma})_t \end{bmatrix}$$

$$= [\alpha_{n\lambda}] \times [\gamma] \times [\alpha_{n\lambda}]_t p^{-1} + [\alpha_{n\rho}] \times [g] \times [\alpha_{n\rho}]_t + [\alpha_{n\sigma}] \times [c] \times [\alpha_{n\sigma}]_t p \tag{64}$$

The expressions

$$[\Gamma] = [\alpha_{n\lambda}] \times [\gamma] \times [\alpha_{n\lambda}]_t$$

$$[G] = [\alpha_{n\rho}] \times [g] \times [\alpha_{n\rho}]_t \tag{65}$$

$$[C] = [\alpha_{n\sigma}] \times [c] \times [\alpha_{n\sigma}]_t$$

are recognized respectively as the *reciprocal inductance*, the *conductance*, and the *capacitance* parameter matrices pertaining to the node basis. In terms of these and the source matrix 62, the equilibrium Eqs. 61 take the somewhat more familiar form

$$([\Gamma]p^{-1} + [G] + [C]p) \times [e] = [i_n] \tag{66}$$

The principal results of the present discussion are the evaluation of the resultant source matrix $[i_n]$ as given in Eq. 61, and the expressions 65 for the pertinent parameter matrices. These are given in terms of the branch-parameter matrices $[\gamma]$, $[g]$, and $[c]$ through triple-matrix products with appropriate portions (and their transpositions) of the α matrix characterizing the cut-set schedule. The formation of these key quantities appearing in the equilibrium Eqs. 66 is thus in every case reduced to a simple, systematic, and straightforward procedure. The equations themselves are a set of simultaneous differential equations in terms of the instantaneous values of the variables.

4   Equilibrium Equations on the Loop Basis

The procedure is in form entirely analogous to that just described. The pertinent tie-set schedule is characterized by the matrix

$$[\beta] = \begin{bmatrix} \beta_{11} & \beta_{12} & \cdots & \beta_{1b} \\ \beta_{21} & \beta_{22} & \cdots & \beta_{2b} \\ \beta_{l1} & \beta_{l2} & \cdots & \beta_{lb} \end{bmatrix} \tag{67}$$

in which the elements of any row are the coefficients in a Kirchhoff voltage-law equation since they correspond to the selection of a tie set (set of branches forming a closed loop). Their values will normally be either ± 1 or zero, depending on whether a pertinent branch does or does not belong to the tie set defined by a given row. Each row has b elements; but there are only l rows since this is the number of independent tie sets or loops. It should be recalled from the discussion in Ch. 1 that $l = b - n = b - n_t + 1$.

It is also shown in Ch. 1 that the elements in any column of the matrix $[\beta]$ are coefficients in an equation expressing the pertinent branch current in terms of the loop currents that are consistent with the tie sets defined by the rows (i.e., currents that circulate upon the closed paths defined by the rows). Therefore, if we make use of column matrices 54 and 55, the relations indicated in Eqs. 56, and write the loop-current variables in the form of a column matrix

$$[i] = \begin{bmatrix} i_1 \\ i_2 \\ \cdot \\ \cdot \\ \cdot \\ i_l \end{bmatrix} \tag{68}$$

then the Kirchhoff-law equations are expressed in matrix form by

$$[\beta] \times [v] = 0 \tag{69}$$

the volt-ampere relations 43 for the branches can be written

$$[v] + [e_s] = [D] \times [j] + [D] \times [i_s] \tag{70}$$

and the branch currents in terms of the loop currents are given by

$$[j] = [\beta]_t \times [i] \tag{71}$$

The desired equilibrium equations are the Kirchhoff-law Eqs. 69 expressed in terms of the loop currents as variables. One obtains this result through substituting the expression for $[j]$ from Eq. 71 into Eq. 70, and the ensuing relation for $[v]$ into Eq. 69. After a slight re-arrangement of the terms, one finds

$$[\beta] \times [D] \times [\beta]_t \times [i] = [\beta] \times ([e_s] - [D] \times [i_s]) = [e_l] \tag{72}$$

in which the right-hand side, representing the net equivalent voltage sources feeding the loops, is abbreviated as a column matrix

$$[e_l] = \begin{bmatrix} e_{l1} \\ e_{l2} \\ \cdot \\ \cdot \\ \cdot \\ e_{ll} \end{bmatrix} \tag{73}$$

It is interesting to note the structure of this matrix as expressed by Eq. 72. Thus the term $[e_s]$ within the parenthesis represents voltage sources associated with the branches, while the term involving $[D] \times [i_s]$

represents the transformation of current sources associated with branches (see Fig. 1) into equivalent voltage sources, the minus sign arising from the opposite reference arrows associated with i_{sk} and e_{sk}. The parenthesis expression, therefore, represents net voltage sources for the branches, and is to be thought of as combining these into a single column matrix. Multiplication of the matrix $[\beta]$ into this column matrix yields again a column matrix whose elements are algebraic sums of the branch sources according to the groups of branches forming tie sets (these are the branches associated with pertinent loops). The elements in this resultant column matrix $[e_l]$ are thus seen to be equivalent loop voltage sources.

Interpretation of the left-hand side of Eq. 72 is facilitated through an appropriate evaluation of the triple-matrix product $[\beta] \times [D] \times [\beta]_t$. A preliminary step toward achieving this end is the partitioning of the columns in the matrix $[\beta]$ into groups of λ, ρ, σ, thus:

$$[\beta] = [\beta_{l\lambda} \mid \beta_{l\rho} \mid \beta_{l\sigma}] \tag{74}$$

The submatrix $[\beta_{l\lambda}]$ consists of the first λ columns in $[\beta]$; $[\beta_{l\rho}]$ represents the succeeding group of ρ columns, and $[\beta_{l\sigma}]$ contains the last σ columns. Using the form for $[D]$ given in Eq. 42, one then finds

$$[\beta] \times [D] \times [\beta]_t = [\beta_{l\lambda} \mid \beta_{l\rho} \mid \beta_{l\sigma}] \times \begin{bmatrix} [l]p & 0 & 0 \\ 0 & [r] & 0 \\ 0 & 0 & [s]p^{-1} \end{bmatrix} \times \begin{bmatrix} [\beta_{l\lambda}]_t \\ [\beta_{l\rho}]_t \\ [\beta_{l\sigma}]_t \end{bmatrix}$$

$$= [\beta_{l\lambda}] \times [l] \times [\beta_{l\lambda}]_t p + [\beta_{l\rho}] \times [r] \times [\beta_{l\rho}]_t + [\beta_{l\sigma}] \times [s] \times [\beta_{l\sigma}]_t p^{-1} \tag{75}$$

The expressions

$$[L] = [\beta_{l\lambda}] \times [l] \times [\beta_{l\lambda}]_t$$

$$[R] = [\beta_{l\rho}] \times [r] \times [\beta_{l\rho}]_t \tag{76}$$

$$[S] = [\beta_{l\sigma}] \times [s] \times [\beta_{l\sigma}]_t$$

are recognized respectively as the *inductance*, the *resistance*, and the *elastance* parameter matrices pertaining to the loop basis. In terms of these and the source matrix 73, the equilibrium Eqs. 72 take the somewhat more familiar form

$$([L]p + [R] + [S]p^{-1}) \times [i] = [e_l] \tag{77}$$

The principal results of the present discussion are the evaluation of the resultant source matrix $[e_l]$ as given in Eq. 72, and the expressions 76 for the pertinent parameter matrices. These are given in terms of the branch-parameter matrices $[l]$, $[r]$, and $[s]$ through triple-matrix products with appropriate portions (and their transpositions) of the β matrix characterizing the tie-set schedule. The formation of these key quantities appearing in the equilibrium Eqs. 77 is thus in every case reduced to a simple, systematic, and straightforward procedure. The equations themselves are a set of simultaneous differential equations in terms of the instantaneous values of the variables.

5   Remarks and Examples

In Ch. 2 it is pointed out that symmetry of the parameter matrices on the node or loop basis comes about if the definitions of the node-pair voltages or loop currents are chosen to be consistent with the Kirchhoff-law equations, a condition that is commonly met but is by no means necessary. The procedures given in the two preceding articles are, therefore, not completely general, for they satisfy the conditions leading to symmetry. In the node method, for example, Eq. 58 expressing Kirchhoff's current law and Eq. 60 defining the node-pair voltage variables are consistent, for they involve the same α matrix (cut-set schedule). Similarly, for the loop method, the Kirchhoff voltage-law Eq. 69 and Eq. 71 defining the loop currents are consistent, for they are based upon the same tie-set schedule (β matrix).

What we should recognize is the fact that one may, on the node basis, choose one set of node pairs for the current-law equations and an altogether different one for the definition of the node-pair voltages; or, on the loop basis, one may choose one set of loops for the voltage-law equations and another as the circulatory paths for the loop currents. Specifically, Eqs. 58 and 60 may involve two different α matrices or cut-set schedules; and Eqs. 69 and 71 may involve two entirely different β matrices or tie-set schedules (so long as the schedules used pertain to the same network, of course). In most instances, however, it is advantageous to adhere to the consistency conditions and obtain symmetrical parameter matrices. Therefore the relations as given in the preceding articles are almost always appropriate and can readily be generalized if desired.

As an illustrative example of the procedure given in the preceding article, suppose we consider the circuit of Fig. 2(a) which involves six mutually coupled windings on the same magnetic core. An appropriate schematic diagram is shown in part (b) of the same figure. It is easily recognized (according to the discussion in Art. 4, Ch. 8) that the scheme for indicating relative polarities of the coils by means of dots is applicable to this simple arrangement, and that the system of dots in the schematic of part (b) is consistent with the physical arrangement indicated in part (a) of Fig. 2.

The reference arrows on the inductive branches of this circuit diagram are all chosen so that the tips of these arrows are at the dot-marked ends. As a result of this simple expedient, all mutual inductances between branches become numerically positive. If we assume that all

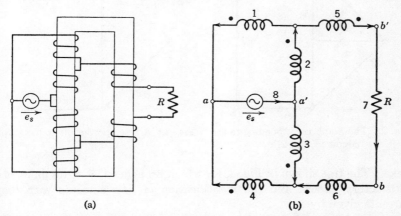

(a)   (b)

FIG. 2. A physical arrangement of coupled coils (a) and their pertinent circuit configuration (b).

six coils have self-inductances equal to unity, and that all mutual inductances are equal to one-half (there is no sense in using more arbitrary numbers in this example), one has the branch-inductance matrix

$$[l] = \begin{bmatrix} 1 & 0.5 & 0.5 & 0.5 & 0.5 & 0.5 \\ 0.5 & 1 & 0.5 & 0.5 & 0.5 & 0.5 \\ 0.5 & 0.5 & 1 & 0.5 & 0.5 & 0.5 \\ 0.5 & 0.5 & 0.5 & 1 & 0.5 & 0.5 \\ 0.5 & 0.5 & 0.5 & 0.5 & 1 & 0.5 \\ 0.5 & 0.5 & 0.5 & 0.5 & 0.5 & 1 \end{bmatrix} \qquad (78)$$

Although the voltage source, which is bridged across a node pair, may readily be replaced by voltage sources in series with branches (as shown in Art. 7, Ch. 2), it is more interesting in this example to consider the voltage source as a degenerate branch; that is, one for which the associated passive element is zero. For the branch numbering indicated in Fig. 2(b), one then obtains the graph shown in Fig. 3.

Since in the given problem we are particularly interested in the current through the resistance R as a function of the source voltage, it is expedient to choose a tree in such a way that branches 7 and 8 become

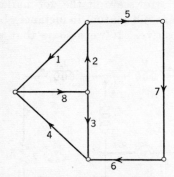

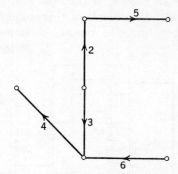

FIG. 3. The graph corresponding to the circuit in Fig. 2(b).

FIG. 4. A tree appropriate to the graph of Fig. 3.

links. The tree shown in Fig. 4, for which branches 1, 7, 8 are links, is a satisfactory choice, and the identification of link currents with loop currents given by

$$i_1 = j_8$$
$$i_2 = j_7 \tag{79}$$
$$i_3 = j_1$$

seems best because it associates i_1 with the source and i_2 with the load.

The matrix of the resulting tie-set schedule is now recognized by inspection to be

$$[\beta] = \begin{bmatrix} 0 & 0 & 1 & 1 & 0 & 0 & 0 & 1 \\ 0 & 1 & -1 & 0 & 1 & 1 & 1 & 0 \\ 1 & 1 & -1 & -1 & 0 & 0 & 0 & 0 \end{bmatrix} \tag{80}$$

and the submatrix $[\beta_{l\lambda}]$ is given by the first six columns. Noting the expression for the inductance matrix in the Eqs. 76, we next evaluate the product

$$[\beta_{l\lambda}] \times [l] = \begin{bmatrix} 1 & 1 & \frac{3}{2} & \frac{3}{2} & 1 & 1 \\ 1 & \frac{3}{2} & \frac{1}{2} & 1 & \frac{3}{2} & \frac{3}{2} \\ \frac{1}{2} & \frac{1}{2} & -\frac{1}{2} & -\frac{1}{2} & 0 & 0 \end{bmatrix} \tag{81}$$

which can be done by inspection, using Eqs. 78 and 80. The desired loop-inductance matrix is then found as shown below

$$[L] \cdot = [\beta_{t\lambda}] \times [l] \times [\beta_{t\lambda}]_t = \begin{bmatrix} 1 & 1 & \frac{3}{2} & \frac{3}{2} & 1 & 1 \\ 1 & \frac{3}{2} & \frac{1}{2} & 1 & \frac{3}{2} & \frac{3}{2} \\ \frac{1}{2} & \frac{1}{2} & -\frac{1}{2} & -\frac{1}{2} & 0 & 0 \end{bmatrix} \times \begin{bmatrix} 0 & 0 & 1 \\ 0 & 1 & 1 \\ 1 & -1 & -1 \\ 1 & 0 & -1 \\ 0 & 1 & 0 \\ 0 & 1 & 0 \end{bmatrix}$$

$$= \begin{bmatrix} 3 & \frac{3}{2} & -1 \\ \frac{3}{2} & 4 & 1 \\ -1 & 1 & 2 \end{bmatrix} \tag{82}$$

The equilibrium equations on the loop basis are thus seen to be given by

$$\begin{bmatrix} 3p & (3/2)p & -p \\ (3/2)p & (4p + R) & p \\ -p & p & 2p \end{bmatrix} \times \begin{bmatrix} i_1 \\ i_2 \\ i_3 \end{bmatrix} = \begin{bmatrix} e_s \\ 0 \\ 0 \end{bmatrix} \tag{83}$$

where the abbreviation $p = d/dt$ is still used. Since we are only interested in i_1 and i_2, it is a good idea to eliminate i_3 immediately. To do this we can consider the so-called *augmented* matrix

$$\begin{bmatrix} 3p & (3/2)p & -p & e_s \\ (3/2)p & (4p + R) & p & 0 \\ -p & p & 2p & 0 \end{bmatrix} \tag{84}$$

and carry out linear combinations of its rows (equivalent to making linear combinations of the Eqs. 83) in such a way as to produce zeros for all elements of the third column except the last.

Thus if we add the $(1/2)$-multiplied elements of the third row to the respective ones of the first row; and then add the $(-1/2)$-multiplied elements of the third row to the respective ones of the second row, there results

$$\begin{bmatrix} (5/2)p & 2p & 0 & e_s \\ 2p & (7/2)p + R & 0 & 0 \\ -p & p & 2p & 0 \end{bmatrix} \tag{85}$$

The third row is now trivial, and the first two yield the equations

$$\begin{bmatrix} (5/2)p & 2p \\ 2p & (7/2)p + R \end{bmatrix} \times \begin{bmatrix} i_1 \\ i_2 \end{bmatrix} = \begin{bmatrix} e_s \\ 0 \end{bmatrix} \tag{86}$$

By inspection one can recognize that the circuit of Fig. 5 involving only self-inductances with the values indicated, has the same loop

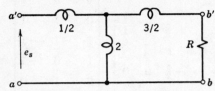

equilibrium equations. One may, therefore, regard this simple circuit as the equivalent of the one given in Fig. 2 so far as the terminal pairs a–a' and b–b' are concerned.

FIG. 5.   Circuit equivalent to that in Fig. 2(b) with respect to the terminal pairs a–a' and b–b'.

As an example of the node method, we will consider the circuit of Fig. 6 in which the three inductances are mutually coupled, and for the indicated reference arrows are characterized by the branch-inductance matrix

$$[l] = \begin{bmatrix} 2 & 4 & -5 \\ 4 & 9 & -11 \\ -5 & -11 & 14 \end{bmatrix} \tag{87}$$

with the inverse

$$[\gamma] = \begin{bmatrix} 5 & -1 & 1 \\ -1 & 3 & 2 \\ 1 & 2 & 2 \end{bmatrix} \tag{88}$$

The resistive branches have conductance values in mhos as indicated in

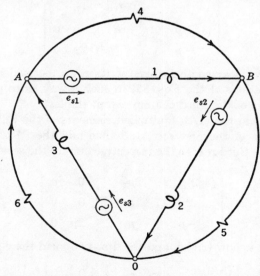

FIG. 6.   A circuit to be characterized on the node basis. The inductances are mutually coupled.

the following branch-conductance matrix for the branch numbering in Fig. 6:

$$[g] = \begin{bmatrix} 2 & 0 & 0 \\ 0 & 8 & 0 \\ 0 & 0 & 3 \end{bmatrix} \tag{89}$$

For the variables we will choose a node-to-datum set of voltages, taking the point 0 as the datum and denoting the potentials of nodes A and B respectively by e_1 and e_2. The appropriate cut-set schedule then has the following matrix:

$$[\alpha] = \begin{bmatrix} 1 & 0 & -1 & 1 & 0 & -1 \\ -1 & 1 & 0 & -1 & 1 & 0 \end{bmatrix} \tag{90}$$

and

$$[\alpha_{n\lambda}] = \begin{bmatrix} 1 & 0 & -1 \\ -1 & 1 & 0 \end{bmatrix}, \qquad [\alpha_{n\rho}] = \begin{bmatrix} 1 & 0 & -1 \\ -1 & 1 & 0 \end{bmatrix} \tag{91}$$

The three voltage sources we will assume to be steady sinusoids with values as indicated in the column matrix

$$[e_s] = \begin{bmatrix} 7 \cos t \\ 2 \sin t \\ 34 \cos t \\ 0 \\ 0 \\ 0 \end{bmatrix} \tag{92}$$

The matrix $[i_s]$ according to 55 is identically zero because there are no current sources associated with any of the branches.

To evaluate $[i_n]$ in Eq. 61 we must form $[D]^{-1}$ which by Eq. 51 becomes

$$[D]^{-1} = \begin{bmatrix} 5p^{-1} & -p^{-1} & p^{-1} & 0 & 0 & 0 \\ -p^{-1} & 3p^{-1} & 2p^{-1} & 0 & 0 & 0 \\ p^{-1} & 2p^{-1} & 2p^{-1} & 0 & 0 & 0 \\ 0 & 0 & 0 & 2 & 0 & 0 \\ 0 & 0 & 0 & 0 & 8 & 0 \\ 0 & 0 & 0 & 0 & 0 & 3 \end{bmatrix} \tag{93}$$

Actually only the first three rows and columns enter into the evaluation of

$$[D]^{-1} \times [e_s] = \begin{bmatrix} 69 \sin t + 2 \cos t \\ 61 \sin t - 6 \cos t \\ 75 \sin t - 4 \cos t \\ 0 \\ 0 \\ 0 \end{bmatrix} \tag{94}$$

as the reader may readily verify by inspection, noting incidentally that $p^{-1} \cos t = \sin t$ and $p^{-1} \sin t = -\cos t$. One thus obtains for the matrix representing the net equivalent current sources feeding the nodes

$$[i_n] = -[\alpha] \times [D]^{-1} \times [e_s] = \begin{bmatrix} 6 \sin t - 6 \cos t \\ 8 \sin t + 8 \cos t \end{bmatrix} = \begin{bmatrix} 6\sqrt{2} \sin (t - 45°) \\ 8\sqrt{2} \sin (t + 45°) \end{bmatrix}$$

$$\tag{95}$$

Straightforward substitution into Eqs. 65 next yields for the parameter matrices

$$[\Gamma] = \begin{bmatrix} 1 & 0 & -1 \\ -1 & 1 & 0 \end{bmatrix} \times \begin{bmatrix} 5 & -1 & 1 \\ -1 & 3 & 2 \\ 1 & 2 & 2 \end{bmatrix} \times \begin{bmatrix} 1 & -1 \\ 0 & 1 \\ -1 & 0 \end{bmatrix} = \begin{bmatrix} 5 & -7 \\ -7 & 10 \end{bmatrix} \tag{96}$$

and

$$[G] = \begin{bmatrix} 1 & 0 & -1 \\ -1 & 1 & 0 \end{bmatrix} \times \begin{bmatrix} 2 & 0 & 0 \\ 0 & 8 & 0 \\ 0 & 0 & 3 \end{bmatrix} \times \begin{bmatrix} 1 & -1 \\ 0 & 1 \\ -1 & 0 \end{bmatrix} = \begin{bmatrix} 5 & -2 \\ -2 & 10 \end{bmatrix} \tag{97}$$

of which the last could have been written down by inspection of Fig. 6. Thus the equilibrium equations for this network become

$$\begin{bmatrix} (5p^{-1} + 5) & -(7p^{-1} + 2) \\ -(7p^{-1} + 2) & (10p^{-1} + 10) \end{bmatrix} \times \begin{bmatrix} e_1 \\ e_2 \end{bmatrix} = \begin{bmatrix} 6\sqrt{2} \sin (t - 45°) \\ 8\sqrt{2} \sin (t + 45°) \end{bmatrix} \tag{98}$$

The computations shown in Eqs. 93, 94, and 95 suggest that it might be a good idea to decompose the matrices $[i_n]$ and $[e_s]$ in a manner consistent with the partitioning of $[D]^{-1}$ and $[\alpha]$ as given in Eqs. 51 and 63, with the object of making the pertinent expressions less unwieldy. In order to carry out this thought both for the loop and node bases, we partition the source matrices 55 pertaining to the branches as indicated by

$$[i_s] = \begin{bmatrix} i_{s\lambda} \\ \hline i_{s\rho} \\ \hline i_{s\sigma} \end{bmatrix} \quad \text{and} \quad [e_s] = \begin{bmatrix} e_{s\lambda} \\ \hline e_{s\rho} \\ \hline e_{s\sigma} \end{bmatrix} \tag{99}$$

Here the submatrices $[i_{s\lambda}]$ and $[e_{s\lambda}]$ contain the first λ elements in the column matrices $[i_s]$ and $[e_s]$, the succeeding ρ elements are represented by the submatrices $[i_{s\rho}]$ and $[e_{s\rho}]$, and the last σ elements are combined in the portions $[i_{s\sigma}]$ and $[e_{s\sigma}]$.

The source matrices $[i_n]$ and $[e_l]$, Eqs. 62 and 73, pertaining to node pairs and loops are appropriately resolved into *additive* components as indicated by

$$[i_n] = [i_n]_\lambda + [i_n]_\rho + [i_n]_\sigma \tag{100}$$

$$[e_l] = [e_l]_\lambda + [e_l]_\rho + [e_l]_\sigma \tag{101}$$

We then find that the expression for $[i_n]$ given in Eq. 61 permits the detailed representation

$$[i_n]_\lambda = [\alpha_{n\lambda}] \times ([i_{s\lambda}] - [\gamma]p^{-1} \times [e_{s\lambda}]) \tag{102}$$

$$[i_n]_\rho = [\alpha_{n\rho}] \times ([i_{s\rho}] - [g] \quad \times [e_{s\rho}]) \tag{103}$$

$$[i_n]_\sigma = [\alpha_{n\sigma}] \times ([i_{s\sigma}] - [c]p \quad \times [e_{s\sigma}]) \tag{104}$$

while the expression for $[e_l]$ given in Eq. 72 may be decomposed into

$$[e_l]_\lambda = [\beta_{l\lambda}] \times ([e_{s\lambda}] - [l]p \quad \times [i_{s\lambda}]) \tag{105}$$

$$[e_l]_\rho = [\beta_{l\rho}] \times ([e_{s\rho}] - [r] \quad \times [i_{s\rho}]) \tag{106}$$

$$[e_l]_\sigma = [\beta_{l\sigma}] \times ([e_{s\sigma}] - [s]p^{-1} \times [i_{s\sigma}]) \tag{107}$$

These components of the matrices $[i_n]$ and $[e_l]$ that are distinguished by the subscripts λ, ρ, σ (not to be confused with submatrices) are those additive portions of these source matrices that are contributed by actual current and voltage sources associated with the inductive, the resistive, and the elastive branches respectively. The separate expressions for these components are far less unwieldy than those for $[i_n]$ and $[e_l]$. Moreover, one may have sources associated only with one kind of element (inductance, resistance, or capacitance) in which case two of the components are obviously zero and need not confuse the calculations. Thus, in the last example above, there are no sources associated with the resistive branches, and so three-fourths of the space occupied by matrix 93 and half the space occupied by 94 could be saved.

Another point worth emphasizing is concerned with the way in which the voltage source in the problem of Fig. 2 is dealt with. Wherever we encounter a voltage source that is not in series with a passive element or a current source that is not in parallel with a passive element, we have the choice either of revising the circuit according to the discussions given in Art. 7 of Ch. 2 or of considering the source as a degenerate branch, as is done in the example above. The latter scheme preserves the given geometry of the network, a feature that may be important to the subsequent interpretation of the analysis. It is well, therefore, to be aware of the possibility of treating sources in these various ways.*

6   Energy Functions

Denoting the elements in the loop-parameter matrices $[L]$, $[R]$, $[S]$ by L_{ik}, R_{ik}, S_{ik} where the indexes i and k may assume any integer values from 1 to l, one may write the equilibrium Eqs. 77 in the following more explicit algebraic form:

$$\sum_{k=1}^{l} \left(L_{ik}\frac{d}{dt} + R_{ik} + S_{ik}\int dt \right) i_k = e_{li}, \qquad i = 1, 2, \cdots, l \quad (108)$$

Since this is still a rather compact form for these equations, the reader will better understand the notation involved through writing them out completely on a large sheet of paper. Thus for $i = 1$ he should write out the terms in the left-hand sum that correspond successively to $k = 1, 2, \cdots, l$ and equate these to e_{l1}. He should then do the same for $i = 2$, $i = 3$, and so forth down to the equation for $i = l$. He will thus understand with ease and clarity how this system of equations appears in detailed form and how the notation in Eq. 108 is to be interpreted.

He should next carry through the detailed evaluation of these same equations starting from the equivalent matrix form 77, writing out all of the matrices explicitly and carrying out the indicated matrix additions and multiplications. A facile understanding of the equivalence of the matrix and the algebraic forms of these equations and their individual detailed interpretation thus gained (and not achievable through any less painful method!) is essential in developing one's ability to comprehend without difficulty the following discussion.

If we interpret the quantities e_{l1}, e_{l2}, $\cdots$, e_{ll} as being actual voltage sources acting in the links of the network and regard the loop currents i_1, i_2, $\cdots$, i_l as the currents in these same links (which is appropriate because the conditions leading to symmetrical parameter matrices are

---

* In this connection see also Probs. 23 and 24 of Ch. 2.

fulfilled), it is clear that the expression

$$P = e_{l1}i_1 + e_{l2}i_2 + \cdots + e_{ll}i_l \tag{109}$$

represents the total instantaneous power delivered to the network by the sources. In order to study this flow of energy throughout the network we need to construct the expression 109 using Eqs. 108. Visualizing these equations written out as suggested above, we may form the desired result through multiplying the equations (on both sides) successively by i_1, i_2, $\cdots$, i_l, and adding all of them.

Through use of the summation sign we can indicate this set of operations very compactly if we multiply on both sides of Eq. 108 by i_i and then sum over the index i from 1 to l. On the left we obtain a double summation, since Eq. 108 already involves a sum with respect to the index k. The result is written

$$P = \sum_{i,\,k=1}^{l} \left(L_{ik}i_i\frac{di_k}{dt} + R_{ik}i_ii_k + S_{ik}i_i\int i_k\,dt \right) = \sum_{i=1}^{l} e_{li}i_i \tag{110}$$

where it is important to note that the time differentiation and integration do not affect i_i.

If we now define three functions as

$$F = \frac{1}{2}\sum_{i,\,k=1}^{l} R_{ik}i_ii_k \tag{111}$$

$$T = \frac{1}{2}\sum_{i,\,k=1}^{l} L_{ik}i_ii_k \tag{112}$$

$$V = \frac{1}{2}\sum_{i,\,k=1}^{l} S_{ik}q_iq_k \tag{113}$$

where q_k in the last of these is used to denote the *loop charge* or indefinite time integral of the loop current as indicated in

$$q_k = \int i_k\,dt \quad \text{or} \quad i_k = \frac{dq_k}{dt} \tag{114}$$

we observe that Eq. 110 is equivalent to

$$P = 2F + \frac{d}{dt}(T + V) = \sum_{i=1}^{l} e_{li}i_i \tag{115}$$

For through straightforward differentiation we see that

$$\frac{dT}{dt} = \frac{1}{2} \sum_{i,\,k=1}^{l} L_{ik} \frac{d}{dt}(i_i i_k) \tag{116}$$

since summation and differentiation are interchangeable operations, and by the rule for the derivative of a product

$$\frac{d}{dt}(i_i i_k) = i_i \frac{di_k}{dt} + i_k \frac{di_i}{dt} \tag{117}$$

so that

$$\frac{dT}{dt} = \frac{1}{2} \left(\sum_{i,\,k=1}^{l} L_{ik} i_i \frac{di_k}{dt} + \sum_{i,\,k=1}^{l} L_{ik} i_k \frac{di_i}{dt} \right) \tag{118}$$

If in the second of these two sums we interchange the summation indexes i and k (which is permissible since each independently assumes all integer values from 1 to l), and make use of the symmetry condition $L_{ik} = L_{ki}$, it becomes clear that the two sums are identical. Hence

$$\frac{dT}{dt} = \sum_{i,\,k=1}^{l} L_{ik} i_i \frac{di_k}{dt} \tag{119}$$

Analogously we find

$$\frac{dV}{dt} = \sum_{i,\,k=1}^{l} S_{ik} q_k \frac{dq_i}{dt} = \sum_{i,\,k=1}^{l} S_{ik} i_i \int i_k \, dt \tag{120}$$

and thus the equivalence of Eqs. 110 and 115 is established.

Comparison with Eq. 32 of Ch. 7 reveals that our present Eqs. 111, 112, 113, and 115 represent a generalization of the previous result pertaining to a simple RLC circuit, and that the functions $2F$, T, and V are respectively the total instantaneous rate of energy dissipation, the instantaneous value of the energy stored in the magnetic fields associated with the inductances, and the instantaneous value of the energy stored in the electric fields associated with the capacitances. Thus Eq. 115 expresses the conservation of energy through showing that the time rate of energy supplied by the sources equals the sum of the rate of energy dissipation in the circuit resistances and the time rate of change of the net stored energy.

Although F dimensionally is power while T and V represent energy, we speak of the three functions F, T, and V as the *energy functions* associated with the network. Specifically, T and V are referred to as stored-energy functions, while F is also called the *loss function* (first introduced into this sort of analysis by Lord Rayleigh). In order to preserve homogeneity in form for the three functions, a factor 1/2 is written before the summation in the expression for F as well as in those for T and V, and for this reason it is $2F$ not F that represents the total instantaneous rate of energy dissipation.

Until the reader has become accustomed to the notation used in Eqs. 111, 112, 113, it is well occasionally to write out an expression of this sort more fully, as, for example,

$$
\begin{aligned}
2T = L_{11}i_1i_1 + L_{12}i_1i_2 &+ \cdots + L_1{}_li_1i_l \\
+ L_{21}i_2i_1 + L_{22}i_2i_2 &+ \cdots + L_2{}_li_2i_l \\
+ \cdots \cdots &\cdots \cdots \cdots \\
+ L_{l1}i_li_1 + L_{l2}i_li_2 &+ \cdots + L_{ll}i_li_l
\end{aligned}
\tag{121}
$$

Thus the first line in this expression is a summation on the index k from 1 to l while the index i remains constant at the value 1; the second line similarly is a summation on k from 1 to l while $i = 2$, and so forth. Since one may just as well add the terms by columns, we see incidentally that one can alternately sum on i from 1 to l holding k constant at 1, then at 2, and so forth. In other words, the double summation is carried out through letting the indexes i and k independently assume all integer values from 1 to l, as stated above.

The expression 121 (compare also with Eq. 154 of Ch. 3 and with Eqs. 39 and 44 of Ch. 8) is thus seen to be homogeneous and quadratic (all terms are quadratic) in the loop-current variables. As mentioned previously, a function of this sort is called by mathematicians a *quadratic form*. The energy functions F, T, and V characterizing a linear passive network are thus seen to be quadratic forms in terms of the network variables.

One may alternately derive the energy functions in terms of the node-pair voltages as variables. Starting from Eqs. 66 pertaining to the node basis, and denoting the elements in the matrices $[\Gamma]$, $[G]$, $[C]$ by Γ_{ik}, G_{ik}, C_{ik}, the equivalent algebraic form for these equations reads

$$
\sum_{k=1}^{n} \left(C_{ik} \frac{d}{dt} + G_{ik} + \Gamma_{ik} \int dt \right) e_k = i_{ni}, \qquad i = 1, 2, \cdots, n \tag{122}
$$

in which $e_1 \cdots e_n$ are the node-pair voltages and $i_{n1} \cdots i_{nn}$ are the equivalent node-pair current sources. Since both sets of quantities refer to the same node pairs, the total instantaneous power supplied to the network by an actual set of current sources feeding the pertinent node pairs is given by

$$
P = i_{n1}e_1 + i_{n2}e_2 + \cdots + i_{nn}e_n \tag{123}
$$

This expression is formed through multiplying the successive equations in set 122 respectively by e_1, e_2, $\cdots$, e_n and adding. The result is compactly written

$$P = \sum_{i,\,k=1}^{n} \left(C_{ik}e_i \frac{de_k}{dt} + G_{ik}e_ie_k + \Gamma_{ik}e_i \int e_k \, dt \right) = \sum_{i=1}^{n} i_{ni}e_i \quad (124)$$

In terms of the energy functions

$$F = \frac{1}{2} \sum_{i,\,k=1}^{n} G_{ik}e_ie_k \quad (125)$$

$$V = \frac{1}{2} \sum_{i,\,k=1}^{n} C_{ik}e_ie_k \quad (126)$$

$$T = \frac{1}{2} \sum_{i,\,k=1}^{n} \Gamma_{ik}\psi_i\psi_k \quad (127)$$

where ψ_k in the last of these is used to denote the node-pair *flux linkages* or indefinite time integrals of the node-pair voltages as indicated in

$$\psi_k = \int e_k \, dt \quad \text{or} \quad e_k = \frac{d\psi_k}{dt} \quad (128)$$

we again find that Eq. 124 is an expression of the conservation of energy, for it is equivalent to

$$P = 2F + \frac{d}{dt}(V + T) = \sum_{i=1}^{n} i_{ni}e_i \quad (129)$$

the detailed justification for this conclusion being entirely similar to that given for the loop basis.

Although initially a given network may be thought of as excited by voltage sources located in the links, we can subsequently assume the sources to be currents having the values of the resulting link currents without altering in any way the rest of the voltages and currents throughout the network. The state of the network, however, is regarded as characterized in terms of loop-current variables or in terms of node-pair voltage variables according to whether the sources are considered to be a set of voltages or currents respectively. In a situation of this sort, the functions 111, 112, 113 have values that are identical with those obtained from Eqs. 125, 126, and 127. The former express the values for the associated energies in terms of loop currents and loop charges as variables while the latter express these same values in terms of node-pair voltages and flux linkages as variables.

So far, the variables and the sources are any time functions. Let us now assume that they are steady sinusoids as they are in many practical applications. For the loop basis we then write

$$i_k = \tfrac{1}{2}(I_k e^{j\omega t} + \bar{I}_k e^{-j\omega t}) \tag{130}$$

$$q_k = \int i_k \, dt = \frac{1}{2j\omega}(I_k e^{j\omega t} - \bar{I}_k e^{-j\omega t}) \tag{131}$$

where the bar signifies the conjugate value. Preparatory to making substitutions into the relations 111, 112, 113 for F, T, and V, we compute

$$i_i i_k = \tfrac{1}{4}(I_i e^{j\omega t} + \bar{I}_i e^{-j\omega t})(I_k e^{j\omega t} + \bar{I}_k e^{-j\omega t}) \tag{132}$$

which yields

$$i_i i_k = \tfrac{1}{4}(I_i I_k e^{j2\omega t} + \bar{I}_i \bar{I}_k e^{-j2\omega t} + I_i \bar{I}_k + \bar{I}_i I_k)$$
$$= \tfrac{1}{2} \operatorname{Re} [I_i \bar{I}_k] + \tfrac{1}{2} \operatorname{Re} [I_i I_k e^{j2\omega t}] \tag{133}$$

where Re is a symbol for "real part of" as used in previous discussions. Similarly we find from Eq. 131 that

$$q_i q_k = \frac{1}{2\omega^2} \operatorname{Re} [I_i \bar{I}_k] - \frac{1}{2\omega^2} \operatorname{Re} [I_i I_k e^{j2\omega t}] \tag{134}$$

and substitution into Eqs. 111, 112, 113 then gives for the energy functions in the sinusoidal steady state

$$F = \frac{1}{4} \sum_{i,\,k=1}^{l} R_{ik} I_i \bar{I}_k + \frac{1}{4} \operatorname{Re} \left[e^{j2\omega t} \sum_{i,\,k=1}^{l} R_{ik} I_i I_k \right] \tag{135}$$

$$T = \frac{1}{4} \sum_{i,\,k=1}^{l} L_{ik} I_i \bar{I}_k + \frac{1}{4} \operatorname{Re} \left[e^{j2\omega t} \sum_{i,\,k=1}^{l} L_{ik} I_i I_k \right] \tag{136}$$

$$V = \frac{1}{4\omega^2} \sum_{i,\,k=1}^{l} S_{ik} I_i \bar{I}_k - \frac{1}{4\omega^2} \operatorname{Re} \left[e^{j2\omega t} \sum_{i,\,k=1}^{l} S_{ik} I_i I_k \right] \tag{137}$$

where it is to be noted that the Re sign is not needed in each first term. For example,

$$\operatorname{Re} \sum_{i,\,k=1}^{l} R_{ik} I_i \bar{I}_k = \sum_{i,\,k=1}^{l} R_{ik} I_i \bar{I}_k \tag{138}$$

that is to say, this sum is real in spite of its complex variables I_i and I_k. The proof of this statement is readily given through showing that the sum on the right-hand side of Eq. 138 is *self-conjugate;* that is to say, it is its own conjugate. Obviously, if a number equals its conjugate, that number must be real. Considering the conjugate of this sum which evidently reads

$$\sum_{i,\,k=1}^{l} R_{ik}\bar{I}_i I_k \tag{139}$$

its value is not changed if we interchange the summation indexes i and k, since any other two symbols could be used in their place. If we then observe that $R_{ki} = R_{ik}$, it is seen that 138 and 139 are identical.

Each of the energy functions F, T, V, according to the Eqs. 135, 136, 137, is given by the sum of a constant term and a double-frequency sinusoid, as is shown in Ch. 7 for the simple RLC circuit. The constant term in each case is the average value of the energy function. We thus have

$$F_{\text{av}} = \frac{1}{4} \sum_{i,\,k=1}^{l} R_{ik} I_i \bar{I}_k \tag{140}$$

$$T_{\text{av}} = \frac{1}{4} \sum_{i,\,k=1}^{l} L_{ik} I_i \bar{I}_k \tag{141}$$

$$V_{\text{av}} = \frac{1}{4\omega^2} \sum_{i,\,k=1}^{l} S_{ik} I_i \bar{I}_k \tag{142}$$

In Art. 7 of Ch. 7, expressions equivalent to Eqs. 136 and 137 are given in terms of branch currents instead of loop currents. These are less general than the present results because the relation for T given there does not provide for the possibility of mutual inductive coupling. Since branch currents, unlike loop currents, do not traverse any common paths, and since the possibility of mutual inductive coupling is not considered in the discussion given in Ch. 7, the sums appearing there (see Eqs. 84 and 85 of Ch. 7) involve no cross-product terms as do the ones given here; rather only square terms are present. For this reason it is clear by inspection that the constant term or average value is greater than or at least equal to the amplitude of the oscillatory component, as a physical consideration obviously requires since the instantaneous value of the function would otherwise become negative during some interval, a condition that is physically impossible.

Although, for the more general expressions 135, 136, 137 considered here, it is not as simply obvious algebraically that the constant terms are at least as large as the amplitudes of the pertinent oscillatory components, such an independent purely algebraic proof can readily be given. Considering any one function by itself, one introduces a linear transformation of the variables which eliminates the cross-product terms, whereupon the desired result is again obvious (as pointed out in the second paragraph of Art. 7, Ch. 7). The algebraic details involved in this demonstration are, however, not justified at this point.

It is useful to obtain analogous results in terms of the node-pair voltages as variables. Considering the functions F, T, V, as given by Eqs. 125, 126, 127 we write for the node-pair voltages and flux linkages

$$e_k = \tfrac{1}{2}(E_k e^{j\omega t} + \overline{E}_k e^{-j\omega t}) \tag{143}$$

and

$$\psi_k = \int e_k \, dt = \frac{1}{2j\omega}(E_k e^{j\omega t} - \overline{E}_k e^{-j\omega t}) \tag{144}$$

It then follows that

$$e_i e_k = \tfrac{1}{2} \operatorname{Re}[E_i \overline{E}_k] + \tfrac{1}{2} \operatorname{Re}[E_i E_k e^{j2\omega t}] \tag{145}$$

and

$$\psi_i \psi_k = \frac{1}{2\omega^2} \operatorname{Re}[E_i \overline{E}_k] - \frac{1}{2\omega^2} \operatorname{Re}[E_i E_k e^{j2\omega t}] \tag{146}$$

whence substitution into Eqs. 125, 126, 127 yields

$$F = \frac{1}{4} \sum_{i,\,k=1}^{n} G_{ik} E_i \overline{E}_k + \frac{1}{4} \operatorname{Re}\left[e^{j2\omega t} \sum_{i,\,k=1}^{n} G_{ik} E_i E_k \right] \tag{147}$$

$$V = \frac{1}{4} \sum_{i,\,k=1}^{n} C_{ik} E_i \overline{E}_k + \frac{1}{4} \operatorname{Re}\left[e^{j2\omega t} \sum_{i,\,k=1}^{n} C_{ik} E_i E_k \right] \tag{148}$$

$$T = \frac{1}{4\omega^2} \sum_{i,\,k=1}^{n} \Gamma_{ik} E_i \overline{E}_k - \frac{1}{4\omega^2} \operatorname{Re}\left[e^{j2\omega t} \sum_{i,\,k=1}^{n} \Gamma_{ik} E_i E_k \right] \tag{149}$$

The Re sign is not needed in each first term for the reason given in the discussion of the analogous situation on the loop basis. The first terms again are the average values and the second terms are double-frequency sinusoids whose amplitudes cannot (for a passive network) exceed the respective values of the constant terms. These average values in terms of the complex amplitudes of the node-pair voltages are

$$F_{\mathrm{av}} = \frac{1}{4} \sum_{i,\,k=1}^{n} G_{ik} E_i \overline{E}_k \tag{150}$$

$$V_{\mathrm{av}} = \frac{1}{4} \sum_{i,\,k=1}^{n} C_{ik} E_i \overline{E}_k \tag{151}$$

$$T_{\mathrm{av}} = \frac{1}{4\omega^2} \sum_{i,\,k=1}^{n} \Gamma_{ik} E_i \overline{E}_k \tag{152}$$

It is now a simple matter to obtain general expressions for active, reactive, and vector power in the sinusoidal steady state. To this end, consider the loop equilibrium Eqs. 108 for the assumptions

$$e_{li} = E_i e^{j\omega t} \quad \text{and} \quad i_k = I_k e^{j\omega t} \tag{153}$$

After cancelation of the exponential factor, one has

$$\sum_{k=1}^{l} \left(L_{ik} j\omega + R_{ik} + \frac{S_{ik}}{j\omega} \right) I_k = E_i, \qquad i = 1, 2, \cdots, l \tag{154}$$

Forming the conjugate value upon both sides and rearranging the terms slightly, we have

$$\bar{E}_i = \sum_{k=1}^{l} \left[R_{ik} - j\omega \left(L_{ik} - \frac{S_{ik}}{\omega^2} \right) \right] \bar{I}_k \tag{155}$$

The total vector power, according to its fundamental definition given in Art. 4, Ch. 7, is now obtained through multiplication by $I_i/2$ and summation over the index i, thus:

$$\frac{1}{2} \sum_{i=1}^{l} \bar{E}_i I_i = \frac{1}{2} \sum_{i,\, k=1}^{l} R_{ik} I_i \bar{I}_k - \frac{j\omega}{2} \left(\sum_{i,\, k=1}^{l} L_{ik} I_i \bar{I}_k - \frac{1}{\omega^2} \sum_{i,\, k=1}^{l} S_{ik} I_i \bar{I}_k \right) \tag{156}$$

In view of the relations 140, 141, 142 this gives

$$\frac{1}{2} \sum_{i=1}^{l} \bar{E}_i I_i = P_{\text{av}} + j Q_{\text{av}} = 2 F_{\text{av}} + j 2\omega (V_{\text{av}} - T_{\text{av}}) \tag{157}$$

whereupon

$$P_{\text{av}} = 2 F_{\text{av}} \tag{158}$$

$$Q_{\text{av}} = 2\omega (V_{\text{av}} - T_{\text{av}}) \tag{159}$$

which agree with the results obtained in Ch. 7 for the simple circuit considered there.

Thus the real part of the vector power is the average power dissipated in the resistances, and the imaginary part or the so-called *reactive power* is proportional to the difference between the average energy stored in the electric fields and that stored in the magnetic fields. When these two average stored energies are equal, the sources are not called upon to take part in an interchange of stored energy, and the net reactive power is zero. As stated in Ch. 7, the reactive power Q_{av} is a measure of the extent to which the sources are called upon to participate in an interchange of stored energy. The actual average power consumed by the network is the so-called *active power* P_{av}.

It is interesting to interpret also Eq. 115, expressing the conservation of energy, in the sinusoidal steady state through substituting the expressions 135, 136, 137 for F, T, V. If we observe that the last two equations yield

$$\frac{dT}{dt} = \frac{1}{2}\,\mathrm{Re}\left[e^{j2\omega t} \sum_{i,\,k=1}^{l} j\omega L_{ik} I_i I_k \right] \qquad (160)$$

and

$$\frac{dV}{dt} = \frac{1}{2}\,\mathrm{Re}\left[e^{j2\omega t} \sum \frac{S_{ik}}{j\omega} I_i I_k \right] \qquad (161)$$

(since the constant terms in 136 and 137 do not contribute to these time derivatives), and group the sinusoidal terms in a single sum, this substitution into Eq. 115 gives

$$P = \frac{1}{2} \sum_{i,\,k=1}^{l} R_{ik} I_i \bar{I}_k + \frac{1}{2}\,\mathrm{Re}\left[e^{j2\omega t} \sum_{i,\,k=1}^{l} \left(R_{ik} + j\omega L_{ik} + \frac{S_{ik}}{j\omega} \right) I_i I_k \right]$$

or

$$P = 2F_{av} + \frac{1}{2}\,\mathrm{Re}\left[e^{j2\omega t} \sum_{i=1}^{l} \left\{ \sum_{k=1}^{l} \left(R_{ik} + j\omega L_{ik} + \frac{S_{ik}}{j\omega} \right) I_k \right\} I_i \right] \qquad (162)$$

where we have separated the double sum into two single sums in order to show that the one inside the curved brackets, according to Eq. 154, is simply E_i. Hence we have

$$P = P_{av} + \frac{1}{2}\,\mathrm{Re}\left[e^{j2\omega t} \sum_{i=1}^{l} E_i I_i \right] \qquad (163)$$

which shows that the total instantaneous power supplied by the sources equals a constant (the average power dissipated by the circuit) plus a double-frequency sinusoid.

From the expression for the double-frequency sinusoid we can see, for example, that, if our network is a balanced polyphase system, this term becomes zero, for the source voltages E_i and the source currents I_i are equal in magnitude and are equally spaced in time phase so that the sum of the products $E_i I_i$ over all sources vanishes. In any balanced polyphase system the total instantaneous power is constant and equal to the average power consumed by the network.

Of particular interest is the result 163 if the network is excited by a single source. Letting this one be E_1, we have in this special case

$$P = P_{\text{av}} + \text{Re}\left[\frac{E_1 I_1}{2} e^{j2\omega t}\right] \qquad (164)$$

Taking E_1 as phase reference and denoting the input admittance angle by φ, we have

$$P = P_{\text{av}} + \frac{|E_1 I_1|}{2} \cos(2\omega t + \varphi) \qquad (165)$$

However, noting Eq. 157,

$$\frac{|E_1 I_1|}{2} = \frac{|\bar{E}_1 I_1|}{2} = \sqrt{P_{\text{av}}^2 + Q_{\text{av}}^2} \qquad (166)$$

so that Eq. 165 can be written

$$P = P_{\text{av}} + \sqrt{P_{\text{av}}^2 + Q_{\text{av}}^2} \cos(2\omega t + \varphi) \qquad (167)$$

a result which shows that the amplitude of the double-frequency sinusoid equals the magnitude of the vector power.

7 Equivalence of Kirchhoff and Lagrange Equations

In this article we wish to show that Lagrange's equations, which express the equilibrium of a system in terms of its associated energy functions, are identical with the Kirchhoff-law equations so far as the end results are concerned. We need first some preliminary relations which can readily be seen from Eqs. 111, 112, 113 for the functions F, T, V in terms of the loop currents. If we differentiate partially with respect to a particular loop current, we find

$$\frac{\partial F}{\partial i_i} = \sum_{k=1}^{l} R_{ik} i_k \qquad (168)$$

$$\frac{\partial T}{\partial i_i} = \sum_{k=1}^{l} L_{ik} i_k \qquad (169)$$

$$\frac{\partial V}{\partial q_i} = \sum_{k=1}^{l} S_{ik} q_k \qquad (170)$$

These results may most easily be obtained if one considers the pertinent function written out completely as T is in Eq. 121. It is then obvious that a particular loop current, say i_2, is contained in all terms of the second row and second column, and only in these terms. Hence, if we differentiate partially with respect to i_2, no other terms are involved, and we find

$$\frac{\partial}{\partial i_2}(2T) = L_{21}i_1 + 2L_{22}i_2 + L_{23}i_3 + \cdots + L_{2l}i_l$$
$$+ L_{12}i_1 + \qquad + L_{32}i_3 + \cdots + L_{l2}i_l \qquad (171)$$

where we note that the term with L_{22} yields a factor 2 because the derivative of $i_2{}^2$ is involved. However, since $L_{ik} = L_{ki}$, we can rewrite this result as

$$\frac{\partial}{\partial i_2}(2T) = 2(L_{21}i_1 + L_{22}i_2 + \cdots + L_{2l}i_l) \qquad (172)$$

from which Eq. 169 follows. Equations 168 and 170 are obtained in the same manner. In all three, the summation involved is a simple summation on the index k.

If we differentiate Eq. 169 totally with respect to time, we have

$$\frac{d}{dt}\left(\frac{\partial T}{\partial i_i}\right) = \sum_{k=1}^{l} L_{ik}\frac{di_k}{dt} \qquad (173)$$

and Eq. 170 can be rewritten as

$$\frac{\partial V}{\partial q_i} = \sum_{k=1}^{l} S_{ik}\int i_k\, dt \qquad (174)$$

so that with Eq. 168 we obtain

$$\frac{d}{dt}\left(\frac{\partial T}{\partial i_i}\right) + \frac{\partial F}{\partial i_i} + \frac{\partial V}{\partial q_i} = \sum_{k=1}^{l}\left(L_{ik}\frac{d}{dt} + R_{ik} + \dot{S}_{ik}\int dt\right)i_k \qquad (175)$$

Reference to the Kirchhoff voltage-law Eqs. 108 now shows that these may alternatively be written

$$\frac{d}{dt}\left(\frac{\partial T}{\partial i_i}\right) + \frac{\partial F}{\partial i_i} + \frac{\partial V}{\partial q_i} = e_{li}, \qquad i = 1, 2, \cdots, l \qquad (176)$$

This form, in which the voltage equilibrium equations are expressed in terms of the energy functions, is known as the *Lagrangian equations*. From the way in which they are here obtained, it is clear that they are equivalent to the Kirchhoff-law equations although their outward appearance does not place this fact in evidence.

The Lagrangian equations may alternately be expressed in terms of the node-pair voltages as variables. To obtain this result we begin with the Eqs. 125, 126, 127 for F, V, T and form

$$\frac{\partial F}{\partial e_i} = \sum_{k=1}^{n} G_{ik} e_k \tag{177}$$

$$\frac{\partial V}{\partial e_i} = \sum_{k=1}^{n} C_{ik} e_k \tag{178}$$

$$\frac{\partial T}{\partial \psi_i} = \sum_{k=1}^{n} \Gamma_{ik} \psi_k \tag{179}$$

Differentiating Eq. 178 totally with respect to time and rewriting Eq. 179 gives

$$\frac{d}{dt}\left(\frac{\partial V}{\partial e_i}\right) = \sum_{k=1}^{n} C_{ik} \frac{de_k}{dt} \tag{180}$$

and

$$\frac{\partial T}{\partial \psi_i} = \sum_{k=1}^{n} \Gamma_{ik} \int e_k \, dt \tag{181}$$

from which one has

$$\frac{d}{dt}\left(\frac{\partial V}{\partial e_i}\right) + \frac{\partial F}{\partial e_i} + \frac{\partial T}{\partial \psi_i} = \sum_{k=1}^{n} \left(C_{ik} \frac{d}{dt} + G_{ik} + \Gamma_{ik} \int dt \right) e_k \tag{182}$$

In view of this result, the Kirchhoff-law Eqs. 122 may be rewritten in the form

$$\frac{d}{dt}\left(\frac{\partial V}{\partial e_i}\right) + \frac{\partial F}{\partial e_i} + \frac{\partial T}{\partial \psi_i} = i_{ni}, \qquad i = 1, 2, \cdots, n \tag{183}$$

These again are the Lagrangian equations expressing the network equilibrium in terms of the associated energy functions.

It is significant to observe that Eqs. 176 and 183 are dual forms of the Lagrangian equations just as the Kirchhoff Eqs. 108 and 122 are dual forms. It is interesting in comparing these two equations to note that the functions T and V interchange places, as should be expected from the fact that T and V are duals.

8   Relation to Impedance Functions

In terms of the previous results of this chapter, it is a simple matter to express the driving-point impedance of a network in terms of its associated energy functions. Thus Eq. 157 for a single driving point (which we can call loop 1) yields

$$\bar{E}_1 I_1 = 4F_{av} + j4\omega(V_{av} - T_{av}) \qquad (184)$$

or, taking the conjugate of each side of this equation,

$$E_1 \bar{I}_1 = 4F_{av} + j4\omega(T_{av} - V_{av}) \qquad (185)$$

Dividing both sides of Eq. 184 by $E_1\bar{E}_1 = |E_1|^2$ or both sides of Eq. 185 by $I_1\bar{I}_1 = |I_1|^2$ yields respectively

$$\frac{I_1}{E_1} = Y_{11}(\omega) = \frac{4F_{av} + j4\omega(V_{av} - T_{av})}{|E_1|^2} \qquad (186)$$

and

$$\frac{E_1}{I_1} = Z_{11}(\omega) = \frac{4F_{av} + j4\omega(T_{av} - V_{av})}{|I_1|^2} \qquad (187)$$

A more effective form for these results reads

$$Y_{11}(\omega) = [4F_{av} + j4\omega(V_{av} - T_{av})]_{E_1=1} \qquad (188)$$

and

$$Z_{11}(\omega) = [4F_{av} + j4\omega(T_{av} - V_{av})]_{I_1=1} \qquad (189)$$

In the interpretation of Eq. 188 one should consider F_{av}, V_{av}, T_{av} to be expressed in terms of *voltages* as in Eqs. 150, 151, 152, for their respective values are then readily recognized to be proportional to the square of the voltage E_1 at the driving point since all other voltages $E_2 \cdots E_n$ are linearly proportional to E_1. In Eq. 188 we say that F_{av}, V_{av}, T_{av} are regarded as being evaluated per volt at the driving point.

Analogously, in the interpretation of Eq. 189 we associate with F_{av}, T_{av}, V_{av} the expressions 140, 141, 142 in terms of currents. Since all other loop currents are linearly proportional to I_1, the average energy functions are seen to be proportional to $I_1{}^2$. Their values per ampere at the driving point may be regarded as *normalized* values. Equation 189 expresses the driving-point impedance in terms of these normalized values of the average energy functions.

As pointed out in Art. 6 of Ch. 7 where these same expressions for the driving-point admittance and impedance functions are derived in terms of the simple RLC circuit, one recognizes by inspection that a resonance condition is one for which the average stored energies are equal, for the input impedance or admittance then becomes purely real. It is also clear that the stored magnetic energy predominates when the reactive part of the impedance is positive, while a negative reactive part indicates that the stored electric energy predominates. Thus these

524   GENERALIZATION OF CIRCUIT EQUATIONS

characteristics of the impedance are more clearly and directly related to the physical properties of the network.

The relations 188 and 189 in a sense permit the same simple correlations between impedance or admittance and the physical network to be made in all cases, that are otherwise only possible with the simple parallel or series RLC circuit. They are, however, restricted in that the impedance or admittance is expressible only for pure imaginary complex frequencies (also referred to as *real frequencies* since they correspond to sinusoids with steady amplitudes). In the following we shall remove this restriction through the introduction of a related set of energy functions that have significance for any complex values of the frequency variable $s = \sigma + j\omega$; and simultaneously we shall generalize the result so as to include all possible transfer impedances or admittances as well as the driving-point functions.*

Starting again with the loop equilibrium Eqs. 108, let us substitute

$$e_{li} = E_i e^{st} \quad \text{and} \quad i_k = I_k e^{st} \tag{190}$$

and obtain after cancelation of the exponential factor

$$\sum_{k=1}^{l} \left(L_{ik}s + R_{ik} + \frac{S_{ik}}{s} \right) I_k = E_i, \qquad i = 1, 2, \cdots, l \tag{191}$$

The successive equations that result for $i = 1$, $i = 2$, and so forth we now multiply respectively by $\bar{I}_1, \bar{I}_2, \cdots, \bar{I}_l$ and add. If we introduce the notation

$$T_0 = \sum_{i,\,k=1}^{l} L_{ik}\bar{I}_i I_k = \sum_{i,\,k=1}^{l} L_{ik}I_i\bar{I}_k \tag{192}$$

$$F_0 = \sum_{i,\,k=1}^{l} R_{ik}\bar{I}_i I_k = \sum_{i,\,k=1}^{l} R_{ik}I_i\bar{I}_k \tag{193}$$

$$V_0 = \sum_{i,\,k=1}^{l} S_{ik}\bar{I}_i I_k = \sum_{i,\,k=1}^{l} S_{ik}I_i\bar{I}_k \tag{194}$$

the result may be written

$$sT_0 + F_0 + \frac{V_0}{s} = \sum_{i=1}^{l} E_i\bar{I}_i \tag{195}$$

The equivalence of the forms for T_0, F_0, V_0 shown in Eqs. 192, 193, 194 is seen to follow if we interchange the letters i and k, which are

* This generalization was first introduced by O. Brune in 1930 as a preliminary step in establishing the positive real character of a driving-point impedance function as being the necessary and sufficient condition for its physical realizability.

merely summation indexes, and then note the symmetry condition $L_{ik} = L_{ki}$ (and so forth) for the parameters. Although T_0 is the only one of these three functions that has the dimensions of energy (F_0 is dimensionally power, and V_0 has the dimensions of the time rate of change of power) we shall for the sake of simplicity refer to all three as energy functions. Their relation to the functions T_{av}, F_{av}, V_{av} is discussed later on.

Our next objective is to extract from Eq. 195 some rather general relations concerning driving-point and transfer impedances. In this regard we observe first of all that in most cases we are not interested in having sources in all the loops of a network. In order, however, to leave this question in a flexible state, we shall assume that, of the l loops in the network, only p will be considered as being points of access, and permit p to be any integer from 1 to l. These p points of access are the terminal pairs of the voltage sources located in p of the loops. The network as a whole we assume to be enclosed in a box with only the accessible terminal pairs brought out.

Since we are interested only in the currents at these p terminal pairs, we wish to eliminate all other currents involved in Eqs. 191. In order to indicate specifically how this elimination is done, we may assume, without introducing any restriction, that the points of access correspond to loops 1 to p. Use of the abbreviation

$$\zeta_{ik} = L_{ik}s + R_{ik} + S_{ik}/s \tag{196}$$

then permits the resulting equilibrium Eqs. 191 to be written

$$\zeta_{11}I_1 + \zeta_{12}I_2 + \cdots + \zeta_{1l}I_l = E_1$$

$$\cdots \cdots \cdots \cdots \cdots \cdots \cdots \cdots \cdots$$

$$\zeta_{p1}I_1 + \zeta_{p2}I_2 + \cdots + \zeta_{pl}I_l = E_p$$

$$\zeta_{p+1,1}I_1 + \zeta_{p+1,2}I_2 + \cdots + \zeta_{p+1,l}I_l = 0 \tag{197}$$

$$\cdots \cdots \cdots \cdots \cdots \cdots \cdots \cdots \cdots$$

$$\zeta_{l1}I_1 + \zeta_{l2}I_2 + \cdots + \zeta_{ll}I_l = 0$$

thus showing that all but the first p loops have no excitation.

The ζ matrix of this set of equations we now represent in the partitioned form

$$[\zeta] = \begin{bmatrix} \zeta_{11} & \zeta_{12} & \cdots & \zeta_{1l} \\ \zeta_{21} & \zeta_{22} & \cdots & \zeta_{2l} \\ \cdot & \cdot & \cdots & \cdot \\ \zeta_{l1} & \zeta_{l2} & \cdots & \zeta_{ll} \end{bmatrix} = \begin{bmatrix} \zeta_{pp} & \vdots & \zeta_{pq} \\ \cdots & & \cdots \\ \zeta_{qp} & \vdots & \zeta_{qq} \end{bmatrix} \tag{198}$$

where the submatrix $[\zeta_{pp}]$ contains the elements of the first p rows and p columns, $[\zeta_{pq}]$ contains the elements of the first p rows and the last q columns where $q = l - p$, and so forth. The column matrices

$$[I] = \begin{bmatrix} I_1 \\ I_2 \\ \cdot \\ \cdot \\ \cdot \\ I_l \end{bmatrix} \quad \text{and} \quad [E] = \begin{bmatrix} E_1 \\ E_2 \\ \cdot \\ \cdot \\ \cdot \\ 0 \end{bmatrix} \tag{199}$$

are correspondingly partitioned as indicated by the forms

$$[I] = \begin{bmatrix} I_p \\ \hline I_q \end{bmatrix} \quad \text{and} \quad [E] = \begin{bmatrix} E_p \\ \hline 0 \end{bmatrix} \tag{200}$$

in which $[I_p]$ and $[E_p]$ are column submatrices containing the first p elements in $[I]$ and $[E]$; $[I_q]$ contains the last q elements in $[I]$, and $[0]$ is a column of q zeros. The Eqs. 197 may then be written more compactly as

$$[\zeta_{pp}] \times [I_p] + [\zeta_{pq}] \times [I_q] = [E_p]$$
$$[\zeta_{qp}] \times [I_p] + [\zeta_{qq}] \times [I_q] = [0] \tag{201}$$

The second of these equations may be solved for $[I_q]$ giving

$$[I_q] = -[\zeta_{qq}]^{-1} \times [\zeta_{qp}] \times [I_p] \tag{202}$$

and substitution into the first equation yields

$$([\zeta_{pp}] - [\zeta_{pq}] \times [\zeta_{qq}]^{-1} \times [\zeta_{qp}]) \times [I_p] = [E_p] \tag{203}$$

which symbolizes the desired set of equations involving only the currents at the accessible terminal pairs.

If we introduce the square impedance matrix of order p

$$[z_{pp}] = [\zeta_{pp}] - [\zeta_{pq}] \times [\zeta_{qq}]^{-1} \times [\zeta_{qp}] = \begin{bmatrix} z_{11} & z_{12} & \cdots & z_{1p} \\ z_{21} & z_{22} & \cdots & z_{2p} \\ \cdot & \cdot & \cdots & \cdot \\ z_{p1} & z_{p2} & \cdots & z_{pp} \end{bmatrix} \tag{204}$$

we may write the Eqs. 203 in the equivalent algebraic form

$$\sum_{k=1}^{p} z_{ik} I_k = E_i, \qquad i = 1, 2, \cdots, p \tag{205}$$

This is an abridged form of the Eqs. 191 appropriate to the situation in which voltage sources are present in the first p loops only. The coefficients z_{ik} in these equations are determined from the ζ_{ik} (Eq. 196) characterizing Eqs. 191, in a manner indicated by the matrix Eq. 204. The transition from Eqs. 191 to Eqs. 205 may be described as a process of suppressing or eliminating the inaccessible or unwanted currents.

Although Eqs. 191 or 205 are derived specifically on the assumption that the E's are sources and the I's are responses, they correctly relate these voltages and currents, even though some or all of the I's may be sources and correspondingly some or all of the E's become responses. If the $I_1 \cdots I_p$ in Eqs. 205 are regarded as sources, then the resulting $E_1 \cdots E_p$ at the respective terminal pairs are *explicitly* given by these equations. Under these circumstances the terminal pairs are all open-circuited, and for this reason the z_{ik} are referred to as a set of *open-circuit driving-point and transfer impedances* characterizing the p terminal-pair network (compare with the analogous quantities described in Art. 7, Ch. 3, for resistance networks).

Specifically, if I_1 is the only nonzero current source, then

$$E_1 = z_{11}I_1$$
$$E_2 = z_{21}I_1$$
$$\cdot \quad \cdot \quad \cdot \quad \cdot \quad \cdot \tag{206}$$
$$E_p = z_{p1}I_1$$

or

$$z_{11} = E_1/I_1$$
$$z_{21} = z_{12} = E_2/I_1$$
$$\cdot \quad \cdot \quad \cdot \quad \cdot \quad \cdot \quad \cdot \quad \cdot \tag{207}$$
$$z_{p1} = z_{1p} = E_p/I_1$$

If I_1 is thought of as being equal in value to one reference ampere, then the complex voltage E_1 at terminal pair 1 is numerically identical with the driving-point impedance z_{11}; the complex voltage E_2 at terminal pair 2 is numerically identical with the transfer impedance $z_{12} = z_{21}$; and so forth. In any of these transfer relations like $E_2 = z_{12}I_1$, it is important to observe that I_1 must be the source and E_2 the response, and that this specific relation is invalid if E_2 now is regarded as a source and I_1 as a response because this change of attitude violates the conditions under which the particular relations 206 are extracted from the general relations 205 (namely, I_2 is no longer zero). Another set of particular relations may be extracted from Eqs. 205

on the assumption that I_2 is the only nonzero current, namely,

$$E_1 = z_{12}I_2$$

$$E_2 = z_{22}I_2$$

$$. \quad . \quad . \quad . \quad .$$

$$E_p = z_{p2}I_2$$

(208)

from which we may again obtain relations for the z's like Eqs. 207 which lend themselves to physical interpretation; and once more it must be emphasized that the transfer relations apply only if I_2 is a source.

The driving-point relations like $E_1 = z_{11}I_1$ or $E_2 = z_{22}I_2$, in contrast, are valid, regardless of whether the voltage or the current is the source because no restriction is placed upon the nonzero I_1 in Eqs. 206 or upon the nonzero I_2 in Eqs. 208. A driving-point relation always remains valid, regardless of which of the quantities E or I is the source and which is the response, while the derivation of a transfer relation invariably involves a restriction which fastens the roles of source and response upon specific ones of the two quantities E and I.

If we now substitute the expression for E_i as given by Eqs. 205 into Eq. 195, the right-hand summation in the latter is restricted to the first p terms, and we have

$$sT_0 + F_0 + \frac{V_0}{s} = \sum_{i,\,k=1}^{p} z_{ik}\bar{I}_i I_k = \sum_{i,\,k=1}^{p} z_{ik}I_i\bar{I}_k$$

(209)

in which the equivalence of the two double sums is seen to follow from the symmetry condition $z_{ik} = z_{ki}$. As later discussions will show, it is possible to determine all the properties of driving-point and transfer impedances from this result. At this time we shall consider only the specific relation obtained for a single driving point ($p = 1$) which reads

$$sT_0 + F_0 + V_0/s = z_{11}I_1\bar{I}_1 = z_{11}\left| I_1 \right|^2$$

(210)

whence

$$z_{11} = \frac{sT_0 + F_0 + V_0/s}{\left| I_1 \right|^2}$$

(211)

or

$$z_{11} = \left(sT_0 + F_0 + \frac{V_0}{s}\right)_{I_1 = 1}$$

(212)

With the expressions 192, 193, 194 for T_0, F_0, V_0, this result is the desired generalization of the one given by Eq. 189 to permit the consideration of any complex frequencies. Its usefulness may be attributed to the fact that the functions T_0, F_0, V_0 are real and positive in spite of any complex values that the I_k's may have as a result of satisfying Eqs. 191 for an arbitrary complex frequency s. This fact may readily be proved through writing

$$I_i = a_i + jb_i, \qquad \bar{I}_k = a_k - jb_k \qquad (213)$$

in which the a's and b's are real but otherwise arbitrary. Then

$$I_i\bar{I}_k = (a_ia_k + b_ib_k) + j(a_kb_i - a_ib_k) \qquad (214)$$

Suppose we substitute into Eq. 192 for T_0, and consider first the imaginary part which may be written as the difference of two sums, thus:

$$\sum_{i,\,k=1}^{l} L_{ik}a_kb_i - \sum_{i,\,k=1}^{l} L_{ik}a_ib_k \qquad (215)$$

If in the first of these we interchange the letters i and k (which we can do because they are merely summation indexes) and then note the symmetry condition $L_{ik} = L_{ki}$, it becomes clear that the two sums in 215 are identical and hence that their difference vanishes. The first part of our above statement, namely that T_0 is real for any complex I_k's, is thus proved.

Substitution of 214 into 192 now yields T_0 in the form

$$T_0 = \sum_{i,\,k=1}^{l} L_{ik}a_ia_k + \sum_{i,\,k=1}^{l} L_{ik}b_ib_k \qquad (216)$$

Reference to Eq. 112 shows that each of these double sums is a quadratic form like T representing the instantaneous value of stored magnetic energy. In Eq. 112 the variables are denoted by the letter i while in the sums 216 the variables involve respectively the letters a and b which, like the instantaneous currents i_k, are real quantities. Since the quadratic form T is related to a passive network, its values cannot become negative, no matter what values (positive or negative) are assigned to the i_k's, since one can through the insertion of current sources force the currents in a network to have *any* set of values, and yet the instantaneous stored magnetic energy must always have a positive value.

The property of a quadratic form like T to have only positive values no matter what the values of its variables may be (it is then referred to as a *positive definite* quadratic form) must clearly be the result of its coefficients L_{ik} having certain relative values; that is to say, it is a property of the matrix $[L]$ characterizing the quadratic form. It follows, therefore, that the quadratic forms in Eq. 216 can have only positive values, and hence T_0 can have only positive values.

Since the quadratic forms 193 and 194 for F_0 and V_0 are identical in form with T_0, the same argument shows that all three functions T_0, F_0, V_0 are real and positive for any complex frequency s, and that this result follows from the positive definite character of the instantaneous energy functions T, F, and V as given by Eqs. 111, 112, 113.

The expression 212 for a driving-point impedance is obviously not an explicit one so far as its dependence upon the complex variable s is concerned, for the functions T_0, F_0, V_0 implicitly are functions of s since they depend upon the I_k's which are solutions of the Eqs. 191 for a specific value of s. Nevertheless the representation for z_{11} as given by Eq. 212 enables one to determine all of the properties pertinent to the driving-point impedance of a linear passive network. Such determinations, which are invaluable to devising methods of synthesis for prescribed impedance functions, will be carried out in the discussions appropriate to these topics.

At present we wish rather to show next that analogous results pertinent to admittance functions are obtained through following a procedure which is precisely dual to the one just given. Thus in the node equilibrium Eqs. 122 we introduce the assumptions

$$i_{ni} = I_i e^{st} \quad \text{and} \quad e_k = E_k e^{st} \tag{217}$$

and, after cancelation of the exponential factor, have

$$\sum_{k=1}^{n} \left(C_{ik}s + G_{ik} + \frac{\Gamma_{ik}}{s} \right) E_k = I_i, \qquad i = 1, 2, \cdots, n \tag{218}$$

The successive equations in this set we multiply by $\bar{E}_1$, $\bar{E}_2$, $\cdots$, $\bar{E}_n$, and then add the results. Introducing the notation

$$V^*_0 = \sum_{i,\,k=1}^{n} C_{ik}\bar{E}_i E_k = \sum_{i,\,k=1}^{n} C_{ik}E_i\bar{E}_k \tag{219}$$

$$F^*_0 = \sum_{i,\,k=1}^{n} G_{ik}\bar{E}_i E_k = \sum_{i,\,k=1}^{n} G_{ik}E_i\bar{E}_k \tag{220}$$

$$T^*_0 = \sum_{i,\,k=1}^{n} \Gamma_{ik}\bar{E}_i E_k = \sum_{i,\,k=1}^{n} \Gamma_{ik}E_i\bar{E}_k \tag{221}$$

in which the equivalence of the two sums in each equation follows from the symmetry condition $C_{ik} = C_{ki}$ etc., the result of these operations yields

$$sV^*_0 + F^*_0 + \frac{T^*_0}{s} = \sum_{i=1}^{n} I_i\bar{E}_i \tag{222}$$

This relation is dual to Eq. 195 obtained on the loop basis, and the quadratic forms V^*_0, F^*_0, T^*_0 are respectively dual to T_0, F_0, V_0. Like the latter, their values are real and positive for all complex E_k values resulting from the solution of Eqs. 218 for a chosen complex s value. In order to consider these equations appropriate to a p terminal-pair network, we shall assume that nonzero current sources are applied only to the first p node pairs, and with the abbreviation

$$\eta_{ik} = C_{ik}s + G_{ik} + \Gamma_{ik}/s \tag{223}$$

write the pertinent Eqs. 218 in the more explicit form

$$\eta_{11}E_1 + \eta_{12}E_2 + \cdots + \eta_{1n}E_n = I_1$$

$$\cdot \quad \cdot \quad \cdot \quad \cdot \quad \cdot \quad \cdot \quad \cdot \quad \cdot \quad \cdot \quad \cdot \quad \cdot \quad \cdot \quad \cdot \quad \cdot \quad \cdot \quad \cdot \quad \cdot$$

$$\eta_{p1}E_1 + \eta_{p2}E_2 + \cdots + \eta_{pn}E_n = I_p$$

$$\eta_{p+1,1}E_1 + \eta_{p+1,2}E_2 + \cdots + \eta_{p+1,n}E_n = 0 \tag{224}$$

$$\cdot \quad \cdot \quad \cdot \quad \cdot \quad \cdot \quad \cdot \quad \cdot \quad \cdot \quad \cdot \quad \cdot \quad \cdot \quad \cdot \quad \cdot \quad \cdot \quad \cdot \quad \cdot \quad \cdot$$

$$\eta_{n1}E_1 + \eta_{n2}E_2 + \cdots + \eta_{nn}E_n = 0$$

The η matrix of this set of equations we now represent in the partitioned form

$$[\eta] = \begin{bmatrix} \eta_{11} & \eta_{12} & \cdots & \eta_{1n} \\ \eta_{21} & \eta_{22} & \cdots & \eta_{2n} \\ \cdot & \cdot & \cdot & \cdot \\ \eta_{n1} & \eta_{n2} & \cdots & \eta_{nn} \end{bmatrix} = \begin{bmatrix} \eta_{pp} & \vdots & \eta_{pq} \\ \cdots & & \cdots \\ \eta_{qp} & \vdots & \eta_{qq} \end{bmatrix} \tag{225}$$

entirely analogous to the partitioning used in Eq. 198 except that here $p + q = n$ instead of l. The column matrices

$$[E] = \begin{bmatrix} E_1 \\ E_2 \\ \cdot \\ \cdot \\ \cdot \\ E_n \end{bmatrix} \quad \text{and} \quad [I] = \begin{bmatrix} I_1 \\ I_2 \\ \cdot \\ \cdot \\ \cdot \\ 0 \end{bmatrix} \tag{226}$$

are correspondingly partitioned as indicated by

$$[E] = \begin{bmatrix} E_p \\ \cdots \\ E_q \end{bmatrix} \quad \text{and} \quad [I] = \begin{bmatrix} I_p \\ \cdots \\ 0 \end{bmatrix} \tag{227}$$

whereupon one may write the Eqs. 224 in the equivalent matrix form

$$[\eta_{pp}] \times [E_p] + [\eta_{pq}] \times [E_q] = [I_p]$$
$$[\eta_{qp}] \times [E_p] + [\eta_{qq}] \times [E_q] = [0] \tag{228}$$

The second of these equations may be solved for $[E_q]$ giving

$$[E_q] = -[\eta_{qq}]^{-1} \times [\eta_{qp}] \times [E_p] \tag{229}$$

whence substitution into the first equation yields

$$([\eta_{pp}] - [\eta_{pq}] \times [\eta_{qq}]^{-1} \times [\eta_{qp}]) \times [E_p] = [I_p] \tag{230}$$

which symbolizes the desired set of equations involving only the voltages at the accessible node pairs.

If we introduce the square admittance matrix of order p

$$[y_{pp}] = [\eta_{pp}] - [\eta_{pq}] \times [\eta_{qq}]^{-1} \times [\eta_{qp}] = \begin{bmatrix} y_{11} & y_{12} & \cdots & y_{1p} \\ y_{21} & y_{22} & \cdots & y_{2p} \\ \cdot & \cdot & \cdots & \cdot \\ y_{p1} & y_{p2} & \cdots & y_{pp} \end{bmatrix} \tag{231}$$

we may write Eqs. 230 in the equivalent algebraic form

$$\sum_{k=1}^{p} y_{ik} E_k = I_i, \qquad i = 1, 2, \cdots, p \tag{232}$$

This is an abridged form of the Eqs. 218 appropriate to the situation in which current sources are feeding only the first p node pairs. The coefficients y_{ik} in these equations are determined from the η_{ik} (Eq. 223) characterizing Eqs. 218, in a manner indicated by the matrix Eq. 231. The transition from Eqs. 218 to 232 may be described as a process of suppressing or eliminating the inaccessible or unwanted node-pair voltages.

Although Eqs. 218 or 232 are derived specifically on the assumption that the I's are sources and the E's are responses, they correctly relate these currents and voltages even though some or all of the E's may be sources and correspondingly some or all of the I's become responses. If the $E_1 \cdots E_p$ in Eqs. 232 are regarded as sources, then the resulting $I_1 \cdots I_p$ at the respective terminal pairs are *explicitly* given by these equations. Under these circumstances the terminal pairs are all short-circuited, and for this reason the y_{ik} are referred to as a set of *short-circuit driving-point and transfer admittances* characterizing the p terminal-pair network (compare with the analogous quantities described in Art. 7, Ch. 3, for resistance networks).

Specifically, if E_1 is the only nonzero voltage source, then

$$I_1 = y_{11}E_1$$

$$I_2 = y_{21}E_1$$

$$\cdots \cdots$$

$$I_p = y_{p1}E_1$$

$$\text{(233)}$$

or

$$y_{11} = I_1/E_1$$

$$y_{21} = y_{12} = I_2/E_1$$

$$\cdots \cdots \cdots$$

$$y_{p1} = y_{1p} = I_p/E_1$$

$$\text{(234)}$$

If E_1 is thought of as being equal in value to one reference volt, then the complex current I_1 at terminal pair 1 is numerically identical with the driving-point admittance y_{11}; the complex current I_2 at terminal pair 2 is numerically identical with the transfer admittance $y_{12} = y_{21}$; and so forth. In any of these transfer relations like $I_2 = y_{12}E_1$, it is important to observe that E_1 must be the source and I_2 the response; and that this relation is invalid if I_2 now is regarded as a source and E_1 as a response because this change of attitude violates the conditions under which the particular relations 233 are extracted from the general relations 232 (namely, E_2 is no longer zero).

Another set of particular relations may be extracted from Eqs. 232 on the assumption that E_2 is the only nonzero voltage source, namely,

$$I_1 = y_{12}E_2$$

$$I_2 = y_{22}E_2$$

$$\cdots \cdots$$

$$I_p = y_{p2}E_2$$

$$\text{(235)}$$

from which we may again obtain relations for the y's like Eqs. 234 which lend themselves to physical interpretation; and once more it must be emphasized that the transfer relations apply only if E_2 is a source.

The driving-point relations like $I_1 = y_{11}E_1$, or $I_2 = y_{22}E_2$, in contrast, are valid regardless of whether the voltage or the current is the source because no restriction is placed upon the nonzero E_1 in Eqs. 233 or upon the nonzero E_2 in Eqs. 235. As stated before, a driving-point relation remains valid regardless of which quantity, E or I, is the source and which is the response, while a transfer relation is valid only for a specific assignment of the roles of source and response, namely that one which is implicit in its derivation.

It is significant to mention in passing that, if the Eqs. 205 and 232 are derived for the same p terminal-pair network, then they must obviously be inverse sets, and the matrices $[z_{pp}]$ and $[y_{pp}]$, Eqs. 204 and 231, are inverse. Specifically, if these matrices have the determinants Z and Y with cofactors Z_{sk} and Y_{sk}, then

$$z_{sk} = Y_{ks}/Y \quad \text{and} \quad y_{sk} = Z_{ks}/Z \tag{236}$$

If we now substitute the expression for I_i as given by Eqs. 232 into Eq. 222, the right-hand summation in the latter is restricted to the first p terms, and we have

$$sV^*{}_0 + F^*{}_0 + \frac{T^*{}_0}{s} = \sum_{i,\,k=1}^{p} y_{ik}\overline{E}_iE_k = \sum_{i,\,k=1}^{p} y_{ik}E_i\overline{E}_k \tag{237}$$

in which the equivalence of the two double sums is seen to follow from the symmetry condition $y_{ik} = y_{ki}$. For $p = 1$ we obtain the specific result pertinent to a single driving point.

$$sV^*{}_0 + F^*{}_0 + T^*{}_0/s = y_{11}E_1\overline{E}_1 = y_{11}\big| E_1 \big|^2 \tag{238}$$

whence

$$y_{11} = \frac{sV^*{}_0 + F^*{}_0 + T^*{}_0/s}{\big| E_1 \big|^2} \tag{239}$$

or

$$y_{11} = \left(sV^*{}_0 + F^*{}_0 + \frac{T^*{}_0}{s}\right)_{E_1=1} \tag{240}$$

Together with the relations 219, 220, 221 for $V^*{}_0$, $F^*{}_0$, $T^*{}_0$ this result is the desired generalization of the one given by Eq. 188 permitting the consideration of any complex frequency. Like the expression 212 for z_{11}, its usefulness stems from the fact that the functions $V^*{}_0$, $F^*{}_0$, $T^*{}_0$ have positive real values for all complex s, the method of proof for this statement being precisely that given in the consideration of T_0, F_0, V_0.

It remains to establish relations between T_0, F_0, V_0 with and without asterisk, and T_{av}, F_{av}, V_{av} that apply to $s = j\omega$. If Eqs. 195 and 222 relate to the same network with sources at p points of access, then the right-hand sums are conjugates, and hence the left-hand sides of these equations must likewise be conjugates; that is,

$$sT_0 + F_0 + V_0/s = \bar{s}V^*{}_0 + F^*{}_0 + T^*{}_0/\bar{s} \tag{241}$$

and so we have

$$F_0 = F^*_0, \qquad V_0 = |s|^2 V^*_0, \qquad T_0 = T^*_0/|s|^2 \qquad (242)$$

Comparison of the expressions for these functions with pertinent ones for F_{av}, T_{av}, V_{av}, moreover, shows that for $s = j\omega$ one may make the identifications

$$F_0 = 4F_{av} = F^*_0, \qquad T_0 = 4T_{av} = T^*_0/\omega^2, \qquad V^*_0 = 4V_{av} = V_0/\omega^2$$

$$(243)$$

For complex s values, a physical interpretation of the functions T_0, F_0, V_0 or V^*_0, F^*_0, T^*_0 is not readily possible, but this fact is of little consequence since it is their mathematical rather than their physical significance that justifies introducing them into the present discussions.

9 Duality Once More

At various places throughout this text the principle of duality is discussed and the method of constructing a network dual to a given one described for various particular situations. It is pointed out, moreover, that, since current and voltage are duals, impedance and admittance likewise are dual quantities. For a given network and a selected driving point, the impedance of one of such a pair of dual networks equals the admittance of the other; whence it follows that the impedances of the two networks are reciprocal. The problem of finding a network whose driving-point impedance is the reciprocal of the impedance of a given network is thus solved if one can construct its dual. This and numerous other useful applications of the principle of duality suggest the appropriateness of discussing in its most general terms the method of constructing dual networks and of recognizing their associated reciprocal impedances or impedance matrices.

The first step in the construction of a dual network does not depend upon the kinds of elements (resistances, inductances, or capacitances)` that constitute the branches in the given network. Thus the first step in any case is that of constructing the dual geometry according to the completely general discussion given in Art. 9 of Ch. 1. Of significance is the condition that the given network graph be mappable on the surface of a sphere; and that the method of construction yields a dual graph with branches appropriately numbered as well as provided with reference arrows corresponding to those on the branches of the given network.

Considering any branch in the given network graph and the corresponding one in the dual graph, the matter of element assignment follows the simple pattern that: A resistance of R ohms in one network becomes a conductance of R mhos in the other (or a conductance of G mhos in one becomes a resistance of G ohms in the other); a self-inductance of L henrys becomes a capacitance of L farads, and a capacitance of C farads becomes a self-inductance of C henrys. Thus to each element (branch) in the given network there corresponds the pertinent dual element in the dual network.

Since capacitances in one network become self-inductances in the dual, it is clear that the latter cannot be constructed if the given network contains mutually coupled inductances because there exists no analogous mutual coupling between capacitances. Under certain circumstances one may be able to find a network involving no mutual inductive coupling and having a restricted equivalence with respect to a given network that does contain mutually coupled inductances (as illustrated by the network of Fig. 5 relative to the one in Fig. 2(a) in the first example discussed in Art. 5 above). In such "equivalent" networks, the original mutual inductances are replaced by one or more self-inductances, and these may be represented by additional branches not present in the original network. Having found such a mutual-inductanceless "equivalent" network, one may, to be sure, construct a dual (provided the graph of the "equivalent" network is still mappable), but the latter is dual to the original network only to the extent that the "equivalent" one is equivalent to it.

One does not use the term "dual" in any situation that involves restrictions. A network is said to be the dual of another one only if it is *completely* dual, in which case this property is a mutual one. Wherever a restriction is involved, we speak of the networks as being *reciprocal* (rather than dual), and, unless the nature of the restriction is obvious, it is best to state specifically that the networks are reciprocal with respect to "so and so." For example, we might have a pair of networks that are reciprocal with respect to a single terminal pair, or with respect to p terminal pairs. In the latter event, impedance matrix 204 for one of these networks is identical with admittance matrix 231 of the other [or their impedance (resp. admittance) matrices are inverse]. It may be shown that the reciprocal of a p terminal-pair network (in the above sense) always exists, regardless of mappability or of the presence of mutual inductive coupling.

Returning our attention to the mappable and mutual-inductanceless network and its dual, we may think of creating points of entry or access (terminal pairs) either by connecting leads to the nodes at the two ends of any branch (the "soldering iron" type of entry) or by cutting into a branch to form a terminal pair (the "pliers" type of entry) as pointed out in Art. 7 of Ch. 2. If entries of both types are made in a given network then it is clear that the original state of that network is left undisturbed if the terminal pairs resulting from the "soldering iron" method are left open-circuited while those created by the "pliers" method are left short-circuited. These two ways of creating terminal pairs or points of access may, therefore, be referred to as having respectively open- and short-circuit character; and thus they are clearly recognized as being dual procedures.

It follows that, if in a given network we create a point of access by the "soldering iron" method, then the corresponding entry in the dual network must be made by the "pliers" method, and vice versa. More specifically, if the "soldering iron" method is applied to the terminals of a certain branch in one of a pair of dual networks, then the pliers method is applied to the *correspondingly numbered* branch in the other network. Both types of entry may, of course, be made in each of the two networks.

If altogether p terminal pairs are thus created in each of the two dual networks, then it follows at once from the dual character of the procedures discussed in the foregoing articles that the set of open-circuit driving-point and transfer impedances z_{sk} defined for one network by matrix 204 must be identical with the set of short-circuit driving-point and transfer admittances y_{sk} defined for the other network by matrix 231; or that the open-circuit impedance (resp. short-circuit admittance) matrices for the two networks must be mutually inverse. Careful interpretation of these statements is essential, and so the following discussion is pertinent.

Suppose we consider a pair of dual networks in which p points of entry (having respectively dual character) are made in each. Let us refer to these as networks A and B; and suppose we define for A the open-circuit impedance matrix $[z_{sk}]_A$ with elements $z_{sk}^{(A)}$ and for B the short-circuit admittance matrix $[y_{sk}]_B$ with elements $y_{sk}^{(B)}$. It follows that $y_{sk}^{(B)} \equiv z_{sk}^{(A)}$ with indexes s and k independently equal to the integer values 1 to p inclusive.

For example, the driving-point impedance $z_{kk}^{(A)}$ at the terminal pair k of network A in which all other terminal pairs are open-circuited is identical with the driving-point admittance $y_{kk}^{(B)}$ at the terminal pair k of network B in which all other terminal pairs are short-circuited (regardless of whether they were created by the "pliers" or by the "soldering iron" method). If we think of both of these driving-point functions as impedances, then clearly they have reciprocal values; and so we have altogether p driving-point impedances in network A that are reciprocal respectively to p driving-point impedances in network

B. Note, however, that in network B all terminal pairs except the one we happen to be looking into are *short-circuited* while in network A they are *open-circuited*.

Regarding the *transfer* functions, we may similarly say that any open-circuit transfer impedance of network A equals the corresponding short-circuit transfer admittance of network B; but it is now *not* appropriate to think of both of these quantities as impedances since the reciprocal of a transfer admittance (although dimensionally an impedance) is not a transfer impedance because the reciprocal of a transfer function is not also a transfer function, as has been emphasized above. That is to say, a transfer impedance, for example, is understood to be the ratio of a voltage output to a current input and thus fastens the roles of input and output upon current and voltage respectively. The reciprocal of $y_{sk}^{(B)}$, while dimensionally an impedance, is not a quantity that will yield a voltage output when multiplied by a current input, but rather it is a quantity that yields an output current when divided into an input voltage. Thus we virtually accomplish nothing through writing $1/y_{sk}^{(B)}$ since the process of division that must be carried out in order to obtain an output from an input *undoes* the reciprocal form of this expression. Observe carefully that similar comment does not apply to the driving-point quantities $z_{kk}^{(A)}$ and $y_{kk}^{(B)}$ since they are response functions whether right side up or upside down.

For the network A we could just as well determine a short-circuit admittance matrix $[y_{sk}]_A$ and for the network B an open-circuit impedance matrix $[z_{sk}]_B$. If we do, we will find that these are identical, and also that $[y_{sk}]_A$ is the inverse of $[z_{sk}]_A$ while $[z_{sk}]_B$ is the inverse of $[y_{sk}]_B$. Regarding the latter matrix pairs, one should not make the mistake of thinking that the elements $y_{sk}^{(A)}$ and $z_{sk}^{(A)}$ or $y_{sk}^{(B)}$ and $z_{sk}^{(B)}$ have reciprocal values, for, as we know from the definition of inverse matrices, their elements do not have reciprocal values.

We have spoken of creating terminal pairs through soldering leads to the terminals of any branch, or through cutting into a branch. In this connection the question always arises as to why we cannot also create terminal pairs through soldering leads to any node pair whether linked by a branch or not. The answer is that we can, but that (a) it may not be immediately clear how we should create the corresponding entry in the dual network, and (b) the latter entry may not exist. Regarding (a) we need merely introduce into the given network an additional branch linking the node pair in question and, for the network graph thus augmented, construct the dual. The added branch in either network is considered to be a zero resistance or an infinite resistance (zero conductance) according to whether the respective entry is there made by the "pliers" or by the "soldering iron" method. Regarding (b) it should be observed that the augmented graph may not be mappable, in which case it possesses no dual, and hence there exists no corresponding way of entering the dual to the original network; the contemplated entry in the original network is pointless except for its significance as an access to that network alone.

In conclusion we may clarify the use of the terms "dual network" and "reciprocal network" through pointing out that the relationship of duality between a pair of networks is a generalized relationship of reciprocity (not to be confused with the so-called reciprocity theorem) since a pair of dual networks are reciprocal with respect to *all creatable points of entry*. The mutual relationship between a pair of reciprocal networks may in the same sense be regarded as a sort of restricted duality; the networks may be regarded as being dual with respect to certain stated points of entry and only with respect to these terminal pairs. They do not necessarily have the same total number of branches (as do dual networks), and in general it is not possible to create additional corresponding points of entry. While the dual network exists only for graphs mappable on a sphere, a reciprocal network with respect to any number of chosen points of entry always exists.*

At this point the student always asks: "If we can choose any number of points of entry in the given nonmappable network and still construct its reciprocal, why not choose all creatable points of entry? Won't the reciprocal then also be the dual?" The answer is: "No, for the reciprocal will have many more branches than the given network and hence will present the possibility of making additional points of entry, none of which possess correspondents in the given network. Therefore the two networks are *not* duals because duality, as has been emphasized all along, is strictly a *mutual* property, and the pair of reciprocal networks that you are proposing to construct do not possess such completely mutual properties." And thus we bring to a close the discussions of this volume.

* There are some writers who do not restrict the term duality with regard to electrical networks in this sense. In fact, several papers have been written showing how one may construct a "dual" network even though the given one does not possess a mappable graph. They suggest moreover that we must differentiate between the use of the term duality as applied to the purely mathematical theory of linear graphs and its use in network theory. I cannot share this view, for the very essence of the concept of duality is its mutual character. If there is any way of distinguishing which is which in a pair of presumably dual networks, then these are *not* duals. It is more appropriate to describe such networks as having specific reciprocal properties.

PROBLEMS

1. In the circuit the capacitance values are 1 farad each, the self-inductances are 1 henry each, and the mutual inductances in magnitude are 1/4 henry each. Assuming that the voltage sources are all equal to $e(t) = \cos t$, determine the equilibrium equations (a) on a loop basis using the mesh currents (with a consistent clockwise rotation) as variables, (b) on a node basis, identifying the branch-voltage drops v_1, v_2, v_3, v_4 with the node variables e_1, e_2, e_3, e_4.

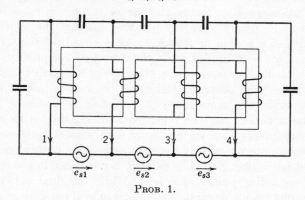

PROB. 1.

2. Choosing the terminals of the voltage source e_{s1} as a driving point, determine the input admittance of the circuit of Prob. 1, and write it in the form of a quotient of polynomials in the complex frequency variable s.

3. With reference to the circuit of Prob. 1, find the impedance function between the terminals of branch 1 and put it into the form of a quotient of polynomials.

4. Show that the expression

$$F = \sum_{i,\,k=1}^{n} a_{ik}x_i x_k$$

for a quadratic form may alternately be written in the matrix form

$$F = \underline{x} \cdot [A] \cdot x]$$

where

$$[A] = \begin{bmatrix} a_{11} & a_{12} & \cdots & a_{1n} \\ a_{21} & a_{22} & \cdots & a_{2n} \\ \cdots\cdots\cdots\cdots\cdots\cdots \\ a_{n1} & a_{n2} & \cdots & a_{nn} \end{bmatrix} \qquad x] = \begin{bmatrix} x_1 \\ x_2 \\ \cdot \\ \cdot \\ x_n \end{bmatrix}$$

5. If new coordinates y_1, y_2, $\cdots$, y_n are introduced through the transformation

$$[P] \cdot x] = y]$$

having the transposed form

$$\underline{x}\,[P]_t = \underline{y}$$

and if the transformation matrix $[P]$ satisfies the condition

$$[A] = [P]_t \cdot [P]$$

show that the quadratic form F in Prob. 4 expressed as a function of the new coordinates has the following so-called *canonic* form

$$F = y_1{}^2 + y_2{}^2 + \cdots + y_n{}^2$$

6. From the result of Prob. 5 deduce that F may be shown to be a positive definite form if its matrix has the representation $[A] = [P]_t \cdot [P]$ wherein $[P]$ is a real nonsingular matrix. Through assuming $[P]$ in the triangular form

$$[P] = \begin{bmatrix} p_{11} & p_{12} & p_{13} & \cdots & p_{1n} \\ 0 & p_{22} & p_{23} & \cdots & p_{2n} \\ 0 & 0 & p_{33} & \cdots & p_{3n} \\ \cdots\cdots\cdots\cdots\cdots\cdots\cdots \\ 0 & 0 & 0 & \cdots & p_{nn} \end{bmatrix}$$

obtain the specific relations

$$a_{11} = p_{11}{}^2, \qquad\qquad a_{1k} = p_{11}p_{1k}, \qquad\qquad (k > 1)$$

$$a_{22} = p_{12}{}^2 + p_{22}{}^2, \qquad a_{2k} = p_{12}p_{1k} + p_{22}p_{2k}, \qquad (k > 2)$$

$$a_{33} = p_{13}{}^2 + p_{23}{}^2 + p_{33}{}^2, \quad a_{3k} = p_{13}p_{1k} + p_{23}p_{2k} + p_{33}p_{3k}, \quad (k > 3)$$

and so forth, from which all the p_{ik} may be computed from a given set of a_{ik} by a straightforward recursion process. The existence of real finite p_{ik} (nonzero for $i = k$) is the necessary and sufficient condition to prove that F is positive definite (assuming that $[A]$ is nonsingular).

7. A set of four inductances are to have the self and mutual values given in the following matrix. Is this physically possible? Is it possible if all the mutual inductances are negative?

$$\begin{bmatrix} 1 & \frac{1}{2} & \frac{1}{2} & \frac{1}{2} \\ \frac{1}{2} & 1 & \frac{1}{2} & \frac{1}{2} \\ \frac{1}{2} & \frac{1}{2} & 1 & \frac{1}{2} \\ \frac{1}{2} & \frac{1}{2} & \frac{1}{2} & 1 \end{bmatrix} = [l]$$

8. If in the sinusoidal steady state all the loop currents in a network are in phase, show that the functions F, T, and V vary between zero and twice their average values. Show that this condition is always true for lossless networks and hence very nearly true for low-loss networks. A single driving point is assumed.

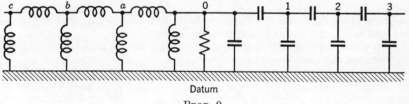

Datum

PROB. 9.

9. If in the set of equilibrium Eqs. 191 we set the determinant equal to zero we have the so-called characteristic (or determinantal) equation which determines those complex s values that are natural frequencies of the network. If we regard the currents as responses and a single voltage (in any loop) as the excitation, then the response functions (ratio of response to excitation) all become infinite for s equal to

a natural frequency. For such an s value the circuit is in resonance; a finite response results even for a vanishingly small excitation.

For such a vanishingly small excitation, the system of Eqs. 191 is homogeneous, and since the determinant is zero we know from the theory of algebraic equations that only the ratios of the currents, one to another, are determined. Specifically, the currents I_1, I_2, I_3, $\cdots$ are to each other as the successive cofactors of the elements in any chosen row, that row by implication referring to the loop in which the vanishingly small excitation is located. Since these ratios are the same for *any* row, we may conclude that, when the circuit is operating at resonance, the current distribution throughout the network is frozen so to speak; that is to say, it is the same regardless of the point of excitation.

These matters will logically be essentially true also for a system operating *near* a pronounced resonance. In order to observe this interesting result, consider the network shown in which the inductances and capacitances have unit values and the resistance equals 1000 ohms. Assuming the excitation to be a steady sinusoidal current fed into one of the nodes, and a response to be the voltage of any node with respect to the datum, compute values of all driving-point and transfer functions for the resonance frequency.

10. Reconsider the network of the previous problem with nodes 3 and c joined.

11. Making use of the results of Prob. 9 and the fact that at resonance $T_{av} = V_{av}$, show that the function $V_0 = \omega_0^2 T_0$ (for $I_1 = 1$) is nearly constant for the vicinity of any pronounced resonance frequency ω_0. Thus obtain for the driving-point impedance in this vicinity the approximate expression

$$Z_1(j\omega) \approx F_0 + jT_0 \left(\frac{\omega^2 - \omega_0^2}{\omega} \right) \approx F_0 + j2T_0(\omega - \omega_0)$$

Defining the Q of the system in the usual manner as $Q = \omega_0/w$ where w is the width of the resonance curve between its half-power points, show that one obtains

$$Q = \frac{\omega_0 T_0}{F_0} = \frac{2\pi T_{peak}}{loss/cycle} = \frac{2\pi V_{peak}}{loss/cycle} = \frac{\omega_0 T_{av}}{F_{av}}$$

12. Continue the previous problem by considering the corresponding dual relationships, and show that any zeros and poles that are much closer to the j axis than they are to the real axis have the approximate representation

$$s_0 = -\frac{F_0}{2T_0} \pm j\omega_0 = -\frac{P_{av}}{4T_{av}} \pm j\omega_0$$

where the ratios F_0/T_0 and P_{av}/T_{av} are to be evaluated at the frequency in question and with appropriate constraints at the driving point.

13. A given three-loop RL network is excited by a voltage source in loop 1. The pertinent loss and stored-energy functions are

$$2F = i_1^2 - 4i_1 i_2 + 2i_1 i_3, \qquad 2T = i_1^2 - 4i_1 i_2 + 2i_1 i_3$$
$$+ 12i_2^2 - 28i_2 i_3 \qquad\qquad + 8i_2^2 - 16i_2 i_3$$
$$+ 31i_3^2 \qquad\qquad\qquad + 14i_3^2$$

If the variables are subjected to the transformation

$$\begin{bmatrix} i_1 \\ i_2 \\ i_3 \end{bmatrix} = \begin{bmatrix} 1 & 1 & 1 \\ 0 & \frac{1}{2} & \frac{3}{4} \\ 0 & 0 & \frac{1}{2} \end{bmatrix} \times \begin{bmatrix} i'_1 \\ i'_2 \\ i'_3 \end{bmatrix}$$

find the expressions for F and T in terms of i'_1, i'_2, i'_3, and construct a simple network pertinent to these new variables. Show that this network has the same driving-point admittance as the original one, and hence that the above manipulations constitute a synthesis procedure for the realization of this admittance. Discuss the limitations of this scheme as a general synthesis method.

14. From the loop resistance and inductance matrices pertinent to the original network of the previous problem, determine the driving-point admittance for loop 1 as a quotient of polynomials, and from its partial fraction expansion obtain by inspection the same network as that found above. Contrast this synthesis procedure with that illustrated in Prob. 13.

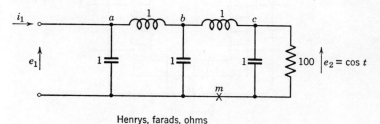

Henrys, farads, ohms

PROB. 15.

15. Show that the above network is operating very nearly at one of its resonance frequencies by computing the values of the energy functions T_{av} and V_{av}. What is the value of the input impedance? What is the Q of the network for this resonance?

16. Show that for $e_2(t) = \cos \sqrt{3}\, t$ the circuit of Prob. 15 is operating in the vicinity of a second resonance frequency. Again compute T_{av}, V_{av}, and Q. What should the parameter values be in order that the resonance frequencies may fall at $\omega = 10$ and $\omega = \sqrt{3} \times 10$ and the Q's remain the same?

17. Compute the impedance of the circuit of Prob. 15 across the node pairs a–b, a–c, b–c, c–m for $\omega = 1$ and $\omega = \sqrt{3}$ to show that these are resonance frequencies (close to the poles) of all these impedances. Compute the impedance for a cut at m and show that the same resonance frequencies now lie near the zeros of this impedance.

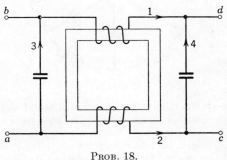

PROB. 18.

18. The above sketch shows a circuit consisting of two inductances wound on a single closed magnetic core and two 1-farad capacitances. The self-inductance values are 1 henry and the magnitude of the mutual inductance is 1/2 henry.

(a) Find the impedances Z_{ab}, Z_{bc}, Z_{bd}, Z_{cd} as quotients of polynomials in the frequency variable s.

(b) Find the open-circuit transfer impedance for the terminal pairs a–b and c–d.

(c) Find an equivalent unbalanced two terminal-pair network for these same terminal pairs, without mutual.

(d) Solve part (c) if the winding sense of one of the inductances is reversed.

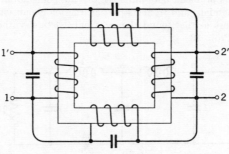

PROB. 19.

19. With reference to the two terminal-pair network shown, the capacitances are 1 farad each, and the inductances wound on the common core are 1 henry each with a mutual between pairs of coils that is 1/4 henry in magnitude. (a) Determine the z matrix of this two terminal-pair network. (b) Find an equivalent unbalanced network involving no mutual inductance.

20. Find networks reciprocal to the two terminal pairs found in Probs. 18 and 19.

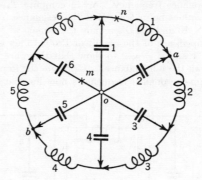

PROB. 21.

21. Element values in the circuit shown here are in henrys and farads. Construct the dual and indicate entries corresponding to the node pairs o–a, a–b and to the cuts at m and n.

22. In the following sketch, the branch numbers may be regarded as also indicating the element values in henrys and farads. (a) Construct the dual network, and indicate entries corresponding to node pairs a–b, c–d and to cuts at m and n. (b) Evaluate the impedances Z_{ab}, Z_{cd}, Z_m, Z_n for the given network and the corresponding ones for the dual network, and thus check that the latter are respectively reciprocal to the former ones.

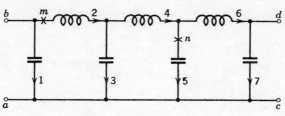

PROB. 22.

23. Element values in the symmetrical lattice shown in the sketch below are in henrys and farads. Find a two terminal-pair network whose z matrix is the inverse of that pertinent to the given network. Evaluate both z matrices and check that they are inverse. Geometrically, what is the dual of the lattice structure?

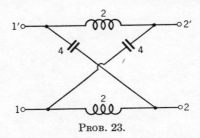

PROB. 23.

24. Apply the statement of Prob. 23 to the symmetrical bridged-tee network shown below. Element values again are in henrys and farads.

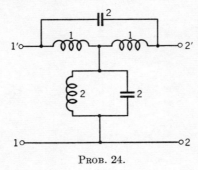

PROB. 24.

I N D E X